Prealgebra

Richard Rusczyk
David Patrick
Art of Problem Solving

Ravi Boppana
Advantage Testing

Art of Problem Solving®

Books • Online Classes • Videos • Interactive Resources

www.aops.com

Published by: AoPS Incorporated
                 10865 Rancho Bernardo Rd Ste 100
                 San Diego, CA 92127-2102
                 (858) 675-4555
                 books@artofproblemsolving.com

ISBN: 978-1-934124-21-5

Art of Problem Solving® is a registered trademark of AoPS Incorporated.

Visit the Art of Problem Solving website at http://www.artofproblemsolving.com

 Scan this code with your mobile device to visit the Art of Problem Solving website, to view our other books, our free videos and interactive resources, our online community, and our online school.

24® is a registered trademark of Suntex International Inc.
MATHCOUNTS® is a registered trademark of the MATHCOUNTS Foundation.

Cover image designed by Vanessa Rusczyk using KaleidoTile software.
Cover includes the original oil painting *Bush Poppy, El Cajon Mountain*, © 2011 Vanessa Rusczyk.

Printed in the United States of America.

Printed in 2019.

For Students—How To Use This Book

Learn by Solving Problems

This book is probably very different from most of the math books that you have read before. We believe that the best way to learn mathematics is by solving problems—lots and lots of problems. In fact, we believe that the best way to learn mathematics is to try to solve problems that you don't know how to do. When you discover something on your own, you'll understand it much better than if someone just tells it to you.

Most of the sections of this book begin with several problems. The solutions to these problems will be covered in the text, but try to solve the problems *before* reading the section. If you can't solve some of the problems, that's OK, because they will all be fully solved as you read the section. Even if you solve all of the problems, it's still important to read the section to make sure that your solution is correct, and also because you may find that the book's solution is simpler or easier to understand than your own.

If you find that the problems are too easy, this means that you should try harder problems. Nobody learns very much by solving problems that are too easy for them.

Explanation of Icons

Throughout the book, you will see various shaded boxes and icons.

Concept: This will be a general problem-solving technique or strategy. These are the "keys" to becoming a better problem solver!

Important: This will be something important that you should learn. It might be a formula, a solution technique, or a caution.

WARNING!! Beware if you see this box! This will point out a common mistake or pitfall.

> **Sidenote:** This box will contain material which, although interesting, is not part of the main material of the text. It's OK to skip over these boxes, but if you read them, you might learn something interesting!

> **Bogus Solution:** Just like the impossible cube shown to the left, there's something wrong with any "solution" that appears in this box.

Exercises, Review Problems, and Challenge Problems

Most sections end with several **Exercises**. These will test your understanding of the material that was covered in that section. You should try to solve *all* of the exercises. Exercises marked with a ★ are more difficult.

Most chapters have several **Review Problems**. These are problems that test your basic understanding of the material covered in the chapter. Your goal should be to solve most or all of the Review Problems for every chapter. If you're unable to do this, you should probably go back and review or reread the chapter.

All of the chapters end with **Challenge Problems**. These problems are generally more difficult than the other problems in the book, and will really test your mastery of the material. Some of them are very, very hard—the hardest ones are marked with a ★. Don't expect to be able to solve all of the Challenge Problems on your first try—these are difficult problems even for experienced problem solvers. If you are able to solve a large number of Challenge Problems, then congratulations, you are on your way to becoming an expert problem solver!

Hints

Many problems come with one or more hints. You can look up the hints in the Hints section in the back of the book. The hints are numbered in random order, so that when you're looking up a hint to a problem you don't accidentally glance at the hint to the next problem at the same time.

It is very important that you first try to solve each problem without resorting to the hints. Only after you've seriously thought about a problem and are stuck should you seek a hint. For problems that have multiple hints, use the hints one at a time; don't go to the second hint until you've thought about the first one.

Solutions

The solutions to all of the Exercises, Review Problems, and Challenge Problems are in the separate *Solutions Manual*. If you are using this textbook in a regular school class, then your teacher may decide not to make the *Solutions Manual* available to you, and instead present the solutions him/herself. However, if you are using this book on your own to learn independently, then you probably have a copy of the *Solutions Manual*, in which case there are some very important things to keep in mind:

1. Make sure that you make a serious attempt at solving the problem before looking at the solution. Don't use the solution book as a crutch to avoid really thinking about a problem first. You should think *hard* about a problem before deciding to give up and look at the solution.

2. After you solve a problem, it's usually a good idea to read the solution, even if you think you know how to solve the problem. The solution in the *Solutions Manual* might show you a quicker or more clever way to solve the problem, or it might have a completely different solution method that you might not have thought of.

3. If you have to look at the solution in order to solve a problem, make sure that you make a note of that problem. Come back to it in a week or two to make sure that you are able to solve it on your own, without resorting to the solution.

Resources

After completing *Prealgebra*, you're ready to continue with Art of Problem Solving's *Introduction* series of texts. The books in the series are:

- *Introduction to Algebra*. This text covers a broad range of introductory topics in algebra, including exponents and radicals, linear equations and inequalities, ratio and proportion, systems of linear equations, factoring quadratics, complex numbers, completing the square, the quadratic formula, graphing, functions, sequences and series, special functions, exponents and logarithms, and more.

- *Introduction to Counting & Probability*. This text offers a thorough introduction to counting and probability topics such as permutations, combinations, Pascal's triangle, geometric probability, basic combinatorial identities, the Binomial Theorem, and more.

- *Introduction to Geometry*. This text is a full geometry course, plus many advanced topics in geometry, including similar triangles, congruent triangles, quadrilaterals, polygons, circles, funky areas, power of a point, three-dimensional geometry, transformations, and more.

- *Introduction to Number Theory*. The text includes topics in number theory such as primes & composites, multiples & divisors, prime factorization and its uses, simple Diophantine equations, base numbers, modular arithmetic, divisibility rules, linear congruences, how to develop number sense, and more.

More detailed descriptions and excerpts from all of the above books are available of the Art of Problem Solving website at www.artofproblemsolving.com. The Art of Problem Solving website also has a wide range of resources for students and teachers, including:

- a very active discussion forum

- online classes

- Alcumus, a free adaptive learning system (includes plenty of Prealgebra practice!)

- hundreds of free instructional videos, including videos aligned to this text

- resource lists of books, contests, and other websites

- and much more!

You can hone your problem solving skills (and perhaps win prizes!) by participating in various math contests. For middle school students in the United States, the major contests are MATHCOUNTS, MOEMS, and the AMC 8. More details about these contests are on page ix, and links to these and many other contests are available on the Art of Problem Solving website.

Extra! Occasionally, you'll see a box like this at the bottom of a page. This is an "Extra!"
⇒⇒⇒⇒ and might be a quote, some biographical or historical background, or perhaps an interesting idea to think about.

A Note To Teachers And Parents

We believe that students learn best when they are challenged with hard problems that at first they may not know how to do. This is the motivating philosophy behind this book.

Rather than first introducing new material and then giving students exercises, we present problems at the start of each section that students should try to solve *before* the new material is presented. The goal is to get students to discover the new material on their own. Often, complicated problems are broken into smaller parts, so that students can discover new techniques one piece at a time. Then the new material is formally presented in the text, and full solutions to each problem are explained, along with problem-solving strategies.

We hope that teachers find that their stronger students will discover most of the material in this book on their own by working through the problems. Other students may learn better from a more traditional approach of first seeing the new material, then working the problems. Teachers have the flexibility to use either approach when teaching from this book.

This book is linear in coverage. Generally, students and teachers should progress straight through the book in order, without skipping chapters. In general, chapters are not equal in length, so different chapters may take different amounts of classroom time.

After completing this book, students should be ready to continue with any book in the Art of Problem Solving's *Introduction* series of textbooks. Brief descriptions of these books are on page v, and more complete descriptions (including excerpts) are available on our website at www.artofproblemsolving.com. The books in the *Introduction* series can be used in any order, although we generally recommend that *Introduction to Geometry* be used last.

We welcome your feedback on this book. Please email comments, corrections, etc. to books@artofproblemsolving.com.

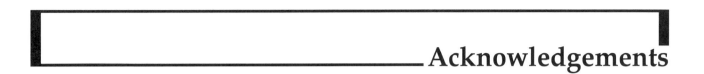

Acknowledgements

Contests

We would like to thank the following contests for allowing us to use a selection of their problems in this book:

- The **American Mathematics Competitions**, a series of contests for U.S. middle and high school students. The **AMC 8**, **AMC 10**, and **AMC 12** contests are multiple-choice tests, which are taken by over 350,000 students every year. Top scorers on the AMC 10 and AMC 12 are invited to take the **American Invitational Mathematics Examination (AIME)**, which is a more difficult, short-answer contest. Approximately 10,000 students every year participate in the AIME. Then, based on the results of the AMC and AIME contests, about 500 students are invited to participate in the **USA Mathematical Olympiad (USAMO)** and the **USA Junior Mathematical Olympiad (USAJMO)**, each of which is a 2-day, 9-hour examination in which each student must show all of his or her work. Results from the USAMO and USAJMO are used to invite a number of students to the Math Olympiad Summer Program, from which the U.S. team for the International Mathematical Olympiad (IMO) is chosen. More information about the AMC contests can be found on the AMC website at `www.maa.org/math-competitions`.

- **MATHCOUNTS®**, the premier math contest for U.S. middle school students. MATH-COUNTS is a national enrichment, coaching, competition, and club program that promotes middle school mathematics achievement through grassroots involvement in every U.S. state and territory. Each year, over 200,000 students in over 6,000 schools utilize MATHCOUNTS materials. Presidents Obama, Bush, Clinton, Bush, and Reagan have all recognized MATHCOUNTS in White House ceremonies. The MATHCOUNTS program has also received two White House citations as an outstanding private sector initiative. More information is available at `www.mathcounts.org`.

- **MOEMS**, an international program for students in grades 4-8. Created in 1977 by Dr. George Lenchner, MOEMS offers beginning problem solvers 5 contests each year. In 2012, nearly 150,000 students worldwide from 6,000 teams participated in MOEMS. More information is available at `www.moems.org`.

How We Wrote This Book

This book was written using the LaTeX document processing system. We sincerely thank the authors of the various LaTeX packages that we used while preparing this book, and also the brilliant authors of *The LaTeX Companion* for writing a reference book that is not only thorough but also very readable. The diagrams were prepared using the Asymptote graphics language. Cover design and publication prepress were completed using Adobe Creative Suite.

If you'd like to learn how to use LaTeX and Asymptote for yourself, and produce documents as spiffy-looking as this book, you can download both LaTeX and Asymptote software for free! Our website has a wiki that includes a how-to guide for downloading the software and a tutorial that will help you get started. Visit www.artofproblemsolving.com and click on "LaTeX Guide" under the "Resources" tab.

People To Thank

This book is a collaborative effort of the staff of the Art of Problem Solving. The three authors listed on the cover would like to particularly thank our colleagues listed below:

Jason Batterson, Jeremy Copeland, Larry Evans, and Shannon Rogers, for providing extensive proofreading, as well as valuable guidance on pedagogy and subject coverage;

Vanessa Rusczyk, for designing the cover and also contributing greatly to the interior design of the book;

Arun Alagappan, Founder and President of Advantage Testing (employer of one of the authors), for supporting this project and for providing a model of educational excellence for the last 25 years; and

Josh Zucker, whose comments about how he learned mathematics inspired the questions-before-the-lessons approach of the text.

Links & Errata

Links to all of the websites mentioned in this book are provided at

http://www.artofproblemsolving.com/booklinks/prealgebra

Also, on the above web page, we maintain a list of known errors from the textbook and solutions manual. If you find an error and it is not already listed on the above page, please let us know at books@artofproblemsolving.com, so that we can add it to the error list and correct it in future editions of the book.

R.B.—I dedicate this book to my mom and dad (Krishna Rao and Jaganmohan Rao), my wife Ranu, and my daughter Meena. Thank you for always believing in me.

D.P.—Personal thanks to my most influential mathematical mentors:
　　　　my parents (when I was very young),
　　　　Gerry Rising (when I was moderately young),
　　　　and Michael Artin (when I was not-so-young).

R.R.—For my students, in the hopes that they learn from me as much as I learn from them.

Contents

Hints to Selected Problems

Index

The 24 Game

See the four numbers on the card below?

Can you combine these four numbers to make the number 24? You may add, subtract, multiply, or divide. You may also use parentheses. You can't use any other symbols. You have to use each of the four numbers exactly once.

In the example above, one solution is $(3 + 1) \times 8 - 8$. Another solution is $(3 - 1) \times 8 + 8$. Yet another solution is $(8 + 1) \times 8 \div 3$.

This game is called the **24®game**. For more information about it, visit `www.24game.com`.

For fun, this book has a few 24 cards at the top of each chapter. Give them a try! Some of them are hard, but each has at least one solution. If you get stuck, you can find solutions in the solutions manual.

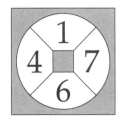 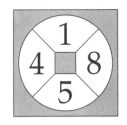 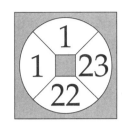 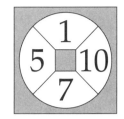

Arithmetic is being able to count up to twenty without taking off your shoes. – Mickey Mouse

CHAPTER 1

Properties of Arithmetic

1.1 Why Start with Arithmetic?

You know how to add, subtract, multiply, and divide. In fact, you may already know how to solve many of the problems in this chapter. So why do we start this book with an entire chapter on arithmetic?

To answer this question, go back to the title of this book: **Prealgebra**. What is prealgebra? Not everybody agrees on what "prealgebra" means, but we (the writers of this book) like to think of prealgebra as the bridge between *arithmetic* and *algebra*.

Arithmetic refers to the basics of adding, subtracting, multiplying, dividing, and (maybe) more exotic things like squares and square roots. You probably learned most of these basics already. The hardest thing that you usually do in arithmetic is "word problems" like "If Jenny has 5 apples and Timmy has 7 apples, then how many apples do they have together?" As you get older, the numbers get bigger, but the problems don't really get much harder. Arithmetic is great when trying to solve simple problems like counting apples. But when the problems get more complicated—like trying to compute a rocket's trajectory, or trying to analyze a financial market, or trying to count the number of ways a text message can be routed through a cellular phone network—we need a more advanced toolbox.

That toolbox is *algebra*. Algebra is the language of all advanced mathematics. Algebra gives us tools to take our concepts from arithmetic and make them *general*, meaning that we can use the concepts not just for arithmetic problems, but for other sorts of problems, too.

To take a simple example, you can use arithmetic to show that

$$2 \times (3 + 5) = (2 \times 3) + (2 \times 5),$$

because the left side equals 2×8, which is 16, and the right side equals $6 + 10$, which is also 16. But algebra gives us the much more general tool that

$$a \times (b + c) = (a \times b) + (a \times c),$$

no matter what numbers a, b, and c are. And in higher mathematics, a, b, and c might not even be numbers as you recognize them now, but might be more complicated mathematical objects. (Even more generally, "+" and "×" might not mean addition and multiplication as you think of them now, but instead might represent more complicated mathematical operations. But we're getting ahead of ourselves a little bit!)

So our initial goal, in Chapter 1, is to carefully lay down the rules of arithmetic, and to give you some ideas as to *why* these rules are true. Once you know the rules, you'll be ready to start thinking algebraically.

Also, by the time you start reading this book, you are mathematically mature enough to start thinking about not just *how* to perform various calculations, but *why* the techniques used in those calculations work. Understanding why mathematics works is the key to solving harder problems. If you only understand how techniques work but not why they work, you'll have a lot more difficulty modifying those techniques to solve more complicated problems. So, throughout this book, we will rarely just tell you how something works—we'll usually show you why it works.

By the end of this chapter, you should be able to explain *why* the following computations are true:

- $(-5) \times (-7) = 35$ (and not -35)

- $(1990 \times 1991) - (1989 \times 1990) = 3980$ (and be able to compute this in your head!)

- $8 \div \frac{1}{7} = 56$

- $(4 \times 10 \times 49) \div (2 \times 5 \times 7) = 28$ (again, in your head!)

You'll know all these things not because you've blindly applied some calculation, or because you've memorized some formula—instead, you'll understand the mathematics behind all these expressions.

Unfortunately, different mathematicians and different textbooks may use slightly different words for the same concept, in the same way that what an American calls a "truck" is called a "lorry" by people in Great Britain. So, before we go any farther, we want to make sure that we all agree on some of the words that we're going to use.

The **number line** is shown above. It goes on forever in both directions. Every number that we will consider in this book is somewhere on the number line. The tick marks on the number line above indicate the **integers**. An integer is a number without a fractional part:

$$\ldots, -7, -6, -5, -4, -3, -2, -1, 0, 1, 2, 3, 4, 5, 6, 7, \ldots$$

(The symbol . . . at either end of the above list means that the list goes on forever in that direction. The . . . symbol is called an **ellipsis**.) However, as you know, there are many numbers on the number line other than integers. For instance, most fractions such as $\frac{1}{2}$ are not integers. (But some fractions are integers—we'll explore this further in Chapter 4.)

A number is called **positive** if it is to the right of 0 on the number line. In other words, a number is positive if it is greater than 0. A number is called **negative** if it is to the left of 0 on the number line. That is, a number is negative if it is less than 0. For example, 2 is positive, while −2 is negative. Note that 0 itself is neither positive nor negative, and that every number is either positive, negative, or 0.

A number is called **nonnegative** if it is not negative. In other words, a nonnegative number is positive or 0. Similarly, a number is called **nonpositive** if it is not positive. Finally, a number is called **nonzero** if it is not equal to 0. Note that 0 is nonnegative and nonpositive.

> **Sidenote:** A lot of people use the term **whole number** to mean a nonnegative integer. In other words, a whole number is one of the numbers 0, 1, 2, ... These same people use the term **natural number** to mean a positive integer. In other words, a natural number is one of the numbers 1, 2, 3, ...
>
> However—and this is the really irritating part—a lot of people use the term **natural number** to mean a nonnegative integer. In other words, a natural number is one of the numbers 0, 1, 2, ... These same people use the term **whole number** to mean a positive integer. In other words, a whole number is one of the numbers 1, 2, 3, ...
>
> And some of both of these groups of people might also use the term **counting number** to mean either whole number or natural number.
>
> These people have been arguing for centuries, and they will likely never agree. Since we don't like to argue, we will stick with the very clear terms **positive integers** for the numbers 1, 2, 3, . . . , and **nonnegative integers** for the numbers 0, 1, 2, ...

1.2 Addition

We'll start by exploring the simplest arithmetic operation: **addition**. There's not a whole lot to explore, but as we'll see, a solid knowledge of the basic properties of addition makes complicated-looking calculations easy.

> **Important:** **How to use this book:** Most sections will begin with problems, like those shown below. You should first try to solve the problems. Then, continue reading the section, and compare your solutions to the solutions presented in the book.

Problem 1.1: Using the two pictures below, explain why $2 + 3 = 3 + 2$.

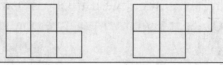

Problem 1.2: Using the two pictures below, explain why $(2 + 3) + 4 = 2 + (3 + 4)$.

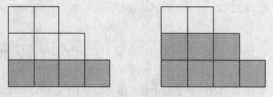

Reminder: The parentheses tell you what to compute first. For example, $(3 + 4) \times 5$ equals 7×5, whereas $3 + (4 \times 5)$ equals $3 + 20$.

Problem 1.3:

(a) Using the properties from Problems 1.1 and 1.2, explain why

$$472 + (219 + 28) = (472 + 28) + 219.$$

(b) Compute the sum $472 + (219 + 28)$. *(Source: MATHCOUNTS)*

Problem 1.4: Compute $(2 + 12 + 22 + 32) + (8 + 18 + 28 + 38)$. *(Source: MATHCOUNTS)*

Problem 1.5: Find the sum $1 + 2 + 3 + \cdots + 19 + 20$. Reminder: The ellipsis $\cdots$ means that we should include all the numbers in the pattern. So we are adding the positive integers from 1 to 20.

Problem 1.6: Using the picture below, explain why $2 + 0 = 2$.

Problem 1.1: Using the two pictures below, explain why $2 + 3 = 3 + 2$.

Solution for Problem 1.1: First let's look at the picture on the left. The first row has 2 squares; the second row has 3 squares. So in total, there are $2 + 3$ squares.

Now let's look at the picture on the right. The first row has 3 squares; the second row has 2 squares. In total, there are $3 + 2$ squares.

The picture on the right, however, is just an upside-down version of the picture on the left. Flipping a picture upside down doesn't change the number of squares. So we conclude that $2 + 3 = 3 + 2$. $\square$

Whenever we add two numbers, the order of the numbers does not matter. For example, $5 + 17 = 17 + 5$ and $32 + 999 = 999 + 32$. There are an infinite number of such examples. Of course, we can't write down an infinite number of examples. Instead, we can write the equation

$$\text{first number} + \text{second number} = \text{second number} + \text{first number}.$$

This is a long equation to write. We can shorten it by letting a represent the first number and b represent the second number. Then our equation becomes

$$a + b = b + a.$$

Here a and b stand for any numbers (and possibly the same number). For instance, if we let $a = 2$ and $b = 3$, then we have our original example: $2 + 3 = 3 + 2$. If we let $a = 100$ and $b = 200$, then we get $100 + 200 = 200 + 100$. Note that a has the same value throughout the equation, as does b; both, however, may change from one problem to the next. Letters such as a and b that represent numbers are called **variables**.

The rule that $a + b = b + a$ for all numbers a and b is called the **commutative property** of addition.

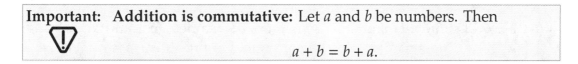

Important: **Addition is commutative:** Let a and b be numbers. Then

$$a + b = b + a.$$

In Problem 1.1, we explained why $a + b = b + a$ is true for one particular example, when $a = 2$ and $b = 3$. But one example doesn't prove that $a + b = b + a$ for all a and b. We don't have the tools in this book to explain why this must hold for any two numbers, but Problem 1.1 should give you good intuition for why it is true for positive integers.

Throughout the rest of this chapter, we will explore many more arithmetic rules. We will use examples and pictures to give intuition for why these rules work. These examples and pictures are not proofs, but they should give you a feel for why these rules must be true.

The commutative property is concerned with adding two numbers. What if we add three numbers?

Problem 1.2: Using the two pictures below, explain why $(2 + 3) + 4 = 2 + (3 + 4)$.

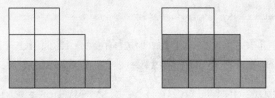

Reminder: The parentheses tell you what to compute first. For example, $(3 + 4) \times 5$ equals 7×5, whereas $3 + (4 \times 5)$ equals $3 + 20$.

Solution for Problem 1.2: For each picture, we will first count the number of light squares, then count the number of dark squares, and finally add the two counts.

Let's start with the picture on the left. It has $(2 + 3)$ light squares and 4 dark squares. So altogether it has $(2 + 3) + 4$ squares.

Next, let's look at the picture on the right. It has 2 light squares and $(3 + 4)$ dark squares. So altogether it has $2 + (3 + 4)$ squares.

What's the difference between the two pictures? The only difference is the color of the middle row. Changing the color doesn't change the number of squares. So we conclude that $(2 + 3) + 4 = 2 + (3 + 4)$. □

We get a similar equation for any three numbers: $(a + b) + c = a + (b + c)$. In other words, first adding a and b and then adding c is the same as adding a to $b + c$. This property is called the **associative property** of addition.

Important: **Addition is associative:** Let a, b, and c be numbers. Then

$$(a + b) + c = a + (b + c).$$

WARNING!! Students sometimes mix up the names "commutative" and "associative." In the commutative property, the numbers are moved around ("commuted") on the two sides of the equation. In the associative property, the numbers stay in the same place, but are grouped ("associated") differently.

Together, the commutative and associative properties are sneakily powerful, as they let us add a list of numbers in any order. The next problem is an illustration of this **any-order principle**.

Problem 1.3:

(a) Using the properties from Problems 1.1 and 1.2, explain why

$$472 + (219 + 28) = (472 + 28) + 219.$$

(b) Compute the sum $472 + (219 + 28)$. *(Source: MATHCOUNTS)*

Solution for Problem 1.3:

(a) Let's start with the left side of the equation:

$$472 + (219 + 28).$$

We will try to make it look like the right side. To do that, we need to switch the order of the 219 and the 28. We can do so by the commutative property. In other words, we replace $472 + (219 + 28)$ with the equal quantity

$$472 + (28 + 219).$$

This expression is close to what we want: $(472 + 28) + 219$. In fact, these two expressions are equal by the associative property.

Let's combine the pieces of our explanation into a nice chain of equations:

$$472 + (219 + 28) = 472 + (28 + 219) \qquad \text{commutative property}$$
$$= (472 + 28) + 219. \qquad \text{associative property}$$

(b) By part (a), the quantities $472 + (219 + 28)$ and $(472 + 28) + 219$ are equal, so we can compute $(472 + 28) + 219$ instead. But this is easy to compute: the sum $472 + 28$ is 500, so we are left with $500 + 219$. The answer is 719.

□

The point of Problem 1.3 is that we can rearrange the numbers in our addition to make the addition easier to compute. It's easier to first compute $472 + 28$, and then compute $500 + 219$, than it would have been to start with $219 + 28$ and then add that sum to 472.

In a similar way, any addition problem can be rearranged without changing the sum. Usually we won't bother to write all the individual steps of the rearrangement, like we did in Problem 1.3. Instead, we'll use our knowledge of the commutative and associative properties to just go ahead and rearrange a sum in whatever way is best. Let's apply that principle to solve the next problem.

Problem 1.4: Compute $(2 + 12 + 22 + 32) + (8 + 18 + 28 + 38)$. *(Source: MATHCOUNTS)*

Solution for Problem 1.4: We could start with 2, then add 12, then add 22, and so on, but that's too much work. Instead, let's try to rearrange the sum in a useful way. Let's pair up the numbers so that each pair has the same sum. Specifically, let's pair each number in the first group with a number in the second group:

$$(2 + 38) + (12 + 28) + (22 + 18) + (32 + 8).$$

The first pair of numbers adds up to 40; so does the second pair, the third pair, and the fourth pair. So our sum becomes

$$40 + 40 + 40 + 40.$$

The answer is 160. $\square$

Let's use the any-order principle to compute a longer sum.

Problem 1.5: Find the sum $1 + 2 + 3 + \cdots + 19 + 20$. Reminder: The ellipsis $\cdots$ means that we should include all the numbers in the pattern. So we are adding the positive integers from 1 to 20.

Solution for Problem 1.5: We definitely don't want to add the 20 numbers one at a time. Instead, let's try again to rearrange the numbers into pairs, so that each pair has the same sum. We pair the smallest number with the largest, the second-smallest with the second-largest, and so on:

$$(1 + 20) + (2 + 19) + (3 + 18) + \cdots + (10 + 11).$$

We have grouped the 20 numbers into 10 pairs. Each pair adds up to 21. So our sum becomes

$$21 + 21 + 21 + 21 + 21 + 21 + 21 + 21 + 21 + 21.$$

Adding 10 copies of 21 is the same as multiplying 10 and 21. So the answer is 210. $\square$

Finally, let's look at one more property of addition. What happens when we add zero to a number?

Problem 1.6: Using the picture below, explain why $2 + 0 = 2$.

Solution for Problem 1.6: On one hand, there are 2 squares. On the other hand, we can say there are 2 light squares and 0 dark squares. So we get the equation $2 + 0 = 2$. $\square$

Adding zero to any number doesn't change the number.

> **Important:** **Adding zero:** Let a be a number. Then
> $$a + 0 = a.$$

Exercises ▶

1.2.1 Compute $99 + 99 + 99 + 101 + 101 + 101$.

1.2.2 Compute $1999 + 2001 + 1999 + 2001 + 1999 + 2001 + 1999 + 2001$.

1.2.3 Compute $(3 + 13 + 23 + 33 + 43) + (7 + 17 + 27 + 37 + 47)$.

1.2.4 Compute $(1 + 2 + 3 + \cdots + 49 + 50) + (99 + 98 + 97 + \cdots + 51 + 50)$.

1.3 Multiplication

Problems ▶

Problem 1.7: Using the two pictures below, explain why $2 \times 3 = 3 \times 2$.

Problem 1.8: By counting the dots in the picture below in two different ways, explain why

$$(2 \times 3) \times 4 = 2 \times (3 \times 4).$$

Problem 1.9: Compute $25 \times 125 \times 4 \times 6 \times 8$.

Problem 1.10: Using the picture below, explain why $2 \times 1 = 2$.

Problem 1.11:

(a) Compute $(5 + 6) \times 7$.

(b) Compute $5 + (6 \times 7)$.

Problem 1.12: Using the picture below, explain why $2 \times (3 + 4) = (2 \times 3) + (2 \times 4)$.

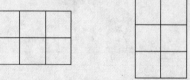

Problem 1.13: Compute $51 \cdot 9 + 51 \cdot 31$.

Problem 1.14: What is the value of $17 \cdot 13 + 51 \cdot 13 + 32 \cdot 13$?

Problem 1.15: Consider the multiplication facts below:

$$5 \times 7 = 35$$
$$4 \times 7 = 28$$
$$3 \times 7 = 21$$
$$2 \times 7 = 14$$
$$1 \times 7 = 7$$
$$0 \times 7 = \underline{\hspace{1cm}}.$$

(a) Find a pattern in the multiplication answers.

(b) Assuming that the pattern continues, predict the answer to the last multiplication.

Problem 1.7: Using the two pictures below, explain why $2 \times 3 = 3 \times 2$.

Solution for Problem 1.7: The picture on the left has 2 rows. Each row has 3 squares. So the total number of squares is $3 + 3$, which is 2×3.

The picture on the right has 3 rows. Each row has 2 squares. So the total number of squares is $2 + 2 + 2$, which is 3×2.

But the picture on the right is just a rotation of the picture on the left. Turning a picture doesn't change how many squares are in it. So we conclude that $2 \times 3 = 3 \times 2$. $\square$

Our example suggests that we can reverse the numbers in multiplication just as we can in addition. In other words, multiplication is commutative. As with addition, this is not a proof that commutativity works for all numbers, but our example does give us a good idea why we have $a \times b = b \times a$ for all positive numbers a and b. We call this the **commutative property of**

multiplication.

We will often write $a \times b$ as $a \cdot b$, using a centered dot. One reason is that it is quicker to write a dot than a cross. Another reason is that the cross $\times$ looks too much like the letter x, which is used a lot in algebra. So we can write $a \cdot b = b \cdot a$ for all numbers a and b.

We will often go a step further, writing $a \cdot b$ as ab. This notation is even quicker to write. We can't always leave out the dot, though. For example, to express $3 \cdot 4$, we can't write 34, because that number is thirty-four. In such cases, we will write either $3 \cdot 4$ or $3(4)$ for multiplication.

So we can write the commutative property of multiplication as:

> **Important:** **Multiplication is commutative:** Let a and b be numbers. Then
> $$ab = ba.$$

Is multiplication associative too? The next example is slightly trickier:

Problem 1.8: By counting the dots in the picture below in two different ways, explain why
$$(2 \times 3) \times 4 = 2 \times (3 \times 4).$$

Solution for Problem 1.8: On one hand, there are (2×3) squares. Each square has 4 dots. So the total number of dots is $(2 \times 3) \times 4$.

On the other hand, there are 2 rows of squares. Each row has (3×4) dots. So the total number of dots is $2 \times (3 \times 4)$.

We have counted the same dots in two different ways. So we conclude that
$$(2 \times 3) \times 4 = 2 \times (3 \times 4).$$

□

Problem 1.8 is an example of the **associative property of multiplication**:

> **Important:** **Multiplication is associative:** Let a, b, and c be numbers. Then
> $$(ab)c = a(bc).$$

Together, the commutative and associative properties let us multiply numbers in any order, just as we can add numbers in any order. Even with more than 3 numbers, this any-order principle applies. Let's see this in action.

Problem 1.9: Compute $25 \times 125 \times 4 \times 6 \times 8$.

Solution for Problem 1.9: Computing 25×125 takes work, so let's reorder the numbers to simplify our task. Let's look for easy pairs such as 4×25 that lead to nice round numbers. For example, let's try

$$6 \times (4 \times 25) \times (8 \times 125).$$

The product of 4 and 25 is 100. The product of 8 and 125 is 1000. So we are left with

$$6 \times 100 \times 1000.$$

The answer is 600,000. □

We've already seen that zero is a special number for addition: adding zero does nothing. Is there a similar number for multiplication?

Problem 1.10: Using the picture below, explain why $2 \times 1 = 2$.

Solution for Problem 1.10: On one hand, there are 2 rows. Each row has 1 square. So there are 2×1 squares in all. On the other hand, there are 2 squares. So we conclude that $2 \times 1 = 2$. □

This example suggests that multiplying a number by 1 does not change the number, and this leads to another rule:

Important: **Multiplying by 1:** Let a be a number. Then

$$1a = a.$$

Before we continue with properties of arithmetic, we need to understand how to combine different operations. We know that if we are just adding or just multiplying, we can move the numbers around and we can perform the operations in any order. But it's a little more complicated if we have both types of operation in the same calculation. For instance, what does $5 + 6 \times 7$ mean?

Problem 1.11:

(a) Compute $(5 + 6) \times 7$.

(b) Compute $5 + (6 \times 7)$.

Solution for Problem 1.11:

(a) The parentheses tell us to add first:

$$(5 + 6) \times 7 = 11 \times 7 = 77.$$

(b) This time, the parentheses tell us to multiply first:

$$5 + (6 \times 7) = 5 + 42 = 47.$$

□

We see that $(5 + 6) \times 7 \neq 5 + (6 \times 7)$. (The symbol "$\neq$" means "not equal to.")

So what if we were presented with just the expression $5 + 6 \times 7$, without any parentheses? We need rules for what order to perform different operations. These rules are shown below. (We've only covered addition and multiplication so far; we will discuss the other operations later.)

> **Important:** **Order of operations:** Perform the operations in an expression in the following order.
>
> 1. Evaluate expressions inside parentheses first.
>
> 2. Compute powers. (We cover powers in Chapter 2.)
>
> 3. Multiply and divide from left to right.
>
> 4. Add and subtract from left to right.

So, to compute $5 + 6 \times 7$, we multiply first, then add:

$$5 + 6 \times 7 = 5 + 42 = 47.$$

In other words, the calculation looks like part (b) of Problem 1.11.

Next, we turn to a powerful rule that connects addition and multiplication. As usual, we'll motivate the rule with a simple example.

Problem 1.12: Using the picture below, explain why $2 \times (3 + 4) = (2 \times 3) + (2 \times 4)$.

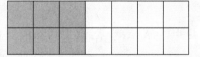

Solution for Problem 1.12: On one hand, there are 2 rows. Each row has $(3 + 4)$ squares. So altogether there are $2 \times (3 + 4)$ squares.

On the other hand, there are (2×3) dark squares, and there are (2×4) light squares. So altogether there are $(2 \times 3) + (2 \times 4)$ squares.

We have counted the same squares in two different ways. So we conclude that

$$2 \times (3 + 4) = (2 \times 3) + (2 \times 4).$$

□

Problem 1.12 is an example of a very useful rule that relates multiplication and addition. For any three numbers, a, b, and c we have

$$a \times (b + c) = (a \times b) + (a \times c).$$

The multiplication is **distributed** (handed out) to the two parts of the addition. For that reason, this property is called the **distributive property of multiplication over addition**, or the **distributive property** for short.

Because multiplication is commutative, we can reverse each of the products above, and write

$$(b + c) \times a = b \times a + c \times a.$$

In other words, the distributive property works when the sum is first, $(b+c) \times a$, or last, $a \times (b+c)$.

To reduce clutter, we can write the distributive property much more simply:

> **Important:** **Multiplication distributes over addition:** Let a, b, and c be numbers. Then
>
> $$a(b + c) = ab + ac \qquad \text{and} \qquad (b + c)a = ba + ca.$$

The equations $a(b+c) = ab+ac$ and $(b+c)a = ba+ca$ are really the same equation. We include them both to highlight the fact that the distributive property can be used when the sum is first or last.

Let's explore the distributive property further. What can this property do for us?

Problem 1.13: Compute $51 \cdot 9 + 51 \cdot 31$.

Solution for Problem 1.13: Instead of separately computing $51 \cdot 9$ and $51 \cdot 31$, we can use the distributive property:

$$51 \cdot 9 + 51 \cdot 31 = 51(9 + 31).$$

On the right side, the sum $9 + 31$ is 40, so our answer is equal to $51 \cdot 40$.

Instead of computing $51 \cdot 40$, we can use the distributive property again to make the multiplication simpler. Writing $51 = 50 + 1$ lets us use the distributive property as

$$51 \cdot 40 = (50 + 1) \cdot 40 = 50 \cdot 40 + 1 \cdot 40.$$

The advantage of using the distributive property as we just did is that the products $50 \cdot 40$ and $1 \cdot 40$ are both easy to compute! Our answer is

$$50 \cdot 40 + 1 \cdot 40 = 2000 + 40 = 2040.$$

□

As we saw in Problem 1.13, we can use the distributive property "in either direction." Using the distributive property to rewrite $a(b+c)$ as $ab+ac$ is called **expanding**. Using the distributive property to rewrite $ab + ac$ as $a(b + c)$ is called **factoring**.

For example, in the first step of the solution to Problem 1.13, we *factored* $51 \cdot 9 + 51 \cdot 31$ to write it as the simpler $51(9 + 31)$. In the second step, we *expanded* $(50 + 1) \cdot 40$ to write it as the easier-to-compute $50 \cdot 40 + 1 \cdot 40$.

> **Concept:** **Factoring** means using the distributive property to rewrite something of the form $ab + ac$ as something of the form $a(b + c)$. For example,
>
> $$51 \cdot 9 + 51 \cdot 31 = 51(9 + 31).$$
>
> In this example, the number 51 is called a **common factor** of both products on the left. We say that we "factor out 51" when we write $51 \cdot 9 + 51 \cdot 31$ as $51(9 + 31)$. We might also say that we "pull out a common factor of 51."

So far, we have used the distributive property with sums of two numbers. What about longer sums?

Problem 1.14: What is the value of $17 \cdot 13 + 51 \cdot 13 + 32 \cdot 13$?

Solution for Problem 1.14: We know that we can use the distributive property if we have two products with a common factor (like ab and ac, which have the common factor a). So we can factor out 13 from the products $17 \cdot 13$ and $51 \cdot 13$:

$$17 \cdot 13 + 51 \cdot 13 + 32 \cdot 13 = (17 + 51) \cdot 13 + 32 \cdot 13.$$

But now the products $(17 + 51) \cdot 13$ and $32 \cdot 13$ also have a common factor of 13. So we can use the distributive property again:

$$(17 + 51) \cdot 13 + 32 \cdot 13 = ((17 + 51) + 32) \cdot 13.$$

By the associative property of addition, we don't need the inner set of parentheses, so our quantity is just $(17 + 51 + 32) \cdot 13$. But $17 + 51 + 32$ equals 100, so our answer is $100 \cdot 13 = 1300$. $\square$

What Problem 1.14 shows us is that the distributive property works on sums of three (or more) numbers too! That is, we can pull out a common factor from a sum of any number of products. Now that we've seen that this works, we don't need to show all the steps like we did in the solution to Problem 1.14. Here's how we can solve the problem more quickly:

Solution for Problem 1.14: We see that all three numbers that we are summing ($17 \cdot 13$, $51 \cdot 13$, and $32 \cdot 13$) have the common factor 13, so we can factor the sum:

$$17 \cdot 13 + 51 \cdot 13 + 32 \cdot 13 = (17 + 51 + 32) \cdot 13.$$

Since $17 + 51 + 32$ equals 100, our answer is $100 \cdot 13 = 1300$. $\square$

> **Concept:** The distributive property works for a sum of any number of products. For example, if a, b, c, d, and e are any numbers, then:
>
> $$ab + ac + ad + ae = a(b + c + d + e).$$
>
> Similarly, we have
>
> $$ba + ca + da + ea = (b + c + d + e)a.$$

You may have learned that multiplying by an integer is the same as "repeated addition." For example,

$$4 \cdot 7 = 7 + 7 + 7 + 7.$$

The distributive property, combined with the rule that $1 \times a = a$ for any number a, tells us why this is true. Since $4 = 1 + 1 + 1 + 1$, we have

$$\begin{aligned} 4 \cdot 7 &= (1 + 1 + 1 + 1) \cdot 7 \\ &= 1 \times 7 + 1 \times 7 + 1 \times 7 + 1 \times 7 \\ &= 7 + 7 + 7 + 7. \end{aligned}$$

What happens when we multiply a number by zero? You probably already know what happens, but let's try to see why it makes sense in the next problem.

> **Problem 1.15:** Consider the multiplication facts below:
>
> $$5 \times 7 = 35$$
> $$4 \times 7 = 28$$
> $$3 \times 7 = 21$$
> $$2 \times 7 = 14$$
> $$1 \times 7 = 7$$
> $$0 \times 7 = \underline{\quad}.$$
>
> (a) Find a pattern in the multiplication answers.
>
> (b) Assuming that the pattern continues, predict the answer to the last multiplication.

Solution for Problem 1.15:

(a) After the first equation, each number on the right-hand side of an equation is 7 less than the number above it.

(b) The last number that we see on the right-hand side is 7. Going down by another 7 brings us to 0. So we predict that 0×7 is 0.

The idea that "multiplication by an integer is repeated addition" also suggests that 0×7 is 0. Just like 2×7 equals the sum of two 7's, and 1×7 equals the sum of one 7, the product

0×7 equals the sum of no 7's at all. Adding nothing gives us nothing, so again we expect that 0×7 is 0. We might also note that $0 \times 7 = 7 \times 0$, and the sum of seven 0's is 0.

□

The same idea shows that multiplying any number by 0 results in 0. It doesn't matter whether the starting number is small or large, a fraction or an integer, positive, negative, or zero—multiplying a number by 0 always results in 0. Multiplying by 0 "destroys" every number.

> **Important:** **Multiplying by zero:** Let x be a number. Then
> $$0x = 0.$$

Exercises ▶

1.3.1 What is the value of the product $25 \cdot 17 \cdot 4 \cdot 20$? *(Source: MOEMS)*

1.3.2 Compute $1 \cdot 100 \cdot 2 \cdot 50 \cdot 4 \cdot 25 \cdot 5 \cdot 20$.

1.3.3 Compute $2 \cdot 2 \cdot 2 \cdot 2 \cdot 2 \cdot 5 \cdot 5 \cdot 5 \cdot 5 \cdot 5$.

1.3.4 Compute $1 \cdot 1995 \cdot 1$.

1.3.5 Compute $1 \cdot 5 \cdot 1 \cdot 5 \cdot 1 \cdot 5$.

1.3.6 Using the distributive property, evaluate the following expressions.

(a) $11 \cdot 43 + 11 \cdot 57$ (b) $22 \cdot 6 + 6 \cdot 38$ (c) $32 \cdot 16 + 16 \cdot 48$.

1.3.7 Find numbers a, b, and c such that $a + (b \cdot c)$ is *not* equal to $(a + b) \cdot (a + c)$. In other words, find an example to illustrate that addition does *not* distribute over multiplication.

1.3.8 Compute $456 + 456 + 456 + 456 + 456 + 456 + 456 + 456 + 456 + 456$.

1.3.9 What is the product of the numbers $1, 2, 3, 4, 5, 6, 7, 8, 9$, and 0? *(Source: MATHCOUNTS)*

1.3.10 Compute $10 + 110 \cdot 0 \cdot 101 + 111$.

1.4 Negation

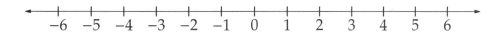

Take a look at the number line above. Note that -2 and 2 are the same distance from 0, but are on opposite sides of 0. What happens when we add $-2 + 2$? Of course, you know that we get 0. We can think of the sum $-2 + 2$ on the number line as starting at the position -2 and moving 2 units to the right, so that we end up at 0.

This idea of two numbers that sum to 0 is the key concept behind **negation**:

Definition: The **negation** of a number x, written $-x$, is the number that we add to x to get 0. That is,

$$-x + x = 0.$$

The negation of x is also called the **opposite** of x or the **additive inverse** of x. We also sometimes pronounce $-x$ as "minus x" or "negative x."

For example, -1 is the negation of 1, since $-1 + 1 = 0$, and -2 is the negation of 2, since $-2 + 2 = 0$. The number line shows us that there is clearly a negation for any positive integer. For example, -288 is the negation of 288, since $-288 + 288 = 0$.

You might ask: why do we bother with a new word "negation" when we already have negative numbers? The reason is that although so far we have mentioned the negations of positive numbers, we can also take the negations of zero and negative numbers. For example, the negation of 0 is -0, whatever that is. (We will find out soon enough.) The negation of -6 is $-(-6)$, whatever that is. (Again, we will soon find out.) Every number—positive, negative, or zero—has a negation.

Problems

Problem 1.16: Consider the negation facts below:

> The negation of 4 is -4.
> The negation of 3 is -3.
> The negation of 2 is -2.
> The negation of 1 is -1.
> The negation of 0 is ____ .
> The negation of -1 is ____ .
> The negation of -2 is ____ .

(a) Consider where the numbers at the ends of the facts above are on the number line. After the first number, how is each number related to the number above it?

(b) Based on the pattern from part (a), what is the negation of 0?

(c) Based on the pattern from part (a), what is the negation of -1?

(d) Based on the pattern from part (a), what is the negation of -2?

Problem 1.17: Consider the multiplication facts below:

$$4 \cdot 3 = 12$$
$$3 \cdot 3 = 9$$
$$2 \cdot 3 = 6$$
$$1 \cdot 3 = 3$$
$$0 \cdot 3 = 0$$
$$(-1) \cdot 3 = \underline{}.$$

(a) Consider where the numbers at the ends of the facts above are on the number line. After the first number, how is each number related to the number above it?

(b) Based on the pattern from part (a), what should $(-1) \cdot 3$ be?

Every number has a negation. What's the negation of zero? What's the negation of a negative number? Let's find out.

Problem 1.16: Consider the negation facts below:

The negation of 4 is −4.

The negation of 3 is −3.

The negation of 2 is −2.

The negation of 1 is −1.

The negation of 0 is ____ .

The negation of −1 is ____ .

The negation of −2 is ____ .

(a) Consider where the numbers at the ends of the facts above are on the number line. After the first number, how is each number related to the number above it?

(b) Based on the pattern from part (a), what is the negation of 0?

(c) Based on the pattern from part (a), what is the negation of −1?

(d) Based on the pattern from part (a), what is the negation of −2?

Solution for Problem 1.16:

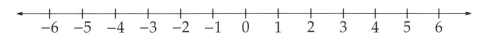

(a) The numbers at the ends of the facts in the list are −4, −3, −2, and −1. After the first number in the list, each number is one unit to the right of the number before it.

(b) The pattern from part (a) suggests that the answer is 1 unit to the right of -1. That number is 0. So -0, the negation of 0, should be 0.

We can also see this from our definition of negation. The negation of 0 was defined as the number that we can add to 0 to get 0. That is, by our definition, the number -0 satisfies

$$-0 + 0 = 0.$$

But adding 0 to a number does nothing, so adding 0 to -0 gives -0:

$$-0 + 0 = -0.$$

Since $-0 + 0$ equals both -0 and 0, we know that $-0 = 0$.

(c) Starting from 0 and moving 1 unit to the right, we get to 1. So $-(-1)$, the negation of -1, is 1.

Again, we can use the definition of negation. We know that 1 and -1 sum to 0:

$$1 + (-1) = 0.$$

But we also know that $-(-1)$ is defined as the number whose sum with -1 is 0:

$$-(-1) + (-1) = 0.$$

Comparing the above two equations indicates that $-(-1) = 1$.

(d) Starting from 1 and moving 1 unit to the right, we get to 2. So $-(-2)$, the negation of -2, is 2. We also know that $2 + (-2) = 0$, and we must have $-(-2) + (-2) = 0$, so we conclude that $-(-2) = 2$.

$\square$

In Problem 1.16, we saw that the negation of -1 is 1, and the negation of -2 is 2. Similarly, for any number x, the negation of $-x$ is the original number x. A double negation seems to "cancel out," giving us the original number back again. So we suspect that $-(-x) = x$ for all numbers x, and indeed in Problem 1.16, we saw this pattern. But a pattern is not enough to be sure that $-(-x) = x$ for all numbers x. How do we know that the pattern continues forever?

We can **prove** that $-(-x) = x$ for all numbers x, using a very clever idea. Consider the sum

$$x + (-x) + (-(-x)).$$

That is, we are adding x, its negation $-x$, and the negation of $-x$. By the associative property of addition, we can add these three in any order. If we start by adding the first two, we have $x + (-x) = 0$, so

$$x + (-x) + (-(-x)) = 0 + (-(-x)) = -(-x).$$

However, suppose we start by adding $(-x) + (-(-x))$ first. Since $(-(-x))$ is the negation of $-x$, we have $(-x) + (-(-x)) = 0$. So, we find

$$x + (-x) + (-(-x)) = x + 0 = x.$$

We just showed that $x + (-x) + (-(-x))$ equals both $-(-x)$ and x, so we must have

$$-(-x) = x.$$

Important: **Negation of negation:** Let x be any number. Then

$$-(-x) = x.$$

WARNING!! Even though $-x$ is sometimes spoken as "negative x," it does not have to be a negative number. For example, when $x = -1$, the value of $-x$ is the positive number 1. The negation of any negative number is positive.

Problem 1.17: Consider the multiplication facts below:

$$4 \cdot 3 = 12$$
$$3 \cdot 3 = 9$$
$$2 \cdot 3 = 6$$
$$1 \cdot 3 = 3$$
$$0 \cdot 3 = 0$$
$$(-1) \cdot 3 = \underline{\quad}.$$

(a) Consider where the numbers at the ends of the facts above are on the number line. After the first number, how is each number related to the number above it?

(b) Based on the pattern from part (a), what should $(-1) \cdot 3$ be?

Solution for Problem 1.17:

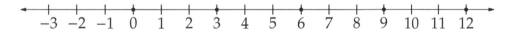

(a) The numbers at the ends of the facts in the list are 12, 9, 6, 3, and 0. On a number line, each number after the first is 3 units to the left of the number before it.

(b) The pattern from part (a) suggests that the answer is 3 units to the left of 0. That number is -3. So $(-1) \cdot 3$ is -3.

□

In words, multiplying a number by -1 appears to be the same as negating the number. This rule is handy. We can replace multiplication by -1 with negation if it helps us. We can also go the other way, replacing negation with multiplication—whichever way helps us solve a problem.

> **Important:** **Multiplying by −1:** Let x be a number. Then
> $$(-1)x = -x.$$

But just as before, a pattern is not a proof. So let's prove that $(-1)x$ is the negation of x. We can do this if we can show that

$$(-1)x + x = 0,$$

because if a number added to x gives 0, then our definition of negation says that the number is the negation of x. The clever idea here is to use that fact that $x = (1)x$, since multiplying by 1 doesn't change a number. Then, we have the following computation:

$$
\begin{aligned}
(-1)x + x &= (-1)x + (1)x && \text{replacing } x \text{ by } (1)x \\
&= ((-1) + 1)x && \text{using the distributive property to factor } x \\
&= (0)x && \text{definition of the negation } -1 \\
&= 0. && \text{multiplication by zero}
\end{aligned}
$$

So indeed, $(-1)x$ is the negation of x, and therefore

$$(-1)x = -x.$$

We can use the fact that $-x = (-1)x$ to understand how to multiply by negative numbers.

Problems

Problem 1.18: Using the fact that $-x = (-1)x$, explain why

$$(-2) \cdot 3 = -(2 \cdot 3).$$

Problem 1.19: Using Problem 1.18, explain why

$$(-2)(-3) = 2 \cdot 3.$$

Problem 1.20: Using the fact that $-x = (-1)x$, explain why

$$-(4 + 5) = (-4) + (-5).$$

Problem 1.18: Using the fact that $-x = (-1)x$, explain why

$$(-2) \cdot 3 = -(2 \cdot 3).$$

Solution for Problem 1.18: We know that negation is the same as multiplying by −1, so let's use that fact twice:

$$(-2) \cdot 3 = \big((-1) \cdot 2\big) \cdot 3 \qquad \text{multiplying by } -1$$
$$= (-1) \cdot (2 \cdot 3) \qquad \text{associative property}$$
$$= -(2 \cdot 3). \qquad \text{multiplying by } -1$$

In particular, since $(-2) \cdot 3 = -(2 \cdot 3)$, we know that $(-2) \cdot 3 = -6$. $\square$

There was nothing particularly special about the numbers "2" or "3" in Problem 1.18. In the same way, we can show that $(-x)y = -(xy)$ for any numbers x and y.

> **Important: Multiplying by negation:** Let x and y be numbers. Then
>
> $$(-x)y = -(xy),$$
> $$x(-y) = -(xy).$$

When x and y are positive, the equation $(-x)y = -(xy)$ says that a negative number times a positive number is negative, or "negative times positive is negative." By the commutative property, we can say the rule the other way around too: "positive times negative is negative."

How do we multiply a negative number by a negative number? Let's try an example.

> **Problem 1.19:** Using Problem 1.18, explain why
>
> $$(-2)(-3) = 2 \cdot 3.$$

Solution for Problem 1.19: We know how to multiply by a negation, so let's do that twice:

$$(-2)(-3) = -\big(2(-3)\big) \qquad \text{multiplying by negation}$$
$$= -\big(-(2 \cdot 3)\big) \qquad \text{multiplying by negation}$$
$$= 2 \cdot 3. \qquad \text{negation of negation}$$

In particular, $(-2)(-3)$ is the positive number 6. $\square$

In the same way, this works for any numbers x and y:

> **Important: Negation times negation:** Let x and y be numbers. Then
>
> $$(-x)(-y) = xy.$$

When x and y are positive, this equation says that a negative number times a negative number is positive. Students are often taught the chant "negative times negative is positive." Now you know why the chant is true!

How do we add negations? Let's find out in the next problem.

Problem 1.20: Using the fact that $-x = (-1)x$, explain why

$$-(4 + 5) = (-4) + (-5).$$

Solution for Problem 1.20: Let's use the fact that negation is the same as multiplying by -1:

$$
\begin{aligned}
-(4 + 5) &= (-1)(4 + 5) & \text{multiplying by } -1 \\
&= (-1)\cdot 4 + (-1)\cdot 5 & \text{distributive property} \\
&= (-4) + (-5). & \text{multiplying by } -1
\end{aligned}
$$

In particular, our work above tells us that $(-4) + (-5)$ is -9. $\square$

Similarly, the negation of $x + y$ equals $(-x) + (-y)$. In fancier words, negation distributes over addition.

> **Important:** **Negation of sum:** Let x and y be numbers. Then
>
> $$-(x + y) = (-x) + (-y).$$

Negation also distributes over longer sums. For example,

$$-(x + y + z) = (-x) + (-y) + (-z).$$

Exercises

1.4.1 Compute $-631 + (114 + 631)$.

1.4.2 What is the sum of all of the negative integers that are greater than -5?

1.4.3 What is the sum $-10 + (-9) + (-8) + \cdots + 9 + 10 + 11 + 12$?

1.4.4 What is the value of $210 \cdot 5 + 105 \cdot (-9)$? *(Source: MATHCOUNTS)*

1.4.5 What is $9342 + (-438)719 + (-9340) + (-438)(-719)$? *(Source: MATHCOUNTS)*

1.5 Subtraction

What do we mean by a subtraction such as $9 - 2$? Of course, you know that $9 - 2 = 7$. But in order to generalize subtraction to work for more complicated numbers (such as negatives or fractions), it will be useful to define subtraction as a combination of addition and negation. This also has the bonus of letting us use the rules and properties that we've already established in this chapter for addition and negation.

Definition: Let a and b be any numbers. Then the **subtraction** $a - b$ (pronounced "a minus b") is defined as
$$a - b = a + (-b).$$
The subtraction $a - b$ is sometimes called the **difference** $a - b$.

In other words:

Concept: Subtracting a number means adding its opposite.

For instance, $9 - 2$ equals $9 + (-2)$ using our new definition. But if this definition is going to make any sense, we had better have this equal to 7. We can check that it is, by writing $9 = 7 + 2$ and using our already-established rules for addition and negation:

$$
\begin{aligned}
9 - 2 &= 9 + (-2) && \text{definition of subtraction} \\
&= (7 + 2) + (-2) && \text{because 9 equals } 7 + 2 \\
&= 7 + \big(2 + (-2)\big) && \text{associative property} \\
&= 7 + 0 && \text{negation property} \\
&= 7. && \text{adding zero}
\end{aligned}
$$

Hurray! Our new definition of subtraction matches up with what we already know about subtracting positive integers! Specifically, using the addition fact $7 + 2 = 9$, we were able to prove that $9 - 2$ is 7. In other words, $9 - 2$ is the number that fills the blank in the addition equation

$$\underline{\quad} + 2 = 9.$$

So we can think of subtraction as the reverse of addition. This is a very useful way to think about subtraction.

Important: Let a, b, and c be numbers. If $a + b = c$, then $a = c - b$ and $b = c - a$.

Our goal is to explain how subtraction works with zero and with negative numbers, and to explain some of the other properties of subtraction.

WARNING!! Negation and subtraction look the same, but are different operations. Negation takes one number and returns its opposite. Subtraction takes two numbers and returns their difference. Even though negation and subtraction use the same symbol (the minus sign), you should distinguish in your mind between negation and subtraction.

Problems

Problem 1.21: Use the definition of subtraction to answer the following questions.

(a) What is $0 - 17$?

(b) What is $17 - 17$?

(c) What is $17 - 0$?

Problem 1.22: Use the definition of subtraction to explain the following equations.

(a) $11 - (-13) = 11 + 13$.

(b) $-11 - 13 = -(11 + 13)$.

(c) $11 - 13 = -(13 - 11)$.

Problem 1.23: Find numbers a and b such that $a - b$ is not equal to $b - a$.

Problem 1.24: Find numbers $a, b,$ and c such that $(a - b) - c$ is not equal to $a - (b - c)$.

Problem 1.25: What is the value of $1643 - 1994 - 1643$?

Problem 1.26: What is the value of $268 + 1375 + 6179 - 168 - 1275 - 6079$? *(Source: MOEMS)*

Problem 1.27:

(a) Explain why $(26 - 24) \cdot 64 = 26 \cdot 64 - 24 \cdot 64$.

(b) Compute $26 \cdot 64 - 24 \cdot 64$. *(Source: MATHCOUNTS)*

Problem 1.28: Use the fact that $999 = 1000 - 1$ to evaluate $999(345)$.

Our first problem confirms our intuition about how subtraction behaves with 0:

Problem 1.21: Use the definition of subtraction to answer the following questions.

(a) What is $0 - 17$?

(b) What is $17 - 17$?

(c) What is $17 - 0$?

Solution for Problem 1.21:

(a) Subtraction is defined as addition of a negation:

$$
\begin{aligned}
0 - 17 &= 0 + (-17) && \text{definition of subtraction} \\
&= -17. && \text{adding zero}
\end{aligned}
$$

(b) In a similar way,

$$17 - 17 = 17 + (-17) \qquad \text{definition of subtraction}$$
$$= 0. \qquad \text{negation property}$$

(c) Again in a similar way,

$$17 - 0 = 17 + (-0) \qquad \text{definition of subtraction}$$
$$= 17 + 0 \qquad \text{negation of zero}$$
$$= 17. \qquad \text{adding zero}$$

□

Of course, there was nothing special about "17" in the previous example, and we can extend these subtraction properties to numbers other than 17.

> **Important:** Let x be any number. Subtraction has the following properties:
>
> **Subtracting from zero:** $0 - x = -x$.
> **Self subtraction:** $x - x = 0$.
> **Subtracting zero:** $x - 0 = x$.

Next, how do we subtract when some of the numbers involved are negative? You may already know some rules about negative numbers and subtraction. In our next problem, we learn why those rules work.

Problem 1.22: Use the definition of subtraction to explain the following equations.
(a) $11 - (-13) = 11 + 13$.
(b) $-11 - 13 = -(11 + 13)$.
(c) $11 - 13 = -(13 - 11)$.

Solution for Problem 1.22:

(a) Let's change the subtraction to an addition:

$$11 - (-13) = 11 + \left(-(-13)\right) \qquad \text{definition of subtraction}$$
$$= 11 + 13. \qquad \text{negation of negation}$$

So $11 - (-13)$ is $11 + 13$.

(b) In a similar way,

$$-11 - 13 = -11 + (-13) \qquad \text{definition of subtraction}$$
$$= -(11 + 13). \qquad \text{negation of sum}$$

So $-11 - 13$ is $-(11 + 13)$.

(c) This part takes a few more steps. We wish to show that $11 - 13 = -(13 - 11)$ are equal. The right-hand side is more complicated than the left-hand side, so we'll start with $-(13 - 11)$ and try to show that it equals $11 - 13$.

> **Concept:** When trying to show that two expressions are equal, it's often easier to start from the more complicated expression.

We have:

$$
\begin{aligned}
-(13 - 11) &= -\big(13 + (-11)\big) & &\text{definition of subtraction} \\
&= -13 + \big(-(-11)\big) & &\text{negation of sum} \\
&= -13 + 11 & &\text{negation of negation} \\
&= 11 + (-13) & &\text{commutative property} \\
&= 11 - 13. & &\text{definition of subtraction}
\end{aligned}
$$

So $11 - 13$ is $-(13 - 11)$.

□

One of our key steps in part (c) of Problem 1.22 was showing that $-(13 - 11) = -13 + 11$. Often we'll stop there rather than continuing to $11 - 13$. More generally, we can write $-(x - y)$ as $-x + y$ or as $y - x$. We can think of $-(x - y) = -x + y$ as distributing the negation:

$$-(x - y) = -x - (-y) = -x + y.$$

We can extend the properties of Problem 1.22 to numbers other than 11 and 13.

> **Important:** Let x and y be any numbers. Then:
>
> **Subtraction of negation:** $x - (-y) = x + y$.
> **Subtraction from negation:** $-x - y = -(x + y)$.
> **Negation of subtraction:** $-(x - y) = -x + y = y - x$.

Remember that addition and multiplication are commutative. Is subtraction commutative?

Problem 1.23: Find numbers a and b such that $a - b$ is not equal to $b - a$.

Solution for Problem 1.23: There are many choices of a and b for which $a - b$ is not equal to $b - a$. For instance, choose $a = 2$ and $b = 1$. The first expression is

$$a - b = 2 - 1 = 1.$$

The second expression is

$$b - a = 1 - 2 = -1.$$

Because 1 and −1 are different, the two expressions 2 − 1 and 1 − 2 are not equal. This one example shows that subtraction is *not* commutative. □

Subtraction is not commutative, because $b - a$ does not necessarily equal $a - b$. In fact, we know that $b - a = -(a - b)$ by the "negation of subtraction" rule. So, $b - a$ is the opposite of $a - b$.

Next, we investigate if subtraction is associative:

Problem 1.24: Find numbers a, b, and c such that $(a - b) - c$ is not equal to $a - (b - c)$.

Solution for Problem 1.24: Again, there are many choices for which $(a - b) - c$ is not equal to $a - (b - c)$. For instance, choose $a = 3$, $b = 2$, and $c = 1$. The first expression is

$$(a - b) - c = (3 - 2) - 1 = 1 - 1 = 0.$$

The second expression is

$$a - (b - c) = 3 - (2 - 1) = 3 - 1 = 2.$$

Because 0 and 2 are different, this example shows that subtraction is *not* associative. □

WARNING!! Subtraction is neither commutative nor associative.

This means that we can't regroup subtraction as we did with addition or multiplication. For example, 1643 − 1994 − 1643 is equal to

$$(1643 - 1994) - 1643,$$

because we subtract from left to right. But we cannot regroup this expression as

$$1643 - (1994 - 1643).$$

There is good news, though. Remember that we defined subtraction in terms of addition (and negation), and addition is commutative and associative. So we can use the following strategy for dealing with subtraction:

Concept: **To solve subtraction problems:**

1. Change all subtractions to additions.

2. Rearrange the additions using the commutative and associative properties.

3. [Optional] Change some of the additions back to subtractions.

Let's see this subtraction-to-addition strategy at work.

Problem 1.25: What is the value of $1643 - 1994 - 1643$?

Solution for Problem 1.25: First, let's convert the two subtractions to additions:

$$1643 + (-1994) + (-1643).$$

Now we can group similar terms together:

$$-1994 + (-1643 + 1643).$$

The sum $(-1643 + 1643)$ is zero, so we have

$$-1994 + 0.$$

Therefore, the answer is -1994. $\square$

Problem 1.26: What is the value of $268 + 1375 + 6179 - 168 - 1275 - 6079$? *(Source: MOEMS)*

Solution for Problem 1.26: Remember that sums and differences are computed from left to right. We could keep the numbers in the given order, but the calculations get ugly. So let's use the properties of addition to rearrange the numbers.

First, we convert all subtractions to additions:

$$268 + 1375 + 6179 + (-168) + (-1275) + (-6079).$$

Second, we bring similar numbers together:

$$\Big(268 + (-168)\Big) + \Big(1375 + (-1275)\Big) + \Big(6179 + (-6079)\Big).$$

Third, we convert some of the sums back to differences:

$$(268 - 168) + (1375 - 1275) + (6179 - 6079).$$

Each of these differences has a value of 100:

$$100 + 100 + 100.$$

So the answer is 300.

With practice, you'll be able to go from the original expression

$$268 + 1375 + 6179 - 168 - 1275 - 6079$$

to the rearrangement

$$(268 - 168) + (1375 - 1275) + (6179 - 6079)$$

without first converting the subtractions to additions. The key idea is that all of the numbers that were originally being added (268, 1375, and 6179) are still being added after the rearrangement, and all of the numbers that were originally being subtracted (168, 1275, and 6079) are still being subtracted after the rearrangement. □

Having discussed the commutative and associative properties, we turn to the distributive property. Remember that multiplication distributes over addition. Does multiplication distribute over subtraction too? The next problem is a test case.

Problem 1.27:
(a) Explain why $(26 - 24) \cdot 64 = 26 \cdot 64 - 24 \cdot 64$.

(b) Compute $26 \cdot 64 - 24 \cdot 64$. *(Source: MATHCOUNTS)*

Solution for Problem 1.27:

(a) Let's convert the difference to a sum and then distribute the 64:

$$
\begin{aligned}
(26 - 24) \cdot 64 &= \big(26 + (-24)\big) \cdot 64 && \text{definition of subtraction} \\
&= 26 \cdot 64 + (-24) \cdot 64 && \text{distributive property (over addition)} \\
&= 26 \cdot 64 + \big(-(24 \cdot 64)\big) && \text{multiplying by negation} \\
&= 26 \cdot 64 - 24 \cdot 64. && \text{definition of subtraction}
\end{aligned}
$$

(b) By the previous part, we can replace $26 \cdot 64 - 24 \cdot 64$ with

$$(26 - 24) \cdot 64.$$

This expression simplifies to

$$2 \cdot 64.$$

So the answer is 128.

□

As part (a) shows, multiplication distributes over subtraction. As part (b) shows, the distributive property is as powerful for subtraction as it is for addition.

> **Important:** **Multiplication distributes over subtraction:** Let a, b, and c be numbers. Then
> $$a(b - c) = ab - ac \qquad \text{and} \qquad (b - c)a = ba - ca.$$

Even better, multiplication distributes over any combination of additions and subtractions. For example, we can expand $a(b - c - d + e)$ into $ab - ac - ad + ae$.

The next problem has a surprising use of the distributive property.

Problem 1.28: Use the fact that $999 = 1000 - 1$ to evaluate $999(345)$.

Solution for Problem 1.28: As prompted by the problem, we can write 999 as $1000 - 1$:

$$999 \cdot 345 = (1000 - 1)345.$$

By the distributive property (over subtraction), we get

$$999 \cdot 345 = 1000(345) - 1(345).$$

Now our difference is just $345{,}000 - 345$, which is $344{,}655$. □

Exercises

1.5.1 What is the value of $85(33 \cdot 22) - 33(22 \cdot 85)$?

1.5.2 Compute $(1992 + 1992)(1992 - 1992)$.

1.5.3 The city of Alexandria had a high temperature of $18°$ and a low temperature of $-5°$ on the same day. By how many degrees did the high temperature exceed the low temperature? *(Source: MATHCOUNTS)*

1.5.4 Evaluate $3 + (-9) - (-5)$.

1.5.5 If x and y are numbers such that $y - x = 7$, what is the value of $x - y$?

1.5.6 Compute $100 - 2 + 101 - 4 + 102 - 6 + 103 - 8 + 104 - 10$. *(Source: MATHCOUNTS)*

1.5.7 Compute $(1901 + 1902 + 1903 + \cdots + 1993) - (101 + 102 + 103 + \cdots + 193)$. *(Source: AMC 8)*

1.5.8 By how much does the sum $19 + 28 + 37 + 46 + 55 + 64 + 73 + 82 + 91$ exceed the sum $18 + 27 + 36 + 45 + 54 + 63 + 72 + 81 + 90$?

1.5.9 Compute $1990 \cdot 1991 - 1989 \cdot 1990$. *(Source: MOEMS)*

1.5.10 Compute $998 \cdot 23$ in your head.

1.5.11★ The sum of the first 10,000 positive even numbers is how much more than the sum of the first 10,000 positive odd numbers?

1.6 Reciprocals

We learned back on page 8 that adding 0 to a number doesn't change the number:

$$0 + x = x$$

for any x. For this reason, we call 0 the **identity** for addition. In Section 1.4 we also learned that for any number x, there is a number called the negation of x (written $-x$) whose sum with

x is this identity, 0. That is, $-x$ is the number that goes in the blank in the equation

$$\underline{\quad} + x = 0.$$

Does multiplication have an identity? It isn't 0, since multiplying any number by 0 gives 0, not the original number. Of course, 1 is the number we seek:

$$1 \cdot x = x$$

for any number x, so 1 is the identity for multiplication.

But the question we really want to ask is: given any number x, what number can we put in the blank to solve the equation

$$\underline{\quad} \cdot x = 1?$$

The answer to this question is called the **reciprocal** of x.

Definition: For any number x, the **reciprocal** of x, written as $\frac{1}{x}$, is the number such that

$$\frac{1}{x} \cdot x = 1.$$

This number is also called the **multiplicative inverse** of x, and we can say $\frac{1}{x}$ as "1 over x."

Of course, you've seen this sort of number before: $\frac{1}{x}$ looks like a fraction. If $x = 2$, then $\frac{1}{2}$ is the fraction one-half; if $x = 3$, then $\frac{1}{3}$ is the fraction one-third, and so on. Later, in Chapter 4, we'll see that reciprocals of positive integers are exactly the same thing as the fractions that you already know. However, for now, we'll just treat a reciprocal as a new kind of number—a number that "magically" multiplies with another number to give a product of 1. In this section, we figure out some properties of reciprocals, and then in Chapter 4, we will use these properties to learn about fractions.

We're going to assume that every number, except for 0, has a reciprocal. However, the number 0 cannot have a reciprocal. We will see why in our first problem.

 **Problems**

Problem 1.29:

(a) What is the product of 0 and any number?

(b) Using part (a), explain why 0 doesn't have a reciprocal.

Problem 1.30: Explain why the reciprocal of 1 is 1.

Problem 1.31:

(a) What is the product of $\frac{1}{2}$ and 2?

(b) Using part (a), explain why the reciprocal of $\frac{1}{2}$ is 2.

Problem 1.32:

(a) What is the product of $5 \cdot 7$ and $\frac{1}{5} \cdot \frac{1}{7}$?

(b) Using part (a), explain why the reciprocal of $5 \cdot 7$ is $\frac{1}{5} \cdot \frac{1}{7}$.

Problem 1.33:

(a) What is the product of -8 and $-\frac{1}{8}$?

(b) Using part (a), explain why the reciprocal of -8 is $-\frac{1}{8}$.

We'd like to assume that every number has a reciprocal. But we can't do this, because the number 0 is special:

Problem 1.29:

(a) What is the product of 0 and any number?

(b) Using part (a), explain why 0 doesn't have a reciprocal.

Solution for Problem 1.29:

(a) We know that 0 times any number is 0. (If you've forgotten why this is true, go back and review page 17.)

(b) If the number $\frac{1}{0}$ existed, then $\frac{1}{0} \cdot 0$ would have to equal 1. But recall part (a): the product of any number and 0 must be 0. So $\frac{1}{0}$ cannot exist! Therefore, 0 can't have a reciprocal.

□

Problem 1.29 tells us that we have to be careful with reciprocals. A number must be nonzero in order to have a reciprocal.

> **WARNING!!** The reciprocal of 0 is undefined.

Every nonzero number does in fact have a reciprocal. Let's now look at some properties of reciprocals. The "nicest" number for multiplication is 1, so it makes sense to first look at $\frac{1}{1}$.

Problem 1.30: Explain why the reciprocal of 1 is 1.

Solution for Problem 1.30: By definition, the reciprocal of 1 is the number that goes in the blank to solve the equation

$$\underline{} \cdot 1 = 1.$$

But we know that $1 \cdot 1 = 1$. So the reciprocal of 1 is 1. $\square$

Problem 1.30 confirms the "obvious" fact that $\frac{1}{1} = 1$. We also saw a general strategy for dealing with reciprocals:

> **Concept:** **Reciprocal strategy:** To show that two numbers are reciprocals of each other, multiply them and check that their product is 1.

Remember that the negation of the negation of a number is the original number. Is there a similar result for reciprocals?

Problem 1.31:

(a) What is the product of $\frac{1}{2}$ and 2?

(b) Using part (a), explain why the reciprocal of $\frac{1}{2}$ is 2.

Solution for Problem 1.31:

(a) By the definition of reciprocal, the product of $\frac{1}{2}$ and 2 is 1.

(b) From part (a), we see that the number that fills in the blank to solve

$$\underline{} \cdot \frac{1}{2} = 1$$

is 2. But that number, by definition, is the reciprocal of $\frac{1}{2}$. So the reciprocal of $\frac{1}{2}$ is 2.

$\square$

We just showed that the reciprocal of the reciprocal of 2 is 2. In the same way, for every nonzero number x, we can show that the reciprocal of $\frac{1}{x}$ is x. We can write that property as

$$\frac{1}{\left(\frac{1}{x}\right)} = x.$$

> **Important:** **Reciprocal of reciprocal:** Let x be a nonzero number. Then $\frac{1}{x}$ is
> nonzero and its reciprocal is x.

How do we multiply reciprocals? The next problem shows how.

> **Problem 1.32:**
>
> (a) What is the product of $5 \cdot 7$ and $\frac{1}{5} \cdot \frac{1}{7}$?
>
> (b) Using part (a), explain why the reciprocal of $5 \cdot 7$ is $\frac{1}{5} \cdot \frac{1}{7}$.

Solution for Problem 1.32:

(a) Let's multiply:

$$(5 \cdot 7)\left(\frac{1}{5} \cdot \frac{1}{7}\right) = \left(\frac{1}{5} \cdot 5\right)\left(\frac{1}{7} \cdot 7\right) \qquad \text{commutative and associative properties}$$
$$= 1 \cdot 1 \qquad \text{definition of reciprocal (twice)}$$
$$= 1. \qquad \text{multiplying by 1}$$

So the product is 1.

(b) From part (a), we see that $5 \cdot 7$ and $\frac{1}{5} \cdot \frac{1}{7}$ are reciprocals of each other because their product is 1. So the reciprocal of $5 \cdot 7$ is $\frac{1}{5} \cdot \frac{1}{7}$. As an equation, we have

$$\frac{1}{5} \cdot \frac{1}{7} = \frac{1}{5 \cdot 7}.$$

□

There was nothing special about the numbers 5 and 7 in Problem 1.32—the same result holds for any two nonzero numbers. We conclude that the reciprocal of a product is the product of reciprocals.

> **Important:** **Reciprocal of product:** Let x and y be nonzero numbers. Then xy
> is nonzero and its reciprocal is $\frac{1}{x} \cdot \frac{1}{y}$. That is,
>
> $$\frac{1}{x} \cdot \frac{1}{y} = \frac{1}{xy}.$$

A similar result holds for longer products. For example,

$$\frac{1}{3} \cdot \frac{1}{5} \cdot \frac{1}{7} = \frac{1}{3 \cdot 5 \cdot 7} = \frac{1}{105}.$$

How do we find the reciprocal of a negative number? The next problem shows the way.

Problem 1.33:

(a) What is the product of -8 and $-\dfrac{1}{8}$?

(b) Using part (a), explain why the reciprocal of -8 is $-\dfrac{1}{8}$.

Solution for Problem 1.33:

(a) Let's multiply the two numbers:

$$\left(-\frac{1}{8}\right)\cdot(-8) = \frac{1}{8}\cdot 8 \qquad \text{negation times negation}$$
$$= 1. \qquad \text{reciprocal property}$$

So the product is 1.

(b) From part (a), -8 and $-\dfrac{1}{8}$ are reciprocals of each other. So the reciprocal of -8 is $-\dfrac{1}{8}$. As an equation,

$$\frac{1}{-8} = -\frac{1}{8}.$$

□

In a similar way, we can take the reciprocal of any negation. The reciprocal of a negation is the negation of the reciprocal.

> **Important:** **Reciprocal of negation:** Let x be a nonzero number. Then
> $$\frac{1}{-x} = -\frac{1}{x}.$$

Exercises

1.6.1 What is the reciprocal of -1?

1.6.2 What number is *not* the reciprocal of any number?

1.6.3 What is the product of any nonzero number and twice its reciprocal?

1.6.4 Multiply the negation of a positive number by the reciprocal of that same positive number. What is the product?

1.6.5 Compute $(2\cdot 3\cdot 4)\left(\dfrac{1}{2}+\dfrac{1}{3}+\dfrac{1}{4}\right)$. *(Source: AMC 8)*

1.7 Division

You certainly already know how to do simple division, such as $10 \div 2 = 5$. You might think of this in words as "if we split 10 items into 2 equal piles, then there will be 5 items in each pile." But this way of thinking about division doesn't generalize very well to negative numbers, or to fractions, or to the stranger numbers that you will see.

We'd like a more general definition of division, but one that gives the same answers as our simpler way of thinking about division. Recall how we defined subtraction in Section 1.5 as a combination of addition and negation. Specifically, we defined

$$a - b = a + (-b).$$

In a similar way, we will define division as a combination of multiplication and reciprocation.

Definition: Let a and b be numbers such that b is not zero. Then the **quotient** $a \div b$ (pronounced "a divided by b") is defined as

$$a \div b = a \cdot \frac{1}{b}.$$

In other words, dividing by a number means multiplying by its reciprocal. For instance, $10 \div 2$ equals $10 \cdot \frac{1}{2}$. But for the definition in the box above to make sense, $10 \div 2$ should equal 5, and indeed our first problem below will show that this is still the case.

Notice that when we defined $a \div b$, we required b to be nonzero. That's because the reciprocal of 0 is undefined.

WARNING!! You can't divide by zero. Division by zero is undefined. Before dividing by a number, be sure that the number is nonzero.

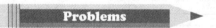
Problems

Problem 1.34: Using our definition of division and the fact that $10 = 5 \cdot 2$, explain why $10 \div 2 = 5$.

Problem 1.35: Let x be any nonzero number. Use the definition of division to answer the following questions.
(a) What is $0 \div x$?
(b) What is $x \div x$?
(c) What is $x \div 1$?
(d) What is $1 \div x$?

Problem 1.36: Use the definition of division to explain why

$$17 \div \frac{1}{5} = 17 \cdot 5.$$

Problem 1.37: Use the definition of division to compute the following quantities:

(a) $(-10) \div 2$　　　　　(b) $10 \div (-2)$　　　　　(c) $(-10) \div (-2)$

Problem 1.38:

(a) Find positive numbers a and b such that $a \div b$ is not equal to $b \div a$.

(b) Find positive numbers a, b, and c such that $(a \div b) \div c$ is not equal to $a \div (b \div c)$.

Problem 1.39: What is $20 \cdot 24 \cdot 28 \cdot 32 \div (10 \cdot 12 \cdot 14 \cdot 16)$? *(Source: MOEMS)*

Problem 1.40: Compute $(116 \cdot 93) \div (116 \cdot 31)$.

Problem 1.41:

(a) Using the definition of division, explain why

$$(12 + 18) \div 3 = 12 \div 3 + 18 \div 3.$$

(b) Is $6 \div (2 + 1)$ equal to $6 \div 2 + 6 \div 1$?

We started our discussion of subtraction by showing that our formal definition of subtraction gives us the expected result $9 - 2 = 7$. Similarly, we start here by showing that our formal definition of division gives us the expected answer for $10 \div 2$.

Problem 1.34: Using our definition of division and the fact that $10 = 5 \cdot 2$, explain why $10 \div 2 = 5$.

Solution for Problem 1.34: By the definition of division,

$$10 \div 2 = 10 \cdot \frac{1}{2}.$$

Let's now use the given multiplication fact:

$$10 \div 2 = (5 \cdot 2) \cdot \frac{1}{2}.$$

Aha! Now we can use the associative property to rewrite this as

$$10 \div 2 = 5 \cdot \left(2 \cdot \frac{1}{2}\right),$$

and by the definition of reciprocal, we have $2 \cdot \frac{1}{2} = 1$. So we finish with

$$10 \div 2 = 5 \cdot 1 = 5.$$

Here are all of our steps on one line:

$$10 \div 2 = 10 \cdot \frac{1}{2} = (5 \cdot 2) \cdot \frac{1}{2} = 5 \cdot \left(2 \cdot \frac{1}{2}\right) = 5 \cdot 1 = 5.$$

$\square$

In Problem 1.34, we used the multiplication fact $5 \cdot 2 = 10$ to show that $10 \div 2$ is 5. Another way to think of this is that $10 \div 2$ is the number that fills the blank in the multiplication equation

$$\underline{\quad} \cdot 2 = 10.$$

So division is the reverse of multiplication. This is a useful way to think about division.

> **Important:** Let a, b, and c be nonzero numbers. If a and b are nonzero and $ab = c$, then $a = c \div b$ and $b = c \div a$.

Let's try some more fundamental division problems.

Problem 1.35: Let x be any nonzero number. Use the definition of division to answer the following questions.
(a) What is $0 \div x$?
(b) What is $x \div x$?
(c) What is $x \div 1$?
(d) What is $1 \div x$?

Solution for Problem 1.35:

(a) Remember that division is multiplication by a reciprocal:

$$0 \div x = 0 \cdot \frac{1}{x} \qquad \text{definition of division}$$
$$= 0. \qquad \text{multiplying by 0}$$

(b) In a similar way,

$$x \div x = x \cdot \frac{1}{x} \qquad \text{definition of division}$$
$$= 1. \qquad \text{reciprocal property}$$

(c) Again, in a similar way,

$$x \div 1 = x \cdot \frac{1}{1} \qquad \text{definition of division}$$

$$= x \cdot 1 \qquad \text{reciprocal of 1}$$

$$= x. \qquad \text{multiplying by 1}$$

(d) Once more, we have

$$1 \div x = 1 \cdot \frac{1}{x} \qquad \text{definition of division}$$

$$= \frac{1}{x} \qquad \text{multiplying by 1}$$

So, the result of dividing a nonzero number x into 1 is the reciprocal of x.

□

Let's summarize our results from Problem 1.35:

> **Important:** Let x be any number.
>
> **Dividing into zero:** If x is nonzero, then $0 \div x = 0$.
> **Self division:** If x is nonzero, then $x \div x = 1$.
> **Dividing by 1:** $x \div 1 = x$.
> **Dividing into 1:** If x is nonzero, then $1 \div x = \frac{1}{x}$.

How do we divide by a reciprocal? Let's find out.

Problem 1.36: Use the definition of division to explain why

$$17 \div \frac{1}{5} = 17 \cdot 5.$$

Solution for Problem 1.36: By the definition of division, $17 \div \frac{1}{5}$ is 17 times the reciprocal of $\frac{1}{5}$. But the reciprocal of $\frac{1}{5}$ is 5. So $17 \div \frac{1}{5}$ is 17 times 5, which is 85. □

> **Important:** **Dividing by reciprocal:** Let x and y be numbers such that y is nonzero. Then
> $$x \div \frac{1}{y} = xy.$$

How do we compute a division that involves a negative number? For example, if we wanted to compute something like $(-10) \div (-2)$, we can't just think in terms of "we want to divide −10 items into −2 piles," because what does that mean? Instead, we'll use our already-discovered rules for division and negation to develop new rules for divisions that involve negative numbers. The next problem shows how.

Problem 1.37: Use the definition of division to compute the following quantities:

(a) $(-10) \div 2$ (b) $10 \div (-2)$ (c) $(-10) \div (-2)$

Solution for Problem 1.37: When working through these calculations, note how we are very careful to use only rules of division, multiplication, negation, and reciprocation that we have already discussed.

(a) Let's convert the division to a multiplication:

$$
\begin{aligned}
(-10) \div 2 &= (-10) \cdot \frac{1}{2} && \text{definition of division} \\
&= -\left(10 \cdot \frac{1}{2}\right) && \text{multiplying by negation} \\
&= -(10 \div 2) && \text{definition of division} \\
&= -5.
\end{aligned}
$$

(b) In a similar way,

$$
\begin{aligned}
10 \div (-2) &= 10 \cdot \frac{1}{-2} && \text{definition of division} \\
&= 10 \cdot \left(-\frac{1}{2}\right) && \text{reciprocal of negation} \\
&= -\left(10 \cdot \frac{1}{2}\right) && \text{multiplying by negation} \\
&= -(10 \div 2) && \text{definition of division} \\
&= -5.
\end{aligned}
$$

(c) Again, in a similar way,

$$
\begin{aligned}
(-10) \div (-2) &= (-10) \cdot \frac{1}{-2} && \text{definition of division} \\
&= (-10) \cdot \left(-\frac{1}{2}\right) && \text{reciprocal of negation} \\
&= 10 \cdot \frac{1}{2} && \text{negation times negation} \\
&= 10 \div 2 && \text{definition of division} \\
&= 5.
\end{aligned}
$$

□

Of course, we can perform the calculations from Problem 1.37 with numbers other than 10 and 2.

> **Important:** Let x and y be numbers such that y is nonzero.
>
> **Division into negation:** $(-x) \div y = -(x \div y)$.
> **Division by negation:** $x \div (-y) = -(x \div y)$.
> **Negation divided by negation:** $(-x) \div (-y) = x \div y$.

Let's focus on the situation when x and y are positive. Then the first equation above says that "negative divided by positive is negative." The second equation says that "positive divided by negative is negative." The third equation says that "negative divided by negative is positive." So the sign (positive or negative) of the answer comes out the same as in multiplication.

Remember that addition and multiplication are commutative and associative, but subtraction is neither commutative nor associative. What about division?

Problem 1.38:

(a) Find positive numbers a and b such that $a \div b$ is not equal to $b \div a$.

(b) Find positive numbers a, b, and c such that $(a \div b) \div c$ is not equal to $a \div (b \div c)$.

Solution for Problem 1.38:

(a) For many choices of a and b, the values of $a \div b$ and $b \div a$ are not equal. For instance, choose $a = 2$ and $b = 1$. The first expression is

$$a \div b = 2 \div 1 = 2 \cdot \frac{1}{1} = 2 \cdot 1 = 2.$$

The second expression is

$$b \div a = 1 \div 2 = 1 \cdot \frac{1}{2} = \frac{1}{2}.$$

So the two expressions are not equal. This example shows that division is *not* commutative.

(b) Again, for many values of the variables, the values of $(a \div b) \div c$ and $a \div (b \div c)$ are not equal. For instance, choose $a = 8$, $b = 4$, and $c = 2$. The first expression is

$$(a \div b) \div c = (8 \div 4) \div 2 = 2 \div 2 = 1.$$

The second expression is

$$a \div (b \div c) = 8 \div (4 \div 2) = 8 \div 2 = 4.$$

So the two expressions are again not equal. This example shows that division is *not* associative.

□

Division isn't commutative or associative. We can't regroup division as we can with addition or multiplication. For example, $8 \div 4 \div 2$ equals $(8 \div 4) \div 2$, because we do divisions from left to right. As we have just seen, we can't regroup the expression as $8 \div (4 \div 2)$.

> **WARNING!!** Division is neither commutative nor associative.

There is good news, though. Remember that we defined division in terms of multiplication (and reciprocals). And multiplication is commutative and associative. Just as we can tackle problems involving subtractions by turning the subtractions into additions, we can solve division problems by turning divisions into multiplications:

> **Concept:** **To solve division problems:**
>
>
> 1. Change all divisions to multiplications.
>
> 2. Rearrange the multiplications using the commutative and associative properties.
>
> 3. [Optional] Change some of the multiplications back to divisions.

Let's see this strategy in action.

Problem 1.39: What is $20 \cdot 24 \cdot 28 \cdot 32 \div (10 \cdot 12 \cdot 14 \cdot 16)$? *(Source: MOEMS)*

Solution for Problem 1.39: First let's convert the division to a multiplication:

$$20 \cdot 24 \cdot 28 \cdot 32 \cdot \frac{1}{10 \cdot 12 \cdot 14 \cdot 16}.$$

The reciprocal of a product is the product of reciprocals:

$$20 \cdot 24 \cdot 28 \cdot 32 \cdot \left(\frac{1}{10} \cdot \frac{1}{12} \cdot \frac{1}{14} \cdot \frac{1}{16}\right).$$

Next, bringing similar numbers together gives

$$\left(20 \cdot \frac{1}{10}\right)\left(24 \cdot \frac{1}{12}\right)\left(28 \cdot \frac{1}{14}\right)\left(32 \cdot \frac{1}{16}\right).$$

We're finished rearranging, so we can go back to division:

$$(20 \div 10)(24 \div 12)(28 \div 14)(32 \div 16).$$

Each of the above quotients is 2, so we have

$$2 \cdot 2 \cdot 2 \cdot 2.$$

So the answer is 16.

With practice, we can go from the original problem

$$20 \cdot 24 \cdot 28 \cdot 32 \div (10 \cdot 12 \cdot 14 \cdot 16)$$

to the rearrangement

$$(20 \div 10)(24 \div 12)(28 \div 14)(32 \div 16)$$

without first converting the divisions to reciprocals. □

We can use the same strategy to show that division has an interesting cancellation property.

Problem 1.40: Compute $(116 \cdot 93) \div (116 \cdot 31)$.

Solution for Problem 1.40: We convert the division to multiplication, apply the product of reciprocals property, and then rearrange the product:

$$(116 \cdot 93) \div (116 \cdot 31) = 116 \cdot 93 \cdot \frac{1}{116 \cdot 31} = 116 \cdot 93 \cdot \frac{1}{116} \cdot \frac{1}{31} = \left(116 \cdot \frac{1}{116}\right)\left(93 \cdot \frac{1}{31}\right).$$

Writing these final two products on the right-hand side as divisions, we have

$$(116 \cdot 93) \div (116 \cdot 31) = (116 \div 116)(93 \div 31).$$

But $116 \div 116 = 1$, so we are left with $93 \div 31 = 3$. □

In this problem, we **canceled** the common factor 116 from both parts of the original division $(116 \cdot 93) \div (116 \cdot 31)$, leaving $93 \div 31$. We can extend this property to other numbers.

> **Important:** **Cancel common factor:** Let a, b, and c be numbers such that a and
> ⚠️ c are nonzero. Then
>
> $$(ab) \div (ac) = b \div c.$$

Now we turn to the distributive property. Remember that multiplication distributes over addition. Does division distribute over addition? The answer depends on whether we mean dividing *by* a particular number or dividing *into* a particular number.

Problem 1.41:
(a) Using the definition of division, explain why

$$(12 + 18) \div 3 = 12 \div 3 + 18 \div 3.$$

(b) Is $6 \div (2 + 1)$ equal to $6 \div 2 + 6 \div 1$?

Solution for Problem 1.41:

(a) Of course, we can compute both sides separately. The left side is $30 \div 3$, which is 10, and the right side is $4 + 6$, which is also 10. So clearly they are equal. But let's see why both sides must be equal, using the arithmetic rules that we have discovered so far. As usual, we'll start by converting the division to a multiplication:

$$(12 + 18) \div 3 = (12 + 18) \cdot \frac{1}{3} \qquad \text{definition of division}$$

$$= 12 \cdot \frac{1}{3} + 18 \cdot \frac{1}{3} \qquad \text{distributive property of multiplication}$$

$$= 12 \div 3 + 18 \div 3. \qquad \text{definition of division (twice)}$$

(b) The first number is
$$6 \div (2 + 1) = 6 \div 3 = 2.$$

The second number is
$$6 \div 2 + 6 \div 1 = 3 + 6 = 9.$$

So the two numbers are not equal.

$\square$

The first part of Problem 1.41 explains why dividing *by* any nonzero number distributes over addition.

> **Important:** Let a, b, and c be numbers such that c is nonzero. Then
> $$(a + b) \div c = a \div c + b \div c.$$

On the other hand, the second part of Problem 1.41 shows that dividing *into* a number does *not* distribute over addition.

> **WARNING!!** Dividing *into* a particular number does *not* distribute over addition. In other words, $a \div (b + c)$ does not have to equal $a \div b + a \div c$.

In other words, we can use the distributive property to divide a sum by a number, but we can't use the distributive property to divide a number by a sum.

Remember that multiplication distributes over a long sum of three or more numbers. Dividing by a nonzero number also distributes over a long sum. For example,

$$(a + b + c) \div d = a \div d + b \div d + c \div d.$$

Similarly, we recall that multiplication distributes over subtraction. Dividing by a nonzero number also distributes over subtraction.

> **Important:** Let a, b, and c be numbers such that c is nonzero. Then
> $$(a - b) \div c = a \div c - b \div c.$$

Exercises

1.7.1 Compute $(2 + 4 + 6 + 8 + 10) \div (10 + 8 + 6 + 4 + 2)$.

1.7.2 Divide $205 \cdot 205$ by 205. What is the result?

1.7.3 What is $64{,}000 \div 800$?

1.7.4 Compute $777{,}777{,}777{,}770 \div 77{,}777{,}777{,}777$.

1.7.5 What is $28 \div \frac{1}{7}$?

1.7.6 What number is 10 more than the quotient when 78 is divided by $\frac{1}{2}$?
(Source: MATHCOUNTS)

1.7.7 What is the value of $\frac{1}{2} \div \frac{1}{2} \div \frac{1}{2} \div \frac{1}{2}$? *(Source: MATHCOUNTS)*

1.7.8 Compute $(27 \cdot 31 \cdot 35 \cdot 39 \cdot 43) \div (43 \cdot 39 \cdot 35 \cdot 31)$.

1.7.9 Compute $(50 \cdot 60 \cdot 70 \cdot 80) \div (5 \cdot 6 \cdot 7 \cdot 8)$.

1.7.10 Compute $(77{,}777{,}777{,}777 + 77{,}077) \div 7$.

1.7.11 Compute $(124 + 104 + 84 + 64 + 44 + 24) \div (62 + 52 + 42 + 32 + 22 + 12)$.

1.8 Summary

In this chapter, we explored the basic arithmetic operations of addition, negation, subtraction, multiplication, reciprocation, and division. Our goal was to derive as many properties about these operations as possible.

> **Important:** **Order of operations:** Perform the operations in an expression in the following order.
>
> 1. Evaluate expressions inside parentheses first.
>
> 2. Compute powers. (We cover powers in Chapter 2.)
>
> 3. Multiply and divide from left to right.
>
> 4. Add and subtract from left to right.

We described that the following properties of arithmetic hold for all numbers:

Important: Let a, b, and c be numbers.

Addition is commutative: $a + b = b + a$.
Addition is associative: $(a + b) + c = a + (b + c)$.
Adding zero: $a + 0 = a$.
Multiplication is commutative: $ab = ba$.
Multiplication is associative: $(ab)c = a(bc)$.
Multiplying by 1: $1a = a$.
Multiplication distributes over addition: $a(b + c) = ab + ac$ and $(b + c)a = ba + ca$.
Negation property: $-a + a = 0$.
Reciprocal property: If a is nonzero, then $\frac{1}{a} \cdot a = 1$.

These nine rules are the only assumptions that we need! Starting from these few properties, we can figure out a surprising number of other useful facts.

We defined subtraction and division in terms of addition and multiplication.

Definitions: Let a and b be numbers.

Subtraction: $a - b = a + (-b)$.

Division: If b is nonzero, then $a \div b = a \cdot \dfrac{1}{b}$.

From these few basic properties and definitions, we proved dozens of other important properties of arithmetic. You shouldn't have to memorize these properties. Instead, you should be comfortable with *why* each of the following rules of arithmetic are true. If you aren't, go back and review the appropriate section of the chapter.

Important: Let a, b, and c be numbers.

Negation of negation: $-(-a) = a$.
Negation of sum: $-(a + b) = (-a) + (-b)$.
Multiplying by zero: $0a = 0$.
Multiplying by -1: $(-1)a = -a$.
Multiplying by negation: $(-a)b = -(ab)$ and $a(-b) = -(ab)$.
Negation times negation: $(-a)(-b) = ab$.

Continued on the following page.

Continued from the previous page. Let a, b, and c be numbers.

Subtracting from zero: $0 - a = -a$.

Self subtraction: $a - a = 0$.

Subtracting zero: $a - 0 = a$.

Subtraction of negation: $a - (-b) = a + b$.

Subtraction from negation: $-a - b = -(a + b)$.

Negation of subtraction: $-(a - b) = b - a$.

Multiplication distributes over subtraction: $a(b - c) = ab - ac$ and $(b - c)a = ba - ca$.

Reciprocal of reciprocal: If a is nonzero, then the reciprocal of $\frac{1}{a}$ is a.

Reciprocal of negation: If a is nonzero, then $\frac{1}{-a} = -\frac{1}{a}$.

Reciprocal of product: If a and b are nonzero, then $\frac{1}{ab} = \frac{1}{a} \cdot \frac{1}{b}$.

Dividing into zero: If a is nonzero, then $0 \div a = 0$.

Self division: If a is nonzero, then $a \div a = 1$.

Dividing by 1: $a \div 1 = a$.

Dividing into 1: If x is nonzero, then $1 \div x = \frac{1}{x}$.

Dividing by reciprocal: If b is nonzero, then $a \div \frac{1}{b} = ab$.

Dividing into negation: If b is nonzero, then $(-a) \div b = -(a \div b)$.

Dividing by negation: If b is nonzero, then $a \div (-b) = -(a \div b)$.

Negation divided by negation: If b is nonzero, then $(-a) \div (-b) = a \div b$.

Cancel common factor: If a and c are nonzero, then $(ab) \div (ac) = b \div c$.

Division by a number distributes over addition: If c is nonzero, then $(a + b) \div c = a \div c + b \div c$.

Division by a number distributes over subtraction: If c is nonzero, then $(a - b) \div c = a \div c - b \div c$.

WARNING!! Keep these arithmetic warnings in mind:

- Subtraction is neither commutative nor associative. That is, $a - b$ and $b - a$ are **not** necessarily equal, and neither are $a - (b - c)$ and $(a - b) - c$.

- You can't divide by zero. Division by zero is undefined. Before dividing by a number, be sure that the number is nonzero.

> **WARNING!!** Watch out for these, too:
>
> ☢
>
> - Division is neither commutative nor associative. That is, $a \div b$ and $b \div a$ are **not** necessarily equal, and neither are $a \div (b \div c)$ and $(a \div b) \div c$.
>
> - We can use the distributive property to divide a sum by a number, but we can't use the distributive property to divide a number by a sum. In other words, $a \div (b + c)$ is **not** necessarily equal to $a \div b + a \div c$. Similarly, $a \div (b - c)$ is **not** the same as $a \div b - a \div c$.

REVIEW PROBLEMS ▶

1.42   Compute $90 + 91 + 92 + 93 + 94 + 95 + 96 + 97 + 98 + 99$. *(Source: AMC 8)*

1.43   Compute the product $25 \cdot (12 \cdot 8)$ in your head.

1.44   Compute $3(101 + 103 + 105 + 107 + 109 + 111 + 113 + 115 + 117 + 119)$.

1.45   Simplify the expression $\big((1 \cdot 2) + (3 \cdot 4) - (5 \cdot 6) + (7 \cdot 8)\big) \cdot (9 \cdot 0)$. *(Source: MATHCOUNTS)*

1.46   What is $42 + 7 - 6 \cdot 6 + 3 \cdot (-1) \cdot 0$ minus $\big(42 + 7 - 6 \cdot 6 + 3 \cdot (-1)\big) \cdot 0$? *(Source: MATHCOUNTS)*

1.47   What is the value of $(185 + 378 + 579) - (85 + 178 + 279)$?

1.48   Calculate $11 + (-15) + 11 - (-15) + 11 - 15 - (11 + 15)$.

1.49   Express in simplest form: $6\big((25 - 98) - (19 - 98)\big)$. *(Source: MATHCOUNTS)*

1.50   Compute: $1 - 3 + 5 - 7 + 9 - 11 + 13 - 15 + 17 - 19 + 21 - 23 + 25$.

1.51   Evaluate $693 \cdot 1587 - 692 \cdot 1587$.

1.52   Express in simplest form: $(-20)\big((-3)(-15) - (-6)(3)\big)$. *(Source: MATHCOUNTS)*

1.53   Compute $4(299) + 3(299) + 2(299) + 298$. *(Source: AMC 8)*

1.54   Evaluate $40 \cdot \dfrac{1}{8} + 40 \div \dfrac{1}{8} + 40 \cdot \dfrac{1}{5} + 40 \div \dfrac{1}{5}$.

1.55   Express in simplest form: $\big(6 \div (-3)\big)(4 - 12)$. *(Source: MATHCOUNTS)*

1.56   Simplify $(-13) + (-13) \div (-13) \cdot (-13) - (-13)$.

1.57   What is the value of $123{,}123$ divided by 1001? *(Source: MATHCOUNTS)*

1.58 What is the reciprocal of $2 \cdot 3 \cdot \dfrac{1}{4} \cdot \dfrac{1}{9}$?

1.59 Compute $\dfrac{1}{2} \div \dfrac{1}{6}$.

1.60 Compute $(3 \cdot 4) \div \left(\dfrac{1}{5} \cdot \dfrac{1}{6} \right)$.

1.61 Sean adds up all the even integers from 2 to 500, inclusive. Julie adds up all the integers from 1 to 250, inclusive. What is Sean's sum divided by Julie's sum? *(Source: MATHCOUNTS)*

1.62 Gary wanted to compute $200 \div 10 \div 2$, and his reasoning was: "Well, $10 \div 2$ is 5, so $200 \div 10 \div 2$ is the same as $200 \div 5$, which is 40, so the answer is 40." Is Gary correct? Why or why not?

Challenge Problems

1.63 What is the sum of the first sixty-one positive integers?

1.64 What is the value of the sum $5 + 10 + 15 + \cdots + 95 + 100$?

1.65 What is the sum $-100 + (-99) + (-98) + \cdots + 97 + 98$?

1.66 Find the sum $(-39) + (-37) + (-35) + \cdots + (-1)$. *(Source: MATHCOUNTS)*

1.67 Find the value of $100 - 98 + 96 - 94 + 92 - 90 + \cdots + 8 - 6 + 4 - 2$. *(Source: MOEMS)*

1.68 What is the product $\big(40 + (-10)\big)\big(36 + (-9)\big)\big(32 + (-8)\big) \cdots \big(-32 + 8\big)\big(-36 + 9\big)\big(-40 + 10\big)$, where the first number in each factor is decreasing by 4, and the second number in each factor is increasing by 1? *(Source: MATHCOUNTS)*

1.69 "Echoing" a one-digit number to make it a two-digit number (for example, making 2 into 22) is equivalent to multiplying by eleven. Echoing a two-digit number to make it a four-digit number (for example, making 23 into 2323) is equivalent to multiplying the two-digit number by what value? *(Source: MATHCOUNTS)*

1.70 The number 222,222 is equal to the product $37{,}037 \cdot 6$. What is the product of 37,037 and 27? *(Source: MATHCOUNTS)*

1.71 Given numbers a and b, let $a @ b$ equal $2a + 2b$. For example, $3 @ 4$ equals 14.

(a) Show that @ is commutative.

(b) Show that @ is *not* associative.

1.72   Given numbers a and b, let $a \# b$ equal a. For example, $3 \# 4$ equals 3.

(a) Show that $\#$ is associative.

(b) Show that $\#$ is *not* commutative.

1.73   Let $a, b, x,$ and y be numbers. Show that $(a + b)(x + y)$ equals $ax + ay + bx + by$.

1.74   Let $a, b,$ and c be numbers. Simplify the expression $\big(a - (b - c)\big) - \big((a - b) - c\big)$. *(Source: MATHCOUNTS)*

1.75★   Find the sum of the digits in the answer to

$$\underbrace{9999\ldots99}_{\text{94 nines}} \times \underbrace{4444\ldots44}_{\text{94 fours}} .$$

The first number has 94 digits, each of which is a 9. The second number also has 94 digits, each of which is a 4. *(Source: AMC 8)* **Hints:** 57, 143

1.76★   Given numbers a and b, define $a \odot b$ to be $a + ab + b$. For example, $2 \odot 3 = 2 + 2(3) + 3 = 11$.

(a) Show that the operation $\odot$ is commutative.

(b) Show that $\odot$ is associative.

(c) What number is the identity of $\odot$? That is, what is the number I such that $x \odot I = x$ for all values of x?

(d) What number is the inverse of 1 with respect to $\odot$? That is, what number goes in the blank to solve ___ $\odot\, 1 = I$, where I is the number that you found in part (c)?

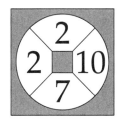 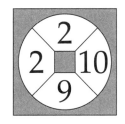 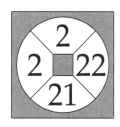 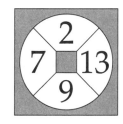

Numbers are friends for me, more or less. It doesn't mean the same for you, does it, 3,844? For you it's just a three and an eight and a four and a four. But I say, "Hi, 62 squared." – Willem Klein

CHAPTER 2

Exponents

We have a special notation for writing a product in which all of the numbers being multiplied are the same. For example, we can write the product

$$2 \cdot 2 \cdot 2 \cdot 2 \cdot 2 \cdot 2$$

as simply

$$2^6.$$

We call the entire expression 2^6 a **power**. More specifically, 2^6 is a power of 2. The number on the bottom is the **base**, and that's the number we repeatedly multiply. The number on top is the **exponent**, and the exponent tells us how many of the base are multiplied. So 2^6 is a power with base 2 and exponent 6. We can evaluate 2^6 by multiplying six 2's, and we find

$$2^6 = 2 \cdot 2 \cdot 2 \cdot 2 \cdot 2 \cdot 2 = 64.$$

In words, we say 2^6 as "2 raised to the 6th power," or "2 raised to the 6th," or just "2 to the 6th." We use the word **exponentiation** to refer generally to raising numbers to powers, much as we use the words addition and multiplication to refer to the processes of adding and multiplying.

In this chapter, we'll explore various useful rules that exponentiations follow. These are sometimes referred to as **exponent laws**. After we become comfortable with the exponent laws, we'll explore what happens if an exponent is 0 or negative.

2.1 Squares

We call the product of a number and itself a **square**. We can write a square as a power using 2 as the exponent. For example, $3^2 = 3 \cdot 3$. When speaking, we say "3 **squared**" to mean 3^2, and "squaring" a number means to multiply the number by itself.

> **Definition:** Let a be a number. The **square** of a, written a^2, is equal to $a \cdot a$.

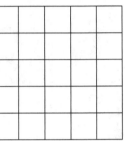

The reason we call a^2 "a squared" comes from geometry. To see why, consider the large square on the right that consists of 5 rows and 5 columns of little squares. The number of little squares is $5 \cdot 5$, which is 25. Of course, we can also write $5 \cdot 5$ as 5^2. That is, the number of little squares at the right is 5 squared. This gives us some intuition about where "square" numbers get their name.

A **perfect square** is the square of an integer. For example, 100 is a perfect square because it is the square of 10. Here is a table of the 30 smallest perfect squares:

$0^2 = 0$	$1^2 = 1$	$2^2 = 4$	$3^2 = 9$	$4^2 = 16$
$5^2 = 25$	$6^2 = 36$	$7^2 = 49$	$8^2 = 64$	$9^2 = 81$
$10^2 = 100$	$11^2 = 121$	$12^2 = 144$	$13^2 = 169$	$14^2 = 196$
$15^2 = 225$	$16^2 = 256$	$17^2 = 289$	$18^2 = 324$	$19^2 = 361$
$20^2 = 400$	$21^2 = 441$	$22^2 = 484$	$23^2 = 529$	$24^2 = 576$
$25^2 = 625$	$26^2 = 676$	$27^2 = 729$	$28^2 = 784$	$29^2 = 841$

How many of the squares above do you know? Over time, you will get to know them well.

As a reminder, we compute powers in the order of operations just after expressions inside parentheses and before multiplication and division:

> **Important:** **Order of operations:** We perform the operations in an expression in the following order.
>
> 1. Evaluate expressions inside parentheses first.
>
> 2. Compute powers.
>
> 3. Multiply and divide from left to right.
>
> 4. Add and subtract from left to right.

For example, in the expression $7 \cdot 3^2$, we first square 3 (making 9), and then multiply by 7 (making 63).

 **Problems** ▶

Problem 2.1: Simplify $180 - 5 \cdot 2^2$.

Problem 2.2: What is the value of $(2x + 5)^2$ when $x = 3$? In other words, in the expression $(2x + 5)^2$, replace the x with 3, and evaluate the new expression.

Problem 2.3:
(a) Evaluate $(-12)^2$.
(b) How are $(-a)^2$ and a^2 related?

Problem 2.4:
(a) What is $(-2)^2$?
(b) The expression -2^2 is the negation of the square of 2. What number does -2^2 equal?
(c) Given $x = -2$, find the value of $2x^2 + 3x + 4$.

Problem 2.5:
(a) Explain why $(8 \cdot 125)^2 = 8^2 \cdot 125^2$.
(b) How does part (a) help us compute $8^2 \cdot 125^2$ quickly?

Problem 2.6: Evaluate $\left(\dfrac{1}{7}\right)^2$.

Problem 2.7: Explain why $(7224 \div 12)^2 = 7224^2 \div 12^2$.

Problem 2.8:
(a) What is the value of $(5 + 6)^2$?
(b) What is the value of $5^2 + 6^2$?
(c) Is $(5 + 6)^2$ equal to $5^2 + 6^2$?

Problem 2.9:
(a) Using the picture at the right, explain why $8^2 = 7^2 + 2(7) + 1$.
(b) Explain why $901^2 = 900^2 + 2(900) + 1$.
(c) What is 901^2?

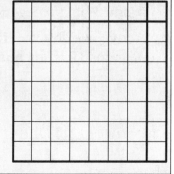

Let's warm up with a quick calculation.

Problem 2.1: Simplify $180 - 5 \cdot 2^2$.

Solution for Problem 2.1: We compute the square first, then multiply, and then subtract:

$$180 - 5 \cdot 2^2 = 180 - 5 \cdot 4 = 180 - 20 = 160.$$

□

The next problem is also about evaluating an expression. It involves the extra step of replacing a variable with a number.

Problem 2.2: What is the value of $(2x + 5)^2$ when $x = 3$? In other words, in the expression $(2x + 5)^2$, replace the x with 3, and evaluate the new expression.

Solution for Problem 2.2: Let's first replace the x with a 3 in the expression $(2x + 5)^2$. Since $2x$ means $2 \cdot x$, we get

$$(2x + 5)^2 = (2 \cdot 3 + 5)^2.$$

Next we evaluate $(2 \cdot 3 + 5)^2$ by following the order of operations:

$$(2 \cdot 3 + 5)^2 = (6 + 5)^2 = (11)^2 = 121.$$

□

Next, let's investigate squares of negations.

Problem 2.3:
(a) Evaluate $(-12)^2$.

(b) How are $(-a)^2$ and a^2 related?

Solution for Problem 2.3:

(a) First, we write the square as a product: $(-12)^2 = (-12)(-12)$. Applying the rule for a product of two negations, we have $(-12)(-12) = 12 \cdot 12 = 144$. So, we have $(-12)^2 = 144$.

(b) Above, we showed that $(-12)^2 = 12 \cdot 12 = 12^2$. We can do the same for the square of any negation. For any number a, we have

$$
\begin{aligned}
(-a)^2 &= (-a)(-a) &&\text{definition of a square} \\
&= a \cdot a &&\text{negation times negation} \\
&= a^2. &&\text{definition of a square}
\end{aligned}
$$

□

As Problem 2.3 shows, squaring the negation of a number produces the same result as squaring the original number produces. For example, $(-1)^2 = 1^2$ and $(-2)^2 = 2^2$. So squaring negative integers won't give us new perfect squares. The only perfect squares are $0^2, 1^2, 2^2$, and so on.

> **Important:** ⚠ **Square of negation:** Let a be a number. Then
>
> $$(-a)^2 = a^2.$$

So, the square of a negative number is positive. The square of a positive number is also positive. The square of 0 is 0. Therefore, every square is either positive or zero. In other words, every square is nonnegative.

> **Important:** ⚠ **Squares are nonnegative:** Let a be a number. Then a^2 is nonnegative.

Let's use what we just learned about squaring negations to solve another problem about replacing a variable with a number.

> **Problem 2.4:**
> (a) What is $(-2)^2$?
> (b) The expression -2^2 is the negation of the square of 2. What number does -2^2 equal?
> (c) Given $x = -2$, find the value of $2x^2 + 3x + 4$.

Solution for Problem 2.4:

(a) Because of the parentheses, this part asks us to square -2. Using what we just learned about squaring negative numbers, we have

$$(-2)^2 = 2^2 = 4.$$

(b) Hmm, this part looks like part (a). But the missing parentheses make all the difference. The expression -2^2 is the negation of the square of 2. In other words, we have to square 2 first, and then negate. So we get

$$-2^2 = -(2^2) = -4.$$

> **WARNING!!** ☢ The square of a negation and the negation of a square are **NOT** the same thing! For example, $(-2)^2$ and -2^2 are **NOT** equal.

(c) In the expression $2x^2 + 3x + 4$, we first replace each x with -2:

$$2x^2 + 3x + 4 = 2(-2)^2 + 3(-2) + 4.$$

Note that we were careful to write (-2) instead of -2. Since x^2 means to square x, we want $(-2)^2$, the square of -2, not -2^2, the negation of 2^2. Similarly, since $3x$ means 3 times x, we want $3(-2)$, which means 3 times -2.

Finally, we evaluate the expression using the order of operations:

$$2(-2)^2 + 3(-2) + 4 = 2(4) + 3(-2) + 4 = 8 + (-6) + 4 = 2 + 4 = 6.$$

□

Now that we know how to handle the square of a negation, let's take a look at the square of a product.

Problem 2.5:

(a) Explain why $(8 \cdot 125)^2 = 8^2 \cdot 125^2$.

(b) How does part (a) help us compute $8^2 \cdot 125^2$ quickly?

Solution for Problem 2.5:

(a) Let's rewrite the square $(8 \cdot 125)^2$ as a product and then group equal numbers:

$$
\begin{aligned}
(8 \cdot 125)^2 &= (8 \cdot 125)(8 \cdot 125) &&\text{definition of a square} \\
&= (8 \cdot 8)(125 \cdot 125) &&\text{commutative and associative properties} \\
&= 8^2 \cdot 125^2. &&\text{definition of a square}
\end{aligned}
$$

So, we see that a square of a product, $(8 \cdot 125)^2$, equals a product of squares, $8^2 \cdot 125^2$.

(b) The product $8 \cdot 125$ is 1000, which is an easy number to square. So, the relationship in part (a) makes $8^2 \cdot 125^2$ easy to compute:

$$8^2 \cdot 125^2 = (8 \cdot 125)^2 = 1000^2 = 1000 \cdot 1000 = 1{,}000{,}000.$$

□

We can replace the 8 and the 125 in part (a) with any two numbers to see that the square of a product is the product of squares.

> **Important: Square of product:** Let a and b be numbers. Then
>
> $$(ab)^2 = a^2 b^2.$$

The same result holds for longer products. For example, we have $(abc)^2 = a^2 b^2 c^2$.

We now know how to square products. Let's move on to squaring quotients. We'll start by learning how to square a reciprocal, since we use reciprocals to define division.

Problem 2.6: Evaluate $\left(\frac{1}{7}\right)^2$.

Solution for Problem 2.6: Again, let's rewrite the square as a product:

$$
\begin{aligned}
\left(\frac{1}{7}\right)^2 &= \frac{1}{7} \cdot \frac{1}{7} && \text{definition of a square} \\
&= \frac{1}{7 \cdot 7} && \text{product of reciprocals} \\
&= \frac{1}{7^2} && \text{definition of a square} \\
&= \frac{1}{49}. && 7^2 = 49
\end{aligned}
$$

□

We can use the steps above to square any reciprocal, and we have:

> **Important:** **Square of reciprocal:** Let a be a nonzero number. Then
> $$
> \left(\frac{1}{a}\right)^2 = \frac{1}{a^2}.
> $$

Now that we know how to square a reciprocal, we're ready to square a quotient.

Problem 2.7: Explain why $(7224 \div 12)^2 = 7224^2 \div 12^2$.

Solution for Problem 2.7: We could compute both $(7224 \div 12)^2$ and $7224^2 \div 12^2$, but squaring 7224 is a lot of work! Instead, let's try using the properties of squares and division. Because division is multiplication by a reciprocal, we can use our rules for the square of a product and the square of a reciprocal:

$$
\begin{aligned}
(7224 \div 12)^2 &= \left(7224 \cdot \frac{1}{12}\right)^2 && \text{definition of division} \\
&= 7224^2 \cdot \left(\frac{1}{12}\right)^2 && \text{square of product} \\
&= 7224^2 \cdot \frac{1}{12^2} && \text{square of reciprocal} \\
&= 7224^2 \div 12^2. && \text{definition of division}
\end{aligned}
$$

So, the square of $7224 \div 12$ is $7224^2 \div 12^2$. □

We can start with $(a \div b)^2$ and follow the same steps as in Problem 2.7 to get the rule below:

> **Important:** **Square of quotient:** Let a and b be numbers such that b is nonzero. Then
> $$(a \div b)^2 = a^2 \div b^2.$$

We have found simple formulas for the square of a negation, the square of a product, the square of a reciprocal, and the square of a quotient. Is there a simple formula for the square of a sum?

Problem 2.8:

(a) What is the value of $(5 + 6)^2$?

(b) What is the value of $5^2 + 6^2$?

(c) Is $(5 + 6)^2$ equal to $5^2 + 6^2$?

Solution for Problem 2.8:

(a) The value of $(5 + 6)^2$ is $(5 + 6)^2 = 11^2 = 121$.

(b) The value of $5^2 + 6^2$ is $5^2 + 6^2 = 25 + 36 = 61$.

(c) No. By the first two parts, $(5 + 6)^2$ is greater than $5^2 + 6^2$, so the two expressions are not equal.

□

> **WARNING!!** If a and b are nonzero, then $(a + b)^2$ is **NOT** equal to $a^2 + b^2$. That is, the square of a sum of two nonzero numbers is **NOT** equal to the sum of the squares of the numbers.

As Problem 2.8 shows, $(a + b)^2$ is typically *not* equal to $a^2 + b^2$. There is a formula for $(a + b)^2$ though. We will start by finding a formula for $(a + 1)^2$.

Problem 2.9:

(a) Using the picture at the right, explain why $8^2 = 7^2 + 2(7) + 1$.

(b) Explain why $901^2 = 900^2 + 2(900) + 1$.

(c) What is 901^2?

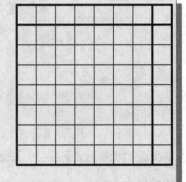

Solution for Problem 2.9:

(a) On one hand, the entire picture is a square with 8 rows and 8 columns. So it has 8^2 little squares.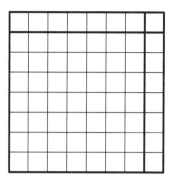

On the other hand, we split the grid of little squares into four pieces with the bold lines inside the square. The big piece is a square with 7 rows and 7 columns, so it has 7^2 little squares. The two skinny rectangles have 7 little squares each. Finally, there is 1 lonely square in the upper right corner. In all, the number of little squares is

$$7^2 + 2(7) + 1.$$

We have counted the same squares in two different ways, so these two counts must be equal. We found 8^2 little squares with our first method and $7^2 + 2(7) + 1$ with the second, so

$$8^2 = 7^2 + 2(7) + 1.$$

Let's check this equation. The left side, 8^2, is 64. The right side, $7^2 + 2(7) + 1$, simplifies to $49 + 14 + 1$, which is also 64. Yes, the equation checks out.

(b) We can use the same argument. Imagine a huge square with 901 rows and 901 columns. It will have 901^2 little squares.

We can also count the little squares by cutting the huge square into the four pieces in the pattern shown at the right:

- A square with 900 rows and 900 columns. This square has 900^2 little squares.

- One skinny rectangle that is a row of 900 little squares.

- One skinny rectangle that is a column of 900 little squares.

- 1 lonely little square.

This gives us a total of $900^2 + 2(900) + 1$ little squares. But this must be the same total as our first count, 901^2, so

$$901^2 = 900^2 + 2(900) + 1.$$

(c) Using part (b), we have

$$901^2 = 900^2 + 2(900) + 1 = 900^2 + 1800 + 1 = 810{,}000 + 1801 = 811{,}801.$$

So we have found a quick way to go from one perfect square to the next.

□

In the same way, we get the formula

$$(a + 1)^2 = a^2 + 2a + 1,$$

whenever a is a positive integer. Using the distributive property, we can show that this formula holds for *every* number a:

$$(a + 1)^2 = (a + 1)(a + 1) = a(a + 1) + 1(a + 1) = a^2 + a + a + 1 = a^2 + 2a + 1.$$

Notice that we can also write $a^2 + a + a + 1$ as

$$(a + 1)^2 = a^2 + a + (a + 1).$$

So, we can get $(a + 1)^2$ by starting with a^2 and adding both a and $(a + 1)$. For example, we can compute 901^2 by adding 900 and 901 to 900^2:

$$901^2 = 900^2 + 900 + 901 = 900^2 + 1801 = 810,000 + 1801 = 811,801.$$

Just as $(a + 1)^2 = a^2 + 2a + 1$ for any value of a, we can square the sum of any two numbers a and b with the formula

$$(a + b)^2 = a^2 + 2ab + b^2.$$

You'll have a chance to explain why this works in Challenge Problem 2.73.

Exercises

2.1.1 Evaluate the following expressions.

(a) $8 + 6(3 - 8)^2$

(b) $5(3 + 4 \cdot 2) - 6^2$

(c) $92 - 45 \div (3 \cdot 5) - 5^2$

(d) $8(6^2 - 3(11)) \div 8 + 3$

2.1.2 Evaluate the following expressions.

(a) $(7 + 5)^2 - 7^2 - 5^2$

(b) $25^2 \cdot 16^2$

(c) $480^2 \div 40^2$

(d) 101^2

2.1.3 What is the value of the expression $x^2 + 2x - 6$ when $x = -3$?

2.1.4 Evaluate $x^2(x - t)$ if $x = -4$ and $t = 2$.

2.1.5 A calculator has a squaring key $\boxed{x^2}$ that replaces the current number displayed with its square. For example, if the display is $\boxed{3}$ when the $\boxed{x^2}$ key is pressed, then the display becomes $\boxed{9}$. If the display reads $\boxed{2}$, how many times must you press the $\boxed{x^2}$ key to produce a displayed number greater than 500? *(Source: AMC 8)*

2.1.6   What perfect square is closest to 5000?

2.1.7   What year in the 19$^\text{th}$ century (the years 1801 through 1900) was a perfect square?

2.1.8   How many positive integers less than 500 are perfect squares?

2.1.9★   How many perfect squares are between 1000 and 2000? *(Source: MOEMS)*

2.1.10★   The sum $1^2 + 2^2 + 3^2 + 4^2 + \cdots + 25^2$ is equal to 5525. Evaluate $2^2 + 4^2 + 6^2 + 8^2 + \cdots + 50^2$. *(Source: MOEMS)* **Hints:** 116, 14

2.2   Higher Exponents

Just as a number raised to the 2$^\text{nd}$ power is called a "square," a number raised to the 3$^\text{rd}$ power is called a **cube**. The cube of an integer is also called a **perfect cube**. So, 7^3 is called "7 cubed," and 7^3 equals $7 \cdot 7 \cdot 7$. We don't have special names for higher powers. We say 7^4 as "7 raised to the 4$^\text{th}$" or just "7 to the 4$^\text{th}$." As a reminder, we call the entire expression 7^4 a **power**. We call the number on the bottom the **base**. We call the number on top the **exponent**. So 7^4 is a power with base 7 and exponent 4. Furthermore, 7^4 is a power of 7 and a 4$^\text{th}$ power.

Of course, there are 5$^\text{th}$ powers, 6$^\text{th}$ powers, and so on. For instance, 7^{20} means

$$7^{20} = 7 \cdot 7 \cdot 7 \cdot 7 \cdot 7 \cdot 7 \cdot 7 \cdot 7 \cdot 7 \cdot 7 \cdot 7 \cdot 7 \cdot 7 \cdot 7 \cdot 7 \cdot 7 \cdot 7 \cdot 7 \cdot 7 \cdot 7.$$

It's a pain to write that many 7's, so we shorten the right-hand side as follows:

$$7^{20} = \underbrace{7 \times 7 \times \cdots \times 7}_{20 \text{ copies of } 7}.$$

The phrase "20 copies of 7" tells us how many 7's we are multiplying together.

Definition: Let a be any number and let n be a positive integer. The **power** a^n, pronounced "a to the n," is defined by the equation

$$a^n = \underbrace{a \times a \times \cdots \times a}_{n \text{ copies of } a}.$$

For example, $a^5 = a \cdot a \cdot a \cdot a \cdot a$.

When the exponent is 2, the equation becomes $a^2 = a \cdot a$, which matches our previous definition of squares. When the exponent is 1, the equation becomes $a^1 = a$. For instance, 17^1 is 17. Any number raised to the exponent 1 equals the original number.

In the last section, we showed how to square products, reciprocals, and quotients. In a similar way, we can raise these expressions to higher exponents.

> **Important:** Let a and b be numbers. Let n be a positive integer.
>
> **Power of product:** $(ab)^n = a^n b^n$.
>
> **Power of reciprocal:** If b is nonzero, then $\left(\frac{1}{b}\right)^n = \frac{1}{b^n}$.
>
> **Power of quotient:** If b is nonzero, then $(a \div b)^n = a^n \div b^n$.

The proofs of these properties are basically the same as the ones we presented in the last section, so we will skip them. The "power of product" rule also holds for longer products. For instance, $(abc)^n = a^n b^n c^n$.

> **WARNING!!** Suppose a and b are nonzero numbers, and n is an integer greater than 2. Just as $(a + b)^2$ is **NOT** equal to $a^2 + b^2$, the expression $(a + b)^n$ is **NOT** necessarily equal to $a^n + b^n$.

As an example why this warning is true, consider what happens if $a = b = 1$ and $n = 3$. Then, we have $(a+b)^n = (1+1)^3 = 8$ and $a^n + b^n = 1^3 + 1^3 = 2$, so $(a+b)^n$ and $a^n + b^n$ are not equal.

Powers have other interesting properties. We will explore those properties in the rest of this section.

Problems

Problem 2.10:

(a) Compute $(-4)^3$.

(b) For how many integers n is n^3 between -50 and 50? *(Source: MATHCOUNTS)*

Problem 2.11: Let a be any number.

(a) Explain why $(-a)^4 = a^4$.

(b) Explain why $(-a)^5 = -a^5$.

Problem 2.12: Evaluate $(-1)^{(5^2)} + 1^{(2^5)}$. *(Source: MATHCOUNTS)*

Problem 2.13: Addition and multiplication are commutative. That is, $a + b = b + a$ and $ab = ba$ for all a and b. In this problem, we explore whether or not exponentiation is commutative.

(a) What is 3^4?

(b) What is 4^3?

(c) Is exponentiation commutative? That is, if a and b are positive integers, then must we have $a^b = b^a$?

Problem 2.14: Addition and multiplication are associative. That is, $(a + b) + c = a + (b + c)$ and $(ab)c = a(bc)$ for any numbers a, b, and c. In this problem, we explore whether or not exponentiation is associative.

(a) What is $(2^2)^3$?

(b) What is $2^{(2^3)}$?

(c) Is exponentiation associative? That is, if a, b, and c are positive integers, must we have $(a^b)^c = a^{(b^c)}$?

Problem 2.15: Let a be any number. Explain why $a^3 \cdot a^5 = a^8$.

Problem 2.16: Express $5^{17} + 5^{17} + 5^{17} + 5^{17} + 5^{17}$ as a power of 5. *(Source: MATHCOUNTS)*

Problem 2.17: Explain why $9^7 \div 9^3 = 9^4$.

Problem 2.18: Explain why $(7^5)^3 = 7^{5 \cdot 3}$.

Problem 2.19: Express each of the following as a power of 2:

(a) $(2^7 \cdot 2^8) \div 2^3$ (b) $(2^6)^4 \div 2^7$ (c) $4^6 \div 8^2$

Problem 2.20:

(a) Express $11^{20,000}$ as a 10,000th power by finding the positive integer a such that $11^{20,000}$ equals $a^{10,000}$.

(b) Express $5^{30,000}$ as a 10,000th power.

(c) Express $2^{70,000}$ as a 10,000th power.

(d) Which of the numbers $11^{20,000}$, $5^{30,000}$, and $2^{70,000}$ is the greatest?

Problem 2.10:

(a) Compute $(-4)^3$.

(b) For how many integers n is n^3 between -50 and 50? *(Source: MATHCOUNTS)*

Solution for Problem 2.10:

(a) The expression $(-4)^3$ means the product of three -4's, so

$$(-4)^3 = (-4)(-4)(-4) = (16)(-4) = -64.$$

This result shows one key difference between squares and cubes. While the square of a negative number is positive, the cube of a negative number is negative. We see why in our computation of $(-4)^3$. The product of the first two -4's in $(-4)(-4)(-4)$ is positive, and then we multiply by one more -4 and have a negative number as a final result. So, while there are no negative squares, there *are* negative cubes.

> **Important:** **Cube of negation:** Let a be any number. Then
> $$(-a)^3 = -a^3.$$

(b) We have
$$0^3 = 0 \cdot 0 \cdot 0 = 0, \qquad 1^3 = 1 \cdot 1 \cdot 1 = 1, \qquad 2^3 = 2 \cdot 2 \cdot 2 = 8,$$
$$3^3 = 3 \cdot 3 \cdot 3 = 27, \qquad 4^3 = 4 \cdot 4 \cdot 4 = 64.$$

We see that 4^3 is greater than 50, and the cube of any number greater than 4 is greater than 4^3. So, the only nonnegative cubes between -50 and 50 are 0^3, 1^3, 2^3, and 3^3. But we have to be careful not to forget about negatives! We have

$$(-1)^3 = -1^3 = -1, \qquad (-2)^3 = -2^3 = -8, \qquad (-3)^3 = -3^3 = -27.$$

Just as all the positive cubes from 4^3 up are greater than 50, the negative cubes from $(-4)^3$ down are less than -50.

Combining these 3 negative cubes with the 4 nonnegative cubes we found first, we see that there are 7 integers n such that n^3 is between -50 and 50.

□

Earlier in this chapter, we showed that the square of a negative number is *positive*. In Problem 2.10, we found that the cube of a negative number is *negative*. What about higher exponents?

> **Problem 2.11:** Let a be any number.
>
> (a) Explain why $(-a)^4 = a^4$.
>
> (b) Explain why $(-a)^5 = -a^5$.

Solution for Problem 2.11:

(a) We rewrite the power on the left side as a product, and then use what we know about the product of negations:

$$
\begin{aligned}
(-a)^4 &= (-a)(-a)(-a)(-a) && \text{definition of an exponent} \\
&= \big((-a)(-a)\big)\big((-a)(-a)\big) && \text{associative property} \\
&= (a \cdot a)(a \cdot a) && \text{negation times negation (twice)} \\
&= a^4. && \text{definition of an exponent}
\end{aligned}
$$

(b) Again, we convert the power on the left side to a product:

$$(-a)^5 = (-a)(-a)(-a)(-a)(-a) \qquad \text{definition of an exponent}$$
$$= (-a)\big((-a)(-a)\big)\big((-a)(-a)\big) \qquad \text{associative property}$$
$$= (-a)(a \cdot a)(a \cdot a) \qquad \text{negation times negation (twice)}$$
$$= -(a \cdot a \cdot a \cdot a \cdot a) \qquad \text{multiplication by negation}$$
$$= -a^5. \qquad \text{definition of an exponent}$$

□

Problem 2.11 shows that the 4th power of a negative number is positive, while the 5th power of a negative number is negative. Similarly, if we raise a negative number to an *even* exponent, the result is positive. This is because such a power is the product of an even number of negative numbers. As shown above for $(-a)^4$, we can pair up the negative numbers in the product, and the product of each pair is a positive number. So, the product of all of the numbers is positive.

On the other hand, if we raise a negative number to an *odd* exponent, the result is negative. Such a power is the product of an odd number of negative numbers. So, as shown above for $(-a)^5$, we can pair up all the negative numbers in the product *except one*. The product of each pair is a positive number, so the product of all the pairs is positive. But then we still have that extra negative number in the product. Multiplying by this extra negative number makes the product negative. Here's another example with a 7th power:

$$(-1)^7 = [(-1)(-1)] \cdot [(-1)(-1)] \cdot [(-1)(-1)] \cdot (-1) = (1)(1)(1)(-1) = -1.$$

> **Important:** **Power of Negation:** Let a be any number. Let n be a positive
> ⚠ integer. If n is even, then $(-a)^n = a^n$. If n is odd, then $(-a)^n = -a^n$.

Problem 2.12: Evaluate $(-1)^{(5^2)} + 1^{(2^5)}$. *(Source: MATHCOUNTS)*

Solution for Problem 2.12: Let's look at the first term of our sum. Because $5^2 = 25$ is odd, we have
$$(-1)^{(5^2)} = (-1)^{25} = -(1^{25}) = -1.$$

For the second term of our sum, any power of 1 is 1, so $1^{(2^5)}$ is 1. Therefore, our sum is $-1 + 1$, which is 0. □

We started our discussion of addition and multiplication in Chapter 1 with the important properties of commutativity and associativity. Let's see if these properties hold for exponents as well.

Problem 2.13: Addition and multiplication are commutative. That is, $a+b = b+a$ and $ab = ba$ for all a and b. In this problem, we explore whether or not exponentiation is commutative.

(a) What is 3^4?

(b) What is 4^3?

(c) Is exponentiation commutative? That is, if a and b are positive integers, then must we have $a^b = b^a$?

Solution for Problem 2.13:

(a) $3^4 = 3 \cdot 3 \cdot 3 \cdot 3 = (3 \cdot 3) \cdot (3 \cdot 3) = 9 \cdot 9 = 81$.

(b) $4^3 = 4 \cdot 4 \cdot 4 = 16 \cdot 4 = 64$.

(c) In parts (a) and (b), we found that 3^4 and 4^3 are not equal. Therefore, we know that exponentiation is not commutative. The order of the numbers in a power matters.

$\square$

Problem 2.14: Addition and multiplication are associative. That is, $(a + b) + c = a + (b + c)$ and $(ab)c = a(bc)$ for any numbers a, b, and c. In this problem, we explore whether or not exponentiation is associative.

(a) What is $\left(2^2\right)^3$?

(b) What is $2^{\left(2^3\right)}$?

(c) Is exponentiation associative? That is, if a, b, and c are positive integers, must we have $(a^b)^c = a^{(b^c)}$?

Solution for Problem 2.14:

(a) We evaluate inside the parentheses first:

$$\left(2^2\right)^3 = 4^3 = 64.$$

(b) Again, we evaluate inside the parentheses first:

$$2^{\left(2^3\right)} = 2^8 = 2 \cdot 2 \cdot 2 \cdot 2 \cdot 2 \cdot 2 \cdot 2 \cdot 2 = (2 \cdot 2 \cdot 2 \cdot 2) \cdot (2 \cdot 2 \cdot 2 \cdot 2) = 16 \cdot 16 = 256.$$

(c) We just showed that $\left(2^2\right)^3$ is different from $2^{\left(2^3\right)}$. So exponentiation is not associative; where we place parentheses in expressions like $(2^2)^3$ and $2^{(2^3)}$ matters.

$\square$

Since $(2^2)^3$ and $2^{(2^3)}$ are different, we need a rule that tells us which one we mean when we write an expression like 2^{2^3}. In 2^{2^3}, we evaluate the powers from top to bottom (you might also think of this as "right to left"). So, we have $2^{2^3} = 2^{(2^3)}$. Fortunately, we don't often see expressions like 2^{2^3}.

At the beginning of this section, we mentioned the product rule $a^n b^n = (ab)^n$. In this rule, the exponent is the same throughout. The next problem is about another product rule, in which the *base* is the same throughout.

Problem 2.15: Let a be any number. Explain why $a^3 \cdot a^5 = a^8$.

Solution for Problem 2.15: We expand the left side as a big product:

$$\begin{aligned}
a^3 \cdot a^5 &= (a \cdot a \cdot a)(a \cdot a \cdot a \cdot a \cdot a) \quad &&\text{definition of an exponent (twice)} \\
&= a \cdot a \cdot a \cdot a \cdot a \cdot a \cdot a \cdot a \quad &&\text{associative property} \\
&= a^8. \quad &&\text{definition of an exponent}
\end{aligned}$$

In other words, a^3 is the product of 3 a's and a^5 is the product of 5 a's. So $a^3 \cdot a^5$ is the product of $3 + 5$ a's, which is a^{3+5}, or a^8. $\square$

In the same way that $a^3 \cdot a^5$ is the product of $3 + 5$ copies of a, the product $a^m \cdot a^n$ is the product of $m + n$ copies of a.

Important: **Product of powers (same base):** Let a be any number. Let m and n be positive integers. Then

$$a^m \cdot a^n = a^{m+n}.$$

This property holds for longer products also. For example, $a^m \cdot a^n \cdot a^p = a^{m+n+p}$.

Problem 2.16: Express $5^{17} + 5^{17} + 5^{17} + 5^{17} + 5^{17}$ as a power of 5. *(Source: MATHCOUNTS)*

Solution for Problem 2.16: Because we are adding 5 copies of a number, we have

$$\begin{aligned}
5^{17} + 5^{17} + 5^{17} + 5^{17} + 5^{17} &= 5 \cdot 5^{17} \quad &&\text{repeated addition} \\
&= 5^1 \cdot 5^{17} \quad &&\text{definition of an exponent} \\
&= 5^{1+17} \quad &&\text{product of powers (same base)} \\
&= 5^{18}. \quad &&\text{addition}
\end{aligned}$$

$\square$

Next, we'll take a look at a quotient of powers with the same base.

Problem 2.17: Explain why $9^7 \div 9^3 = 9^4$.

Solution for Problem 2.17: We start by using the product rule "backwards" to write $9^7 = 9^4 \cdot 9^3$.

This allows us to cancel the common factor 9^3:

$$9^7 \div 9^3 = (9^4 \cdot 9^3) \div 9^3 \qquad \text{product of powers (same base)}$$
$$= 9^4 \div 1 \qquad\qquad \text{cancel factor of } 9^3$$
$$= 9^4. \qquad\qquad\quad \text{division by 1}$$

Again, this result makes sense; 9^7 is the product of 7 nines and 9^3 is the product of 3 nines. So in $9^7 \div 9^3$, we can cancel 3 of the nines in 9^7 with the 3 nines of 9^3. This leaves $7 - 3$ nines, or 9^{7-3}, which is 9^4. $\square$

We can work through essentially the same steps as in Problem 2.17 with any quotient of powers with the same base.

> **Important:** **Quotient of powers (same base):** Let a be a nonzero number. Let m and n be positive integers such that m is greater than n. Then
> $$a^m \div a^n = a^{m-n}.$$

Next, we investigate a power of a power.

Problem 2.18: Explain why $\left(7^5\right)^3 = 7^{5 \cdot 3}$.

Solution for Problem 2.18: We will use the product rule:

$$\left(7^5\right)^3 = 7^5 \cdot 7^5 \cdot 7^5 \qquad \text{definition of an exponent}$$
$$= 7^{5+5+5} \qquad\qquad \text{product of powers (same base)}$$
$$= 7^{5 \cdot 3} \qquad\qquad\quad \text{repeated addition}$$
$$= 7^{15}. \qquad\qquad\quad \text{multiplication}$$

Once again, this result makes sense when we count how many 7's must be multiplied to get $\left(7^5\right)^3$. First, the exponent 3 means that we multiply 3 copies of 7^5:

$$\left(7^5\right)^3 = 7^5 \cdot 7^5 \cdot 7^5.$$

Each of these 3 copies of 7^5 is the product of 5 copies of 7:

$$7^5 \cdot 7^5 \cdot 7^5 = (7 \cdot 7 \cdot 7 \cdot 7 \cdot 7) \cdot (7 \cdot 7 \cdot 7 \cdot 7 \cdot 7) \cdot (7 \cdot 7 \cdot 7 \cdot 7 \cdot 7).$$

So, altogether, the product has $5 \cdot 3$ copies of 7. Therefore, $\left(7^5\right)^3 = 7^{5 \cdot 3}$. $\square$

We can use the same reasoning as in Problem 2.18 any time we have a power raised to another power.

> **Important:** **Power of power:** Let a be any number. Let m and n be positive integers. Then
> $$(a^m)^n = a^{mn}.$$

Let's put our new exponent laws to work.

Problem 2.19: Express each of the following as a power of 2:

(a) $(2^7 \cdot 2^8) \div 2^3$ (b) $(2^6)^4 \div 2^7$ (c) $4^6 \div 8^2$

Solution for Problem 2.19:

(a) We have

$$\begin{aligned}
(2^7 \cdot 2^8) \div 2^3 &= 2^{7+8} \div 2^3 && \text{product of powers (same base)} \\
&= 2^{7+8-3} && \text{quotient of powers (same base)} \\
&= 2^{12}. && \text{addition and subtraction}
\end{aligned}$$

(b) We have

$$\begin{aligned}
(2^6)^4 \div 2^7 &= 2^{6\cdot4} \div 2^7 && \text{power of a power} \\
&= 2^{6\cdot4-7} && \text{quotient of powers (same base)} \\
&= 2^{17}. && \text{multiplication and subtraction}
\end{aligned}$$

(c) This part is a little trickier because the bases are 4 and 8, not 2. However, both 4 and 8 are powers of 2. Since $4 = 2^2$ and $8 = 2^3$, we can use exponent laws to write $4^6 \div 8^2$ as a power of 2:

$$\begin{aligned}
4^6 \div 8^2 &= (2^2)^6 \div (2^3)^2 && \text{powers of 2} \\
&= 2^{2\cdot6} \div 2^{3\cdot2} && \text{power of a power (twice)} \\
&= 2^{12} \div 2^6 && \text{multiplication} \\
&= 2^{12-6} && \text{quotient of powers (same base)} \\
&= 2^6. && \text{subtraction}
\end{aligned}$$

$\square$

Problem 2.20:

(a) Express $11^{20,000}$ as a $10,000^{\text{th}}$ power by finding the positive integer a such that $11^{20,000}$ equals $a^{10,000}$.

(b) Express $5^{30,000}$ as a $10,000^{\text{th}}$ power.

(c) Express $2^{70,000}$ as a $10,000^{\text{th}}$ power.

(d) Which of the numbers $11^{20,000}$, $5^{30,000}$, and $2^{70,000}$ is the greatest?

Solution for Problem 2.20:

(a) Since the problem asks for a 10,000th power, let's write $11^{20,000}$ as $11^{2 \cdot 10,000}$. By the "power of a power" rule, we can write $11^{2 \cdot 10,000}$ as $(11^2)^{10,000}$. Since $11^2 = 121$, we can write $(11^2)^{10,000}$ as $121^{10,000}$. As requested, we have expressed the original expression as a 10,000th power.

(b) Similarly, we have
$$5^{30,000} = 5^{3 \cdot 10,000} = (5^3)^{10,000} = 125^{10,000}.$$

(c) Again, we have
$$2^{70,000} = 2^{7 \cdot 10,000} = (2^7)^{10,000} = 128^{10,000}.$$

(d) Yikes, the three numbers are enormous! We don't want to actually calculate them. Luckily, in the three previous parts, we expressed each number as a 10,000th power. The three 10,000th powers are $121^{10,000}$, $125^{10,000}$, and $128^{10,000}$. The exponents in these three powers are the same, and 128 is the largest base, so the largest of these three powers is $128^{10,000}$. So the largest of our original expressions is $2^{70,000}$.

$\square$

Exercises

2.2.1 Let $A = 2^5$, $B = 3^4$, $C = 4^3$, and $D = 5^2$. Write A, B, C, and D in order from smallest to largest. *(Source: MOEMS)*

2.2.2 Compute the difference between the square of the cube of 2 and the cube of the square of 2.

2.2.3 The sum $3^3 + 3^3 + 3^3$ is equal to which one of the following: 3^4, 9^3, 3^9, 27^3, or 3^{27}? *(Source: AMC 8)*

2.2.4 Evaluate the following expressions.

(a) $2^4 + 2^4 + 2^4 + 2^4$

(b) $(2^5 + 2^6 + 2^7) \div 2^3$

(c) $3^4 - 5 \cdot 8$

(d) $2^5 - 2^4 - 2^3$

(e) $\left(1 - (-1)^{11}\right)^2$

(f) $-1^{2008} + (-1)^{2007}$

(g) $5 - 7(5^2 - 3^3)^4$

(h) $3^5(2^3) - 2^4(3^4)$

(i) $88,888^4 \div 22,222^4$

2.2.5 Find the value of the sum $1^2 + 1^4 + 1^6 + 1^8 + \cdots + 1^{100}$.

2.2.6 Express each of the following numbers as a power of 2.

(a) $(2^3)^4$

(b) $4 \cdot 4 \cdot 4 \cdot 4 \cdot 4$

(c) $2^{40} \cdot 2^{13} \div 2^6$

(d) $2^{10} \cdot 4^{20} \cdot 8^{30}$

(e) $4^4 \cdot 8^8 \cdot 16^{16}$

(f) $4^3 \div 2^2$

(g) $\frac{1}{2} \cdot 8^{50}$

(h) 256

(i) $2^{50} + 2^{50} + 2^{50} + 2^{50}$

(j)$\star$ $4^4 + 4(4^4) + 6(4^4) + 4(4^4) + 4^4$

(k)$\star$ $4^{3^3} \div (4^3)^3$

(l)$\star$ $2^{20} - 2^{19}$

2.2.7 How many digits are in the product of 91 and 10^{17}? *(Source: MATHCOUNTS)*

2.2.8 Determine the number of digits in the value of $2^{16} \cdot 5^{13}$.

2.2.9 Which of the numbers 2^{100}, 3^{75}, and 5^{50} is the largest? *(Source: MATHCOUNTS)*

2.2.10★ When $10^{93} - 93$ is expressed as a single number, what is the sum of its digits? *(Source: AMC 8)* **Hints:** 34, 29

2.2.11★ Which of the numbers

$$2^{3^4}, \quad 2^{4^3}, \quad 3^{4^2}, \quad 4^{3^2}, \quad 4^{2^3}$$

has the greatest value? *(Source: MATHCOUNTS)*

2.3 Zero as an Exponent

In the last two sections, we defined a^1, a^2, a^3, a^4, and so on. What about a^0? We will define it in this section.

Problems

Problem 2.21: Consider the exponent facts below:

$$2^4 = 16$$
$$2^3 = 8$$
$$2^2 = 4$$
$$2^1 = 2$$
$$2^0 = \underline{\quad}.$$

(a) In these equations, what pattern do you see in the numbers on the right?

(b) Assuming that your pattern continues, predict the value of 2^0.

Problem 2.22: Let m and n be positive integers such that m is greater than n. In the last section, we introduced the quotient of powers (same base) rule:

$$2^{m-n} = 2^m \div 2^n.$$

Suppose that this quotient rule is true even when m is equal to n. What is 2^0?

In our first problem, we will predict the value of 2^0.

Problem 2.21: Consider the exponent facts below:

$$2^4 = 16$$
$$2^3 = 8$$
$$2^2 = 4$$
$$2^1 = 2$$
$$2^0 = \underline{\ \ 1\ \ }.$$

$2^{1-1} = 2^1 \div 2^1 = 2 \div 2 = 1$

(a) In these equations, what pattern do you see in the numbers on the right?

(b) Assuming that your pattern continues, predict the value of 2^0.

Solution for Problem 2.21:

(a) Each number on the right is the number above it divided by 2. For instance, 16 divided by 2 is 8, and 8 divided by 2 is 4.

(b) According to the pattern, the missing number should be 2 divided by 2, which is 1. So we predict 2^0 is 1.

□

Let's take a look at another reason we might expect 2^0 to equal 1.

Problem 2.22: Let m and n be positive integers such that m is greater than n. In the last section, we introduced the quotient of powers (same base) rule:

$$2^{m-n} = 2^m \div 2^n.$$

Suppose that this quotient rule is true even when m is equal to n. What is 2^0?

Solution for Problem 2.22: Let's choose $m = 1$ and $n = 1$. Then the equation becomes

$$2^{1-1} = 2^1 \div 2^1.$$

Since $1 - 1 = 0$, the left-hand side is 2^0. The right-hand side equals 1, since any nonzero number divided by itself is 1. So, the equation above becomes

$$2^0 = 1.$$

□

Problems 2.21 and 2.22 give us two reasons why it is convenient to define $2^0 = 1$. Similarly, we can see why we define $a^0 = 1$ for any number a.

Definition: Let a be any number. Then a^0 is defined to be 1.

Our definition includes $0^0 = 1$, even though we can't use our explanations in Problems 2.21 and 2.22 to see why we should define 0^0 this way. You won't see the expression 0^0 often; we define it to be 1 in part to avoid having to write "except when the base is 0" in statements like $a^0 \cdot a^n = a^n$.

Now, let's solve a few problems that contain 0th powers.

Problems

Problem 2.23: Evaluate $6^0 + 6^1 + 6^2$.

Problem 2.24: Let a be any number. Simplify $4a^0(4a)^0$.

Problem 2.25: Let $P = (2 - 3 - 4 + 7)^{2347}$ and $Q = (-2 + 3 + 4 - 7)^{2347}$. What is the value of

$$(2 + 3 + 4 + 7)^{P+Q}?$$

(Source: MATHCOUNTS)

Problem 2.23: Evaluate $6^0 + 6^1 + 6^2$.

Solution for Problem 2.23: Because $6^0 = 1$, we have

$$6^0 + 6^1 + 6^2 = 1 + 6 + 36 = 43.$$

$\square$

Problem 2.24: Let a be any number. Simplify $4a^0(4a)^0$.

Solution for Problem 2.24: Both 0th powers are equal to 1, so $4a^0(4a)^0 = 4 \cdot 1 \cdot 1 = 4$. $\square$

The next problem doesn't involve 0th powers ... or does it?

Problem 2.25: Let $P = (2 - 3 - 4 + 7)^{2347}$ and $Q = (-2 + 3 + 4 - 7)^{2347}$. What is the value of

$$(2 + 3 + 4 + 7)^{P+Q}?$$

(Source: MATHCOUNTS)

Solution for Problem 2.25: The exponent 2347 is scary. Let's first try to simplify P and Q. The value of P is

$$P = (2 - 3 - 4 + 7)^{2347} = 2^{2347}.$$

Because 2347 is odd, the value of Q is

$$Q = (-2 + 3 + 4 - 7)^{2347} = (-2)^{2347} = -2^{2347}.$$

Aha! The values of P and Q are negations of each other. In other words, $P + Q$ is zero. So the expression we want is

$$(2 + 3 + 4 + 7)^{P+Q} = (2 + 3 + 4 + 7)^0 = 1.$$

$\square$

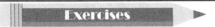

2.3.1 Evaluate the following expressions.

(a) $56 \div 4 + 3 \cdot 2^0$

(b) $7^4(8 - 2^3) + 11^{4(8)-32}$

(c) $7^0 + 3^2 \cdot 4 - 2(14 - 8 \div 2)$

2.3.2 Consecutive powers of 3 are added to form this sequence: 3^0, $3^0 + 3^1$, $3^0 + 3^1 + 3^2$, and so on. What is the value of the fourth term of this sequence? *(Source: MATHCOUNTS)*

2.3.3 When $x = 2$ and $y = -2$, what is the value of $x^{x+y} + y^{x-y}$?

2.3.4 Let n be a number. Evaluate $3n^0 \cdot (7n)^0$.

2.3.5 Let x be a number. Simplify $6^0 x^2 + 6x^2$. Express your answer as a number times a power of x. *(Source: MATHCOUNTS)*

2.4 Negative Exponents

We just learned that $10^0 = 1$. What about powers with negative exponents such as 10^{-1} or 10^{-2}? We will define them in this section.

Problems

Problem 2.26: Consider the exponent facts below:

$$3^3 = 27$$
$$3^2 = 9$$
$$3^1 = 3$$
$$3^0 = 1$$
$$3^{-1} = \underline{\quad}$$
$$3^{-2} = \underline{\quad}$$
$$3^{-3} = \underline{\quad}.$$

(a) In these equations, what pattern do you see in the numbers on the right?

(b) Assuming that your pattern continues, predict the values of the missing numbers.

(c) What is the connection between 3^3 and your predicted value for 3^{-3}?

Problem 2.27: We know that if m and n are nonnegative integers such that m is greater than or equal to n, then the quotient of powers (same base) rule tells us that

$$3^{m-n} = 3^m \div 3^n.$$

Suppose that this quotient rule is true even when m is less than n. What is 3^{-2}?

Problem 2.26: Consider the exponent facts below:

$$3^3 = 27$$
$$3^2 = 9$$
$$3^1 = 3$$
$$3^0 = 1$$
$$3^{-1} = \underline{\quad}$$
$$3^{-2} = \underline{\quad}$$
$$3^{-3} = \underline{\quad}.$$

(a) In these equations, what pattern do you see in the numbers on the right?

(b) Assuming that your pattern continues, predict the values of the missing numbers.

(c) What is the connection between 3^3 and your predicted value for 3^{-3}?

Solution for Problem 2.26:

(a) Each number on the right is the number above it divided by 3. For example, 81 divided by 3 is 27.

(b) According to the pattern, the value of 3^{-1} should be 1 divided by 3, which is $\frac{1}{3}$. The value of 3^{-2} should be $\frac{1}{3}$ divided by 3, which is $\frac{1}{9}$. The value of 3^{-3} should be $\frac{1}{9}$ divided by 3, which is $\frac{1}{27}$.

(c) Because 3^3 is 27 and our prediction for 3^{-3} is $\frac{1}{27}$, the two values are reciprocals of each other.

$\square$

Problem 2.27: We know that if m and n are nonnegative integers such that m is greater than or equal to n, then the quotient of powers (same base) rule tells us that

$$3^{m-n} = 3^m \div 3^n.$$

Suppose that this quotient rule is true even when m is less than n. What is 3^{-2}?

Solution for Problem 2.27: One easy way to get a 3^{-2} term in the equation $3^{m-n} = 3^m \div 3^n$ is to let $m = 0$ and $n = 2$. This gives us 3^{-2} on the left-hand side, and we find that

$$3^{-2} = 3^0 \div 3^2.$$

Because $3^0 = 1$, we can simplify the right-hand side:

$$3^{-2} = 1 \div 3^2.$$

Because $1 \div 3^2 = \frac{1}{3^2}$, we have

$$3^{-2} = \frac{1}{3^2},$$

so $3^{-2} = \frac{1}{9}$. This matches our intuition from Problem 2.26. $\square$

Our results from Problems 2.26 and 2.27 give us some insight into the definition for a nonzero number raised to a negative power:

Definition: Let a be a nonzero number. Let n be a positive integer. Then a^{-n} is defined to be the reciprocal of a^n, so

$$a^{-n} = \frac{1}{a^n}.$$

For instance, when n is 2, the equation becomes $a^{-2} = \frac{1}{a^2}$. When n is 1, the equation becomes $a^{-1} = \frac{1}{a}$. So a^{-1} is the reciprocal of a.

The powers $0^{-1}, 0^{-2}, 0^{-3}$, and so on are undefined, because they would involve the reciprocal of 0, but we know that 0 does not have a reciprocal.

Now that we know how to raise a nonzero number to a negative power, let's try some problems to learn more about working with negative exponents.

Problems

Problem 2.28: Evaluate the following expressions.

(a) 1^{-5}

(b) 10^{-4}

(c) 2^{-3}

(d) $56 \cdot 2^{-3}$

(e) $56 \div 2^{-3}$

Problem 2.29: Compute each of the following:

(a) $3^5 \cdot 3^{-5}$

(b) $3^6 \cdot 3^{-4}$

(c) $3^{-1} \cdot 3^{-2}$

(d) $3^{15} \cdot 3^{-5} \cdot 3^{-4} \cdot 3^{-3}$

Problem 2.30:

(a) Evaluate $\frac{1}{2^{-3}}$.

(b) Evaluate $\frac{1}{5^{-2}}$.

(c) Let a be nonzero and n be a positive integer. How are $\frac{1}{a^{-n}}$ and a^n related?

Problem 2.31:

(a) Evaluate $\left(\frac{1}{2}\right)^{-1}$, $\left(\frac{1}{2}\right)^{-2}$, and $\left(\frac{1}{2}\right)^{-3}$.

(b) Let a be nonzero and n be a positive integer. How are $\left(\frac{1}{a}\right)^{-n}$ and a^n related?

Problem 2.32: Evaluate the following expressions.

(a) -3^{-2} (b) $(-3)^{-2}$ (c) $(-2)^{-3}$ (d) $\dfrac{1}{(-3)^{-2}}$ (e) $\dfrac{1}{(-2)^{-3}}$

Problem 2.33:

(a) How are 2^{-3} and $\left(2^{-1}\right)^3$ related?

(b) Let n be a positive integer. How are 2^{-n} and $\left(2^{-1}\right)^n$ related?

(c) Let a be a nonzero number and let n be a positive integer. How are a^{-n} and $\left(a^{-1}\right)^n$ related?

Problem 2.34: Let a and b be nonzero numbers. Explain why

$$a^{-6}b^{-6} = (ab)^{-6}.$$

Problem 2.35:

(a) Express each of 4^{16}, $(-2)^{34}$, and 16^8 as a power of 2.

(b) Express each of $\left(\dfrac{1}{8}\right)^{-11}$ and $(2^{-4})^{-8}$ as a power of 2.

(c) Which of the following five numbers is the largest?

$$\left(\frac{1}{8}\right)^{-11}, \quad 4^{16}, \quad (-2)^{34}, \quad 16^8, \quad (2^{-4})^{-8}$$

(Source: MATHCOUNTS)

Problem 2.36: Let x and y be nonzero numbers. Simplify $(x^4 y^{-2})(x^{-1} y^5)$. Express your answer as a power of x times a power of y. *(Source: MATHCOUNTS)*

Problem 2.28: Evaluate the following expressions.

(a) 1^{-5}

(b) 10^{-4}

(c) 2^{-3}

(d) $56 \cdot 2^{-3}$

(e) $56 \div 2^{-3}$

Solution for Problem 2.28:

(a) We have $1^{-5} = \dfrac{1}{1^5} = \dfrac{1}{1} = 1$.

(b) We have $10^{-4} = \dfrac{1}{10^4} = \dfrac{1}{10{,}000}$.

(c) We have $2^{-3} = \dfrac{1}{2^3} = \dfrac{1}{8}$.

(d) Using part (c), we have $56 \cdot 2^{-3} = 56 \cdot \dfrac{1}{8}$. Using the definition of division gives

$$56 \cdot 2^{-3} = 56 \cdot \frac{1}{8} = 56 \div 8 = 7.$$

(e) Again using part (c), we have

$$56 \div 2^{-3} = 56 \div \frac{1}{8}.$$

The reciprocal of $\frac{1}{8}$ is 8, so dividing by $\frac{1}{8}$ is the same as multiplying by 8:

$$56 \div \frac{1}{8} = 56 \cdot 8 = 448.$$

$\square$

Problem 2.29: Compute each of the following:

(a) $3^5 \cdot 3^{-5}$

(b) $3^6 \cdot 3^{-4}$

(c) $3^{-1} \cdot 3^{-2}$

(d) $3^{15} \cdot 3^{-5} \cdot 3^{-4} \cdot 3^{-3}$

Solution for Problem 2.29:

(a) By the definition of negative exponents, we have $3^{-5} = \frac{1}{3^5}$, so $3^5 \cdot 3^{-5} = 3^5 \cdot \frac{1}{3^5}$. But 3^5 and $\frac{1}{3^5}$ are reciprocals of each other, so

$$3^5 \cdot 3^{-5} = 3^5 \cdot \frac{1}{3^5} = 1.$$

Notice that $3^0 = 1$, so $3^5 \cdot 3^{-5} = 3^0$. That is, $3^5 \cdot 3^{-5} = 3^{5+(-5)}$.

(b) We have

$$3^6 \cdot 3^{-4} = 3^6 \cdot \frac{1}{3^4} \qquad \text{definition of negative exponent}$$
$$= 3^6 \div 3^4 \qquad \text{definition of division}$$
$$= 3^{6-4} \qquad \text{quotient of powers (same base)}$$
$$= 3^2. \qquad \text{subtraction}$$

So, we have $3^6 \cdot 3^{-4} = 3^2 = 9$. Notice that this means $3^6 \cdot 3^{-4} = 3^{6+(-4)}$.

(c) We have

$$3^{-1} \cdot 3^{-2} = \frac{1}{3^1} \cdot \frac{1}{3^2} \qquad \text{definition of negative exponent (twice)}$$
$$= \frac{1}{3^1 \cdot 3^2} \qquad \text{product of reciprocals}$$
$$= \frac{1}{3^{1+2}}. \qquad \text{product of powers (same base)}$$

Therefore, we have

$$3^{-1} \cdot 3^{-2} = \frac{1}{3^{1+2}} = \frac{1}{3^3} = \frac{1}{27}.$$

If we instead write $\frac{1}{3^3}$ as 3^{-3}, then we have $3^{-1} \cdot 3^{-2} = 3^{-3}$. In other words, we have the equation $3^{-1} \cdot 3^{-2} = 3^{-1+(-2)}$.

(d) As suggested by parts (a) through (c), we can apply the product rule (same base) with negative exponents.

> **Important:** **Product of powers (same base):** Let a be a nonzero number and
> m and n be integers. Then, we have
> $$a^m a^n = a^{m+n}.$$

Repeatedly applying this fact to $3^{15} \cdot 3^{-5} \cdot 3^{-4} \cdot 3^{-3}$, we have

$$3^{15} \cdot 3^{-5} \cdot 3^{-4} \cdot 3^{-3} = 3^{15+(-5)} \cdot 3^{-4} \cdot 3^{-3} = 3^{15+(-5)+(-4)} \cdot 3^{-3} = 3^{15+(-5)+(-4)+(-3)} = 3^3 = 27.$$

□

Problem 2.30:

(a) Evaluate $\frac{1}{2^{-3}}$.

(b) Evaluate $\frac{1}{5^{-2}}$.

(c) Let a be nonzero and n be a positive integer. How are $\frac{1}{a^{-n}}$ and a^n related?

Solution for Problem 2.30:

(a) The expression $\frac{1}{2^{-3}}$ is the reciprocal of 2^{-3}, and $2^{-3} = \frac{1}{2^3} = \frac{1}{8}$. So the reciprocal of 2^{-3} is the reciprocal of $\frac{1}{8}$, which is 8. That is,

$$\frac{1}{2^{-3}} = \frac{1}{\frac{1}{8}} = 8.$$

Notice that $8 = 2^3$, so we have just shown that $\frac{1}{2^{-3}} = 2^3$.

(b) The expression $\frac{1}{5^{-2}}$ is the reciprocal of 5^{-2}, and $5^{-2} = \frac{1}{5^2} = \frac{1}{25}$. So the reciprocal of 5^{-2} is the reciprocal of $\frac{1}{25}$, which is 25. That is,

$$\frac{1}{5^{-2}} = \frac{1}{\frac{1}{25}} = 25.$$

Notice that $25 = 5^2$, so we have just shown that $\frac{1}{5^{-2}} = 5^2$.

(c) Our first two parts suggest that $\frac{1}{a^{-n}}$ and a^n are equal. We can use the same steps to show that this is true. The expression $\frac{1}{a^{-n}}$ is the reciprocal of a^{-n}, and $a^{-n} = \frac{1}{a^n}$. So the reciprocal of a^{-n} is the reciprocal of $\frac{1}{a^n}$, which is just a^n. That is,

$$\frac{1}{a^{-n}} = \frac{1}{\frac{1}{a^n}} = a^n.$$

□

In Problem 2.30, we learned the following:

> **Important:** Let a be nonzero and let n be a positive integer. Then, we have
>
> $$\frac{1}{a^{-n}} = a^n.$$

This really isn't something new. The equation $\frac{1}{a^{-n}} = a^n$ tells us that a^n and a^{-n} are reciprocals. But that's exactly what our original definition of a^{-n} told us!

Now that we know how to handle expressions like $\frac{1}{2^{-3}}$, let's move on to expressions like $\left(\frac{1}{2}\right)^{-3}$. As you'll see, we won't have to move very far!

Problem 2.31:

(a) Evaluate $\left(\frac{1}{2}\right)^{-1}$, $\left(\frac{1}{2}\right)^{-2}$, and $\left(\frac{1}{2}\right)^{-3}$.

(b) Let a be nonzero and n be a positive integer. How are $\left(\frac{1}{a}\right)^{-n}$ and a^n related?

Solution for Problem 2.31:

(a) Raising a number to the -1 power is the same as taking the reciprocal of the number. So, $\left(\frac{1}{2}\right)^{-1}$ equals the reciprocal of $\frac{1}{2}$, which is 2:

$$\left(\frac{1}{2}\right)^{-1} = \frac{1}{\left(\frac{1}{2}\right)^1} = \frac{1}{\frac{1}{2}} = 2.$$

Similarly, we have

$$\left(\frac{1}{2}\right)^{-2} = \frac{1}{\left(\frac{1}{2}\right)^2} = \frac{1}{\frac{1}{2^2}} = 2^2 = 4.$$

And we have

$$\left(\frac{1}{2}\right)^{-3} = \frac{1}{\left(\frac{1}{2}\right)^3} = \frac{1}{\frac{1}{2^3}} = 2^3 = 8.$$

(b) Part (a) gives us a pretty clear path to follow:

$$\left(\frac{1}{a}\right)^{-n} = \frac{1}{\left(\frac{1}{a}\right)^n} \qquad \text{definition of negative exponent}$$

$$= \frac{1}{\frac{1}{a^n}} \qquad \text{power of reciprocal}$$

$$= a^n. \qquad \text{reciprocal of reciprocal}$$

□

> **Important:** **Power of reciprocal:** Let a be nonzero and n be a positive integer.
> Then, we have
> $$\left(\frac{1}{a}\right)^{-n} = a^n.$$

This gives us a quick way to compute the result when a reciprocal is raised to a negative power. For example,

$$\left(\frac{1}{5}\right)^{-3} = 5^3 = 5 \cdot 5 \cdot 5 = 125.$$

In Problem 2.30 we saw that $\frac{1}{a^{-n}} = a^n$, and in Problem 2.31 we found that $\left(\frac{1}{a}\right)^{-n} = a^n$. Combining these, we see that

$$\left(\frac{1}{a}\right)^{-n} = \frac{1}{a^{-n}}.$$

In other words, the rule we have for a power of a reciprocal works when the exponent is negative, too. In fact, all of the laws of exponents we explored in Section 2.2 for powers with positive exponents also work with negative exponents.

Problem 2.32: Evaluate the following expressions.

(a) -3^{-2} (b) $(-3)^{-2}$ (c) $(-2)^{-3}$ (d) $\dfrac{1}{(-3)^{-2}}$ (e) $\dfrac{1}{(-2)^{-3}}$

Solution for Problem 2.32:

(a) By the order of operations, we compute the power before we negate:
$$-3^{-2} = -\frac{1}{3^2} = -\frac{1}{9}.$$

(b) By the definition of negative exponents, we have
$$(-3)^{-2} = \frac{1}{(-3)^2} = \frac{1}{3^2} = \frac{1}{9}.$$

The answer is positive because the exponent is even.

(c) In a similar way, we have
$$(-2)^{-3} = \frac{1}{(-2)^3} = \frac{1}{-2^3} = \frac{1}{-8} = -\frac{1}{8}.$$

The answer is negative because the exponent is odd.

Parts (b) and (c) are examples of the fact that our law for a power of a negation also holds for negative exponents. That is, if a is nonzero and n is an integer, then $(-a)^n = -a^n$ if n is odd and $(-a)^n = a^n$ if n is even. This law is true even if n is negative.

(d) Since $\dfrac{1}{a^{-n}} = a^n$, we have $\dfrac{1}{(-3)^{-2}} = (-3)^2 = 9$.

(e) Since $\dfrac{1}{a^{-n}} = a^n$, we have $\dfrac{1}{(-2)^{-3}} = (-2)^3 = -8$.

$\square$

Let's take a look at a couple more examples of exponent laws that work for negative exponents just like they work for positive exponents.

Problem 2.33:

(a) How are 2^{-3} and $\left(2^{-1}\right)^3$ related?

(b) Let n be a positive integer. How are 2^{-n} and $\left(2^{-1}\right)^n$ related?

(c) Let a be a nonzero number and let n be a positive integer. How are a^{-n} and $\left(a^{-1}\right)^n$ related?

Solution for Problem 2.33:

(a) We have

$$2^{-3} = \frac{1}{2^3} = \frac{1}{8} \quad \text{and} \quad \left(2^{-1}\right)^3 = \left(\frac{1}{2}\right)^3 = \frac{1}{2} \cdot \frac{1}{2} \cdot \frac{1}{2} = \frac{1}{2 \cdot 2 \cdot 2} = \frac{1}{8},$$

so $2^{-3} = \left(2^{-1}\right)^3$.

(b) By the definition of negation in an exponent, we have $2^{-n} = \frac{1}{2^n}$. By the power of a reciprocal rule, we have $\left(2^{-1}\right)^n = \left(\frac{1}{2}\right)^n = \frac{1}{2^n}$. So, we have $2^{-n} = \left(2^{-1}\right)^n$.

(c) We use exactly the same steps as in part (b), but replace 2 with a:

$$
\begin{aligned}
a^{-n} &= \frac{1}{a^n} & \text{definition of negative exponent} \\
&= \left(\frac{1}{a}\right)^n & \text{power of reciprocal} \\
&= \left(a^{-1}\right)^n & \text{definition of negative exponent}
\end{aligned}
$$

□

> **Important:** Let a be a nonzero number. Let n be a positive integer. Then, we have
> $$a^{-n} = \left(a^{-1}\right)^n.$$

Since $-n = (-1)(n)$, the rule $a^{-n} = (a^{-1})^n$ suggests that the power of a power rule works for negative exponents, too. Let's look at another example of an exponent law that works for negative exponents just like it does for positive exponents.

Problem 2.34: Let a and b be nonzero numbers. Explain why

$$a^{-6}b^{-6} = (ab)^{-6}.$$

Solution for Problem 2.34: Let's convert the negative exponents to positive exponents:

$$
\begin{aligned}
a^{-6}b^{-6} &= \frac{1}{a^6} \cdot \frac{1}{b^6} & \text{definition of negative exponents (twice)} \\
&= \frac{1}{a^6 b^6} & \text{product of reciprocals} \\
&= \frac{1}{(ab)^6} & \text{product of powers (same exponent)} \\
&= (ab)^{-6}. & \text{definition of negative exponents}
\end{aligned}
$$

□

The point of this problem is to show that the product law (same exponents) holds for negative exponents too. In a similar way, we can extend our other exponent laws to negative exponents. Here is a list of such exponent laws.

> **Important:** Let a and b be numbers. Let m and n be integers.
>
> **Product of powers (same base):** $a^m a^n = a^{m+n}$.
> **Product of powers (same exponent):** $a^n b^n = (ab)^n$.
> **Quotient of powers (same base):** If a is nonzero, then
> $$a^m \div a^n = a^{m-n}.$$
> **Quotient of powers (same exponent):** If b is nonzero, then
> $$a^n \div b^n = (a \div b)^n.$$
> **Power of power:** $(a^m)^n = a^{mn}$.
> **Power of reciprocal:** If a is nonzero, then $\left(\frac{1}{a}\right)^n = \frac{1}{a^n}$.
> **Power of negation:** If n is even, then $(-a)^n = a^n$. If n is odd, then $(-a)^n = -a^n$.

Before using each law, make sure that the powers in it are defined. For example, in the product law $a^n b^n = (ab)^n$, we can't choose $a = 0$ and $n = -2$, because 0^{-2} is undefined.

Problem 2.35:

(a) Express each of 4^{16}, $(-2)^{34}$, and 16^8 as a power of 2.

(b) Express each of $\left(\frac{1}{8}\right)^{-11}$ and $(2^{-4})^{-8}$ as a power of 2.

(c) Which of the following five numbers is the largest?

$$\left(\frac{1}{8}\right)^{-11}, \quad 4^{16}, \quad (-2)^{34}, \quad 16^8, \quad (2^{-4})^{-8}$$

(Source: MATHCOUNTS)

Solution for Problem 2.35:

(a) Since $4 = 2^2$, we can write 4^{16} as

$$4^{16} = \left(2^2\right)^{16} = 2^{2 \cdot 16} = 2^{32}.$$

Because the exponent in $(-2)^{34}$ is even, we have

$$(-2)^{34} = 2^{34}.$$

Since $16 = 2^4$, we can write 16^8 as $16^8 = \left(2^4\right)^8 = 2^{4 \cdot 8} = 2^{32}$.

(b) Applying the property we learned in Problem 2.31 for a reciprocal raised to a negative exponent, we have
$$\left(\frac{1}{8}\right)^{-11} = 8^{11}.$$

Since $8 = 2^3$, we then have $8^{11} = (2^3)^{11} = 2^{3 \cdot 11} = 2^{33}$.

For $(2^{-4})^{-8}$, we use the power of a power law:
$$(2^{-4})^{-8} = 2^{(-4)(-8)} = 2^{32}.$$

(c) Combining the results from parts (a) and (b), we have expressed all five numbers as powers of 2:
$$\left(\frac{1}{8}\right)^{-11} = 2^{33}, \qquad 4^{16} = 2^{32}, \qquad (-2)^{34} = 2^{34}, \qquad 16^8 = 2^{32}, \qquad (2^{-4})^{-8} = 2^{32}.$$

To compare these powers of 2, we can just look at their exponents. The largest of these powers of 2 is 2^{34}, the third number. Going back to the original expressions, the largest number is $(-2)^{34}$.

Expressing all the numbers as powers of the same number (2) helped us compare them.

□

Problem 2.36: Let x and y be nonzero numbers. Simplify $(x^4 y^{-2})(x^{-1} y^5)$. Express your answer as a power of x times a power of y. *(Source: MATHCOUNTS)*

Solution for Problem 2.36: Let's bring the x's together and the y's together. Then we can use the product rule:

$$\begin{aligned}
(x^4 y^{-2})(x^{-1} y^5) &= (x^4 x^{-1})(y^{-2} y^5) && \text{commutative and associative properties} \\
&= x^{4+(-1)} y^{-2+5} && \text{product of powers (same base)} \\
&= x^3 y^3. && \text{addition facts}
\end{aligned}$$

So the answer is $x^3 y^3$. □

Exercises

2.4.1 Evaluate the following expressions.

(a) $2^{(-1)^{11}}$

(b) $3^7 \cdot 3^{-4}$

(c) $2^3 \div 2^{-4}$

(d) $1 \div 5^{-2}$

(e) $(-3)^{-5} \cdot 3^3$

(f) $\left(\frac{1}{4}\right)^{-3} \cdot 8^{-2}$

2.4.2 What is the value of $a \div a^{-4}$ when $a = 2$?

2.4.3 For $x = 1$ and $y = -1$, give the value of the expression $15x^2y^{-3} + 18yx^{-1} + 27xy^4$. *(Source: MATHCOUNTS)*

2.4.4 Find the integer k such that $3^3 + 3^3 + 3^3 = 243 \cdot 3^k$. *(Source: MATHCOUNTS)*

2.4.5★ Express 2^{12} as a power of $\frac{1}{8}$. **Hints:** 49

2.4.6★ Let a and b be nonzero numbers. Simplify $\left(6a^2b\right)^2 \div (3a^2b^3)$. Express your answer as a number times a power of a times a power of b. *(Source: MATHCOUNTS)*

2.5 Summary

In this chapter, we introduced the concept of exponents.

Definition: Let a be any number. Let n be an integer. If n is positive, then

$$a^n = \underbrace{a \times a \times \cdots \times a}_{n \text{ copies of } a}.$$

For instance, $a^4 = a \cdot a \cdot a \cdot a$. If n is zero, then $a^n = 1$. If a is nonzero and n is positive, then

$$a^{-n} = \frac{1}{a^n}.$$

The expression a^n is called a **power**, with **base** a and **exponent** n.

Important: Let a and b be numbers. Let m and n be integers.

⚠️

Product of powers (same base): $a^m a^n = a^{m+n}$.
Product of powers (same exponent): $a^n b^n = (ab)^n$.
Quotient of powers (same base): $a^m \div a^n = a^{m-n}$.
Quotient of powers (same exponent): $a^n \div b^n = (a \div b)^n$.
Power of power: $(a^m)^n = a^{mn}$.
Power of reciprocal: $\left(\frac{1}{a}\right)^n = \frac{1}{a^n}$.
Negation in exponent: $a^{-n} = \frac{1}{a^n}$.
Power of negation: If n is even, then $(-a)^n = a^n$. If n is odd, then $(-a)^n = -a^n$.

Before using each property, make sure that the powers in it are defined. For example, in the product rule $a^m a^n = a^{m+n}$, we can't choose $a = 0$ and $m = -1$, because 0^{-1} is undefined.

2.37 Evaluate the following expressions.

(a) $4 - 8\big((-2)^2 - 4(-3)\big)$

(b) $(5-2)^2 + (2-5)^3$

(c) $5 \cdot 2^5 - (2 \cdot 3)^2$

(d) $5 + (-6)^3 \div (2 \cdot 3^2)$

2.38 By how much does 3^5 exceed 5^3?

2.39 What is the value of the sum $-1^{2004} + (-1)^{2005} + 1^{2006} - 1^{2007}$? *(Source: MATHCOUNTS)*

2.40 For what positive integer n is $n^2 = 2^6$? *(Source: MATHCOUNTS)*

2.41 What year in the 20th century (the years 1901 through 2000) was a perfect square?

2.42 What is the value of $x^5 - 2x$ when $x = 3$?

2.43 If $x = -4$, what is the value of $-2x^3 - 3x^2$?

2.44 How many positive perfect squares are less than 10,000?

2.45 Let n be a positive integer. If $(1 + 2 + 3 + 4 + 5 + 6)^2 = 1^3 + 2^3 + \cdots + n^3$, what is the value of n? *(Source: MATHCOUNTS)*

2.46 N is an integer such that $N^3 = 4913$. What is the value of N? *(Source: MOEMS)*

2.47 Susan's calculator has a key that replaces the number displayed with its cube. If a 2 is displayed, how many times must Susan press the "cubing" key to display a number that is greater than 10^9? *(Source: MATHCOUNTS)*

2.48 The integer 91 is the smallest positive integer that can be expressed as the sum of two perfect cubes in two different ways—provided that we allow negative cubes.

(a) Express 91 as the sum of two positive perfect cubes.

(b) Express 91 as the sum of a positive and a negative perfect cube.

2.49 How many positive integers less than 333 are powers of 3?

2.50 Find the integer n such that 695,000 is between 10^n and 10^{n+1}. *(Source: MATHCOUNTS)*

2.51 Evaluate $3x^y + 4y^x$ when $x = 3$ and $y = 4$.

2.52 Express each of the following numbers as a power of 2.

(a) $2^3 \cdot 4 \cdot 8$

(b) $\frac{1}{2}(2^{15})$

(c) $(2^5)^6 \div 4^3$

(d)★ $2^{20} - 2^{19} - 2^{18}$

2.53 Express 100^3 as a power of 10.

2.54 Compute each of the following. As an extra challenge, try computing them without writing anything.

(a) $40^3 \cdot 5^3$

(b) $27^5 \div 9^5$

(c) $5^4 \cdot 3^2 \cdot 2^5$

(d) $(2^8 + 2^9 + 2^{10} + 2^{11}) \div 32$

2.55 Compute each of the following:

(a) $2^0 + 3^0 + (-4)^0 - (2 + 3 - 4)^0$

(b) $(5^2 - 2^3 + 10^0 - 4^2)^{-2}$

(c) $\left(\dfrac{1}{2}\right)^{-3}$

(d) $(-2)^{-1}$

(e) $(-1)^{-14}$

(f) $\dfrac{1}{4^{-3}}$

2.56 Express each of the following as a power of 3:

(a) $\dfrac{1}{9}$

(b) $3^{-4} \cdot 3^2 \div 3^3$

(c) $\left(\dfrac{1}{3^{-2}}\right)^{-3} \cdot 3^2$

(d) $27^2 \div 3^{-3}$

Challenge Problems

2.57 The squares of two consecutive positive integers differ by 67. What is the smaller of the two integers? **Hints:** 35

2.58 The Indian mathematician Srinivasa Ramanujan (1887–1920) knew that there are four different positive integers A, B, C, and D such that $A^3 + B^3 = 1729$ and $C^3 + D^3 = 1729$. What is the sum $A + B + C + D$? *(Source: MATHCOUNTS)*

2.59 Express $2^5 \cdot 8^3 \cdot 16^2$ as a power of 4.

2.60 What five-digit positive integer with an 8 in the ten-thousands place is the cube of an integer?

2.61 Express 3^{16} as a power of $\dfrac{1}{9}$. **Hints:** 119

2.62 Express $2^2 \times 4^2 \times 8^2 \times 16^2 \times \cdots \times 1024^2$ as a power of 2. *(Source: MATHCOUNTS)*

2.63 When the expression $8^{10} \cdot 5^{22}$ is multiplied out, how many digits does the number have? *(Source: MATHCOUNTS)* **Hints:** 61, 73

2.64 For what value of n does $500{,}000^2 \cdot 200{,}000^2 = 10^n$?

2.65 Find the number n such that $n \cdot 3^4 \cdot 2^5 = 6^6$.

2.66 What is the sum of the digits of the number $2^{2005} \cdot 5^{2007} \cdot 3$? *(Source: MATHCOUNTS)*

2.67 What is the positive integer N for which $22^2 \cdot 55^2 = 10^2 \cdot N^2$? *(Source: MATHCOUNTS)*

2.68 Let a and b be numbers. Simplify the following expressions. Express each of your answers as a number times a power of a times a power of b.

(a) $(2ab^2)^3$

(b) $5a^2b(2ab)^3$

2.69 Let a, b, and c be numbers. Simplify the following expressions. In each of your answers, the variables a, b, and c should each appear only once.

(a) $a^2b \cdot 8ab^6c^2$

(b) $(a^2)^4(ab)^3c^3$

2.70 What is the largest integer n for which n^{2000} is less than 5^{3000}? *(Source: MATHCOUNTS)*
Hints: 84

2.71 For what value of x is $125 \cdot 5^5 = 5^x + 5^x + 5^x + 5^x + 5^x$?

2.72 What is the value of x in the equation $(2^x)(30^3) = (2^3)(3^3)(4^3)(5^3)$?
(Source: MATHCOUNTS)

2.73 Let a and b be numbers.

(a) Show that $(a + b)^2 = a^2 + 2ab + b^2$.

(b) Show that $(a - b)^2 = a^2 - 2ab + b^2$.

(c)★ Show that $(a + b)^3 = a^3 + 3a^2b + 3ab^2 + b^3$.

2.74 Let a and b be numbers.

(a) Show that $(a - b)(a + b) = a^2 - b^2$.

(b)★ Show that $(a - b)(a^2 + ab + b^2) = a^3 - b^3$. **Hints:** 102

(c)★ Show that $(a + b)(a^2 - ab + b^2) = a^3 + b^3$.

2.75★ What integer n has the property that 5^{96} is greater than n^{72} and 5^{96} is less than $(n + 1)^{72}$? *(Source: MATHCOUNTS)* **Hints:** 84

2.76★ The perfect squares from 1 through 1225 are printed as a sequence of digits

$$1491625\ldots1225.$$

How many digits are in the sequence? *(Source: MATHCOUNTS)*

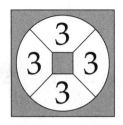 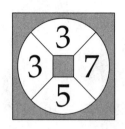 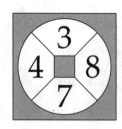 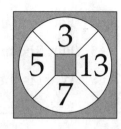

I was interviewed on the Israeli radio for five minutes and I said that more than 2000 years ago, Euclid proved that there are infinitely many primes. Immediately the host interrupted me and asked, "Are there still infinitely many primes?" – Noga Alon

CHAPTER 3

Number Theory

Number theory is the study of integers.

3.1 Multiples

We know that 12 equals 3 times 4. In other words, 12 equals some integer times 4. For that reason, we say that 12 is a **multiple** of 4.

> **Definition:** Let a and b be numbers. We say that a is a **multiple** of b if a equals b times some integer. In other words, a is a multiple of b if there is an integer n such that $a = bn$.

For instance, 7 is *not* a multiple of 4, because we cannot write 7 as the product of 4 and an integer. Note that −12 is a multiple of 4, because −12 equals −3 times 4. Similarly, 0 is a multiple of 4, because 0 equals 0 times 4.

In this chapter, we'll talk about division differently than we did in Chapter 1. We'll use the "quotient and remainder" concept of division, which you probably used when you first learned about division. As an example, when we divide 13 by 4, the quotient is 3 and the remainder is 1.

Using this view of division, we can say that an integer a is a multiple of an integer b if a divided by b has remainder 0. So, for example, 12 is a multiple of 4 because 12 divided by 4 has remainder 0, while 13 is not a multiple of 4 because 13 divided by 4 has remainder 1.

Problems

Problem 3.1:

(a) Both 147 and 357 are multiples of 7. Is $147 + 357$ a multiple of 7?

(b) Suppose k is a multiple of 7. Must $k + 7$ be a multiple of 7?

(c) Suppose r and s are multiples of 7. Must $r + s$ be a multiple of 7?

(d) Suppose k is a multiple of 7. Is it possible for $k + 23$ to be a multiple of 7?

Problem 3.2: What number between 100 and 200 is both a perfect square and a multiple of 7?
(Source: MOEMS)

Problem 3.3: What is the greatest three-digit number that is a multiple of 13?
(Source: MATHCOUNTS)

Problem 3.4:

(a) How many integers between 2 and 1004 are multiples of 5?

(b) How many integers between 150 and 300 are multiples of 9?

Problem 3.5:

(a) Must every multiple of 15 also be a multiple of 3?

(b) Must every multiple of 3 also be a multiple of 15?

Problem 3.1:

(a) Both 147 and 357 are multiples of 7. Is $147 + 357$ a multiple of 7?

(b) Suppose k is a multiple of 7. Must $k + 7$ be a multiple of 7?

(c) Suppose r and s are multiples of 7. Must $r + s$ be a multiple of 7?

(d) Suppose k is a multiple of 7. Is it possible for $k + 23$ to be a multiple of 7?

Solution for Problem 3.1:

(a) We have $147 = 7 \cdot 21$ and $357 = 7 \cdot 51$. We can add these two using the distributive property:
$$147 + 357 = 7 \cdot 21 + 7 \cdot 51 = 7 \cdot (21 + 51) = 7 \cdot 72.$$

So, $147 + 357$ can be written as 7 times an integer, which means that $147 + 357$ is a multiple of 7.

(b) Because k is a multiple of 7, there is an integer a for which $k = 7a$. So, adding 7 to k gives $k + 7 = 7a + 7$. We can then factor out 7 to write
$$k + 7 = 7a + 7 = 7 \cdot a + 7 \cdot 1 = 7(a + 1).$$

Since a is an integer, so is $a + 1$. Therefore, we can write $k + 7$ as 7 times some integer, which means that $k + 7$ is indeed a multiple of 7. Moreover, our work above tells us that adding 7 to a multiple of 7 produces the next multiple of 7.

(c) We can use our solution to part (b) of as a guide. Because r is a multiple of 7, there is an integer m such that $r = 7m$. Similarly, because s is a multiple of 7, there is an integer n such that $s = 7n$. We then have $r + s = 7m + 7n$, and factoring out 7 gives

$$r + s = 7m + 7n = 7(m + n).$$

Because m and n are integers, $m + n$ is an integer. So the equation $r + s = 7(m + n)$ says that $r + s$ is 7 times some integer. In other words, $r + s$ is a multiple of 7.

(d) Part (c) tells us that the sum of any two multiples of 7 is a multiple of 7. So, if k is a multiple of 7, then $k + 21$ and $k + 28$ are both multiples of 7. Moreover, because $k + 21$ and $k + 28$ are 7 apart, they are consecutive multiples of 7. So, there are no multiples of 7 between $k + 21$ and $k + 28$. Specifically, $k + 23$ is not a multiple of 7.

We might also have thought about division to see why $k + 23$ is not a multiple of 7. Since $k + 21$ is a multiple of 7 and $k + 23$ is 2 greater than $k + 21$, we know that $k + 23$ divided by 7 has a remainder of 2. So, $k + 23$ is not a multiple of 7.

$\square$

Part (b) of Problem 3.1 tells us that if we start at any multiple of 7 and count by 7's, we'll generate multiples of 7 from our starting point onward. Similarly, we can also generate multiples of 7 by starting from some multiple of 7 and subtracting 7 over and over. For example, the following are all multiples of 7:

$$700, 693, 686, 679, 672, 665, 658, 651, \ldots.$$

> **Important:** If we start from any multiple of n and count either upward or downward by n's, all the numbers we hit will be multiples of n.

Part (c) of Problem 3.1 is an example of a neat property of multiples. If we add two multiples of a number, we get another multiple of the same number. Similarly, the difference between any two multiples of a number is another multiple of that same number.

> **Important:** If a and b are multiples of c, then both $a + b$ and $a - b$ are multiples of c.

Finally, part (d) of Problem 3.1 is an example of why we know that we don't skip any multiples of 7 when we count by 7's starting from a multiple of 7. We can go through basically the same steps to see that if we add a multiple of 7 and a number that is not a multiple of 7, then the resulting sum is not a multiple of 7.

> **Important:** If we start with a multiple of n and add (or subtract) a number
> that is not a multiple of n, then the resulting sum (or difference) is
> not a multiple of n.

Problem 3.2: What number between 100 and 200 is both a perfect square and a multiple of 7? *(Source: MOEMS)*

> **WARNING!!** In this book, when we say "between 100 and 200," we don't
> include 100 and 200.

Solution for Problem 3.2: The perfect squares between 100 and 200 are 121, 144, 169, and 196. When we divide each of these squares by 7, we find that only 196 is a multiple of 7. To be specific, 196 is 28 times 7. So the answer is 196.

Here's another way to see that 196 is a multiple of 7. Note that 196 is 14 times 14, and 14 is a multiple of 7. Specifically, we have $14 = 2 \cdot 7$, so $196 = 14 \cdot 14 = 14 \cdot 2 \cdot 7 = 28 \cdot 7$. Therefore, 196 is a multiple of 7. $\square$

Problem 3.3: What is the greatest three-digit number that is a multiple of 13? *(Source: MATHCOUNTS)*

Solution for Problem 3.3: The three-digit numbers are the integers from 100 to 999. We are looking for the *greatest* such integer that is a multiple of 13. So let's divide 999 by 13. We get a quotient of 76 and a remainder of 11. In other words, 999 is 11 more than a multiple of 13. So the multiple of 13 we want is $999 - 11$, which is 988.

We also can solve this problem using our insights about multiples from Problem 3.1. We find a multiple of 13 near 1000, and then add or subtract multiples of 13 to find the largest three-digit multiple of 13. For example, we know that 1300 and 130 are multiples of 13, so $1300 - 130 = 1170$ is a multiple of 13, as is $1170 - 130 = 1040$. Therefore, $1040 - 3(13) = 1040 - 39 = 1001$ is a multiple of 13, which means that the largest multiple of 13 less than 1000 is $1001 - 13 = 988$. $\square$

Let's try some counting problems involving multiples.

Problem 3.4:

(a) How many integers between 2 and 1004 are multiples of 5?

(b) How many integers between 150 and 300 are multiples of 9?

(Source: MATHCOUNTS)

Solution for Problem 3.4:

(a) The multiples of 5 between 2 and 1004 are

$$5, 10, 15, \ldots, 995, 1000.$$

How many numbers is that? To make the counting easier, let's express each number as an integer times 5:

$$1 \cdot 5, 2 \cdot 5, 3 \cdot 5, \ldots, 199 \cdot 5, 200 \cdot 5.$$

In other words, we are multiplying 5 by 1, 2, 3, up through 200. So the number of such multiples is 200.

(b) Let's simplify the problem a bit by temporarily ignoring the 150, which makes this problem look like part (a).

> **Concept:** One way to approach a difficult problem is to relate the problem to an easier problem you already know how to do.

The positive multiples of 9 less than 300 are

$$9, 18, \ldots, 297.$$

Let's express these numbers as an integer times 9:

$$1 \cdot 9, 2 \cdot 9, \ldots, 33 \cdot 9.$$

So there are 33 such multiples.

We need to remove the numbers less than 150. The positive multiples of 9 less than 150 are

$$9, 18, \ldots, 144.$$

We can express each as an integer times 9:

$$1 \cdot 9, 2 \cdot 9, \ldots, 16 \cdot 9.$$

So there are 16 such multiples.

If we remove these 16 multiples of 9 less than 150 from the 33 multiples of 9 less than 300, we are left with $33 - 16 = 17$ multiples between 150 and 300.

□

Problem 3.5:
 (a) Must every multiple of 15 also be a multiple of 3?
 (b) Must every multiple of 3 also be a multiple of 15?

Solution for Problem 3.5:

(a) Suppose that m is a multiple of 15, so we have $m = 15n$ for some integer n. Since $15 = 3 \cdot 5$, we can write $m = 3 \cdot 5n$, which means m is 3 times the integer $5n$. Therefore, m is a multiple of 3, as well.

(b) Not every multiple of 3 is a multiple of 15. For example, 3, 6, 9, 12, and 18 are all multiples of 3, but none of these numbers is a multiple of 15.

□

Part (a) of Problem 3.5 tells us that because 15 is a multiple of 3, every multiple of 15 is also a multiple of 3. This is an example of another neat property of multiples:

> **Important:** If a is a multiple of b, then every multiple of a is also a multiple of b.

Exercises

3.1.1   What are the 10 smallest positive multiples of 6?

3.1.2   There are many positive two-digit multiples of 7, but only two of these multiples have a digit sum of 10. (The **digit sum** of an integer is the sum of its digits.) What are these two multiples of 7? *(Source: AMC 8)*

3.1.3   What is the sum of all positive integers less than 100 that are multiples of 13?

3.1.4   What is the least positive number that can be added to 173 so that the result is a multiple of 20?

3.1.5   What is the smallest positive four-digit multiple of 17?

3.1.6   What is the greatest four-digit multiple of 18?

3.1.7   What is the greatest three-digit multiple of 33 that can be written using three different digits? *(Source: MATHCOUNTS)*

3.1.8   How many integers between 17 and 2678 are multiples of 11? *(Source: MATHCOUNTS)*

3.2   Divisibility Tests

Another way to say that 12 is a multiple of 4 is to say that 12 is **divisible** by 4.

> **Definition:**   Let a be a number, and let b be a nonzero number. We say that a is **divisible** by b if $a \div b$ is an integer.

So, for example, 12 is divisible by 4 because $12 \div 4$ equals the integer 3. Similarly, 0 is divisible by every nonzero integer, since 0 divided by any nonzero integer is the integer 0.

The concept of "divisible" is a lot like the concept of "multiple." As long as a and b are not both 0, then "a is divisible by b" and "a is a multiple of b" say the same thing. (If $a = b = 0$, then a is still a multiple of b, but a is not divisible by b, since we can't divide by 0.)

In this section, we explore some shortcuts for determining whether or not one number is divisible by another. You're probably familiar with several of these shortcuts already, but by the end of this section, you'll also understand why these shortcuts work.

Problems

Problem 3.6:

(a) Note that

$$121212 = 120000 + 1200 + 12.$$

How can we use this fact to tell that 121212 is divisible by 3?

(b) How can we quickly tell that 363637 is *not* divisible by 3?

Problem 3.7: How can we tell at a glance whether or not a number is a multiple of 10?

Problem 3.8:

(a) Is every multiple of 10 also a multiple of 5?

(b) How can we tell at a glance whether or not a number is a multiple of 5?

(c) How can we tell at a glance whether or not a number is a multiple of 2?

Problem 3.9:

(a) Which of the following numbers are divisible by 4:

$$12, \quad 312, \quad 512, \quad 2512, \quad 4312?$$

(b) Is every multiple of 100 also a multiple of 4?

(c) Use your answer to part (b) to explain why 5,687,623,688 is divisible by 4.

(d) Use your answer to part (b) to explain why 4,650,310 is *not* divisible by 4.

Problem 3.10: In this problem, we discover a method for determining whether or not a number is divisible by 9. Notice that

$$\begin{aligned}
765 &= 7 \cdot 100 + 6 \cdot 10 + 5 \\
&= 7 \cdot (99 + 1) + 6 \cdot (9 + 1) + 5 \\
&= 7 \cdot 99 + 7 + 6 \cdot 9 + 6 + 5 \\
&= 7 \cdot 99 + 6 \cdot 9 + (7 + 6 + 5)
\end{aligned}$$

(a) As shown above, 765 equals $7 \cdot 99 + 6 \cdot 9 + (7 + 6 + 5)$. Notice that $7 + 6 + 5$ is divisible by 9. Explain why this tells us that 765 is divisible by 9.

(b) Notice that $8 + 5 + 1 + 4 = 18$. Explain why this tells us that 8514 is divisible by 9.

(c) Determine whether or not 59814 is divisible by 9 *without dividing 9 into 59814*.

Problem 3.11: In the previous problem, we noted that $765 = 7 \cdot 99 + 6 \cdot 9 + (7 + 6 + 5)$.

(a) Are both 99 and 9 divisible by 3?

(b) Is 765 divisible by 3?

(c) Is 67242 divisible by 3?

(d) Explain why 6148 is not divisible by 3 *without dividing 6148 by 3*.

Problem 3.12: A is the units digit in the four-digit number 4,63A. If 4,63A is divisible by 3 and by 4, then what are all the possible values of A?

Problem 3.13: N is the tens digit in the five-digit number 24,6N8. If 24,6N8 is divisible by 9, then must 24,6N8 also be divisible by 4?

Problem 3.6:

(a) Note that $121212 = 120000 + 1200 + 12$. How can we use this fact to tell that 121212 is divisible by 3?

(b) How can we quickly tell that 363637 is *not* divisible by 3?

Solution for Problem 3.6:

(a) Since 12 is a multiple of 3, we know that 120000, 1200, and 12 are all multiples of 3. From our work in Section 3.1, we know that the sum of multiples of 3 must be a multiple of 3. So, the sum $120000 + 1200 + 12 = 121212$ is a multiple of 3, which means that 121212 is divisible by 3.

(b) Looking back at the previous part, we know that $363636 = 360000 + 3600 + 36$ is a multiple of 3 because 36 is a multiple of 3. Since 363637 is 1 more than a multiple of 3, we know that dividing 363637 by 3 will give a remainder of 1. Therefore, 363637 is not divisible by 3.

□

Our work in Problem 3.6 gives us two strategies for testing whether a number a is divisible by some other number b:

- Write a as a sum of numbers that are divisible by b. We did this when we wrote 121212 as $120000 + 1200 + 12$.

- Compare a to nearby numbers that are obviously divisible by b. We did this when we noted that 363637 is 1 greater than 363636.

For the rest of this section, we will use these two tactics to develop strategies for testing for divisibility by specific numbers.

Problem 3.7: How can we tell at a glance whether or not a number is a multiple of 10?

Solution for Problem 3.7: We compute the product of 10 and an integer by placing a 0 at the end of the integer. For example, $9572 \cdot 10 = 95720$. So, any number that equals 10 times an integer must end in 0. Also, any integer that ends in 0 is a multiple of 10, since it equals 10 times the integer that remains when its units digit is removed: $95720 = 10 \cdot 9572$. □

Problem 3.8:

(a) Is every multiple of 10 also a multiple of 5?

(b) How can we tell at a glance whether or not a number is a multiple of 5?

(c) How can we tell at a glance whether or not a number is a multiple of 2?

Solution for Problem 3.8:

(a) Because 10 is a multiple of 5, every multiple of 10 is also a multiple of 5.

(b) The multiples of 10 are the numbers that have 0 as the units digit. So, every number with 0 as the units digit is a multiple of both 5 and 10. But there are other multiples of 5, such as 5, 15, and 25. Each of these has 5 as the units digit.

   It appears that every multiple of 5 has either 0 or 5 as the units digit. To focus on the units digit of a number we can write the number as some multiple of 10 plus the units digit of the number. For example, we can write 435 as

$$435 = 430 + 5.$$

Every multiple of 10 is also a multiple of 5, so 430 is a multiple of 5. Since 5 is obviously a multiple of 5, the sum $430 + 5$ is the sum of two multiples of 5. The sum of two multiples of 5 must be a multiple of 5, so 435 is a multiple of 5.

   We can do the same with any positive integer. That is, we can write any integer as the sum of a multiple of 10 and the units digit of the original integer. The multiple of 10 is a multiple of 5, so the sum is a multiple of 5 whenever the units digit is also a multiple of 5. The only single digits that are multiples of 5 are 0 and 5, so any number that has 0 or 5 as its units digit must be a multiple of 5.

   Any number that does not have 0 or 5 as its units digit is between two consecutive multiples of 5. Such a number cannot be a multiple of 5. For example, 813 is between 810 and $810 + 5 = 815$, so 813 cannot be a multiple of 5.

> **Important:** Any integer that has 0 or 5 as its units digit is a multiple of 5. Any integer that does not have 0 or 5 as its units digit is not a multiple of 5.

(c) Our key observation in the previous part is that 10 is a multiple of 5. But 10 is also a multiple of 2. So, we can go through the same steps to see that the last digit of a number tells us whether or not the number is a multiple of 2. For example, we can write 838 as 830 + 8. Since 830 is a multiple of 10, we know it is a multiple of 2. Since 830 and 8 are both multiples of 2, we know that 830 + 8 = 838 is a multiple of 2.

> **Important:** Any integer that has an even units digit (0, 2, 4, 6, 8) is a multiple of 2. Any integer that has an odd units digit (1, 3, 5, 7, 9) is not a multiple of 2.

□

Problem 3.9:

(a) Which of the following numbers are divisible by 4:

$$12, \quad 312, \quad 512, \quad 2512, \quad 4312?$$

(b) Is every multiple of 100 also a multiple of 4?

(c) Use your answer to part (b) to explain why 5,687,623,688 is divisible by 4.

(d) Use your answer to part (b) to explain why 4,650,310 is *not* divisible by 4.

Solution for Problem 3.9:

(a) All of the numbers are divisible by 4! And all of the numbers end in the same two digits. Perhaps these two facts are related.

(b) Since 100 is a multiple of 4, every multiple of 100 is also a multiple of 4.

(c) The multiples of 100 are the numbers that have 0 as both the tens and the units digit. We know that every multiple of 100 is a multiple of 4, so we write the number as a multiple of 100 plus a two-digit number:

$$5,687,623,688 = 5,687,623,600 + 88.$$

Since 5,687,623,600 is a multiple of 100, it is also a multiple of 4. We also have 88 = 4 · 22, so 88 is a multiple of 4. Since 5,687,623,600 and 88 are both multiples of 4, their sum is also a multiple of 4.

Similarly, we can write any positive integer as a multiple of 100 plus the number formed by the last two digits of the original integer. If this number formed by the last two digits is divisible by 4, then the original integer is divisible by 4, as well.

(d) The number formed by the last two digits of 4,650,310 is 10, which is not divisible by 4. So, we expect that 4,650,310 is not divisible by 4. To be sure, we write 4,650,310 as

$$4,650,310 = 4,650,300 + 10.$$

Since 4,650,300 is a multiple of 100, it is a multiple of 4. Therefore, 4,650,300 + 10 is between two multiples of 4, namely

$$4,650,300 + 8 \qquad \text{and} \qquad 4,650,300 + 12.$$

So, 4,650,310 is not a multiple of 4.

We also might have noted that since 10 is not a multiple of 4, adding 10 to a multiple of 4 gives a sum that is not a multiple of 4. (See Problem 3.1 on pages 93–95 if you don't remember why.) Therefore, 4,650,300 + 10 is not a multiple of 4.

□

> **Important:** A positive integer is divisible by 4 if the number formed by the last
> ⚠ two digits of the original integer is divisible by 4. If this number
> is not divisible by 4, then the original integer is not divisible by 4.

Problem 3.10: In this problem, we discover a method for determining whether or not a number is divisible by 9. Notice that

$$765 = 7 \cdot 100 + 6 \cdot 10 + 5$$
$$= 7 \cdot (99 + 1) + 6 \cdot (9 + 1) + 5$$
$$= 7 \cdot 99 + 7 + 6 \cdot 9 + 6 + 5$$
$$= 7 \cdot 99 + 6 \cdot 9 + (7 + 6 + 5).$$

(a) As shown above, 765 equals $7 \cdot 99 + 6 \cdot 9 + (7 + 6 + 5)$. Notice that $7 + 6 + 5$ is divisible by 9. Explain why this tells us that 765 is divisible by 9.

(b) Notice that $8 + 5 + 1 + 4 = 18$. Explain why this tells us that 8514 is divisible by 9.

(c) Determine whether or not 59814 is divisible by 9 *without dividing 9 into 59814*.

Solution for Problem 3.10:

(a) Since 99 is a multiple of 9, so is $7 \cdot 99$. Therefore, the sum $7 \cdot 99 + 6 \cdot 9 + (7 + 6 + 5)$ is the sum of three multiples of 9, namely, $7 \cdot 99$, $6 \cdot 9$, and $7 + 6 + 5$. This means that the sum itself, which equals 765, is a multiple of 9.

(b) Just as $765 = 7 \cdot 99 + 6 \cdot 9 + (7 + 6 + 5)$, we have

$$8514 = 8 \cdot 1000 + 5 \cdot 100 + 1 \cdot 10 + 4$$
$$= 8 \cdot (999 + 1) + 5 \cdot (99 + 1) + 1 \cdot (9 + 1) + 4$$
$$= 8 \cdot 999 + 8 + 5 \cdot 99 + 5 + 1 \cdot 9 + 1 + 4$$
$$= 8 \cdot 999 + 5 \cdot 99 + 1 \cdot 9 + (8 + 5 + 1 + 4).$$

We have $8 + 5 + 1 + 4 = 18$, which is a multiple of 9. Each of $8 \cdot 999$, $5 \cdot 99$, and $1 \cdot 9$ is also a multiple of 9. So, we have written 8514 as the sum of multiples of 9, which means that 8514 is itself a multiple of 9.

Notice that our key step here is to write 8514 as the sum of several multiples of 9 plus the sum of the digits of 8514:

$$8514 = 8 \cdot 999 + 5 \cdot 99 + 1 \cdot 9 + (8 + 5 + 1 + 4).$$

Similarly, we can write any positive integer as the sum of multiples of 9 plus the sum of the digits of the integer. The sum of the digits then tells us whether or not the original integer is a multiple of 9.

> **Important:** If the sum of the digits of an integer is a multiple of 9, then the integer is divisible by 9. Otherwise, the integer is not divisible by 9.

(c) The sum of the digits of 59814 is $5 + 9 + 8 + 1 + 4 = 27$. This sum is divisible by 9, so 59814 is divisible by 9.

$\square$

Problem 3.11: In the previous problem, we noted that $765 = (7 \cdot 99 + 6 \cdot 9) + (7 + 6 + 5)$.

(a) Are both 99 and 9 divisible by 3?

(b) Is 765 divisible by 3?

(c) Is 67242 divisible by 3?

(d) Explain why 6148 is not divisible by 3 *without dividing 6148 by 3*.

Solution for Problem 3.11:

(a) We have $99 = 3 \cdot 33$ and $9 = 3 \cdot 3$, so both 99 and 9 are divisible by 3.

(b) In Problem 3.10, we wrote 765 as

$$765 = 7 \cdot 99 + 6 \cdot 9 + (7 + 6 + 5).$$

Both 99 and 9 are multiples of 3, so $7 \cdot 99$ and $6 \cdot 9$ are multiples of 3. The sum $7 + 6 + 5 = 18$ is a multiple of 3. So, the sum $7 \cdot 99 + 6 \cdot 9 + (7 + 6 + 5)$ is the sum of three multiples of 3, namely, $7 \cdot 99$, $6 \cdot 9$, and $7 + 6 + 5$. Therefore, 765 is a multiple of 3.

(c) We have

$$\begin{aligned}
67242 &= 6 \cdot 10000 + 7 \cdot 1000 + 2 \cdot 100 + 4 \cdot 10 + 2 \\
&= 6 \cdot (9999 + 1) + 7 \cdot (999 + 1) + 2 \cdot (99 + 1) + 4 \cdot (9 + 1) + 2 \\
&= 6 \cdot 9999 + 7 \cdot 999 + 2 \cdot 99 + 4 \cdot 9 + (6 + 7 + 2 + 4 + 2).
\end{aligned}$$

Any number consisting only of 9's is a multiple of 9, and is therefore a multiple of 3. So, each product in the sum $6 \cdot 9999 + 7 \cdot 999 + 2 \cdot 99 + 4 \cdot 9$ is itself a multiple of 3. This means that this sum is a multiple of 3. Since $6 + 7 + 2 + 4 + 2 = 21$ is also a multiple of 3, we know that 67242 is the sum of multiples of 3. Therefore, 67242 is a multiple of 3.

Similarly, if the sum of the digits of an integer is a multiple of 3, then the integer is divisible by 3.

(d) When we follow the same process as in part (c), we get

$$6148 = 6 \cdot 1000 + 1 \cdot 100 + 4 \cdot 10 + 8$$
$$= 6 \cdot (999 + 1) + 1 \cdot (99 + 1) + 4 \cdot (9 + 1) + 8$$
$$= 6 \cdot 999 + 1 \cdot 99 + 4 \cdot 9 + (6 + 1 + 4 + 8)$$

Since $6 \cdot 999$, $1 \cdot 99$, and $4 \cdot 9$ are multiples of 3, the sum $6 \cdot 999 + 1 \cdot 99 + 4 \cdot 9$ is a multiple of 3. So, we see that 6148 is $6 + 1 + 4 + 8 = 19$ more than a multiple of 3. But 19 is not a multiple of 3. From our work on Problem 3.1 on pages 93–95, we know that if we add a multiple of 3 to a number is not a multiple of 3, then the resulting sum is not a multiple of 3. Therefore, 6148 is not a multiple of 3.

□

Our work in Problem 3.11 suggests the following rule for divisibility by 3, which looks a lot like our rule for divisibility by 9:

> **Important:** If the sum of the digits of an integer is a multiple of 3, then the integer is divisible by 3. Otherwise, the integer is not divisible by 3.

Problem 3.12: A is the units digit in the four-digit number 4,63A. If 4,63A is divisible by 3 and by 4, then what are all the possible values of A?

Solution for Problem 3.12: Since the number is divisible by 4, the number formed by its last two digits, $3A$, must be divisible by 4. The only two-digit multiples of 4 with 3 as the tens digit are 32 and 36, which makes the two possible four-digit numbers 4,632 and 4,636.

The four-digit number 4,63A must also be divisible by 3. To check for divisibility by 3, we find the sums of the digits of 4,632 and 4,636. We have $4 + 6 + 3 + 2 = 15$, which is divisible by 3, so 4632 is divisible by 3. We also have $4 + 6 + 3 + 6 = 19$, which is not divisible by 3, so 4636 is not divisible by 3. Therefore, the only possible value of A is 2. □

Problem 3.13: N is the tens digit in the five-digit number 24,6N8. If 24,6N8 is divisible by 9, then must 24,6N8 also be divisible by 4?

Solution for Problem 3.13: Since the number is divisible by 9, the sum of its digits is divisible by 9. The sum of the digits of the number is $2 + 4 + 6 + N + 8 = 20 + N$. The only digit N that makes $20 + N$ a multiple of 9 is 7, so our five-digit number is 24,678. The number formed by the last two digits of 24,678 is 78. Since 78 is not divisible by 4, we know that 24,678 is not divisible by 4. □

Here is a summary of all of the divisibility tests we learned in this section:

Number	Condition under which n is divisible by the number
2	Units digit of n is 0, 2, 4, 6, or 8
3	Sum of the digits of n is a multiple of 3
4	Number formed by last two digits of n is a multiple of 4
5	Units digit of n is 0 or 5
9	Sum of the digits of n is a multiple of 9
10	Units digit of n is 0

Exercises ▶

3.2.1   Which of the following numbers are divisible by 5:

$$46{,}624, \qquad 560{,}335, \qquad 60{,}231{,}060 \qquad 9{,}671{,}118?$$

3.2.2   Which of the following numbers are divisible by 4:

$$46{,}624, \qquad 560{,}335, \qquad 60{,}231{,}060 \qquad 9{,}671{,}118?$$

3.2.3   Which of the following numbers are divisible by 3:

$$46{,}624, \qquad 560{,}335, \qquad 60{,}231{,}060 \qquad 9{,}671{,}118?$$

3.2.4   Which of the following numbers are *not* divisible by 7:

$$7{,}000{,}014, \qquad 14{,}035, \qquad 7{,}777{,}728, \qquad 42{,}721{,}034, \qquad 49{,}763?$$

3.2.5   How many numbers from 1 through 400 have a 2 in the units place (ones place) and are divisible by 4?

3.2.6   Both ABC and $3D8$ are three-digit numbers such that $ABC - 3D8 = 269$. If $3D8$ is divisible by 9, then what number does ABC represent? *(Source: MOEMS)*

3.2.7   What is the largest digit d for which the number $214{,}d07$ is divisible by 3?

3.2.8★   Consider the rules we found to test for divisibility by 2 and by 4. Can you find a similar rule for divisibility by 8?

3.3   Prime Numbers

Every positive integer is divisible by 1 and by itself. Some numbers are not divisible by any other positive integers. For example, 5 is divisible by 1 and 5, but not by any other positive integer. Meanwhile, 6 is divisible by 1 and 6, but also by 2 and 3.

Definition: A **prime number** is a positive integer that is divisible by exactly two positive integers: 1 and the number itself. A **composite number** is a positive integer that is divisible by more than two positive integers. This means that a number is composite if it is divisible by some positive integer besides 1 and the number itself.

For example, 2 is divisible by 1 and by 2, but it is not divisible by any other positive number. Therefore, 2 is prime. Meanwhile, 12 is divisible by 3, so 12 is composite. The number 1 is the only positive integer that is neither prime nor composite. Each integer greater than 1 is either prime or composite.

We often use the word "prime" as a noun, as in, "2 is a prime."

Problem 3.14: List every prime that is less than 20.

Problem 3.15: Meena is trying to determine whether or not 113 is prime. She's doing so by checking 113 for divisibility by each positive integer starting with 2. She sees that 113 is odd, so it is not divisible by 2. She then checks if 113 is divisible by 3. Since $1 + 1 + 3 = 5$ is not divisible by 3, she knows that 113 is not divisible by 3.

(a) Meena says, "Since 113 is not divisible by 2, I know that 113 isn't divisible by 4." Is she right? Why or why not?

(b) How does Meena know at a glance that 113 is not divisible by 5?

(c) She then says, "Since 113 is not divisible by 2, I know that it isn't divisible by 6." Is she right? Why or why not?

(d) Meena divides 113 by 7 and finds a remainder of 1, so she knows that 113 is not divisible by 7. She then says, "I don't have to test 8, 9, or 10. I know that 113 isn't divisible by any of those." How does she know without testing?

(e) Meena then says, "Since 11^2 is 121, I don't have to test any numbers higher than 10. I now know that 113 is prime." Why doesn't Meena have to test any more numbers?

Problem 3.16: Describe each of the following numbers as prime or composite:

(a) 61

(b) 91

(c) 143

(d) 157

Problem 3.17: Find the largest two-digit composite number in which both digits are prime.

Problem 3.18: Find all pairs of primes whose sum is 61.

Problem 3.19: Start with the grid of numbers on the right, and perform the following process:	2 3 4 5 6 7 8 9 10
	11 12 13 14 15 16 17 18 19 20
Step 1. Circle the smallest number that is not already circled or crossed out.	21 22 23 24 25 26 27 28 29 30
	31 32 33 34 35 36 37 38 39 40
Step 2. Cross out all of the multiples of the number you circled in Step 1, except for the circled number itself.	41 42 43 44 45 46 47 48 49 50
	51 52 53 54 55 56 57 58 59 60
Step 3. If every number is either circled or crossed out, then stop. Otherwise, go back to Step 1.	61 62 63 64 65 66 67 68 69 70
	71 72 73 74 75 76 77 78 79 80
When you finish, do you notice anything interesting about the circled numbers?	81 82 83 84 85 86 87 88 89 90
	91 92 93 94 95 96 97 98 99 100

Problem 3.14: List every prime that is less than 20.

Solution for Problem 3.14: In the introduction, we noted that 1 is not prime and 2 is prime.

The number 3 is divisible by 1 and by 3, but not by 2. A positive number cannot be divisible by a number greater than itself, so we don't have to check if 3 is divisible by 4 or 5 or any other number greater than 3. Therefore, we know that 3 is prime.

Since 4 is divisible by 2, we know that 4 is composite. Similarly, 6, 8, 10, 12, 14, 16, and 18 are all divisible by 2 and therefore are composite. Of course, you probably recognize these as even numbers. Any number that is divisible by 2 is even, and any integer that is not divisible by 2 is an odd number. Since every even number is divisible by 2, the only even prime is 2. So, we don't have to check any more even numbers.

Continuing in this manner, we find that the only primes less than 20 are 2, 3, 5, 7, 11, 13, 17, and 19. To see why the other numbers are not prime, we note that 1 is not prime by definition, all the other even numbers are divisible by 2, and both 9 and 15 are multiples of 3. □

Extra! Finding large prime numbers is a thrill for some mathematicians and computer scientists. As of this writing, the largest known prime is

$$2^{82,589,933} - 1,$$

which has 24,862,048 digits! This prime was discovered in 2018 by the **Great Internet Mersenne Prime Search** (**GIMPS**), which is a collaborative internet-based search for large primes. Visit www.mersenne.org to join the search!

Problem 3.15: Meena is trying to determine whether or not 113 is prime. She's doing so by checking 113 for divisibility by each positive integer starting with 2. She sees that 113 is odd, so it is not divisible by 2. She then checks if 113 is divisible by 3. Since $1 + 1 + 3 = 5$ is not divisible by 3, she knows that 113 is not divisible by 3.

(a) Meena says, "Since 113 is not divisible by 2, I know that 113 isn't divisible by 4." Is she right? Why or why not?

(b) How does Meena know at a glance that 113 is not divisible by 5?

(c) She then says, "Since 113 is not divisible by 2, I know that it isn't divisible by 6." Is she right? Why or why not?

(d) Meena divides 113 by 7 and finds a remainder of 1, so she knows that 113 is not divisible by 7. She then says, "I don't have to test 8, 9, or 10. I know that 113 isn't divisible by any of those." How does she know without testing?

(e) Meena then says, "Since 11^2 is 121, I don't have to test any numbers higher than 10. I now know that 113 is prime." Why doesn't Meena have to test any more numbers?

Solution for Problem 3.15:

(a) Yes, she is right. Every multiple of 4 is also a multiple of 2, since 4 is a multiple of 2. But Meena already knows that 113 is not a multiple of 2, so she knows that 113 cannot possibly be a multiple of 4.

(b) The last digit of 113 is not 0 or 5, so she knows that 113 is not divisible by 5.

(c) Yes, she is right. As in part (a), every multiple of 6 is also a multiple of 2, since 6 is a multiple of 2. Meena knows that 113 is not a multiple of 2, so she knows that 113 cannot be a multiple of 6.

(d) She doesn't have to test 8 or 10 because these are both multiples of 2. Since 113 is not a multiple of 2, Meena knows that 113 is not divisible by any even number.

Every multiple of 9 is also a multiple of 3. Since Meena knows that 113 is not a multiple of 3, she knows that 113 cannot be a multiple of 9, either. Therefore, Meena doesn't have to test 8, 9, or 10.

(e) Meena knows that 113 is not a multiple of any integer from 2 through 10. So, if 113 is the product of two integers, and neither integer is 1, then both of the integers must be greater than 10.

The smallest possible product of two integers greater than 10 is $11 \cdot 11 = 121$, which is larger than 113. Any other product of two integers greater than 10 will be even larger. So, 113 cannot be written as the product of two integers that are greater than 1. This means that 113 is divisible only by 1 and by itself, so 113 is prime.

□

Our work in Problem 3.15 revealed two very important points about testing whether or not a number is prime.

> **Important:** If a number is not divisible by a prime, then it is not divisible by any multiple of that prime. So, in testing whether or not a number is prime, we only need to test if that number is divisible by prime numbers.

> **Important:** To check if a number is prime, we only need to test if it is divisible by primes whose squares are less than or equal to the number we are testing.

For example, to test whether or not 59 is prime, we only need to check if it is divisible by 2, 3, 5, or 7. Since 11^2 is greater than 59, we don't need to test any other primes.

Problem 3.16: Describe each of the following numbers as prime or composite:

(a) 61   (b) 91   (c) 143   (d) 157

Solution for Problem 3.16:

(a) Since $11^2 = 121$ is greater than 61, we only need to test for divisibility by 2, 3, 5, and 7. Since 61 is not divisible by any of these primes, we know that 61 is prime.

(b) $91 = 7 \cdot 13$, so 91 is composite.

(c) $143 = 11 \cdot 13$, so 143 is composite.

(d) Since $13^2 = 169$ is greater than 157, we only need to test for divisibility by 2, 3, 5, 7, and 11. Since 157 is not divisible by any of these primes, we know that 157 is prime.

□

Problem 3.17: Find the largest two-digit composite number in which both digits are prime.

Solution for Problem 3.17: The one-digit primes are 2, 3, 5, and 7. The largest two-digit number we can form with these digits is 77, which is indeed composite because $77 = 7 \cdot 11$. □

Problem 3.18: Find all pairs of primes whose sum is 61.

Solution for Problem 3.18: If two integers sum to 61, then one of the integers must be even and the other odd. The only even prime is 2, so one of the primes must be 2. We have $61 - 2 = 59$, and 59 is prime, so 2 and 59 is the only pair of primes whose sum is 61. □

Problem 3.19: Start with the grid of numbers on the right, and perform the following process:

Step 1. Circle the smallest number that is not already circled or crossed out.

Step 2. Cross out all of the multiples of the number you circled in Step 1, except for the circled number itself.

Step 3. If every number is either circled or crossed out, then stop. Otherwise, go back to Step 1.

When you finish, do you notice anything interesting about the circled numbers?

```
    2  3  4  5  6  7  8  9 10
11 12 13 14 15 16 17 18 19 20
21 22 23 24 25 26 27 28 29 30
31 32 33 34 35 36 37 38 39 40
41 42 43 44 45 46 47 48 49 50
51 52 53 54 55 56 57 58 59 60
61 62 63 64 65 66 67 68 69 70
71 72 73 74 75 76 77 78 79 80
81 82 83 84 85 86 87 88 89 90
91 92 93 94 95 96 97 98 99 100
```

Solution for Problem 3.19: The smallest number in the grid is 2, so we start by circling 2 in Step 1. Step 2 then tells us to cross out all of the multiples of 2 except for 2, so we cross out all the even numbers except 2. Moving on to Step 3, we still have plenty of numbers that are not circled or crossed out, so we go back to Step 1.

The smallest number that was not circled or crossed out already is 3, so we circle 3. We then cross out all the other multiples of 3. As we go, we notice that a bunch of these multiples of 3 are already crossed out—these are the numbers that are also multiples of 2. After crossing out all the multiples of 3 besides 3, we still have many numbers that are not circled or crossed out. Back to Step 1 we go.

Now the smallest number that was not circled or crossed out already is 5, so we circle 5. We then cross out all of the other multiples of 5. There are still plenty of numbers to go. Back to Step 1.

The smallest number that was not circled or crossed out is now 7, so we circle that and then cross out the other multiples of 7. Sigh, still a bunch of numbers to go.

The next number we'll circle is 11. But there are no other multiples of 11 in the grid that are not circled or crossed out. This is because we have circled or crossed out all the multiples of 2, 3, 5, and 7 already. That means we have crossed out $2 \cdot 11$, $3 \cdot 11$, $5 \cdot 11$, and $7 \cdot 11$. We also crossed out $4 \cdot 11$, $6 \cdot 11$, and $8 \cdot 11$ when we crossed out multiples of 2, and we crossed out $9 \cdot 11$ when we crossed out multiples of 3.

We circle 11 and still have plenty of numbers left. But for each number we circle, there are no more un-crossed-out multiples of the circled number left in the grid. So, as we repeat the three steps over and over, we circle all the remaining numbers in the grid. In the end, we have the grid at the right.

The circled numbers are the primes less than 100! Why?

Each time we cross out numbers in Step 2, the numbers we cross out are multiples of the number we just circled in Step 1. So, all of the crossed out numbers are composite. We'll never cross out a prime number, because a prime number isn't a multiple of any of the numbers in the grid besides itself. Therefore, eventually each prime number will become the smallest available number in the grid in Step 1. It will then be circled and all its multiples crossed out. Since each prime gets circled and all its multiples get crossed out, every composite number will get crossed out in the step after we circle the smallest prime that evenly divides the composite number. So, we must have all primes in the grid circled and all composite numbers crossed out when we finish.

This process is called the **Sieve of Eratosthenes** after the ancient Greek mathematician who developed it. There's nothing special about 100 in our example above of the Sieve of Eratosthenes. We could have started with a much larger grid to find many more primes. □

> **Sidenote:** The Sieve of Eratosthenes is a very efficient way to generate long lists of prime numbers. For example, if you wanted to write a computer program to list of all the primes that are less than 1,000,000, you'd be much better off using the Sieve of Eratosthenes rather than checking each number one at time with the process we used in Problem 3.15.

 Exercises

3.3.1 What is the sum of all the prime numbers between 80 and 90?

3.3.2 Find every number between 70 and 80 that is not prime and is not a multiple of 2, 3, or 5. *(Source: MATHCOUNTS)*

3.3.3 What is the largest prime number p such that 8 times p is less than 1000?

3.3.4 How many pairs of primes are there such that sum of the pair is 40?

3.3.5

(a) The product of all prime numbers between 1 and 80 is divided by 10. What is the remainder?

(b)★ The product of all prime numbers between 1 and 80 is divided by 4. What is the remainder?

3.3.6 How many groups of three prime numbers add to 22? Note: $(2, 3, 5)$ is considered the same group of three primes as $(3, 2, 5)$.

3.3.7★ Suppose P and Q both represent prime numbers such that

$$5P + 7Q = 109.$$

Find the value of the prime P. *(Source: MOEMS)*

3.4 Prime Factorization

When we **factor** an integer, we write it as a product of integers. So, if a number is composite, then we can factor it by writing it as the product of two smaller integers. For example, we can factor 12 as $12 = 2 \cdot 6$. Since 6 is composite, we also can factor 6, writing it as the product of 2 and 3:

$$12 = 2 \cdot 6 = 2 \cdot 2 \cdot 3.$$

Since 2 and 3 are prime, we cannot write either of them as the product of two smaller positive integers. We have expressed 12 as a product of primes. We call this the **prime factorization** of 12. The primes that appear in the prime factorization of 12 are the **prime factors** of 12. So, 2 and 3 are the prime factors of 12.

We usually write prime factorizations using powers. For example, the prime factorization of 12 is $2^2 \cdot 3^1$. Note that we write the primes in increasing order. In this chapter, we will often include exponents of 1, but usually these are left out elsewhere.

It's easy to keep track of your work when finding the prime factorization of a small number like 12. When finding the prime factorization of a larger number, we sometimes use a **factor tree** to organize our work.

We'll build a sample factor tree for the prime factorization of 12. We start by writing 12. We can factor 12 as $12 = 2 \cdot 6$; we show this in the factor tree by splitting 12 into a 2 and a 6. We circle primes we encounter in the tree, so we circle the 2 as shown. We can't factor primes into a product of smaller positive integers, so we know there won't be any branches going downward from circled numbers.

Since 6 isn't prime, we can factor it into the product of two smaller numbers, 2 and 3. Each of these are prime, so we circle both. There are no uncircled numbers left to factor, so we have our prime factorization. We can now easily read the prime factorization of 12 from our factor tree: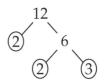

$$12 = 2 \cdot 2 \cdot 3 = 2^2 \cdot 3^1.$$

▌▌▌ **Problems** ▶

Problem 3.20: Find the prime factorization of each of the following numbers:

(a) 30   (b) 60   (c) 252   (d) 288

Problem 3.21: Find the prime factorization of each of the following perfect squares:

(a) 16   (b) 36   (c) 81   (d) 144

How can we use the prime factorization of a number to tell whether or not the number is a perfect square?

Problem 3.22: What positive integer squared equals $96 \cdot 486$?

Problem 3.23: Paul multiplies two positive integers and gets a product of 16000. If neither of Paul's integers ends in 0, then what is the sum of Paul's integers?

Problem 3.24:

(a) Let N be the product of the 10 smallest prime numbers. Explain why the prime factorization of $N + 1$ must include a prime that isn't among the 10 smallest prime numbers.

(b) Let N be the product of the 100 smallest prime numbers. Explain why the prime factorization of $N + 1$ must include a prime that isn't among the 100 smallest prime numbers.

(c)★ Explain why there is not a largest prime number. That is, explain why there are infinitely many primes.

Problem 3.20: Find the prime factorization of each of the following numbers:

(a) 30   (b) 60   (c) 252   (d) 288

Solution for Problem 3.20:

(a) We have $30 = 5 \cdot 6$, and then $6 = 2 \cdot 3$, which gives us the factor tree shown at the right. We then have

$$30 = 2^1 \cdot 3^1 \cdot 5^1$$

as the prime factorization of 30.

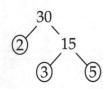

Of course, this isn't the only factor tree we could have built for 30. We could have started with $30 = 2 \cdot 15$, and produced the factor tree shown at the left. This factor tree also produces the prime factorization

$$30 = 2^1 \cdot 3^1 \cdot 5^1.$$

(b) We start with $60 = 6 \cdot 10$, and then note that $6 = 2 \cdot 3$ and $10 = 2 \cdot 5$. This produces the factor tree on the right. Reading the primes from the factor tree gives the prime factorization

$$60 = 2^2 \cdot 3^1 \cdot 5^1.$$

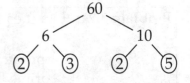

We also could have used our result from part (a). There, we found that $30 = 2^1 \cdot 3^1 \cdot 5^1$. Since $60 = 2 \cdot 30$, we have

$$60 = 2 \cdot 30 = 2 \cdot 2^1 \cdot 3^1 \cdot 5^1 = 2^2 \cdot 3^1 \cdot 5^1.$$

(c) We can easily divide 252 by 2, so we start with $252 = 2 \cdot 126$. We then have $126 = 2 \cdot 63$ and $63 = 7 \cdot 9$. We finish with $9 = 3 \cdot 3$, as shown at the right. Reading the primes from the factor tree gives the prime factorization

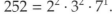

$$252 = 2^2 \cdot 3^2 \cdot 7^1.$$

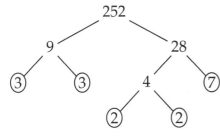

We didn't have to start off dividing by 2. Since the sum of the digits of 252 is 9, we know that 252 is divisible by 9. That gives us a first step of the factor tree for 252 shown on the left: $252 = 9 \cdot 28$. We then have $9 = 3 \cdot 3$ on the left side of the factor tree, and $28 = 4 \cdot 7$ and $4 = 2 \cdot 2$ on the right side. This tree gives us the same prime factorization as before, $252 = 2^2 \cdot 3^2 \cdot 7^1$.

(d) We can easily divide 288 by 2, so we start with $288 = 2 \cdot 144$. We recognize 144 as $12 \cdot 12$, and each 12 is $4 \cdot 3$. Rather than breaking each 4 into two 2's in the tree, we use the tree at the right to write

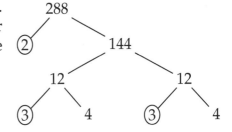

$$288 = 2 \cdot 3 \cdot 4 \cdot 3 \cdot 4 = 2 \cdot 3 \cdot 2^2 \cdot 3 \cdot 2^2 = 2^5 \cdot 3^2.$$

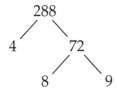

We also might have seen that 288 is easily divided by 4, and started our factor tree with $288 = 4 \cdot 72$. We recognize 72 as $8 \cdot 9$. We now have the factor tree shown at the left. We could continue with the factor tree, but we recognize 4, 8, and 9 as powers of primes. So, once again we can use an incomplete tree to finish:

$$288 = 4 \cdot 8 \cdot 9 = 2^2 \cdot 2^3 \cdot 3^2 = 2^{2+3} \cdot 3^2 = 2^5 \cdot 3^2.$$

□

Every positive integer has a prime factorization. We can see why by considering the primes, the composites, and 1 separately:

- **Primes**. The prime factorization of a prime number is simply the number itself. For example, the prime factorization of 5 is 5.

- **Composites**. We can look to our factor trees to explain why every composite number has a prime factorization. Any composite number can be written as the product of two smaller numbers. We then continue our tree-building process with these smaller positive numbers. For each number, we either identify the number as prime and circle it, or we break the number into a product of smaller positive integers. But we can't continue this process forever, because we can't keep producing smaller and smaller positive integers. So, we must reach a point at which we can't continue the factor tree. At this point, all of the numbers at the ends of the factor tree must be prime, because they cannot be factored. This means we are guaranteed to find a prime factorization of any composite integer.

- **1.** We define the prime factorization of 1 to be simply 1. This isn't a product of primes, but this definition does allow us to write statements about "prime factorizations of positive integers" without having to include "except 1" every time.

Not only does every positive integer have a prime factorization, but the prime factorization of each number is unique. That is, for any positive integer besides 1, there is only one group of primes whose product equals the integer. (Note that we are disregarding the order of the primes in the prime factorization. So, $2^3 \cdot 3$ is the same prime factorization as $3 \cdot 2^3$.) This powerful result is called the **Fundamental Theorem of Arithmetic**. We won't prove this powerful theorem here, because the tools needed for the proof are too advanced for this book.

> **Important:** **Fundamental Theorem of Arithmetic**. Every positive integer has a unique prime factorization.

As you become more experienced with primes and prime factorizations, you probably won't use factor trees to find prime factorizations of many numbers. You'll often be able to reason your way to a prime factorization without a tree. For example, to find the prime factorization of 30, you might reason as follows:

$$30 = 6 \cdot 5 = 2^1 \cdot 3^1 \cdot 5^1.$$

We'll take this approach to finding the prime factorizations of numbers for the rest of this section.

For the next three problems, we'll use prime factorizations to tackle problems about products of integers.

> **Concept:** We can think of primes as the building blocks of integers. Because every integer greater than 1 can be written as a product of primes in exactly one way, prime factorizations can be particularly useful in problems involving products of integers.

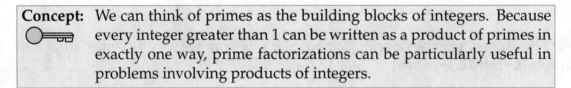

Problem 3.21: Find the prime factorization of each of the following perfect squares:

(a) 16　　　　(b) 36　　　　(c) 81　　　　(d) 144

How can we use the prime factorization of a number to tell whether or not the number is a perfect square?

Solution for Problem 3.21:

(a) $16 = 4^2 = (2^2)^2 = 2^{2 \cdot 2} = 2^4$.

(b) $36 = 6^2 = (2 \cdot 3)^2 = 2^2 \cdot 3^2$.

(c) $81 = 9^2 = (3^2)^2 = 3^{2 \cdot 2} = 3^4$.

(d) $144 = 12^2 = (2^2 \cdot 3)^2 = (2^2)^2 \cdot 3^2 = 2^4 \cdot 3^2$.

All of the exponents in these prime factorizations are even. Our steps for finding the prime factorizations tell us why. In each part, we found the prime factorization of a square n^2 by finding the prime factorization of n, and then squaring the resulting prime factorization. When squaring, we multiply the exponent of each prime in the prime factorization of n by 2. This makes the exponent of each prime in the prime factorization of n^2 even.

We can run this logic in reverse, too! If we start with a prime factorization in which each exponent is even, then we can write that prime factorization as the square of another prime factorization whose exponents are half the exponents of the original prime factorization. For example, consider the prime factorization $2^2 \cdot 5^4 \cdot 11^8$. We have

$$2^2 \cdot 5^4 \cdot 11^8 = 2^{1 \cdot 2} \cdot 5^{2 \cdot 2} \cdot 11^{4 \cdot 2} = (2^1 \cdot 5^2 \cdot 11^4)^2,$$

so we see that $2^2 \cdot 5^4 \cdot 11^8$ is the square of $2^1 \cdot 5^2 \cdot 11^4$. Similarly, any prime factorization in which all of the exponents are even is the prime factorization of a perfect square. $\square$

> **Important:** All of the exponents in the prime factorization of a perfect square are even. Any prime factorization in which all of the exponents are even is the prime factorization of a perfect square.

Problem 3.22: What positive integer squared equals $96 \cdot 486$?

Solution for Problem 3.22: We start by finding the prime factorizations of 96 and 486:

$$96 = 32 \cdot 3 = (4 \cdot 8) \cdot 3 = 2^2 \cdot 2^3 \cdot 3 = 2^{2+3} \cdot 3 = 2^5 \cdot 3^1,$$
$$486 = 6 \cdot 81 = (2 \cdot 3) \cdot (9 \cdot 9) = 2^1 \cdot 3^1 \cdot 3^2 \cdot 3^2 = 2^1 \cdot 3^{1+2+2} = 2^1 \cdot 3^5.$$

Next, we multiply these prime factorizations:

$$96 \cdot 486 = (2^5 \cdot 3^1) \cdot (2^1 \cdot 3^5) = 2^5 \cdot 3^1 \cdot 2^1 \cdot 3^5 = (2^5 \cdot 2^1) \cdot (3^1 \cdot 3^5) = 2^6 \cdot 3^6.$$

Both of the exponents are even, so $2^6 \cdot 3^6$ is a perfect square. Specifically, we have

$$2^6 \cdot 3^6 = 2^{3 \cdot 2} \cdot 3^{3 \cdot 2} = (2^3 \cdot 3^3)^2 = (8 \cdot 27)^2 = 216^2.$$

So, the number we seek is 216. $\square$

Problem 3.23: Paul multiplies two positive integers and gets a product of 16000. If neither of Paul's integers ends in 0, then what is the sum of Paul's integers?

Solution for Problem 3.23: Once again we have a problem about a product of integers, so we'll think about prime factorizations. The prime factorization of 16000 is

$$16000 = 16 \cdot 1000 = (4 \cdot 4) \cdot 10^3 = 2^2 \cdot 2^2 \cdot (2 \cdot 5)^3 = 2^2 \cdot 2^2 \cdot 2^3 \cdot 5^3 = 2^{2+2+3} \cdot 5^3 = 2^7 \cdot 5^3.$$

We therefore seek two numbers whose product is $2^7 \cdot 5^3$, and such that neither number ends in 0. Any multiple of 10 ends in 0, and any number with both a 2 and a 5 in its prime factorization must be a multiple of 10. So, neither of Paul's integers can have both a 2 and a 5 in its prime factorization. This means that all the 2's in Paul's product $2^7 \cdot 5^3$ must come from one of his integers, and all of the 5's come from the other integer. Therefore, the only two possible numbers that fit our problem are $2^7 = 128$ and $5^3 = 125$, which means that the sum of Paul's integers is $128 + 125 = 253$. $\square$

Now that we know that prime numbers are important, we might wonder how many primes there are.

Problem 3.24:

(a) Let N be the product of the 10 smallest prime numbers. Explain why the prime factorization of $N + 1$ must include a prime that isn't among the 10 smallest prime numbers.

(b) Let N be the product of the 100 smallest prime numbers. Explain why the prime factorization of $N + 1$ must include a prime that isn't among the 100 smallest prime numbers.

(c)$\star$ Explain why there is not a largest prime number. That is, explain why there are infinitely many primes.

Solution for Problem 3.24:

(a) The 10 smallest prime numbers are 2, 3, 5, 7, 11, 13, 17, 19, 23, and 29. So,

$$N + 1 = 2 \cdot 3 \cdot 5 \cdot 7 \cdot 11 \cdot 13 \cdot 17 \cdot 19 \cdot 23 \cdot 29 + 1.$$

We see that $N + 1$ is 1 more than 2 times some integer, so $N + 1$ must be odd. Therefore, $N + 1$ is not divisible by 2.

Similarly, $N + 1$ is 1 more than 3 times some integer, so $N + 1$ is not divisible by 3. Next, $N + 1$ is 1 more than 5 times some integer, so $N + 1$ is not divisible by 5. Continuing in this way, we see that $N + 1$ is 1 more than a multiple of each of the first 10 primes, so $N + 1$ is not divisible by any of the 10 smallest prime numbers. This means that the prime factorization of $N + 1$ doesn't include any of these 10 smallest primes. That tells us that all of the prime factors of $N + 1$ are greater than 29.

For the record, the number $N + 1$ is 6469693231, and the prime factorization of this number is $331 \cdot 571 \cdot 34231$. (Yes, we used a computer to figure this out!)

Of course, we know already that there are more primes than just the smallest ten primes. Let's see what this approach tells us if we start with more primes.

(b) It'll take a long time to figure out the 100 smallest primes. Fortunately, we don't have to. By the same argument as in part (a), if N is the product of the 100 smallest primes, then $N + 1$ is not divisible by any of these primes. This is because N is a multiple of each of these primes, so $N + 1$ divided by any one of these primes leaves a remainder of 1.

Since the prime factorization $N + 1$ cannot include any of the 100 smallest primes, it must consist of primes that are larger than these 100 smallest primes. As in part (a), this tells us that there must be some primes besides these 100 primes.

> **Sidenote:** Just in case you're curious, $N + 1$ for this part has 220 digits:
>
>
> 47119307999061849531624878347602604220205747734096755201886348396164153358450342212052892567055446819724391040977771579918043802842183150387194449439904925790307206359905384523125283398643529993103984817917300172010 31091.
>
> Good luck finding the prime factorization of that, but at least you now know that you don't have to check the first 100 primes!

(c) Suppose we made a finite list (meaning a list that ends) that we thought included all of the primes. If we let N equal the product of all the numbers in the list, then N is a multiple of all of the primes in our list. So, just as in parts (a) and (b), $N + 1$ is not a multiple of *any* of the primes in our list. That means that the prime factorization of $N + 1$ must have primes that aren't in our list! No matter how long we make our list, this argument tells us that there will be other primes that are not on the list. So, it is impossible to make a finite list of all the primes. There are infinitely many prime numbers.

$\square$

Exercises

3.4.1 Find the prime factorization of each of the following numbers:

(a) 72

(b) 210

(c) 243

(d) 539

(e) 5525

(f) 26136

3.4.2 What is the largest prime factor of 6,886?

3.4.3 If x, y, and z are positive integers and $2^x \cdot 3^y \cdot 5^z = 54{,}000$, what is the value of $x + y + z$? *(Source: MATHCOUNTS)*

3.4.4

(a) What is the smallest positive perfect square that is divisible by the four smallest primes?

(b) How does the answer to part (a) change if we remove the word "positive"?

3.4.5 The product of two positive integers is 504 and each of the numbers is divisible by 6. However, neither of the two integers is 6. What is the larger of the two integers? *(Source: MOEMS)*

3.4.6 In the equation $858 = a \cdot b$, the numbers a and b are both positive two-digit integers. What is the greatest possible value of $a + b$? *(Source: MATHCOUNTS)*

3.4.7 In Problem 3.21, we learned that all of the exponents must be even in the prime factorization of a perfect square. Is there a similar fact for perfect cubes? How can we tell from looking at the prime factorization of a positive integer whether or not the integer is a perfect cube?

3.4.8★

(a) The number 40! (40! is spoken, "40 **factorial**") is defined as the product of all integers from 1 through 40:
$$40! = 1 \times 2 \times 3 \times 4 \times 5 \times \cdots \times 38 \times 39 \times 40.$$

In the prime factorization of 40!, what is the power of 5?

(b) If a number ends in zeros, those zeros are called **terminal zeros**. For example, 40,000 has four terminal zeros, but 104,000 has just three terminal zeros. How many terminal zeros does 40! have?

3.5 Least Common Multiple

Suppose a and b are positive integers. If a number is a multiple of both a and b, then we say that the number is a **common multiple** of a and b. The smallest positive integer that is a multiple of both a and b is called the **least common multiple** of a and b. For example, 12 is a common multiple of 2 and 3, and the least common multiple of 2 and 3 is 6.

We can refer to the least common multiple of a and b as lcm$[a, b]$. So, we have lcm$[2, 3] = 6$.

We can extend the concept of a common multiple to any number of integers. For example, 12 is a common multiple of the three integers 2, 3, and 4, because 12 is a multiple of all three integers. Moreover, we can write lcm$[2, 3, 4] = 12$.

Problems

> **Problem 3.25:**
>
> (a) List the five smallest positive multiples of 18.
>
> (b) List the five smallest positive multiples of 24.
>
> (c) List the three smallest positive common multiples of 18 and 24.
>
> (d) What is the least common multiple of 18 and 24? How are the common multiples you found in part (c) related to the least common multiple?

Problem 3.26: Find the prime factorizations of the five smallest positive multiples of 18. Compare these prime factorizations to the prime factorization of 18. Do you notice anything interesting?

Problem 3.27: The prime factorization of 72 is $2^3 \cdot 3^2$. Use the given prime factorization of each number below to determine if the number is a multiple of 72.

(a) $864 = 2^5 \cdot 3^3$

(b) $400 = 2^4 \cdot 5^2$

(c) $1008 = 2^4 \cdot 3^2 \cdot 7^1$

(d) $2916 = 2^2 \cdot 3^6$

Suppose we have the prime factorizations of two positive integers m and n. How can we use these prime factorizations to tell if m is a multiple of n?

Problem 3.28: How can we use the prime factorizations of 24 and 90 to find lcm[24, 90]?

Problem 3.29: Compute each of the following:

(a) lcm[96, 144]

(b) lcm[28, 35]

(c) lcm[$2^2 \cdot 3^3 \cdot 5^1, 3^3 \cdot 5^2 \cdot 7^1$]

(d) lcm[24, 36, 42]

Problem 3.30:

(a) Are lcm[$2 \cdot 500, 2 \cdot 300$] and 2 lcm[500, 300] equal?

(b) Let a and b be positive integers. Must we have lcm[$2a, 2b$] = 2 lcm[a, b]?

(c) Let a and b be positive integers. Must we have lcm[$15a, 15b$] = 15 lcm[a, b]?

(d) Compute lcm[606060, 707070].

Problem 3.31: A church rings its bells every 15 minutes, the school rings its bells every 20 minutes, and the day care center rings its bells every 25 minutes. If they all ring their bells at noon on the same day, at what time will they next all ring their bells together? *(Source: MATHCOUNTS)*

Problem 3.32: The number 16128 is a multiple of 6, 7, and 8. What is the smallest multiple of 6, 7, and 8 that is greater than 16128?

Problem 3.33:

(a) What is the smallest positive integer greater than 1 that leaves a remainder of 1 when divided by each of 6, 7, and 8?

(b) Find the smallest positive number that leaves a remainder of 5 when divided by 6, a remainder of 6 when divided by 7, and a remainder of 7 when divided by 8.

Problem 3.25:

(a) List the five smallest positive multiples of 18.

(b) List the five smallest positive multiples of 24.

(c) List the three smallest positive common multiples of 18 and 24.

(d) What is the least common multiple of 18 and 24? How are the common multiples you found in part (c) related to the least common multiple?

Solution for Problem 3.25:

(a) The five smallest positive multiples of 18 are

$$18 \cdot 1 = 18, \qquad 18 \cdot 2 = 36, \qquad 18 \cdot 3 = 54, \qquad 18 \cdot 4 = 72, \qquad 18 \cdot 5 = 90.$$

(b) The five smallest positive multiples of 24 are

$$24 \cdot 1 = 24, \qquad 24 \cdot 2 = 48, \qquad 24 \cdot 3 = 72, \qquad 24 \cdot 4 = 96, \qquad 24 \cdot 5 = 120.$$

(c) From the first two parts, we see that 72 is one common multiple of 18 and 24. If we continue listing multiples of 18 and 24, we will form the following two lists:

$$\text{Multiples of 18}: \ 18, 36, 54, \underline{72}, 90, 108, 126, \underline{144}, 162, 180, 198, \underline{216}, \ldots,$$
$$\text{Multiples of 24}: \ 24, 48, \underline{72}, 96, 120, \underline{144}, 168, 192, \underline{216}, \ldots.$$

The numbers 72, 144, and 216 appear in both lists; these are the three smallest positive common multiples of 18 and 24.

(d) The smallest of the positive common multiples we found in part (c) is 72, so $\text{lcm}[18, 24] = 72$. Notice that each common multiple of 18 and 24 we found in part (c) is a multiple of $\text{lcm}[18, 24]$. This isn't a coincidence. Later in this section we figure out why this must be the case.

□

Making lists of multiples can be a pretty tedious way to find the least common multiple. Fortunately, prime factorization gives us a slick method. We'll start by seeing how the prime factorizations of a number are related to the prime factorizations of multiples of the number.

Problem 3.26: Find the prime factorizations of the five smallest positive multiples of 18. Compare these prime factorizations to the prime factorization of 18. Do you notice anything interesting?

Solution for Problem 3.26: The prime factorization of 18 is $2^1 \cdot 3^2$. The prime factorizations of the five smallest positive multiples of 18 are

$$1 \cdot 18 = 1 \cdot (2^1 \cdot 3^2) = 2^1 \cdot 3^2,$$
$$2 \cdot 18 = 2 \cdot (2^1 \cdot 3^2) = 2^2 \cdot 3^2,$$
$$3 \cdot 18 = 3 \cdot (2^1 \cdot 3^2) = 2^1 \cdot 3^3,$$
$$4 \cdot 18 = 2^2 \cdot (2^1 \cdot 3^2) = 2^3 \cdot 3^2,$$
$$5 \cdot 18 = 5 \cdot (2^1 \cdot 3^2) = 2^1 \cdot 3^2 \cdot 5^1.$$

Each positive multiple of 18 is the product of 18 and some positive integer. So, the prime factorization of any multiple of 18 must include the prime factors in the prime factorization of 18. That is, the prime factorization of any multiple of 18 must have 2 raised to at least the 1st power and 3 raised to at least the 2nd power. $\square$

Problem 3.27: The prime factorization of 72 is $2^3 \cdot 3^2$. Use the given prime factorization of each number below to determine if the number is a multiple of 72.

(a) $864 = 2^5 \cdot 3^3$

(b) $400 = 2^4 \cdot 5^2$

(c) $1008 = 2^4 \cdot 3^2 \cdot 7^1$

(d) $2916 = 2^2 \cdot 3^6$

Suppose we have the prime factorizations of two positive integers m and n. How can we use these prime factorizations to tell if m is a multiple of n?

Solution for Problem 3.27:

(a) $2^3 \cdot 3^2$ is the product of three 2's and two 3's, while $2^5 \cdot 3^3$ is the product of five 2's and three 3's. So, we can multiply $2^3 \cdot 3^2$ by two 2's and one 3 to get $2^5 \cdot 3^3$:

$$(2^2 \cdot 3^1) \cdot (2^3 \cdot 3^2) = 2^5 \cdot 3^3.$$

Therefore, $2^5 \cdot 3^3$ is a multiple of $2^3 \cdot 3^2$. Multiplying out the prime factorizations in the equation above, we have $12 \cdot 72 = 864$, so 864 is a multiple of 72.

(b) The product of any integer and $2^3 \cdot 3^2$ must have 3's in its prime factorization. But the prime factorization of 400, which is $2^4 \cdot 5^2$, doesn't have 3 as a prime factor. So, $2^4 \cdot 5^2$ is not a multiple of $2^3 \cdot 3^2$, which means 400 is not a multiple of 72.

(c) $2^4 \cdot 3^2 \cdot 7^1$ has one more 2 and one more 7 than $2^3 \cdot 3^2$, so we can write

$$2^4 \cdot 3^2 \cdot 7^1 = (2^1 \cdot 7^1) \cdot (2^3 \cdot 3^2).$$

Therefore, $2^4 \cdot 3^2 \cdot 7^1$ is a multiple of $2^3 \cdot 3^2$. Multiplying out the prime factorizations in the equation above, we have $1008 = 14 \cdot 72$, and 1008 is a multiple of 72.

(d) When we multiply $2^3 \cdot 3^2$ by any positive integer, the resulting product must have at least three 2's in its prime factorization. Therefore, the prime factorization of any positive multiple of $2^3 \cdot 3^2$ must have at least three 2's. But $2^2 \cdot 3^6$ only has two 2's, so it cannot possibly be a multiple of $2^3 \cdot 3^2$. Therefore, 2916 is not a multiple of 72.

Let's take a closer look at how we can use the prime factorization of a positive integer n to identify multiples of n. We get a multiple of n by multiplying n by an integer. We can think of this as multiplying n's prime factorization by an integer. So, for example, if 2^3 appears in the prime factorization of n, then 2 must be raised to at least the 3rd power in the prime factorization of any multiple of n.

Similarly, the prime factorization of any multiple of n includes the entire prime factorization of n. That is, every prime in the prime factorization of n is in the prime factorization of every multiple of n, and is raised to at least as great a power in the multiple as it is in n.

The numbers in parts (a) and (c) have 2 raised to at least the 3rd power and 3 raised to at least the 2nd power, so they are multiples of $2^3 \cdot 3^2$. Meanwhile, the number in part (b) doesn't have a large enough power of 3 to be a multiple of $2^3 \cdot 3^2$, and the number in part (d) doesn't have a large enough power of 2.

> **Important:** Let n be a positive integer. The prime factorization of any multiple of n includes the prime factorization of n. That is, every prime in the prime factorization of n is in the prime factorization of every multiple of n, and is raised to at least as great a power in the multiple as it is in n.

In part (c) of Problem 3.27, we wish to test whether or not $2^4 \cdot 3^2 \cdot 7^1$ is a multiple of $2^3 \cdot 3^2$. We look at each of the prime factors of $2^3 \cdot 3^2$ in turn:

- The exponent of 2 in $2^4 \cdot 3^2 \cdot 7^1$ (which is 4) is at least the exponent of $2^3 \cdot 3^2$ (which is 3).

- The exponent of 3 in $2^4 \cdot 3^2 \cdot 7^1$ (which is 2) is at least the exponent of 3 in $2^3 \cdot 3^2$ (which is also 2).

Since each prime in the prime factorization $2^3 \cdot 3^2$ is raised to at least as large a power in $2^4 \cdot 3^2 \cdot 7^1$ as in $2^3 \cdot 3^2$, we conclude that $2^4 \cdot 3^2 \cdot 7^1$ is a multiple of $2^3 \cdot 3^2$. $\square$

Now that we know how to identify multiples of a number using prime factorizations, let's try finding the least common multiple of two numbers using prime factorizations.

Problem 3.28: How can we use the prime factorizations of 24 and 90 to find lcm[24, 90]?

Solution for Problem 3.28: The prime factorizations of 24 and 90 are

$$24 = 2^3 \cdot 3^1,$$
$$90 = 2^1 \cdot 3^2 \cdot 5^1.$$

The power of 2 in the prime factorization of a multiple of 24 must be at least 2^3. The power of 2 in the prime factorization of a multiple of 90 must be at least 2^1. To satisfy both of these conditions, the power of 2 in a common multiple of 24 and 90 must be at least 2^3. So, the smallest power of 2 we can include in the prime factorization of lcm[24, 90] is 2^3.

Similarly, the power of 3 in the prime factorization of a multiple of 24 must be at least 3^1, and the power of 3 in the prime factorization of a multiple of 90 must be at least 3^2. To satisfy both of these conditions, the smallest power of 3 we can include in the prime factorization of lcm[24, 90] is 3^2

Finally, we have 5 raised to at least the 1st power in any multiple of 90, so we include 5^1 in the prime factorization of lcm[24, 90].

So, now we know that the prime factorization of lcm[24, 90] must include 2^3, 3^2, and 5^1. Looking back at our reasoning, we see how to use the prime factorizations of 24 and 90 to find the prime factorization of lcm[24, 90]. We take the higher power of each prime factor that appears in the prime factorization of either 24 or 90. Below, the higher power of each prime factor is in bold and underlined:

$$24 = \underline{\mathbf{2^3}} \cdot 3^1, \qquad 90 = 2^1 \cdot \underline{\mathbf{3^2}} \cdot \underline{\mathbf{5^1}}.$$

We then combine these higher powers to form lcm[24, 90]:

$$\text{lcm}[24, 90] = \underline{\mathbf{2^3}} \cdot \underline{\mathbf{3^2}} \cdot \underline{\mathbf{5^1}} = 360.$$

To check that 360 is indeed the least common multiple of 24 and 90, we can list the multiples of 90 up to 360:

$$90, 180, 270, 360.$$

The first three numbers in this list are not also multiples of 24, while $360 = 15 \cdot 24$ is a multiple of 24. So, 360 is indeed the least common multiple of 24 and 90. □

We can follow essentially the same process as in Problem 3.28 to find the least common multiple of any group of numbers.

> **Important:** To find the prime factorization of the least common multiple of a group of numbers, we first find the prime factorization of each number. The prime factorization of the least common multiple is the product of the highest power of each prime factor that appears in the prime factorizations of the numbers.

Our explanation in Problem 3.28 not only tells us how to find the prime factorization of the least common multiple of 24 and 90. It also tells us that this prime factorization must be included in any common multiple of 24 and 90. That is, any positive common multiple's prime factorization must have 2 raised to at least the 3rd power, 3 raised to at least the 2nd power, and 5 raised to at least the 1st power. Also, any multiple of lcm[24, 90] must also be a common multiple of 24 and 90.

> **Important:** Let a and b be positive integers. Every multiple of $\text{lcm}[a, b]$ is a common multiple of a and b, and every common multiple of a and b is a multiple of $\text{lcm}[a, b]$.

Problem 3.29: Compute each of the following:

(a) $\text{lcm}[96, 144]$

(b) $\text{lcm}[28, 35]$

(c) $\text{lcm}[2^2 \cdot 3^3 \cdot 5^1, 3^3 \cdot 5^2 \cdot 7^1]$

(d) $\text{lcm}[24, 36, 42]$

Solution for Problem 3.29: In each part, we use the prime factorizations of the numbers to construct the desired least common multiple. In each set of prime factorizations, we bold and underline the highest power of each prime. Note that if the highest power of a particular prime appears in both prime factorizations, then we only need to include it once in the prime factorization of the least common multiple. So, we'll just bold and underline one of them. (You'll see an example of this in part (b).)

(a) We have
$$96 = \underline{\mathbf{2^5}} \cdot 3^1, \qquad 144 = 2^4 \cdot \underline{\mathbf{3^2}}.$$
So, $\text{lcm}[96, 144] = 2^5 \cdot 3^2 = 32 \cdot 9 = 288$.

(b) We have
$$28 = \underline{\mathbf{2^2}} \cdot \underline{\mathbf{7^1}}, \qquad 35 = \underline{\mathbf{5^1}} \cdot 7^1.$$
So, $\text{lcm}[28, 35] = 2^2 \cdot 5^1 \cdot 7^1 = 4 \cdot 5 \cdot 7 = 140$.

(c) We already have our prime factorizations, so we simply pick out the highest power of each prime:
$$\underline{\mathbf{2^2}} \cdot \underline{\mathbf{3^3}} \cdot 5^1, \qquad 3^3 \cdot \underline{\mathbf{5^2}} \cdot \underline{\mathbf{7^1}}.$$
So, $\text{lcm}[2^2 \cdot 3^3 \cdot 5^1, 3^3 \cdot 5^2 \cdot 7^1] = 2^2 \cdot 3^3 \cdot 5^2 \cdot 7^1 = 4 \cdot 27 \cdot 25 \cdot 7 = (4 \cdot 25) \cdot (27 \cdot 7) = 100 \cdot 189 = 18900$.

(d) We have
$$24 = \underline{\mathbf{2^3}} \cdot 3^1, \qquad 36 = 2^2 \cdot \underline{\mathbf{3^2}}, \qquad 42 = 2^1 \cdot 3^1 \cdot \underline{\mathbf{7^1}}.$$
So, $\text{lcm}[24, 36, 42] = 2^3 \cdot 3^2 \cdot 7^1 = 8 \cdot 9 \cdot 7 = 504$.

$\square$

Problem 3.30:

(a) Are $\text{lcm}[2 \cdot 500, 2 \cdot 300]$ and $2 \, \text{lcm}[500, 300]$ equal?

(b) Let a and b be positive integers. Must we have $\text{lcm}[2a, 2b] = 2 \, \text{lcm}[a, b]$?

(c) Let a and b be positive integers. Must we have $\text{lcm}[15a, 15b] = 15 \, \text{lcm}[a, b]$?

(d) Compute $\text{lcm}[606060, 707070]$.

Solution for Problem 3.30:

(a) We start with prime factorizations. We have

$$500 = 2^2 \cdot 5^3 \qquad \text{and} \qquad 300 = 2^2 \cdot 3^1 \cdot 5^2,$$

so $\text{lcm}[500, 300] = 2^2 \cdot 3^1 \cdot 5^3 = 1500$. Also,

$$2 \cdot 500 = 2^3 \cdot 5^3 \qquad \text{and} \qquad 2 \cdot 300 = 2^3 \cdot 3^1 \cdot 5^2,$$

so $\text{lcm}[2 \cdot 500, 2 \cdot 300] = 2^3 \cdot 3^1 \cdot 5^3 = 3000$. Since $3000 = 2 \cdot 1500$, we find

$$\text{lcm}[2 \cdot 500, 2 \cdot 300] = 2 \, \text{lcm}[500, 300].$$

(b) Each of the prime factorizations of $2a$ and $2b$ has one more factor of 2 than the corresponding prime factorization of a and b. So, the greatest power of 2 that appears in the prime factorization of either $2a$ or $2b$ has exponent one greater than the greatest power of 2 that appears in the prime factorization of either a or b. This tells us that the prime factorization of $\text{lcm}[2a, 2b]$ has one more factor of 2 than the prime factorization of $\text{lcm}[a, b]$. Since these two prime factorizations are otherwise the same, we must have $\text{lcm}[2a, 2b] = 2 \, \text{lcm}[a, b]$.

(c) We can go through the same steps as in part (b) and replace 2 with any prime. That is, for any prime p, we have $\text{lcm}[pa, pb] = p \, \text{lcm}[a, b]$. Therefore, we have

$$\text{lcm}[15a, 15b] = \text{lcm}[3 \cdot 5a, 3 \cdot 5b] = 3 \, \text{lcm}[5a, 5b] = 3(5 \, \text{lcm}[a, b]) = 15 \, \text{lcm}[a, b].$$

Similarly, we can "factor out" any number in a least common multiple computation:

> **Important:** For any positive integers a, b, and n, we have
> $$\text{lcm}[na, nb] = n \, \text{lcm}[a, b].$$

(d) Finding the prime factorizations of 606060 and 707070 sure would be a chore. Fortunately, we can write both numbers as 101010 times some integer, so we can apply our strategy from part (c):

$$\text{lcm}[606060, 707070] = \text{lcm}[101010 \cdot 6, 101010 \cdot 7] = 101010 \, \text{lcm}[6, 7] = 101010 \cdot 42 = 4242420.$$

$\square$

Problem 3.31: A church rings its bells every 15 minutes, the school rings its bells every 20 minutes, and the day care center rings its bells every 25 minutes. If they all ring their bells at noon on the same day, at what time will they next all ring their bells together? *(Source: MATHCOUNTS)*

Solution for Problem 3.31: Since the church rings its bells every 15 minutes and its bells ring at noon, the church bells ring every multiple of 15 minutes after noon. Similarly, the school bells ring every multiple of 20 minutes after noon and the day care center bells ring every multiple of 25 minutes after noon. So, the next time all three bells ring at the same time must be a multiple of 15 minutes, a multiple of 20 minutes, and a multiple of 25 minutes after noon. In other words, the next time the bells ring together is at lcm[15, 20, 25] minutes after noon. Again we turn to prime factorizations to find the least common multiple:

$$15 = \underline{3^1} \cdot 5^1, \qquad 20 = \underline{2^2} \cdot 5^1, \qquad 25 = \underline{5^2}.$$

So, lcm[15, 20, 25] $= 2^2 \cdot 3^1 \cdot 5^2 = 4 \cdot 3 \cdot 25 = 300$. Therefore, the bells next ring together 300 minutes after noon. There are 60 minutes in an hour, so 300 minutes is $300 \div 60 = 5$ hours, which means the next time the bells ring together is 5 p.m. □

Problem 3.32: The number 16128 is a multiple of 6, 7, and 8. What is the smallest multiple of 6, 7, and 8 that is greater than 16128?

Solution for Problem 3.32: The common multiples of 6, 7, and 8 are the multiples of the least common multiple of 6, 7, and 8. So, we find the smallest multiple of lcm[6, 7, 8] that is greater than 16128.

We have $6 = 2^1 \cdot 3^1$, $7 = 7^1$, and $8 = 2^3$, so lcm[6, 7, 8] $= 2^3 \cdot 3^1 \cdot 7^1 = 168$. Since 16128 is a multiple of 6, 7, and 8, we know that 16128 is also a multiple of lcm[6, 7, 8]. Therefore, the smallest multiple of 6, 7, and 8 that is greater than 16128 is $16128 + 168 = 16296$. □

Problem 3.33:

(a) What is the smallest positive integer greater than 1 that leaves a remainder of 1 when divided by each of 6, 7, and 8?

(b) Find the smallest positive number that leaves a remainder of 5 when divided by 6, a remainder of 6 when divided by 7, and a remainder of 7 when divided by 8.

Solution for Problem 3.33:

(a) A number that leaves a remainder of 1 when divided by 6 is 1 more than a multiple of 6. Similarly, our desired number is 1 more than a multiple of 7, and 1 more than a multiple of 8. So, our desired number is 1 more than a common multiple of 6, 7, and 8. In the previous problem, we found that lcm[6, 7, 8] $= 168$, so our solution is $168 + 1 = 169$.

(b) A number that leaves a remainder of 5 when divided by 6 is 1 less than a multiple of 6. Similarly, our desired number is 1 less than a multiple of 7, and 1 less than a multiple of 8. So, our desired number is 1 less than a common multiple of 6, 7, and 8. Since lcm[6, 7, 8] $= 168$, the smallest number that fits our problem is $168 - 1 = 167$.

□

▶

3.5.1 Compute the following:

(a) lcm[14, 21]   (c) lcm[27, 63]   (e) lcm[72, 108]

(b) lcm[24, 32]   (d) lcm[54, 60]   (f) lcm[5096, 117]

3.5.2 Compute the following:

(a) lcm[12, 18, 30]   (b) lcm[36, 48, 27]   (c) lcm[24, 54, 144]

3.5.3 In this section, we defined the least common multiple of two positive integers. Why didn't we define the *greatest* common multiple?

3.5.4 What is the largest common multiple of 8 and 12 that is less than 200?

3.5.5 What is the smallest positive four-digit number that is divisible by 2, 3, 4, 5, 6, and 7?

3.5.6 Alex counted to 2400 by 6's beginning with 6. Matthew counted to 2400 by 4's starting with 4. How many of the numbers counted by Alex were also counted by Matthew? *(Source: MATHCOUNTS)*

3.5.7 The people at a party tried to form teams with the same number of people on each team, but when they tried to split up into teams of 2, 3, 5, or 7, exactly one person was left without a team. What is the smallest number of people (greater than 1) who could have been at the party? *(Source: MATHCOUNTS)*

3.5.8★ One owl hoots every 3 hours, a second owl hoots every 8 hours, and a third owl hoots every 12 hours. If they all hoot together at the start, how many times during the next 80 hours will just two of the owls hoot together? *(Source: MOEMS)*

3.6 Divisors

In Section 3.1, we learned that 12 is a multiple of 4, because 12 equals 4 times an integer. We can also express this fact by saying, "4 is a **divisor** of 12."

Definition: Let a be a nonzero integer and b be an integer. We say that a is a **divisor** of b if b is a multiple of a. In other words, b is a times some integer.

We can also say that 4 is a **factor** of 12. The nouns "divisor" and "factor" mean the same thing. For example, the positive factors of 6 are 1, 2, 3, and 6. The negative factors of 6 are -1, -2, -3, and -6.

One way we sometimes think of divisors is as "a is a divisor of b if dividing b by a leaves no remainder." So, because 60 divided by 6 has no remainder, 6 is a divisor of 60. Since 72 divided by 5 has remainder 2, we know that 5 is not a divisor of 72.

> **Important:** If a and b are nonzero integers, then all of the following statements mean the same thing:
>
> - a is a divisor of b.
>
> - a is a factor of b.
>
> - b is a multiple of a.
>
> - b is divisible by a.

 Problems

Problem 3.34: Find all of the positive divisors of 84.

Problem 3.35:

(a) Count the positive divisors of each integer from 8 to 18. Which of these integers have an odd number of positive divisors?

(b) There is one integer between 20 and 30 that has an odd number of positive divisors. Which one?

(c) Which positive integers have an odd number of positive divisors?

Problem 3.36: Note that 20 is a divisor of 60.

(a) Must every divisor of 20 also be a divisor of 60?

(b) Must every divisor of 60 also be a divisor of 20?

Problem 3.37:

(a) Suppose 3 is a divisor of k. Is 3 a divisor of $k + 3$?

(b) Suppose 3 is a divisor both of b and of c. Must 3 be a divisor of $b + c$?

(c) Suppose 3 is a divisor of $b + c$. Must 3 be a divisor both of b and of c?

Problem 3.34: Find all of the positive divisors of 84.

Solution for Problem 3.34: We start off testing each positive integer, starting with 1.

Is 1 a divisor of 84? Yes, because $84 = 1 \cdot 84$. This equation shows that both 1 and 84 are divisors of 84.

Is 2 a divisor of 84? Yes, because $84 = 2 \cdot 42$. Both 2 and 42 are divisors of 84.

In the same way, we can find other pairs that multiply to 84:

$$3 \cdot 28 = 84, \qquad 4 \cdot 21 = 84, \qquad 6 \cdot 14 = 84, \qquad 7 \cdot 12 = 84.$$

None of 5, 8, or 9 is a divisor of 84. Rather than continuing to test the numbers from 10 up to 84 to see if they are divisors of 84, we notice that $10 \cdot 10$ is greater than 84. So, it's impossible to find two numbers greater than 9 whose product is 84. We've already tested all the numbers from 1 to 9, so we have found all the pairs of integers whose product is 84.

In summary, 84 has 12 positive divisors: 1, 2, 3, 4, 6, 7, 12, 14, 21, 28, 42, and 84. □

As we saw in Problem 3.34, when hunting for pairs of positive integers that multiply to n, we only have to test numbers up to the first integer whose square is greater than n.

Problem 3.35:

(a) Count the positive divisors of each integer from 8 to 18. Which of these integers have an odd number of positive divisors?

(b) There is one integer between 20 and 30 that has an odd number of positive divisors. Which one?

(c) Which positive integers have an odd number of positive divisors?

Solution for Problem 3.35:

(a) Below is a table of the positive divisors of each integer from 8 to 18, as well as a count of the positive divisors of each integer.

Number	Divisors	Count	Number	Divisors	Count
8	1, 2, 4, 8	4	14	1, 2, 7, 14	4
9	1, 3, 9	3	15	1, 3, 5, 15	4
10	1, 2, 5, 10	4	16	1, 2, 4, 8, 16	5
11	1, 11	2	17	1, 17	2
12	1, 2, 3, 4, 6, 12	6	18	1, 2, 3, 6, 9, 18	6
13	1, 13	2			

The only integers from 8 to 18 that have an odd number of positive divisors are 9 and 16.

(b) The perfect squares 9 and 16 are the only numbers in part (a) that have an odd number of positive divisors. So, we guess that the perfect square 25 is the number between 20 and 30 that has an odd number of positive divisors. Checking, we find that the only positive divisors of 25 are 1, 5, and 25. Indeed, 25 is the integer between 20 and 30 that has an odd number of positive divisors.

(c) From the previous two parts, we suspect that perfect squares have an odd number of positive divisors, and the rest of the positive integers have an even number of positive divisors.

The positive divisors of an integer come in pairs of numbers whose product is that integer. If an integer is not a perfect square, the two numbers in a such a pair cannot ever be the same. When we count the positive divisors of a non-square integer, they come in pairs, so the count is even:

$$12 = 1 \cdot 12 = 2 \cdot 6 = 3 \cdot 4.$$

If an integer is a perfect square, then one pair has two numbers that are the same. All the rest of the positive divisors of the integer come in pairs of different numbers:

$$36 = 1 \cdot 36 = 2 \cdot 18 = 3 \cdot 12 = 4 \cdot 9 = 6 \cdot 6.$$

So, when we count the positive divisors of a perfect square, we count by twos for the pairs with different numbers, and then count only one divisor for the pair that has two numbers that are the same. This final divisor makes the count of positive divisors odd.

□

Problem 3.36: Note that 20 is a divisor of 60.

(a) Must every divisor of 20 also be a divisor of 60?

(b) Must every divisor of 60 also be a divisor of 20?

Solution for Problem 3.36:

(a) Yes. If an integer d is a divisor of 20, then 20 is a multiple of d. This means that every multiple of 20 is also a multiple of d. Specifically, 60 is a multiple of 20, so 60 is a multiple of d. Therefore, d is a divisor of 60.

(b) No. For example, 30 is a divisor of 60, but 30 is not a divisor of 20.

□

Important: If a is a divisor of b, then every divisor of a is also a divisor of b.

Problem 3.37:

(a) Suppose 3 is a divisor of k. Is 3 a divisor of $k + 3$?

(b) Suppose 3 is a divisor both of b and of c. Must 3 be a divisor of $b + c$?

(c) Suppose 3 is a divisor of $b + c$. Must 3 be a divisor both of b and of c?

Solution for Problem 3.37:

(a) 3 is a divisor of k, so k is a multiple of 3. Adding 3 to a multiple of 3 gives another multiple of 3, so $k + 3$ is a multiple of 3. Therefore, 3 is a divisor of $k + 3$.

(b) Since 3 is a divisor of both b and c, we know that both b and c are multiples of 3. The sum of two multiples of 3 must also be a multiple of 3. (See Problem 3.1 if you don't remember why.) Therefore, $b + c$ is a multiple of 3, which means that 3 is a divisor of $b + c$.

(c) No. Suppose $b = 2$ and $c = 1$. Then, 3 is a divisor of $b + c$, but 3 is not a divisor of b or c.

$\square$

The principles we explored in Problem 3.37 are the same as the rules we learned about multiples in Problem 3.1. Here are the rules written in terms of "divisors" instead of "multiples":

> **Important:** Let a, b, and c be integers. If c is a divisor of a and of b, then c is a divisor of $a + b$ and of $a - b$.

Exercises

3.6.1 What is the product of all positive factors of 6?

3.6.2 What is the sum of the positive divisors of 18?

3.6.3 How many positive factors does 32 have?

3.6.4 For how many integers n is $28 \div n$ an integer?

3.6.5 The product of two positive integers is 2005. If neither integer is 1, what is the sum of the two integers? *(Source: MATHCOUNTS)*

3.6.6 The product of the three-digit number ABC and the single-digit number D is 1673. If A, B, C, and D represent different digits, then what three-digit number does ABC represent? *(Source: MOEMS)*

3.6.7 A *lucky* year is one in which at least one date, when written in the form month/day/year, has the following property: the product of the month times the day equals the last two digits of the year. For example, 1956 is a lucky year because it has the date 7/8/56 and $7 \cdot 8 = 56$. Which of the following is NOT a lucky year: 1990, 1991, 1992, 1993, or 1994? *(Source: AMC 8)*

3.6.8 What is the greatest positive integer less than 100 that has an odd number of positive divisors?

3.6.9 What is the greatest integer less than 10000 that is a factor of $11000 + 1100 + 11$? *(Source: MATHCOUNTS)*

3.7 Greatest Common Divisor

If a number is a divisor of both a and b, then we say that the number is a **common divisor** of a and b. Common divisors are also referred to as **common factors**.

For example, the divisors of 30 are 1, 2, 3, 5, 6, 10, 15, and 30 (and their negations). The divisors of 96 are 1, 2, 3, 4, 6, 8, 12, 16, 24, 32, 48, and 96 (and their negations). The numbers in both lists are 1, 2, 3, and 6 (and their negations); these are the common divisors of 30 and 96.

The greatest positive integer that is a divisor of both a and b is called the **greatest common divisor** of a and b. Among all the common divisors of 30 and 96, the largest is 6. So the greatest common divisor, or **greatest common factor**, of 30 and 96 is 6. We sometimes shorten "greatest common divisor" to "gcd," and we write $\gcd(30, 96) = 6$ to indicate that 6 is the greatest common divisor of 30 and 96.

Problems

Problem 3.38:

(a) List the positive divisors of 18.

(b) List the positive divisors of 24.

(c) List the positive common divisors of 18 and 24.

(d) What is the greatest common divisor of 18 and 24?

Problem 3.39: Find the prime factorization of each of the positive divisors of 24. Compare these prime factorizations to the prime factorization of 24. Do you notice anything interesting?

Problem 3.40: The prime factorization of 1944 is $2^3 \cdot 3^5$. Below are three numbers and their prime factorizations. In each part, use the prime factorization of the number to determine if the number is a divisor of 1944.

(a) $108 = 2^2 \cdot 3^3$

(b) $45 = 3^2 \cdot 5^1$

(c) $48 = 2^4 \cdot 3^1$

Suppose we have two positive integers, m and n. How can we tell from the prime factorizations of m and n whether or not m is a divisor of n?

Problem 3.41: How can we use the prime factorizations of 360 and 48 to find $\gcd(360, 48)$?

Problem 3.42: Compute each of the following:

(a) $\gcd(27, 39)$

(b) $\gcd(100, 63)$

(c) $\gcd(2^3 \cdot 5^3 \cdot 11^2, 3^2 \cdot 5^2 \cdot 11^1)$

(d) $\gcd(72, 240, 288)$

Problem 3.43:

(a) Are $\gcd(2 \cdot 500, 2 \cdot 300)$ and $2 \gcd(500, 300)$ equal?

(b) Let a and b be positive integers. Must we have $\gcd(2a, 2b) = 2 \gcd(a, b)$?

(c) Let a and b be positive integers. Must we have $\gcd(15a, 15b) = 15 \gcd(a, b)$?

(d) Compute $\gcd(606060, 707070)$.

Problem 3.44: Every bag of candy in the Grab-bag Candy store has the same number of candies. Tony and Kaya each grab some bags of candies. Tony gets a total of 70 candies and Kaya gets a total of 42 candies. What is the smallest possible number of bags Tony could have grabbed?

Problem 3.45:

(a) Find $\gcd(4, 9)$ and $\text{lcm}[4, 9]$.

(b) Find $\gcd(10, 27)$ and $\text{lcm}[10, 27]$.

(c) Let a and b be positive integers such that $\gcd(a, b) = 1$. Explain why $\text{lcm}[a, b] = ab$.

Problem 3.46:

(a) Must a number that is a multiple of 4 and of 9 be a multiple of 36?

(b) Must a number that is a multiple of 3 and of 12 be a multiple of 36?

(c) Find the digit A such that $59,7A6$ is a multiple of 36.

Problem 3.38:

(a) List the positive divisors of 18.

(b) List the positive divisors of 24.

(c) List the positive common divisors of 18 and 24.

(d) What is the greatest common divisor of 18 and 24?

Solution for Problem 3.38:

(a) We have $18 = 1 \cdot 18 = 2 \cdot 9 = 3 \cdot 6$, so the positive divisors of 18 are

$$1, 2, 3, 6, 9, 18.$$

(b) We have $24 = 1 \cdot 24 = 2 \cdot 12 = 3 \cdot 8 = 4 \cdot 6$, so the positive divisors of 24 are

$$1, 2, 3, 4, 6, 8, 12, 24.$$

(c) The divisors that appear in both of our lists are the positive common divisors of 18 and 24. These are 1, 2, 3, and 6.

(d) The greatest of the common divisors in part (c) is 6, so gcd(18, 24) = 6. Notice that the positive common divisors of 18 and 24 are the positive divisors of gcd(18, 24).

□

Just as prime factorization gives us a methodical way to find the least common multiple of two numbers, prime factorization also offers a way to find the greatest common divisor of two numbers. We start by using prime factorizations to identify divisors of a number.

Problem 3.39: Find the prime factorization of each of the positive divisors of 24. Compare these prime factorizations to the prime factorization of 24. Do you notice anything interesting?

Solution for Problem 3.39: The prime factorization of 24 is $2^3 \cdot 3^1$. The prime factorizations of its divisors are

$$
\begin{array}{ll}
1 & 3 = 3^1 \\
2 = 2^1 & 6 = 2^1 \cdot 3^1 \\
4 = 2^2 & 12 = 2^2 \cdot 3^1 \\
8 = 2^3 & 24 = 2^3 \cdot 3^1
\end{array}
$$

First, we see that the only primes that appear in any of these prime factorizations are 2 and 3, which are the primes in the prime factorization of 24. Next, we see that no divisor's prime factorization has a power of 2 greater than the 2^3 that appears in 24's prime factorization. Similarly, no divisor's prime factorization has a power of 3 greater than the 3^1 that appears in 24's prime factorization.

In other words, the prime factorization of 24 includes the prime factorization of each of its divisors. This makes sense, since 24 must be a multiple of each of its divisors. □

Problem 3.40: The prime factorization of 1944 is $2^3 \cdot 3^5$. Below are three numbers and their prime factorizations. In each part, use the prime factorization of the number to determine if the number is a divisor of 1944.

(a) $108 = 2^2 \cdot 3^3$

(b) $45 = 3^2 \cdot 5^1$

(c) $48 = 2^4 \cdot 3^1$

Suppose we have two positive integers, m and n. How can we tell from the prime factorizations of m and n whether or not m is a divisor of n?

Solution for Problem 3.40: In each case, the given number is a divisor of $2^3 \cdot 3^5$ if $2^3 \cdot 3^5$ is a multiple of the given number.

(a) Since $2^3 \cdot 3^5$ has at least as many 2's and at least as many 3's as $2^2 \cdot 3^3$, we know that $2^3 \cdot 3^5$

is a multiple of $2^2 \cdot 3^3$. So, $2^2 \cdot 3^3$ is a divisor of $2^3 \cdot 3^5$. That is, 108 is a divisor of 1944. (Specifically, $18 \cdot 108 = 1944$.)

(b) The prime factorization of any multiple of $3^2 \cdot 5^1$ must include a 5. So, $2^3 \cdot 3^5$ cannot be a multiple of $3^2 \cdot 5^1$, which means $3^2 \cdot 5^1$ is not a divisor of $2^3 \cdot 3^5$.

(c) The prime factorization of any multiple of $2^4 \cdot 3^1$ must have 2 raised to at least the 4th power. So, $2^3 \cdot 3^5$ cannot be a multiple of $2^4 \cdot 3^1$. This means that $2^4 \cdot 3^1$ is not a divisor of $2^3 \cdot 3^5$.

Back on page 124 we learned how to use prime factorizations to determine if one number is a multiple of another:

> **Important:** Let n be a positive integer. The prime factorization of any multiple of n includes the prime factorization of n. That is, every prime in the prime factorization of n is in the prime factorization of every multiple of n, and is raised to at least as great a power in the multiple as it is in n.

Since an integer is a multiple of each of its divisors, an integer must include the prime factorization of each of its divisors. (The prime factorization of 1 is "included" in any prime factorization.)

Consider part (a) of Problem 3.40, in which we found that 108, or $2^2 \cdot 3^3$, is a divisor of 1944, or $2^3 \cdot 3^5$. We write the prime factorization of 1944 without exponents, and we see that it includes the two 2's and three 3's of the prime factorization of 108 (these are bolded and underlined below):

$$1944 = \underline{\mathbf{2}} \cdot \underline{\mathbf{2}} \cdot 2 \cdot \underline{\mathbf{3}} \cdot \underline{\mathbf{3}} \cdot \underline{\mathbf{3}} \cdot 3 \cdot 3.$$

In other words, each prime can appear no more times in the prime factorization of the divisor of a number than that prime appears in the prime factorization of the original number.

> **Important:** Let n be a positive integer. The prime factorization of n includes the prime factorization of each divisor of n. That is, every prime in the prime factorization of each divisor of n is in the prime factorization of n, and is raised to no greater a power in the divisor than it is in n.

For example, in part (a) above, we wish to determine if $2^2 \cdot 3^3$ is a divisor of $2^3 \cdot 3^5$. We consider each of the primes in the prime factorization of $2^2 \cdot 3^3$:

- The exponent of 2 in $2^2 \cdot 3^3$ (which is 2) is no greater than the exponent of 2 in $2^3 \cdot 3^5$ (which is 3).

- The exponent of 3 in $2^2 \cdot 3^3$ (which is 3) is no greater than the exponent of 3 in $2^3 \cdot 3^5$ (which is 5).

Since each exponent in the prime factorization $2^2 \cdot 3^3$ is no greater than the corresponding exponent in the prime factorization $2^3 \cdot 3^5$, we conclude that $2^2 \cdot 3^3$ is a divisor of $2^3 \cdot 3^5$. $\square$

Problem 3.41: How can we use the prime factorizations of 360 and 48 to find gcd(360, 48)?

Solution for Problem 3.41: The prime factorizations of 360 and 48 are

$$360 = 2^3 \cdot 3^2 \cdot 5^1,$$
$$48 = 2^4 \cdot 3^1.$$

The power of 2 in the prime factorization of a divisor of 360 cannot be greater than 2^3. The power of 2 in the prime factorization of a divisor of 48 cannot be greater than 2^4. To satisfy both of these conditions, the power of 2 in a common divisor of 360 and 48 is no greater than 2^3. So, the greatest power of 2 we can include in the prime factorization of gcd(360, 48) is 2^3.

Similarly, the prime factorization of a divisor of 360 cannot have a power of 3 greater than 3^2, and the prime factorization of a divisor of 48 cannot have a power of 3 greater than 3^1. To satisfy both of these conditions, the greatest power of 3 we can include in the prime factorization of gcd(360, 48) is 3^1.

Finally, a divisor of 48 cannot have 5 in its prime factorization, so the prime factorization of gcd(360, 48) cannot include 5. Similarly, the prime factorization of gcd(360, 48) cannot include any larger primes, since no primes besides 2 and 3 appear in the prime factorizations of both 360 and 48.

So, now we know that the prime factorization of gcd(360, 48) can only include the primes 2 and 3. The greatest power of 2 the prime factorization can include is 2^3, while the greatest power of 3 it can include is 3^1. Looking back over our reasoning, we see how to use the prime factorizations of 360 and 48 to find the prime factorization of gcd(360, 48). We take the smallest power of each prime factor that appears in the prime factorizations of *both* 360 and 48. Below, the smallest power of each prime factor is in bold and underlined:

$$360 = \underline{\mathbf{2^3}} \cdot 3^2 \cdot 5^1, \qquad 48 = 2^4 \cdot \underline{\mathbf{3^1}}.$$

We then combine these smallest powers to form gcd(360, 48):

$$\text{gcd}(360, 48) = \underline{\mathbf{2^3}} \cdot \underline{\mathbf{3^1}} = 24.$$

Notice that we don't include a power of 5 in the prime factorization of gcd(360, 48). The prime factors of gcd(360, 48) are the primes that are prime factors of both 360 and 48. While 5 is a prime factor of 360, it is not a prime factor of 48, so 5 is not a prime factor of gcd(360, 48). $\square$

We can follow essentially the same process as in Problem 3.41 to find the greatest common divisor of any two numbers.

> **Important:** We can find the greatest common divisor of a group of numbers
> with the following process:
>
> Step 1: Find the prime factorization of each number.
>
> Step 2: Identify the primes that appear in *all* of the prime factorizations.
>
> Step 3: Among the prime factorizations, find the smallest power of each prime from Step 2.
>
> Step 4: Multiply the powers of primes found in Step 3.

But what happens if there aren't any primes that appear in all of the prime factorizations? Then we can't have any primes at all in the prime factorization of the greatest common divisor. This means that the greatest common divisor is 1. We say that two integers are **relatively prime** if their greatest common divisor is 1.

> **Important:** If two integers do not have any prime factors in common, then the integers are relatively prime.

In our solution to Problem 3.38, we saw that the common divisors of 18 and 24 are divisors of the greatest common divisor of 18 and 24. See if you can explain why using our new process for identifying the greatest common divisor of two numbers.

> **Important:** Let a and b be positive integers. Every common divisor of a and b is a divisor of $\gcd(a, b)$, and every divisor of $\gcd(a, b)$ is a common divisor of a and b.

Problem 3.42: Compute each of the following:

(a) $\gcd(27, 39)$

(b) $\gcd(100, 63)$

(c) $\gcd(2^3 \cdot 5^3 \cdot 11^2, 3^2 \cdot 5^2 \cdot 11^1)$

(d) $\gcd(72, 240, 288)$

Solution for Problem 3.42:

(a) We have $27 = 3^3$ and $39 = \underline{3^1} \cdot 13^1$, so $\gcd(27, 39) = 3$.

(b) We have
$$100 = 2^2 \cdot 5^2, \qquad 63 = 3^2 \cdot 7^1.$$

These two prime factorizations have no primes in common. Therefore, $\gcd(100, 63)$ cannot have any primes in its prime factorization. This means that $\gcd(100, 63) = 1$. In other words, 100 and 63 are relatively prime.

(c) We already have our prime factorizations, so we simply pick out the smallest power of each prime that the prime factorizations have in common:

$$2^3 \cdot 5^3 \cdot 11^2, \qquad 3^2 \cdot \underline{\mathbf{5^2}} \cdot \underline{\mathbf{11^1}}.$$

So, $\gcd(2^3 \cdot 5^3 \cdot 11^2, 3^2 \cdot 5^2 \cdot 11^1) = 5^2 \cdot 11^1 = 25 \cdot 11 = 275$. Notice that we don't have a power of 2 or of 3 in the prime factorization of the greatest common divisor, even though each appears in the prime factorization of one of the original numbers.

> **WARNING!!** A prime must appear in the prime factorizations of *all* of the numbers in a group in order to appear in the prime factorization of the greatest common divisor of the group.

(d) We have

$$72 = \underline{\mathbf{2^3}} \cdot 3^2,$$
$$240 = 2^4 \cdot \underline{\mathbf{3^1}} \cdot 5^1,$$
$$288 = 2^5 \cdot 3^2.$$

So, $\gcd(72, 240, 288) = 2^3 \cdot 3^1 = 8 \cdot 3 = 24$. Notice that 5 is not in the prime factorization of $\gcd(72, 240, 288)$.

$\square$

> **Problem 3.43:**
> (a) Are $\gcd(2 \cdot 500, 2 \cdot 300)$ and $2 \gcd(500, 300)$ equal?
> (b) Let a and b be positive integers. Must we have $\gcd(2a, 2b) = 2 \gcd(a, b)$?
> (c) Let a and b be positive integers. Must we have $\gcd(15a, 15b) = 15 \gcd(a, b)$?
> (d) Compute $\gcd(606060, 707070)$.

Solution for Problem 3.43: We follow essentially the same reasoning we used in Problem 3.30, where we learned that $\text{lcm}[na, nb] = n \, \text{lcm}[a, b]$ for any positive integers a, b, and n.

(a) We start with prime factorizations. We have

$$500 = 2^2 \cdot 5^3 \qquad \text{and} \qquad 300 = 2^2 \cdot 3^1 \cdot 5^2,$$

so $\gcd(500, 300) = 2^2 \cdot 5^2 = 100$. Also,

$$2 \cdot 500 = 2^3 \cdot 5^3 \qquad \text{and} \qquad 2 \cdot 300 = 2^3 \cdot 3^1 \cdot 5^2,$$

so $\gcd(2 \cdot 500, 2 \cdot 300) = 2^3 \cdot 5^2 = 200$. Since $200 = 2 \cdot 100$, we have

$$\gcd(2 \cdot 500, 2 \cdot 300) = 2 \gcd(500, 300).$$

(b) Each of the prime factorizations of $2a$ and $2b$ has one more factor of 2 than the corresponding prime factorization of a and b. So, the least power of 2 that appears in the prime factorization of either $2a$ or $2b$ has exponent one greater than the least power of 2 that appears in the prime factorization of either a or b. This tells us that the prime factorization of $\gcd(2a, 2b)$ has one more factor of 2 than the prime factorization of $\gcd(a, b)$. Since these two prime factorizations are otherwise the same, we must have $\gcd(2a, 2b) = 2\gcd(a, b)$.

(c) We can go through the same steps as in part (b) and replace 2 with any prime. That is, for any prime p, we have $\gcd(pa, pb) = p\gcd(a, b)$. Therefore, we have

$$\gcd(15a, 15b) = \gcd(3 \cdot 5a, 3 \cdot 5b) = 3\gcd(5a, 5b) = 3(5\gcd(a, b)) = 15\gcd(a, b).$$

Similarly, we can "factor out" any number when computing the greatest common divisor of two numbers:

> **Important:** For any positive integers a, b, and n, we have
> $$\gcd(na, nb) = n\gcd(a, b).$$

(d) We can write both numbers as 101010 times some integer, so we can apply our strategy from part (c):

$$\gcd(606060, 707070) = \gcd(101010 \cdot 6, 101010 \cdot 7) = 101010\gcd(6, 7) = 101010 \cdot 1 = 101010.$$

$\square$

> **Problem 3.44:** Every bag of candy in the Grab-bag Candy store has the same number of candies. Tony and Kaya each grab some bags of candies. Tony gets a total of 70 candies and Kaya gets a total of 42 candies. What is the smallest possible number of bags Tony could have grabbed?

Solution for Problem 3.44: Every bag has the same number of candies, so

(Number of bags Tony grabbed) · (Number of candies in each bag) = 70.

Therefore, the number of bags and the number of candies in each bag are both divisors of 70. At first, we might think that the smallest number of bags Tony could grab is 1 bag, with 70 candies in it. But then we remember Kaya. There can't possibly be 70 candies in each bag, since Kaya only has 42 candies. This means we must have

(Number of bags Kaya grabbed) · (Number of candies in each bag) = 42.

Therefore, the number of candies in each bag must be a divisor of 42 as well. So, the number of candies in each bag is a common divisor of 42 and 70. Which common divisor is the number of candies in the bag that makes the number of bags Tony grabbed as small as possible?

We know that the number of bags Tony grabbed is 70 divided by the number of candies in each bag. So, the number of bags Tony grabbed is as small as possible when the number of candies in each bag is as large as possible. That means the number of candies in each bag must be the greatest common divisor of 42 and 70.

Since $42 = 2^1 \cdot 3^1 \cdot 7^1$ and $70 = 2^1 \cdot 5^1 \cdot 7^1$, we have $\gcd(42, 70) = 2^1 \cdot 7^1 = 14$. This means that the largest possible number of candies in each bag is 14. If there are 14 candies in each bag, then Tony must have $70 \div 14 = 5$ bags and Kaya must have $42 \div 14 = 3$ bags. So, the smallest possible number of bags Tony could have grabbed is 5. $\square$

Problem 3.45:

(a) Find $\gcd(4, 9)$ and $\text{lcm}[4, 9]$.

(b) Find $\gcd(10, 27)$ and $\text{lcm}[10, 27]$.

(c) Let a and b be positive integers such that $\gcd(a, b) = 1$. Explain why $\text{lcm}[a, b] = ab$.

Solution for Problem 3.45:

(a) Since $4 = 2^2$ and $9 = 3^2$, we have $\gcd(4, 9) = 1$ and $\text{lcm}[4, 9] = 2^2 \cdot 3^2 = 4 \cdot 9 = 36$.

(b) Since $10 = 2^1 \cdot 5^1$ and $27 = 3^3$, we have $\gcd(10, 27) = 1$ and $\text{lcm}[10, 27] = 2^1 \cdot 5^1 \cdot 3^3 = 10 \cdot 27 = 270$.

(c) Our work in the first two parts gives us a pretty good guide as to what's going on. In part (a), the prime factorizations of 4 and 9 are 2^2 and 3^2. These have no prime factors in common, so 4 and 9 are relatively prime. (As a reminder, two numbers are relatively prime if their greatest common divisor is 1.) Moreover, both 2^2 and 3^2 must appear in the prime factorization of $\text{lcm}[4, 9]$, so $\text{lcm}[4, 9]$ is the product of 4 and 9.

In part (b), the prime factorizations of 10 and 27 are $2^1 \cdot 5^1$ and 3^3. Again, these have no prime factors in common, so 10 and 27 are relatively prime. Because the prime factorizations have no primes in common, we form the prime factorization of $\text{lcm}[10, 27]$ by combining the prime factorizations of 10 and 27. Since the prime factorization of $\text{lcm}[10, 27]$ is the product of the prime factorizations of 10 and 27, we have $\text{lcm}[10, 27] = 10 \cdot 27$.

Similarly, if a and b are relatively prime, then their prime factorizations cannot share any prime factors. So, the prime factorization of $\text{lcm}[a, b]$ is the product of the prime factorizations of a and b. This means that $\text{lcm}[a, b] = ab$.

$\square$

Problem 3.46:

(a) Must a number that is a multiple of 4 and of 9 be a multiple of 36?

(b) Must a number that is a multiple of 3 and of 12 be a multiple of 36?

(c) Find the digit A such that $59,7A6$ is a multiple of 36.

Solution for Problem 3.46:

(a) Yes. Every common multiple of 4 and 9 must be a multiple of the least common multiple of 4 and 9. Since lcm[4, 9] = 36, every multiple of both 4 and 9 is a multiple of 36.

(b) No. Since lcm[3, 12] = 12, every common multiple of 3 and 12 is a multiple of 12. But there are multiples of 12 that are not multiples of 36. For example, 12 itself is a multiple of both 3 and 12, but 12 is not a multiple of 36.

(c) We don't yet have a divisibility rule for 36, but we do have rules for 4 and 9. In part (a), we saw that every common multiple of 4 and 9 is a multiple of 36. So, if we find A such that 59,7A6 is divisible by both 4 and 9, then the resulting 59,7A6 must be divisible by 36.

Since 59,7A6 must be divisible by 9, the sum $5 + 9 + 7 + A + 6$ must be divisible by 9. This sum equals $27 + A$, so the digit A must be 0 or 9. In order for the number 59,7A6 to be divisible by 4, the number formed by its last two digits must be divisible by 4. Since 06 is not divisible by 4 but 96 is divisible by 4, the only possible value of A is 9. Checking, we find that $59{,}796 \div 36 = 1661$, so 59,796 is indeed divisible by 36. □

The first two parts of Problem 3.46 exhibit an important fact about divisibility. To test for divisibility by 36, we can instead test for divisibility by 4 and by 9, since $4 \cdot 9 = 36$ and lcm[4, 9] = 36. However, we can't test for divisibility by 36 through testing for divisibility by 3 and by 12, even though $3 \cdot 12 = 36$ as well. This is because lcm[3, 12] = 12, not 36. So, for example, $2 \cdot 12 = 24$ is a multiple of both 3 and 12, but 24 is not a multiple of 36.

Similarly, suppose a and b are positive integers, and we want to be able to test if some other number is divisible by the product ab. We can only perform this test by testing separately for divisibility by a and by b if lcm[a, b] = ab. Our result from Problem 3.45 tells us that if $\gcd(a, b) = 1$, then lcm[a, b] = ab. So, to test a number for divisibility by some composite number, we can test for divisibility by two relatively prime numbers whose product is the composite number. Problem 3.46 gave us one example of this: we tested for divisibility by 36 through testing for divisibility by 4 and 9. Similarly, we can test for divisibility by 12 through testing for divisibility by 3 and 4, but not through testing by divisibility by 2 and 6 (since 2 and 6 aren't relatively prime).

> **Important:** To test for divisibility by a composite number, we can test for divisibility by two relatively prime numbers whose product is the composite number.

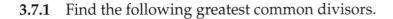

3.7.1 Find the following greatest common divisors.

(a) gcd(32, 48)

(b) gcd(99, 100)

(c) gcd(315, 108)

(d) gcd(99, 726)

(e) gcd(365, 1985)

(f) gcd(9009, 14014)

3.7.2 What is the greatest common factor of 36, 90, and 60?

3.7.3 If a and b are positive integers and $\gcd(a, b) = 8$, then what are the positive common divisors of a and b?

3.7.4 Which one of the following pairs of numbers consists of relatively prime integers: 15 and 18, 12 and 18, 5 and 18, or 9 and 18? *(Source: MATHCOUNTS)*

3.7.5 If $661,17A$ is a multiple of 12, then what is A?

3.7.6 Let a, b, and c be integers such that a and b are relatively prime, and b and c are relatively prime. Must a and c be relatively prime?

3.7.7 The positive divisors of 175, except 1, are arranged around a circle so that every pair of adjacent integers has a common factor greater than 1. What is the sum of the two integers adjacent to 7? *(Source: MATHCOUNTS)*

3.8 Summary

Definition: A **prime number** is a positive integer that is divisible by exactly 2 positive integers: 1 and the number itself. A **composite number** is a positive integer that is divisible by some positive integer besides 1 and the number itself.

Important: **Fundamental Theorem of Arithmetic**. Every integer greater than 1 can be written as the product of one or more primes in exactly one way (disregarding the order of the primes in the product).

Definition: Let a and b be integers. We say that a is a **multiple** of b if a equals b times some integer. In other words, a is a multiple of b if there is an integer n such that $a = bn$. If a is a multiple of b and b is nonzero, then we say that b is a **divisor**, or **factor**, of a, and that a is **divisible** by b.

Important: Let a, b, and c be numbers.

- If a and b are multiples of c, then both $a + b$ and $a - b$ are multiples of c.

- If a is a multiple of b, then every multiple of a is also a multiple of b.

We developed several useful divisibility tests:

Number	Condition under which n is divisible by the number
2	Units digit of n is 0, 2, 4, 6, or 8
3	Sum of the digits of n is a multiple of 3
4	Number formed by last two digits of n is a multiple of 4
5	Units digit of n is 0 or 5
6	Divisible by 2 and by 3
9	Sum of the digits of n is a multiple of 9
10	Units digit of n is 0

If a number is a multiple of both a and b, then we say that the number is a **common multiple** of a and b. The smallest positive integer that is a multiple of both a and b is called the **least common multiple** of a and b. We refer to the least common multiple of a and b as lcm$[a, b]$. Every multiple of lcm$[a, b]$ is a common multiple of a and b, and every common multiple of a and b is a multiple of lcm$[a, b]$.

> **Important:** To find the prime factorization of the least common multiple of a group of numbers, we first find the prime factorization of each of the numbers. The prime factorization of the least common multiple is the product of the highest power of each prime factor that appears in the prime factorizations of the numbers.

If a number is a divisor of both a and b, then we say that the number is a **common divisor** of a and b. The greatest positive integer that is a divisor of both a and b is called the **greatest common divisor** of a and b. We refer to the greatest common divisor of a and b as gcd(a, b). Every divisor of gcd(a, b) is a common divisor of a and b, and every common divisor of a and b is a divisor of gcd(a, b). We say that two integers are **relatively prime** if their greatest common divisor is 1.

> **Important:** We can find the greatest common divisor of a group of numbers with the following process:
>
> Step 1: Find the prime factorization of each number.
>
> Step 2: Identify the primes that appear in *all* of the prime factorizations. If no primes appear in all of the prime factorizations, then the greatest common divisor of the numbers is 1.
>
> Step 3: Among the prime factorizations, find the smallest power of each prime from Step 2.
>
> Step 4: Multiply the powers of primes found in Step 3.

> **Important:** For any positive integers a, b, and n, we have
>
> $$\text{lcm}[na, nb] = n\,\text{lcm}[a, b],$$
> $$\gcd(na, nb) = n\,\gcd(a, b).$$

REVIEW PROBLEMS

3.47 Find the prime factorization of each of the following numbers:

(a) 693

(b) 5423

(c) 35100

3.48 What is the remainder when (99)(237) is divided by 9?

3.49 What is the sum of the two smallest multiples of 6 that are greater than 103?

3.50 What is the largest multiple of 73 that is less than 2000?

3.51 Which of the following numbers is divisible by 9:

$$45{,}624, \quad 560{,}335, \quad 60{,}231{,}060 \quad 9{,}671{,}011?$$

3.52 Which one of the following four-digit numbers is *not* divisible by 4: 2544, 2554, 2564, 2572, or 2576?

3.53 We learned that a number is divisible by 5 if its units digit is 0 or 5. What is a similar rule that we can use to test if a number is divisible by 25?

3.54 Amanda arranges the digits 1, 3, 5, and 7 to write a four-digit number. The 7 is next to the 1 but not to the 5. The 3 is next to the 7 but not to the 5. The four-digit number is divisible by 5. What is Amanda's four-digit number? *(Source: MOEMS)*

3.55 Compute each of the following:

(a) $\text{lcm}[26, 65]$

(b) $\text{lcm}[96, 72]$

(c) $\text{lcm}[16, 21, 28]$

(d) $\text{lcm}[45, 60, 75]$

3.56 Compute each of the following:

(a) $\gcd(45, 75)$

(b) $\gcd(144, 405)$

(c) $\gcd(238, 374)$

(d) $\gcd(970, 485, 1330)$

3.57 If the 4-digit number 7,2d2 is divisible by 6, then what is the largest possible value of the digit d?

3.58 Which of the following numbers is *not* divisible by 8:

$$8{,}024, \quad 168{,}640, \quad 8{,}648{,}034, \quad 720{,}032, \quad 64{,}856?$$

3.59 What is the units digit (ones digit) of the product of any six consecutive positive integers? *(Source: AMC 8)*

3.60 What is the smallest prime factor of $11^7 + 7^5$?

3.61 If 12 is a factor of n, what other positive numbers must be factors of n?

3.62 What is the greatest odd factor of 12,024?

3.63 How many positive integers less than 20 have exactly two positive divisors?

3.64 If x, y, and z are integers such that $2^x \cdot 3^y \cdot 7^z = 392$, then what is xyz?

3.65 The number 206,496 is divisible by each of 2, 3, 6, and 8. What is the next larger integer that is divisible by 2, 3, 6, and 8?

3.66 A positive integer is 3 more than a multiple of 4, and 4 more than a multiple of 5. What is the least integer it could be?

3.67 A light flashes every 1 minute 15 seconds. Another flashes every 1 minute 40 seconds. Suppose they flash together at a certain time. What is the shortest amount of time that will elapse before both lights will again flash together? *(Source: MOEMS)*

3.68 What is the difference between the greatest positive factor of 121 and the least positive factor of 6? *(Source: MATHCOUNTS)*

3.69 The number 6545 can be written as a product of a pair of positive two-digit integers. What are these two integers? *(Source: AMC 8)*

3.70 In the sequence 1, 7, 13, 19, ..., each number is 6 more than the number before it. In the sequence 1, 9, 17, 25, ..., each number is 8 more than the number before it. The two sequences have infinitely many numbers in common. Find the sum of the first three common numbers. *(Source: MATHCOUNTS)*

3.71 Let a and b be positive integers such that a is a divisor of b.

(a) What is the greatest common divisor of a and b?

(b) What is the least common multiple of a and b?

Challenge Problems ▶

3.72 When the six-digit number $3456n7$ is divided by 8, the remainder is 5. List both possible values of the digit n. *(Source: MOEMS)* **Hints:** 37

3.73 If two positive integers have a greatest common divisor of 1 and a least common multiple of 57, what are the possible values of the larger of the two integers?

3.74 What is the largest multiple of 12 that can be written using each digit $0, 1, 2, \ldots, 9$ exactly once? *(Source: MATHCOUNTS)*

3.75 The four-digit number $A55B$ is divisible by 36. What is the sum of A and B? *(Source: MOEMS)*

3.76 The number $A4273B$ is a six-digit integer in which A and B are digits, and the number is divisible by 72. Find the value of A and the value of B. *(Source: MOEMS)*

3.77 Find the largest factor of 2520 that is not divisible by 6. *(Source: MOEMS)* **Hints:** 31, 13

3.78 Jack finds the product of three different prime numbers. Is it possible for the sum of the digits of Jack's product to be 18? Why or why not? **Hints:** 124

3.79 The least common multiple of 12, 15, 20, and k is 420. What is the least possible value of the positive integer k? *(Source: MATHCOUNTS)* **Hints:** 7

3.80 For each of the following pairs of numbers, find the product of the numbers, and then find the product of the greatest common divisor and least common multiple of the numbers.

(a) $18, 24$ (b) $35, 42$ (c) $66, 84$

Do you see an interesting pattern in your answers? Will that pattern hold for any two positive integers you start with? If so, why?

3.81 How many terminal zeros does the integer equal to $80^{16} \cdot 75^8$ have? **Hints:** 91, 131

3.82 The number 64 is both a perfect cube and a perfect square, since $4^3 = 64$ and $8^2 = 64$. What is the next larger number that is both a perfect cube and a perfect square? **Hints:** 82

3.83★ Suppose that a and b are positive integers with a greater than b, and with $\operatorname{lcm}[a, b] = 462$ and $\gcd(a, b) = 33$. Find the largest prime factor of a that is not a prime factor of b. *(Source: MATHCOUNTS)* **Hints:** 138, 78

3.84★ What is the smallest positive multiple of 45 that has only 0's and 1's as digits? **Hints:** 87

3.85★ What is the sum of the digits of the number $(10^{22} + 8) \div 9$? *(Source: MATHCOUNTS)* **Hints:** 154

3.86★ How many positive integers less than 1000 are divisible by 2 and 3 but not 5? **Hints:** 144, 122

3.87★ The lockers in my school are numbered in order from 1 to 1000. Initially, they are all closed. There are 1000 students in my school. The 1st student goes through the school and opens every locker. The 2nd student goes through the school and for every 2nd locker, if the locker is closed, she opens it, and if the locker is open, she closes it. The 3rd student does the same for every 3rd locker, the 4th student does the same for every 4th locker, and so on until all 1000 students have gone through the school. After all of the students have finished, how many lockers are open? **Hints:** 15

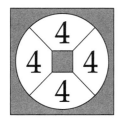 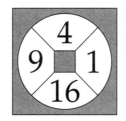 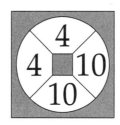 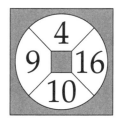

Five out of four people have trouble with fractions. – Steven Wright

CHAPTER 4

Fractions

4.1   What is a Fraction?

In Section 1.7, we discussed division. For example, $12 \div 3$ is 4 and $72 \div 9$ is 8. But what is $2 \div 3$? It is a number too, though not an integer. We often write the number equal to $2 \div 3$ as $\frac{2}{3}$. We call $\frac{2}{3}$ a **fraction**.

Definition: If a is a number and b is a nonzero number, then the **fraction** $\frac{a}{b}$ equals $a \div b$.

A fraction such as $\frac{3}{5}$ has three parts: a top (namely 3), a bottom (5), and a line in the middle called a **fraction bar**. We call the top the **numerator**, and we call the bottom the **denominator**. When typing, we often write fractions in horizontal form, such as 5/7. Here a slash separates the numerator and the denominator.

A fraction is a number, so we can locate any fraction on the number line. This is easy if the fraction equals an integer. For example, since $\frac{0}{3} = 0 \div 3 = 0$, the number $\frac{0}{3}$ is 0 on the number line. Similarly, we have $\frac{3}{3} = 3 \div 3 = 1$, so $\frac{3}{3}$ is 1 on the number line.

Where is $\frac{1}{3}$? Since 1 is between 0 and 3, we guess that $\frac{1}{3}$ is between $\frac{0}{3}$ and $\frac{3}{3}$. The fraction $\frac{1}{3}$ equals 1 divided by 3. So, to locate $\frac{1}{3}$ on the number line, we divide the number line between 0 and 1 into 3 equal pieces. The fraction $\frac{1}{3}$ is the point at the right end of the first piece, $\frac{2}{3}$ is the point at the right end of the second piece, and $\frac{3}{3}$ is the point at the right end of the third piece.

As shown below, we can continue rightward beyond 1, and we can go leftward from 0 to locate negations of fractions.

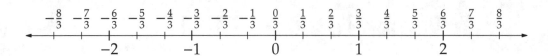

Of course, you've already seen fraction notation in this book, when we talked about reciprocals. When n is nonzero, the reciprocal $\frac{1}{n}$ is simply $1 \div n$.

Because every fraction is a division, we can use the properties of division we learned in Chapter 1 to work with fractions. Here are some properties we will need in this section, written with fraction notation.

> **Important:** **Dividing into zero:** If a is not zero, then $\frac{0}{a} = 0$.
> **Self division:** If a is not zero, then $\frac{a}{a} = 1$.
> **Dividing by 1:** $\frac{a}{1} = a$.
> **Dividing into a negation:** If b is not zero, then $\frac{-a}{b} = -\frac{a}{b}$.
> **Dividing by a negation:** If b is not zero, then $\frac{a}{-b} = -\frac{a}{b}$.
> **Negation divided by negation:** If b is not zero, then $\frac{-a}{-b} = \frac{a}{b}$.

Above, we repeatedly warn that denominators of fractions cannot be 0. This is because $\frac{a}{b} = a \div b$, and division by 0 is not defined.

Problems

Problem 4.1: Simplify each of the following fractions.

(a) $\frac{0}{7}$

(b) $\frac{5}{5}$

(c) $\frac{2}{1}$

(d) $\frac{12}{6}$

(e) $\frac{-12}{3}$

(f) $\frac{22+13}{-4-3}$

Problem 4.2: For what values of n between 1 and 40 is $\frac{n}{7}$ an integer?

Problem 4.3: Each segment between two consecutive integers on the number line below is divided into five equal pieces. For each lettered dot, find a number that corresponds to that point on the number line.

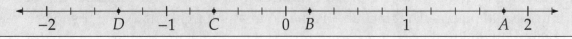

Problem 4.4:

(a) Use the number line to explain why $\frac{3}{7}$ is between 0 and 1.

(b) Between what two consecutive integers is $\frac{43}{5}$?

Problem 4.5: The points A, B, C, and D on the number line below correspond to the numbers $-\frac{4}{7}$, $\frac{21}{7}$, $\frac{15}{7}$, and $\frac{4}{8}$ in some order. Match each point to the correct number.

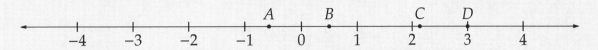

Problem 4.6: Use the number line to explain why $\frac{4}{8} = \frac{1}{2}$.

Problem 4.7: Find two fractions that are equal to $\frac{2}{3}$.

Problem 4.1: Simplify each of the following fractions.

(a) $\frac{0}{7}$

(b) $\frac{5}{5}$

(c) $\frac{2}{1}$

(d) $\frac{12}{6}$

(e) $\frac{-12}{3}$

(f) $\frac{22+13}{-4-3}$

Solution for Problem 4.1:

(a) Dividing 0 by any nonzero number gives 0, so we have $\frac{0}{7} = 0 \div 7 = 0$.

(b) Any nonzero number divided by itself is 1, so we have $\frac{5}{5} = 5 \div 5 = 1$.

(c) Dividing any number by 1 equals the original number, so we have $\frac{2}{1} = 2$.

(d) We have $\frac{12}{6} = 12 \div 6 = 2$.

(e) The result of dividing a negative number by a positive number is negative: $\frac{-12}{3} = -\frac{12}{3} = -4$.

(f) We first compute the numerator and the denominator. Since $22 + 13 = 35$ and $-4 - 3 = -7$, we have

$$\frac{22+13}{-4-3} = \frac{35}{-7}.$$

Next, the result of dividing a positive number by a negative number is negative:

$$\frac{35}{-7} = -\frac{35}{7} = -5.$$

$\square$

Problem 4.2: For what values of n between 1 and 40 is $\frac{n}{7}$ an integer?

Solution for Problem 4.2: Since $\frac{n}{7} = n \div 7$, the number n must be a multiple of 7 in order for $\frac{n}{7}$ to be an integer. The only multiples of 7 between 1 and 40 are 7, 14, 21, 28, and 35. $\square$

Problem 4.3: Each segment between two consecutive integers on the number line below is divided into five equal pieces. For each lettered dot, find a number that corresponds to that point on the number line.

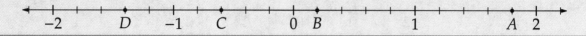

Solution for Problem 4.3: Because the dots divide the number line between 0 and 1 into 5 equal pieces, the right end of the first of these pieces is $\frac{1}{5}$. The right end of the second piece is $\frac{2}{5}$, of the third piece is $\frac{3}{5}$, and so on.

Going in the other direction from 0, the number line corresponds to negative numbers. So, starting from 0 and going leftward, the left end of the first piece is $-\frac{1}{5}$. The left end of the second piece is $-\frac{2}{5}$, of the third piece is $-\frac{3}{5}$, and so on. Continuing in this way, we can label the number line as shown below.

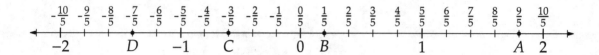

We find that $A = \frac{9}{5}$, $B = \frac{1}{5}$, $C = -\frac{3}{5}$, and $D = -\frac{7}{5}$. □

Problem 4.4:

(a) Use the number line to explain why $\frac{3}{7}$ is between 0 and 1.

(b) Between what two consecutive integers is $\frac{43}{5}$?

Solution for Problem 4.4:

(a) We locate the number $\frac{3}{7}$ on the number line by dividing the segment between 0 and 1 into 7 equal pieces. $\frac{3}{7}$ is the point at the right end of the third of these pieces.

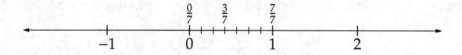

Since $\frac{7}{7}$ is at the right end of the seventh of these pieces, we see that $\frac{3}{7}$ is between $\frac{0}{7}$ and $\frac{7}{7}$. So, $\frac{3}{7}$ is between 0 and 1.

Similarly, if the numerator and denominator of a fraction are positive, we can quickly compare the fraction to 1.

Important: Suppose a and b are positive.

- $\frac{a}{b}$ is less than 1 if a is less than b.

- $\frac{a}{b}$ equals 1 if $a = b$.

- $\frac{a}{b}$ is greater than 1 if a is greater than b.

(b) We can write a fraction $\frac{a}{5}$ as an integer if a is a multiple of 5. So, to determine which consecutive integers $\frac{43}{5}$ is between, we must find the consecutive multiples of 5 that 43 is between. Since 43 is between 40 and 45, we know that $\frac{43}{5}$ is between $\frac{40}{5}$ and $\frac{45}{5}$.

Therefore, $\frac{43}{5}$ is between 8 and 9.

$\square$

Problem 4.5: The points A, B, C, and D on the number line below correspond to the numbers $-\frac{4}{7}$, $\frac{21}{7}$, $\frac{15}{7}$, and $\frac{4}{8}$ in some order. Match each point to the correct number.

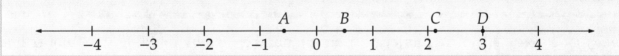

Solution for Problem 4.5: Point A is the only labeled point to the left of 0, so it must correspond to the only negative number in the list, which is $-\frac{4}{7}$.

Point B is between 0 and 1. Of the three positive numbers in our list, only $\frac{4}{8}$ has a numerator that is less than its denominator. Therefore, $\frac{4}{8}$ is the only positive number in the list that is less than 1. So, point B corresponds to $\frac{4}{8}$.

Since $\frac{21}{7} = 21 \div 7 = 3$, point D must be $\frac{21}{7}$. That leaves point C for $\frac{15}{7}$. As a quick check, we note that 15 is between 14 and 21, so $\frac{15}{7}$ is between $\frac{14}{7} = 2$ and $\frac{21}{7} = 3$. Point C is indeed between 2 and 3 on the number line. $\square$

In our solution to Problem 4.5, the point we identified as corresponding to $\frac{4}{8}$ appears to be exactly halfway between 0 and 1. But the point halfway between 0 and 1 corresponds to $\frac{1}{2}$. This suggests that it's possible to write the same number in more than one way with fractions. It's clear that we can do this with integers. For example, $4 = \frac{4}{1} = \frac{8}{2} = \frac{12}{3}$. Let's use the number line to see why non-integers $\frac{4}{8}$ and $\frac{1}{2}$ are equal.

Problem 4.6: Use the number line to explain why $\frac{4}{8} = \frac{1}{2}$.

Solution for Problem 4.6: To locate $\frac{1}{2}$ on the number line, we divide the number line between 0 and 1 into two equal pieces. $\frac{1}{2}$ is at the right end of the first piece.

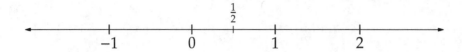

To locate $\frac{4}{8}$ on the number line, we divide the number line between 0 and 1 into eight equal pieces. We can do so by dividing each of the two pieces we already have between 0 and 1 into four equal pieces.

So, the right end of the fourth of these eight small pieces between 0 and 1 is the same as the right end of the first of the two equal pieces we used to locate $\frac{1}{2}$. Since $\frac{4}{8}$ and $\frac{1}{2}$ correspond to the same point on the number line, we have $\frac{4}{8} = \frac{1}{2}$. $\square$

Problem 4.7: Find two fractions that are equal to $\frac{2}{3}$.

Solution for Problem 4.7: We can locate $\frac{2}{3}$ on the number line by dividing the number line between 0 and 1 into three equal pieces. $\frac{2}{3}$ is the right end of the second of these pieces.

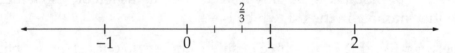

We can divide each of these three equal pieces between 0 and 1 into two equal pieces, so that we now have six equal pieces between 0 and 1. The point corresponding to $\frac{2}{3}$ is at the right end of the 4th of these 6 pieces, so we see that $\frac{2}{3} = \frac{4}{6}$.

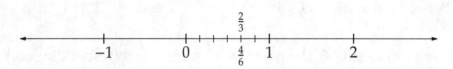

Similarly, we could have divided each of our original three equal pieces into three equal pieces, so that there are 9 equal pieces between 0 and 1. The point corresponding to $\frac{2}{3}$ is at the right end of the 6th of these 9 pieces, so we see that $\frac{2}{3} = \frac{6}{9}$.

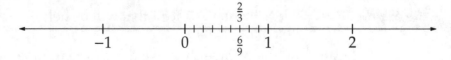

Therefore, both $\frac{4}{6}$ and $\frac{6}{9}$ equal $\frac{2}{3}$. These are not the only fractions that equal $\frac{2}{3}$. For example, $\frac{8}{12}, \frac{12}{18}, \frac{20}{30}$, and $\frac{138}{207}$ all equal $\frac{2}{3}$. We'll learn why in Section 4.5. □

Exercises

4.1.1 Find the value of each of the following:

(a) $\frac{-6}{6}$

(b) $\frac{18}{3}$

(c) $\frac{-23}{-23}$

(d) $\frac{0}{-5}$

4.1.2 Compute $\frac{16+6}{4-2}$.

4.1.3 Compute $\frac{1+5+9+13+17+21}{6}$. *(Source: MATHCOUNTS)*

4.1.4 Which integer is closest to $\frac{43}{7}$?

4.1.5 If $x = -12$ and $y = 4$, find the value of $xy - \frac{x}{y}$.

4.1.6 The points A, B, C, and D on the number line below correspond to the numbers $-\frac{8}{4}, \frac{11}{6}$, $\frac{7}{6}$, and $-\frac{1}{3}$ in some order. Match each point to the correct number.

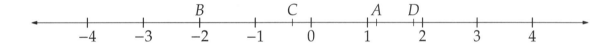

4.1.7 Find three fractions that are equal to $\frac{3}{5}$.

4.1.8★ For how many positive integer values of n is the expression $\frac{36}{n+1}$ an integer? **Hints:** 28

4.2 Multiplying Fractions

We often use the word "of" to mean multiplication. For example, suppose there are 12 apples in each apple basket at the grocery store. To count how many total apples there are in 3 *of* these baskets, we compute $3 \cdot 12 = 36$. We often avoid using "of" with integers, saying "3 baskets" rather than "3 of the baskets." But with fractions, we frequently use "of," saying "$\frac{2}{3}$ of a basket" instead of "$\frac{2}{3}$ basket."

So, how many apples are in $\frac{2}{3}$ of a basket if there are 12 apples in each basket? Since "of" means multiply, there are $\frac{2}{3} \cdot 12$ apples. To compute $\frac{2}{3} \cdot 12$, we must learn how to multiply by fractions.

Here are a couple of properties we learned in Chapter 1 that will be helpful in learning how to multiply fractions.

> **Important:** **Definition of division:** If b is not zero, then $\frac{a}{b} = a \cdot \frac{1}{b}$.
>
> ⚠ **Reciprocal of product:** If a and b are not zero, then $\frac{1}{ab} = \frac{1}{a} \cdot \frac{1}{b}$.

Problems

Problem 4.8: What is $2 \cdot \frac{1}{3}$?

Problem 4.9: In this problem, we compute $3 \cdot \frac{4}{5}$.

(a) Use our definition of division to write $\frac{4}{5}$ as the product of an integer and the reciprocal of an integer.

(b) Use the appropriate properties of multiplication and your result from part (a) to compute $3 \cdot \frac{4}{5}$. (By "compute," we mean find a number that equals $3 \cdot \frac{4}{5}$.)

Problem 4.10: In this problem, we compute $66666 \cdot \frac{7}{6}$.

(a) Explain why $66666 \cdot \frac{7}{6}$ equals $\frac{66666}{6} \cdot 7$.

(b) Compute $66666 \cdot \frac{7}{6}$.

Problem 4.11: What is $\frac{1}{3} \cdot \frac{1}{2}$?

Problem 4.12: In this problem, we compute $\frac{2}{3} \cdot \frac{4}{5}$.

(a) Use the definition of division to write each of $\frac{2}{3}$ and $\frac{4}{5}$ as the product of an integer and the reciprocal of an integer.

(b) Use the appropriate properties of multiplication and your result from part (a) to compute $\frac{2}{3} \cdot \frac{4}{5}$.

Problem 4.13: Compute $\frac{35}{6} \cdot \frac{48}{7}$.

Problem 4.14:

(a) What is $\frac{2}{3}$ of 90?

(b) What is $\frac{3}{4}$ of $\frac{11}{8}$?

Problem 4.15: Maya starts with 160 pennies. She gives $\frac{3}{5}$ of her pennies to her brother Mitch. Mitch then gives $\frac{3}{4}$ of the pennies he receives to his mother. How many pennies does Mitch give to his mother?

Problem 4.8: What is $2 \cdot \frac{1}{3}$?

Solution for Problem 4.8: Our definition of division tells us that $a \cdot \frac{1}{b} = a \div b = \frac{a}{b}$. Applying this to $2 \cdot \frac{1}{3}$ gives $2 \cdot \frac{1}{3} = \frac{2}{3}$.

We can also see that $2 \cdot \frac{1}{3} = \frac{2}{3}$ on the number line. We locate $\frac{1}{3}$ on the number line by dividing the number line between 0 and 1 into three equal pieces. $\frac{1}{3}$ is at the right end of the first piece. $2 \cdot \frac{1}{3}$ is twice as far from 0 as $\frac{1}{3}$ is, so $2 \cdot \frac{1}{3}$ is at the right end of the second of these three equal pieces between 0 and 1:

$\square$

Problem 4.9: What is $3 \cdot \frac{4}{5}$?

Solution for Problem 4.9: In the previous problem, we saw how to multiply an integer and the reciprocal of an integer using the definition of division. So, we start by writing $\frac{4}{5}$ as such a product:

$$3 \cdot \frac{4}{5} = 3 \cdot \left(4 \cdot \frac{1}{5}\right).$$

Applying the associative property of multiplication gives

$$3 \cdot \left(4 \cdot \frac{1}{5}\right) = (3 \cdot 4) \cdot \frac{1}{5} = 12 \cdot \frac{1}{5}.$$

Finally, applying the definition of division gives

$$12 \cdot \frac{1}{5} = \frac{12}{5}.$$

We can also describe the product $3 \cdot \frac{4}{5}$ with the number line. We first divide the number line between 0 and 1 into 5 equal pieces. The number $\frac{4}{5}$ is at the right end of the 4th of these 5 equal pieces. The number $3 \cdot \frac{4}{5}$ is 3 times as far from 0 as $\frac{4}{5}$ is from 0, so $3 \cdot \frac{4}{5}$ is at the right end of 3 times as many of these pieces. That is, $3 \cdot \frac{4}{5}$ is at the right end of the $3 \cdot 4 = 12^{\text{th}}$ piece:

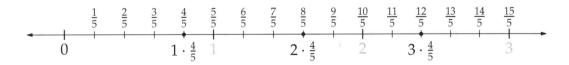

$\square$

We can similarly handle any product $a \cdot \frac{c}{d}$, where d is not 0:

$$a \cdot \frac{c}{d} = a \cdot \left(c \cdot \frac{1}{d} \right) \qquad \text{definition of division}$$

$$= (a \cdot c) \cdot \frac{1}{d} \qquad \text{associative property}$$

$$= \frac{a \cdot c}{d}. \qquad \text{definition of division}$$

> **Important:** If d is nonzero, then $a \cdot \frac{c}{d} = \frac{ac}{d}$.

Since $a \cdot \frac{c}{d} = \frac{c}{d} \cdot a$, we have $\frac{c}{d} \cdot a = \frac{ac}{d}$ as well.

Problem 4.10: Compute $66666 \cdot \frac{7}{6}$.

Solution for Problem 4.10: We know that $66666 \cdot \frac{7}{6} = \frac{66666 \cdot 7}{6}$, but computing $66666 \cdot 7$ is quite a chore. Instead, we see that 66666 is clearly a multiple of 6. Using the rule $\frac{ac}{d} = \frac{a}{d} \cdot c$ that we just learned, we have

$$\frac{66666 \cdot 7}{6} = \frac{66666}{6} \cdot 7.$$

Since $66666 \div 6 = 11111$, we have $\frac{66666}{6} \cdot 7 = 11111 \cdot 7 = 77777$. □

> **Concept:** We can sometimes use the fact that $a \cdot \frac{c}{d} = \frac{ac}{d} = \frac{a}{d} \cdot c$ (when d is not 0) to simplify computations.

Problem 4.11: What is $\frac{1}{3} \cdot \frac{1}{2}$?

Solution for Problem 4.11: The product of reciprocals rule tells us that $\frac{1}{a} \cdot \frac{1}{b} = \frac{1}{ab}$ if a and b are not zero. Applying this to $\frac{1}{3} \cdot \frac{1}{2}$ gives $\frac{1}{3} \cdot \frac{1}{2} = \frac{1}{3 \cdot 2} = \frac{1}{6}$.

Once again, we interpret this result on the number line. We start with the location of $\frac{1}{2}$, dividing the number line between 0 and 1 into 2 equal pieces:

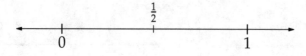

We locate $\frac{1}{3}$ on the number line by dividing the number line between 0 and 1 into 3 equal pieces, and place $\frac{1}{3}$ at the right end of the first of these pieces. We use a similar procedure to locate the number $\frac{1}{3} \cdot \frac{1}{2}$, which is $\frac{1}{3}$ of $\frac{1}{2}$. We divide the number line between 0 and $\frac{1}{2}$ (instead of between 0 and 1) into three equal pieces, and place $\frac{1}{3} \cdot \frac{1}{2}$ at the right end of the first of these pieces:

But why does the point on the number line corresponding to $\frac{1}{3} \cdot \frac{1}{2}$ also correspond to $\frac{1}{6}$? We start by dividing each of our initial 2 equal pieces between 0 and 1 into 3 equal pieces. So, there are now 6 equal pieces between 0 and 1. The right end of the first of these pieces corresponds to $\frac{1}{6}$:

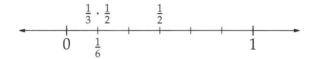

The point that corresponds to $\frac{1}{6}$ also corresponds to $\frac{1}{3} \cdot \frac{1}{2}$, so we have $\frac{1}{3} \cdot \frac{1}{2} = \frac{1}{6}$. □

Problem 4.12: What is $\frac{2}{3} \cdot \frac{4}{5}$?

Solution for Problem 4.12:   We follow the same strategy we used to compute $3 \cdot \frac{4}{5}$. We use the definition of division to write each of $\frac{2}{3}$ and $\frac{4}{5}$ as the product of an integer and a reciprocal:

$$\frac{2}{3} \cdot \frac{4}{5} = \left(2 \cdot \frac{1}{3}\right) \cdot \left(4 \cdot \frac{1}{5}\right).$$

We then use the associative and commutative properties of multiplication to group the integers and the reciprocals:

$$\left(2 \cdot \frac{1}{3}\right) \cdot \left(4 \cdot \frac{1}{5}\right) = (2 \cdot 4) \cdot \left(\frac{1}{3} \cdot \frac{1}{5}\right).$$

Finally, applying the reciprocal of a product property and the definition of division, we have

$$(2 \cdot 4) \cdot \left(\frac{1}{3} \cdot \frac{1}{5}\right) = 8 \cdot \frac{1}{3 \cdot 5} = 8 \cdot \frac{1}{15} = \frac{8}{15}.$$

Once again, we can interpret this result on the number line. We start by locating $\frac{4}{5}$ on the number line:

Then, we find $\frac{2}{3} \cdot \frac{4}{5}$ on the number line by dividing the number line between 0 and $\frac{4}{5}$ into three equal pieces. The product $\frac{2}{3} \cdot \frac{4}{5}$ is at the right end of the second of these pieces:

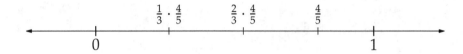

To see that $\frac{8}{15}$ is also at the right end of the second of these pieces, we divide each of our initial five equal pieces between 0 and 1 into 3 equal pieces each. This gives us $3 \cdot 5 = 15$ equal pieces:

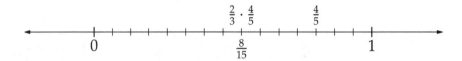

Between 0 and $\frac{4}{5}$, there are $3 \cdot 4 = 12$ of these pieces. Since $\frac{2}{3}$ of these 12 pieces is $\frac{2}{3} \cdot 12 = \frac{24}{3} = 8$ pieces, the number equal to $\frac{2}{3} \cdot \frac{4}{5}$ is at the right end of the 8th of the 15 equal pieces between 0 and 1. $\square$

We can similarly handle any product $\frac{a}{b} \cdot \frac{c}{d}$, where b and d are nonzero:

$$\frac{a}{b} \cdot \frac{c}{d} = \left(a \cdot \frac{1}{b}\right) \cdot \left(c \cdot \frac{1}{d}\right) \qquad \text{definition of division}$$

$$= (a \cdot c) \cdot \left(\frac{1}{b} \cdot \frac{1}{d}\right) \qquad \text{associative and commutative properties}$$

$$= (a \cdot c) \cdot \left(\frac{1}{b \cdot d}\right) \qquad \text{product of reciprocals}$$

$$= \frac{a \cdot c}{b \cdot d}. \qquad \text{definition of division}$$

Important: If b and d are nonzero, then $\dfrac{a}{b} \cdot \dfrac{c}{d} = \dfrac{ac}{bd}$.

Problem 4.13: Compute $\frac{35}{6} \cdot \frac{48}{7}$.

Solution for Problem 4.13: Applying the rule for multiplying fractions gives

$$\frac{35}{6} \cdot \frac{48}{7} = \frac{35 \cdot 48}{6 \cdot 7}.$$

Rather than multiplying out the numerator and the denominator, we notice that 35 is a multiple of 7 and 48 is a multiple of 6. This allows us to simplify the computation. We apply the commutative property in the numerator, and then use the fraction multiplication rule in reverse:

$$\frac{35 \cdot 48}{6 \cdot 7} = \frac{48 \cdot 35}{6 \cdot 7} = \frac{48}{6} \cdot \frac{35}{7} = 8 \cdot 5 = 40.$$

□

Problem 4.14:

(a) What is $\frac{2}{3}$ of 90?　　　　　　　(b) What is $\frac{3}{4}$ of $\frac{11}{8}$?

Solution for Problem 4.14:

(a) $\frac{2}{3}$ of 90 is $\frac{2}{3} \cdot 90 = \frac{2 \cdot 90}{3} = \frac{180}{3} = 60$.

(b) We apply the rule we just discovered for multiplying fractions: $\frac{3}{4} \cdot \frac{11}{8} = \frac{3 \cdot 11}{4 \cdot 8} = \frac{33}{32}$.

□

Problem 4.15: Maya starts with 160 pennies. She gives $\frac{3}{5}$ of her pennies to her brother Mitch. Mitch then gives $\frac{3}{4}$ of the pennies he receives to his mother. How many pennies does Mitch give to his mother?

Solution for Problem 4.15: Here are two different approaches to the problem:

Method 1: Figure out how many pennies Mitch receives. Since Maya gives $\frac{3}{5}$ of her 160 pennies to Mitch, she gives him

$$\frac{3}{5} \cdot 160 = \frac{480}{5} = 480 \div 5 = 96$$

pennies. Mitch then gives $\frac{3}{4}$ of these pennies to his mother, which is

$$\frac{3}{4} \cdot 96 = \frac{3 \cdot 96}{4} = 3 \cdot \frac{96}{4} = 3 \cdot 24 = 72$$

pennies.

Method 2: Figure out what fraction of Maya's pennies Mitch gives to his mother. Mitch gives $\frac{3}{4}$ of $\frac{3}{5}$ of Maya's pennies to his mother. So, the fraction of Maya's pennies that Mitch gives to his mother is

$$\frac{3}{4} \cdot \frac{3}{5} = \frac{3 \cdot 3}{4 \cdot 5} = \frac{9}{20}.$$

Since Mitch gives $\frac{9}{20}$ of Maya's 160 pennies to his mother, he gives his mother

$$\frac{9}{20} \cdot 160 = \frac{9 \cdot 160}{20} = 9 \cdot \frac{160}{20} = 9 \cdot 8 = 72$$

pennies, which matches our answer from before. □

Exercises

4.2.1 Compute each of the following products:

(a) $\frac{5}{6} \cdot \frac{11}{7}$

(b) $\frac{1}{5} \cdot (-75) \cdot \frac{2}{3}$

(c) $\left(-\frac{80}{7}\right)\left(\frac{14}{9}\right)\left(-\frac{63}{16}\right)$

4.2.2 Find an integer that equals the following fraction: $\dfrac{30 \cdot 28 \cdot 26 \cdot 24}{12 \cdot 13 \cdot 14 \cdot 15}$.

4.2.3 Compute $\dfrac{3 \cdot 5}{9 \cdot 11} \times \dfrac{7 \cdot 9 \cdot 11}{3 \cdot 5 \cdot 7}$. *(Source: AMC 8)*

4.2.4 What number is $\frac{3}{4}$ of $\frac{8}{9}$ of 180?

4.2.5 What is $\frac{1}{2}$ of $\frac{2}{3}$ of $\frac{3}{4}$ of $\frac{4}{5}$ of 100? *(Source: MOEMS)*

4.2.6 What is the product $\frac{5}{8} \cdot \frac{8}{11} \cdot \frac{11}{14} \cdot \frac{14}{17} \cdot \frac{17}{20} \cdot \frac{20}{23}$?

4.2.7

(a) $\frac{5}{6}$ times what fraction equals $\frac{5}{7}$?

(b)★ $\frac{5}{6}$ times what fraction equals $\frac{4}{7}$?

4.2.8★ If a is divided by b, the result is $\frac{3}{4}$. If b is divided by c, the result is $\frac{11}{13}$. What is the result when a is divided by c? **Hints:** 46

4.3 Dividing by a Fraction

Recall that we define division in terms of multiplication:

$$a \div b = a \cdot \frac{1}{b}.$$

In this section, we combine this definition with the rule for multiplying fractions to learn how to divide by fractions.

Problems

Problem 4.16: What is $\frac{3}{7} \div 2$?

Problem 4.17:

(a) What is the reciprocal of $\frac{2}{3}$?

(b) If a and b are nonzero, then what is the reciprocal of $\frac{a}{b}$?

Problem 4.18: What is $3 \div \frac{5}{8}$?

Problem 4.19: What is $\frac{2}{7} \div \frac{9}{5}$?

Problem 4.20: What is $\frac{14/3}{-2/9}$?

Problem 4.21: 32 is $\frac{2}{5}$ of what number?

Problem 4.22: Each panel of fencing material is $\frac{20}{3}$ feet long. How many panels do I need to build a 60-foot fence?

Problem 4.16: What is $\frac{3}{7} \div 2$?

Solution for Problem 4.16: Since $a \div b = a \cdot \frac{1}{b}$, we have
$$\frac{3}{7} \div 2 = \frac{3}{7} \cdot \frac{1}{2} = \frac{3 \cdot 1}{7 \cdot 2} = \frac{3}{14}.$$

□

What about dividing by a fraction? Our definition of division tells us that to divide by a fraction, we multiply by the reciprocal of the fraction. So, we'll have to figure out how to find the reciprocal of a fraction.

Problem 4.17:

(a) What is the reciprocal of $\frac{2}{3}$?

(b) If a and b are nonzero, then what is the reciprocal of $\frac{a}{b}$?

Solution for Problem 4.17:

(a) We seek a number such that the product of $\frac{2}{3}$ and the number is 1. Suppose that this number is a fraction, $\frac{m}{n}$. Applying the rule for multiplying fractions, we have
$$\frac{2}{3} \cdot \frac{m}{n} = \frac{2m}{3n}.$$

The fraction $\frac{2m}{3n}$ equals 1 if the numerator and denominator are equal. One easy way to accomplish this is by letting $m = 3$ and $n = 2$:
$$\frac{2m}{3n} = \frac{2 \cdot 3}{3 \cdot 2} = \frac{2 \cdot 3}{2 \cdot 3} = 1.$$

So, $\frac{3}{2}$ is the reciprocal of $\frac{2}{3}$:
$$\frac{2}{3} \cdot \frac{3}{2} = \frac{2 \cdot 3}{3 \cdot 2} = \frac{2 \cdot 3}{2 \cdot 3} = 1.$$

We also could have found the answer by applying the definition of division together with the rule for the product of reciprocals:

$$\frac{1}{\frac{2}{3}} = \frac{1}{2 \cdot \frac{1}{3}} = \frac{1}{2} \cdot \frac{1}{\frac{1}{3}}.$$

Since the reciprocal of $\frac{1}{3}$ is 3, we have

$$\frac{1}{2} \cdot \frac{1}{\frac{1}{3}} = \frac{1}{2} \cdot 3 = \frac{3}{2}.$$

(b) In part (a), we found that the reciprocal of $\frac{2}{3}$ is formed by swapping the numerator and denominator to get $\frac{3}{2}$. Maybe we can find the reciprocal of any fraction the same way! Let's check if the reciprocal of $\frac{a}{b}$ is $\frac{b}{a}$:

$$\frac{a}{b} \cdot \frac{b}{a} = \frac{ab}{ba} = \frac{ab}{ab} = 1.$$

Since $\frac{a}{b} \cdot \frac{b}{a} = 1$, the reciprocal of $\frac{a}{b}$ is $\frac{b}{a}$.

As in part (a), we could have applied the definition of division together with the rule for the product of reciprocals:

$$\frac{1}{\frac{a}{b}} = \frac{1}{a \cdot \frac{1}{b}} = \frac{1}{a} \cdot \frac{1}{\frac{1}{b}} = \frac{1}{a} \cdot b = \frac{b}{a}.$$

$\square$

Important: If a and b are nonzero, then the reciprocal of $\frac{a}{b}$ is $\frac{b}{a}$. In other words,

$$\frac{1}{a/b} = \frac{b}{a}.$$

Problem 4.18: What is $3 \div \frac{5}{8}$?

Solution for Problem 4.18: The definition of division tells us that $3 \div \frac{5}{8}$ equals 3 times the reciprocal of $\frac{5}{8}$. The reciprocal of $\frac{5}{8}$ is $\frac{8}{5}$, so we have

$$3 \div \frac{5}{8} = 3 \cdot \frac{1}{5/8} = 3 \cdot \frac{8}{5} = \frac{3 \cdot 8}{5} = \frac{24}{5}.$$

$\square$

Usually, we leave out the intermediate step $\frac{1}{5/8}$ above and just write $3 \div \frac{5}{8} = 3 \cdot \frac{8}{5}$.

Problem 4.19: What is $\frac{2}{7} \div \frac{9}{5}$?

Solution for Problem 4.19: Since the reciprocal of $\frac{9}{5}$ is $\frac{5}{9}$, we have

$$\frac{2}{7} \div \frac{9}{5} = \frac{2}{7} \cdot \frac{5}{9} = \frac{2 \cdot 5}{7 \cdot 9} = \frac{10}{63}.$$

☐

Similarly, we can now write a rule for dividing by a fraction:

Important: If b, c, and d are nonzero, then

$$\frac{a}{b} \div \frac{c}{d} = \frac{a}{b} \cdot \frac{d}{c} = \frac{ad}{bc}.$$

Problem 4.20: What is $\frac{14/3}{-2/9}$?

Solution for Problem 4.20: Here we have a fraction in which the numerator and the denominator are both fractions. All this means is that we are dividing the fraction in the numerator, $\frac{14}{3}$, by the fraction in the denominator, $-\frac{2}{9}$. In order to divide by $-\frac{2}{9}$, we need to find the reciprocal of a negative fraction. Fortunately, on page 37 we learned the rule for the reciprocal of a negation:

$$\frac{1}{-x} = -\frac{1}{x}.$$

So, we have $\frac{1}{-2/9} = -\frac{1}{2/9} = -\frac{9}{2}$. Now, we can perform our division:

$$\frac{14/3}{-2/9} = \frac{14}{3} \div \left(-\frac{2}{9}\right) = \frac{14}{3} \cdot \left(-\frac{9}{2}\right) = -\frac{14 \cdot 9}{3 \cdot 2}.$$

Since 14 is a multiple of 2 and 9 is a multiple of 3, we can simplify the final computation:

$$-\frac{14 \cdot 9}{3 \cdot 2} = -\frac{14 \cdot 9}{2 \cdot 3} = -\frac{14}{2} \cdot \frac{9}{3} = -7 \cdot 3 = -21.$$

☐

Problem 4.21: 32 is $\frac{2}{5}$ of what number?

Solution for Problem 4.21: Since "of" means "multiply," the question asks, "32 equals $\frac{2}{5}$ times what number?" This means we seek the number that fills the box in the equation

$$32 = \frac{2}{5} \cdot \boxed{}.$$

If we still don't know what to do to fill in the box here, we can use a very powerful problem-solving strategy:

> **Concept:** If you don't know how to solve a problem at first, try solving a
> simpler version of the problem.

It's probably the fraction that makes this problem difficult, so we think about how to solve a similar problem without a fraction. Imagine instead that the problem were to find the number that fills the box in the equation

$$32 = 4 \cdot \boxed{}.$$

This is more familiar. We learned back in Section 1.7 that we can think of division as the reverse of multiplication, and the number that fills this box is $32 \div 4 = 8$.

Let's return to the equation with the fraction:

$$32 = \frac{2}{5} \cdot \boxed{}.$$

Now, we know to use division to find the number that fills the box:

$$32 \div \frac{2}{5} = 32 \cdot \frac{5}{2} = \frac{32 \cdot 5}{2} = \frac{32}{2} \cdot 5 = 16 \cdot 5 = 80.$$

We also could have used some number sense to solve this problem. Since $\frac{2}{5}$ of a number is 32, we know that $\frac{1}{5}$ of that same number is half of 32, or 16. Since $\frac{1}{5}$ of the number equals 16, the number is 5 times 16, or 80. Notice that in this solution, we divided 32 by 2 and then multiplied the result by 5. Compare these two steps to the steps we used to compute $32 \div \frac{2}{5}$ above—they're the same steps! □

> **Problem 4.22:** Each panel of fencing material is $\frac{20}{3}$ feet long. How many panels do I need to build a 60-foot fence?

Solution for Problem 4.22: Once again, we can start by simplifying the problem to get a better handle on it. Suppose the problem were instead:

> Each panel of fencing material is 5 feet long. How many panels do I need to build a 60-foot fence?

Now it's more clear that we have to divide. Each panel is 5 feet, so I need $60 \div 5 = 12$ panels to have 60 feet of fence.

Returning to our original problem, we see that if each panel is $\frac{20}{3}$ feet, then the number of panels needed for a 60-foot fence is

$$60 \div \frac{20}{3} = 60 \cdot \frac{3}{20} = \frac{60 \cdot 3}{20} = \frac{60}{20} \cdot 3 = 3 \cdot 3 = 9.$$

As a check, we confirm that 9 panels do indeed provide $9 \cdot \frac{20}{3} = \frac{9 \cdot 20}{3} = \frac{180}{3} = 60$ feet of fence. □

Exercises

4.3.1 Evaluate each of the following:

(a) $\frac{3}{5} \div 2$ 　　　　 (b) $7 \div \frac{7}{8}$ 　　　　 (c) $\frac{14/3}{5/4}$ 　　　　 (d) $\left(-\frac{5}{6}\right) \div \left(-\frac{12}{7}\right)$

4.3.2 What is the quotient when $\frac{3}{7}$ is divided by $\frac{7}{3}$?

4.3.3 If $x = \frac{3}{4}$, what is the value of $\frac{36}{x}$?

4.3.4

(a) 40 is $\frac{2}{3}$ of what number?

(b) $\frac{9}{5}$ is $\frac{2}{3}$ of what number?

4.3.5

(a) Dividing $\frac{6}{7}$ by what number gives $\frac{3}{7}$?

(b) Dividing $\frac{6}{7}$ by what number gives $\frac{6}{5}$?

(c) Dividing $\frac{6}{7}$ by what number gives $\frac{2}{3}$?

4.3.6 Dividing $\frac{3}{5}$ into what number gives a quotient of 20?

4.3.7 Multiplying a number by $\frac{3}{4}$ and then dividing the result by $\frac{3}{5}$ has the same effect as multiplying the original number by what number? *(Source: AMC 8)*

4.3.8 I have a scoop that holds $\frac{2}{3}$ cup of flour. If my recipe calls for 6 cups of flour, how many scoops do I need?

4.4 Raising Fractions to Powers

Problems

> **Problem 4.23:**
>
> (a) Compute $\left(\frac{2}{5}\right)^3$.
>
> (b) Let b be nonzero and let n be a positive integer. Explain why $\left(\frac{a}{b}\right)^n = \frac{a^n}{b^n}$.

> **Problem 4.24:**
>
> (a) Evaluate $\left(\frac{5}{7}\right)^{-1}$.
>
> (b) Evaluate $\left(\frac{4}{3}\right)^{-3}$.

Problem 4.25: Suppose a and b are nonzero, and n is a positive integer. Explain why

$$\left(\frac{a}{b}\right)^{-n} = \frac{b^n}{a^n}.$$

Problem 4.26: Compute $\dfrac{(21/31)^5(31/21)^3}{(21/31)^2}$.

Problem 4.23:

(a) Compute $\left(\frac{2}{5}\right)^3$.

(b) Let b be nonzero and let n be a positive integer. Explain why $\left(\frac{a}{b}\right)^n = \frac{a^n}{b^n}$.

Solution for Problem 4.23:

(a) We apply the rule for fraction multiplication:

$$\left(\frac{2}{5}\right)^3 = \frac{2}{5} \cdot \frac{2}{5} \cdot \frac{2}{5} = \frac{2 \cdot 2}{5 \cdot 5} \cdot \frac{2}{5} = \frac{2 \cdot 2 \cdot 2}{5 \cdot 5 \cdot 5} = \frac{2^3}{5^3} = \frac{8}{125}.$$

(b) If n is a positive integer, then $\left(\frac{a}{b}\right)^n$ is a product of n copies of $\frac{a}{b}$. Applying the rule for multiplying fractions tells us that such a product equals $\frac{a^n}{b^n}$:

$$\left(\frac{a}{b}\right)^n = \underbrace{\frac{a}{b} \times \frac{a}{b} \times \cdots \times \frac{a}{b}}_{n \text{ copies}} = \frac{\overbrace{a \times a \times \cdots \times a}^{n \text{ copies}}}{\underbrace{b \times b \times \cdots \times b}_{n \text{ copies}}} = \frac{a^n}{b^n}.$$

$\square$

Important: If n is a positive integer and b is not 0, then

$$\left(\frac{a}{b}\right)^n = \frac{a^n}{b^n}.$$

This isn't something new. It's just the quotient of powers rule $(a \div b)^n = a^n \div b^n$ written using fractions.

Problem 4.24:

(a) Evaluate $\left(\frac{5}{7}\right)^{-1}$.

(b) Evaluate $\left(\frac{4}{3}\right)^{-3}$.

Solution for Problem 4.24:

(a) Back in Section 2.4, we defined a^{-1} for any nonzero a to be the reciprocal of a. Since the reciprocal of $\frac{5}{7}$ is $\frac{7}{5}$, we have

$$\left(\frac{5}{7}\right)^{-1} = \frac{7}{5}.$$

Similarly, we have:

> **Important:** If a and b are nonzero, then
>
> $$\left(\frac{a}{b}\right)^{-1} = \frac{b}{a}.$$

This is just another way to write our earlier rule for finding the reciprocal of a fraction.

(b) In Section 2.4, we also defined a^{-n} for any nonzero a and any positive integer n as follows:

$$a^{-n} = \frac{1}{a^n}.$$

So, $\left(\frac{4}{3}\right)^{-3}$ equals the reciprocal of $\left(\frac{4}{3}\right)^3$. Applying the rule we discovered on page 168 for raising a fraction to a positive integer power gives

$$\left(\frac{4}{3}\right)^{-3} = \frac{1}{(4/3)^3} = \frac{1}{4^3/3^3} = \frac{3^3}{4^3} = \frac{27}{64}.$$

Often, a more helpful way to think about negative powers of fractions is to apply the exponent rule

$$a^{-n} = (a^{-1})^n,$$

which we learned on page 85. Applying this rule to $\left(\frac{4}{3}\right)^{-3}$, together with the rule for finding the reciprocal of a fraction, we have

$$\left(\frac{4}{3}\right)^{-3} = \left(\left(\frac{4}{3}\right)^{-1}\right)^3 = \left(\frac{3}{4}\right)^3 = \frac{3^3}{4^3} = \frac{27}{64}.$$

□

Our second solution to part (b) is the way we usually compute negative powers of fractions.

> **Problem 4.25:** Suppose a and b are nonzero, and n is a positive integer. Explain why
> $$\left(\frac{a}{b}\right)^{-n} = \frac{b^n}{a^n}.$$

Solution for Problem 4.25: We have

$$\left(\frac{a}{b}\right)^{-n} = \left(\left(\frac{a}{b}\right)^{-1}\right)^{n} \qquad \text{power of a power}$$

$$= \left(\frac{b}{a}\right)^{n} \qquad \text{reciprocal of a fraction}$$

$$= \frac{b^n}{a^n}. \qquad \text{power of a fraction}$$

$\square$

> **Important:** If a and b are nonzero and n is a positive integer, then
>
> $$\left(\frac{a}{b}\right)^{-n} = \frac{b^n}{a^n}.$$

Rather than memorizing this as a separate formula, we usually think of this with the intermediate step

$$\left(\frac{a}{b}\right)^{-n} = \left(\frac{b}{a}\right)^{n} = \frac{b^n}{a^n}.$$

As an Exercise, you'll use $\left(\frac{a}{b}\right)^{-n} = \frac{b^n}{a^n}$ to explain why we can apply the same rule to negative powers of fractions that we use for positive powers of fractions:

> **Important:** If a and b are nonzero and n is any integer, then
>
> $$\left(\frac{a}{b}\right)^{n} = \frac{a^n}{b^n}.$$

Problem 4.26: Compute $\dfrac{(21/31)^5(31/21)^3}{(21/31)^2}$.

Solution for Problem 4.26: We could compute this the long way, multiplying out each of the powers of fractions. But instead, we notice that $\frac{21}{31}$ appears in both the numerator and the denominator. We can use an exponent law to simplify:

$$\frac{(21/31)^5(31/21)^3}{(21/31)^2} = \frac{(21/31)^5}{(21/31)^2} \cdot (31/21)^3 = (21/31)^{5-2} \cdot (31/21)^3 = (21/31)^3 \cdot (31/21)^3.$$

Here are two solutions from this point:

Solution 1: Use the rule for raising fractions to powers. We have

$$\left(\frac{21}{31}\right)^3 \cdot \left(\frac{31}{21}\right)^3 = \frac{21^3}{31^3} \cdot \frac{31^3}{21^3} = \frac{21^3 \cdot 31^3}{31^3 \cdot 21^3}.$$

The numerator and the denominator of the final fraction are equal, so the fraction equals 1.

Solution 2: Notice that the powers are the same. Since both fractions in $(21/31)^3 \cdot (31/21)^3$ are raised to the same power, we apply an exponent law:

$$\left(\frac{21}{31}\right)^3 \cdot \left(\frac{31}{21}\right)^3 = \left(\frac{21}{31} \cdot \frac{31}{21}\right)^3.$$

Since $\frac{31}{21}$ is the reciprocal of $\frac{21}{31}$, the product $\frac{21}{31} \cdot \frac{31}{21}$ equals 1. This means our expression equals 1^3, which is 1. $\square$

Exercises

▶

4.4.1 Compute each of the following:

(a) $\left(\frac{3}{5}\right)^2$

(b) $\left(-\frac{2}{7}\right)^0$

(c) $\left(\frac{4}{9}\right)^{-2}$

(d) $\left(\frac{-3}{2}\right)^5$

(e) $\frac{1}{(1/5)^3}$

(f) $\frac{(2/9)^2}{(5/3)^4}$

4.4.2

(a) $\frac{3}{4}$ raised to what power equals $\frac{27}{64}$?

(b) $\frac{3}{4}$ raised to what power equals $\frac{16}{9}$?

4.4.3 Compute $\frac{(2/1641)^4}{(3/1641)^4}$.

4.4.4 Compute $\frac{(5/3)^4(5/3)^3}{(5/3)^5}$.

4.4.5 Compute $\left(\frac{7}{4}\right)^3 \left(\frac{4}{7}\right)^5 \left(\frac{7}{4}\right)^3$.

4.4.6★ Suppose a and b are nonzero, and n is a positive integer. In the text, we showed that $\left(\frac{a}{b}\right)^{-n} = \frac{b^n}{a^n}$. Explain why

$$\left(\frac{a}{b}\right)^{-n} = \frac{a^{-n}}{b^{-n}}$$

by showing that $\frac{a^{-n}}{b^{-n}}$ also equals $\frac{b^n}{a^n}$.

4.5 Simplest Form of a Fraction

A fraction is in **simplest form** if its numerator and denominator have no positive common divisor besides 1. For example, the numerator and the denominator of $\frac{4}{8}$ have 4 as a common divisor, so $\frac{4}{8}$ is not in simplest form. The only positive common divisor of the numerator and denominator of $\frac{1}{2}$ is 1, so $\frac{1}{2}$ is in simplest form. We saw back in Problem 4.6 that the fractions $\frac{4}{8}$ and $\frac{1}{2}$ are equal. So, we can write $\frac{4}{8}$ in simplest form as $\frac{1}{2}$.

Problems

Problem 4.27: Write $\frac{12}{30}$ in simplest form.

Problem 4.28: One of the properties of division that we learned in Section 1.7 was the "cancel common factor" property: If b and c are not zero, then

$$(ac) \div (bc) = a \div b.$$

Use fraction multiplication to explain why the cancel common factor property works.

Problem 4.29: Write $\frac{225}{540}$ in simplest form.

Problem 4.30: Compute each of the following in simplest form:

(a) $\frac{6}{8} \cdot \frac{12}{8}$

(b) $\left(-\frac{24}{32}\right) \cdot \left(-\frac{36}{45}\right)$

(c) $\left(-\frac{40}{27}\right) \cdot \frac{21}{160}$

(d) $\frac{34}{33} \div \frac{51}{44}$

Problem 4.31: What fraction of 96 is 64? Answer as a fraction in simplest form.

Problem 4.32:
(a) Simplify $\frac{2 \cdot 5^2}{3 \cdot 5^3}$.

(b) Simplify $\frac{2 \cdot 7^2}{3 \cdot 7^3}$.

(c) Suppose x is nonzero. Simplify $\frac{2x^2}{3x^3}$.

Problem 4.33: If c and d are not zero, then simplify $\frac{40c^3 d^2}{16c^5 d}$.

Problem 4.27: Write $\frac{12}{30}$ in simplest form.

Solution for Problem 4.27: Since 12 and 30 have 6 as a common divisor, we have

$$\frac{12}{30} = \frac{2 \cdot 6}{5 \cdot 6} = \frac{2}{5} \cdot \frac{6}{6} = \frac{2}{5}.$$

2 and 5 have only 1 as a positive common divisor, so $\frac{2}{5}$ is in simplest form. $\square$

Problem 4.28: One of the properties of division that we learned in Section 1.7 was the "cancel common factor" property: If b and c are not zero, then

$$(ac) \div (bc) = a \div b.$$

Use fraction multiplication to explain why the cancel common factor property works.

Solution for Problem 4.28: We start by writing $(ac) \div (bc)$ as the fraction $\frac{ac}{bc}$. From our discussion of multiplying fractions, we know that $\frac{ac}{bc} = \frac{a}{b} \cdot \frac{c}{c}$. Since $\frac{c}{c} = 1$, we have $\frac{ac}{bc} = \frac{a}{b}$. Finally, since $\frac{a}{b} = a \div b$, we have $(ac) \div (bc) = a \div b$. $\square$

When the numerator and the denominator of a fraction have a positive common factor besides 1, we can use the fact that $\frac{ac}{bc} = \frac{a}{b}$ to simplify the fraction.

Problem 4.29: Write $\frac{225}{540}$ in simplest form.

Solution for Problem 4.29: 5 is a common divisor of 225 and 540, and we have $\frac{225}{540} = \frac{45 \cdot 5}{108 \cdot 5} = \frac{45}{108}$. But $\frac{45}{108}$ is not in simplest form because 45 and 108 are both divisible by 9:

$$\frac{45}{108} = \frac{5 \cdot 9}{12 \cdot 9} = \frac{5}{12}.$$

The only positive common divisor of 5 and 12 is 1, so $\frac{5}{12}$ is in simplest form.

We also could have used the prime factorizations of 225 and 540 to help us find common divisors. Since $225 = 3^2 \cdot 5^2$ and $540 = 2^2 \cdot 3^3 \cdot 5$, we see that 225 and 540 have two factors of 3 and one factor of 5 in common, so

$$\frac{225}{540} = \frac{3^2 \cdot 5^2}{2^2 \cdot 3^3 \cdot 5} = \frac{5 \cdot (3^2 \cdot 5)}{2^2 \cdot 3 \cdot (3^2 \cdot 5)} = \frac{5}{2^2 \cdot 3} \cdot \frac{3^2 \cdot 5}{3^2 \cdot 5} = \frac{5}{2^2 \cdot 3} = \frac{5}{12}.$$

$\square$

Concept: We can use the prime factorizations of the numerator and denominator of a fraction to simplify the fraction.

Problem 4.30: Compute each of the following in simplest form:

(a) $\frac{6}{8} \cdot \frac{12}{8}$ (b) $\left(-\frac{24}{32}\right) \cdot \left(-\frac{36}{45}\right)$ (c) $\left(-\frac{40}{27}\right) \cdot \frac{21}{160}$ (d) $\frac{34}{33} \div \frac{51}{44}$

Solution for Problem 4.30:

(a) We have

$$\frac{6}{8} \cdot \frac{12}{8} = \frac{6 \cdot 12}{8 \cdot 8} = \frac{72}{64} = \frac{9 \cdot 8}{8 \cdot 8} = \frac{9}{8}.$$

We also could have simplified $\frac{6}{8}$ and $\frac{12}{8}$ before multiplying. Since $\frac{6}{8} = \frac{3\cdot2}{4\cdot2} = \frac{3}{4}$ and $\frac{12}{8} = \frac{3\cdot4}{2\cdot4} = \frac{3}{2}$, we have

$$\frac{6}{8}\cdot\frac{12}{8} = \frac{3}{4}\cdot\frac{3}{2} = \frac{9}{8}.$$

(b) The product of two negative numbers is positive; we have

$$\left(-\frac{24}{32}\right)\cdot\left(-\frac{36}{45}\right) = \frac{24}{32}\cdot\frac{36}{45}.$$

We still have to compute $\frac{24}{32}\cdot\frac{36}{45}$. We could multiply out $24\cdot36$ and $32\cdot45$, and then hunt for common factors. However, we can save a lot of time by simplifying the two fractions before multiplying. We have $\frac{24}{32} = \frac{3\cdot8}{4\cdot8} = \frac{3}{4}$ and $\frac{36}{45} = \frac{4\cdot9}{5\cdot9} = \frac{4}{5}$, so

$$\frac{24}{32}\cdot\frac{36}{45} = \frac{3}{4}\cdot\frac{4}{5} = \frac{3\cdot4}{4\cdot5} = \frac{3}{5}.$$

We say that we **canceled** a common divisor of 4 in the final step above. We sometimes express this cancellation with a slash through the numbers being canceled:

$$\frac{3}{4}\cdot\frac{4}{5} = \frac{3\cdot\cancel{4}}{\cancel{4}\cdot5} = \frac{3}{5}.$$

(c) The product of a positive number and a negative number is negative; we have

$$\left(-\frac{40}{27}\right)\cdot\frac{21}{160} = -\left(\frac{40}{27}\cdot\frac{21}{160}\right).$$

We still must compute $\frac{40}{27}\cdot\frac{21}{160}$. We can't simplify either fraction. However, the numerator of each fraction has divisors in common with the denominator of the other fraction. We can perform a clever manipulation to allow us to take advantage of these common factors:

$$-\left(\frac{40}{27}\cdot\frac{21}{160}\right) = -\frac{40\cdot21}{27\cdot160} = -\frac{40\cdot21}{160\cdot27} = -\left(\frac{40}{160}\cdot\frac{21}{27}\right).$$

Since $\frac{40}{160} = \frac{1\cdot40}{4\cdot40} = \frac{1}{4}$ and $\frac{21}{27} = \frac{7\cdot3}{9\cdot3} = \frac{7}{9}$, we have

$$-\left(\frac{40}{27}\cdot\frac{21}{160}\right) = -\left(\frac{40}{160}\cdot\frac{21}{27}\right) = -\left(\frac{1}{4}\cdot\frac{7}{9}\right) = -\frac{7}{36}.$$

(d) First, we write the division as a multiplication: $\frac{34}{33}\div\frac{51}{44} = \frac{34}{33}\cdot\frac{44}{51}$. Now, we notice that the denominator of $\frac{34}{33}$ and the numerator of $\frac{44}{51}$ have 11 as a common divisor. Rearranging the product will allow us to cancel this common divisor:

$$\frac{34}{33}\cdot\frac{44}{51} = \frac{34\cdot44}{33\cdot51} = \frac{44\cdot34}{33\cdot51} = \frac{44}{33}\cdot\frac{34}{51}.$$

We have $\frac{44}{33} = \frac{4\cdot11}{3\cdot11} = \frac{4}{3}$ and $\frac{34}{51} = \frac{2\cdot17}{3\cdot17} = \frac{2}{3}$, so $\frac{44}{33}\cdot\frac{34}{51} = \frac{4}{3}\cdot\frac{2}{3} = \frac{8}{9}$.

As you get more comfortable with fraction multiplication, you won't have to rearrange products in the numerator and denominator in order to cancel common factors. For example, in the product $\frac{34}{33} \cdot \frac{44}{51}$ above, you might cancel out the common factor of 17 in 34 and 51, and cancel out the common factor of 11 in 33 and 44:

$$\frac{\overset{2}{\cancel{34}}}{\underset{3}{\cancel{33}}} \cdot \frac{\overset{4}{\cancel{44}}}{\underset{3}{\cancel{51}}} = \frac{2}{3} \cdot \frac{4}{3}.$$

Notice the small 2 above the 34 and small 3 below the 51. These are the factors that remain when we cancel the common factor of 17 from 34 and 51. Similarly, the 4 above the 44 and the 3 below the 33 are the factors that remain when we cancel the common factor of 11 from 44 and 33.

☐

> **Concept:** When finding the product of fractions in simplest form, we usually cancel common divisors as much as possible before computing any products. Moreover, we can cancel a common divisor from the numerator of one fraction and the denominator of another.

Problem 4.31: What fraction of 96 is 64? Answer as a fraction in simplest form.

Solution for Problem 4.31: Because "of" means "multiply," we seek the fraction that goes in the blank in the equation

$$\underline{\qquad} \cdot 96 = 64.$$

We know how to handle equations like this. Thinking of division as the reverse of multiplication, the number that goes in the blank is $64 \div 96$. Expressing this as a fraction, we have

$$64 \div 96 = \frac{64}{96} = \frac{2 \cdot \cancel{32}}{3 \cdot \cancel{32}} = \frac{2}{3}.$$

To check our answer, we compute that $\frac{2}{3}$ of 96 is

$$\frac{2}{3} \cdot 96 = \frac{2 \cdot 96}{3} = 2 \cdot \frac{96}{3} = 2 \cdot 32 = 64.$$

☐

Problem 4.32:

(a) Simplify $\frac{2 \cdot 5^2}{3 \cdot 5^3}$.

(b) Simplify $\frac{2 \cdot 7^2}{3 \cdot 7^3}$.

(c) Suppose x is nonzero. Simplify $\frac{2x^2}{3x^3}$.

Solution for Problem 4.32:

(a) Since 5^2 is a common divisor of the numerator and denominator, we have

$$\frac{2 \cdot 5^2}{3 \cdot 5^3} = \frac{2 \cdot \cancel{5^2}}{(3 \cdot 5) \cdot \cancel{5^2}} = \frac{2}{3 \cdot 5} = \frac{2}{15}.$$

(b) Since 7^2 is a common divisor of the numerator and denominator, we have

$$\frac{2 \cdot 7^2}{3 \cdot 7^3} = \frac{2 \cdot \cancel{7^2}}{(3 \cdot 7) \cdot \cancel{7^2}} = \frac{2}{3 \cdot 7} = \frac{2}{21}.$$

(c) Our first two parts guide the way. We have a factor of x^2 in the numerator and the denominator, so we can cancel it out:

$$\frac{2x^2}{3x^3} = \frac{2 \cdot x^2}{3x \cdot x^2} = \frac{2}{3x} \cdot \frac{x^2}{x^2} = \frac{2}{3x} \cdot 1 = \frac{2}{3x}.$$

Of course, if x were even, we could simplify $\frac{2}{3x}$ further. But we aren't given a value of x, so we can't cancel x with any number. We can only cancel x with x. So, we cannot simplify any further.

$\square$

Problem 4.33: If c and d are not zero, then write $\frac{40c^3d^2}{16c^5d}$ in simplest form.

Solution for Problem 4.33: Writing $\frac{40c^3d^2}{16c^5d} = \frac{40}{16} \cdot \frac{c^3}{c^5} \cdot \frac{d^2}{d}$ allows us to simplify piece-by-piece.

We have $\frac{40}{16} = \frac{5 \cdot 8}{2 \cdot 8} = \frac{5}{2}$.

To simplify $\frac{c^3}{c^5}$, we note that there are two more factors of c in the denominator than in the numerator, so

$$\frac{c^3}{c^5} = \frac{1 \cdot c^3}{c^2 \cdot c^3} = \frac{1}{c^2}.$$

In $\frac{d^2}{d}$, there is one more factor of d in the numerator than in the denominator, so $\frac{d^2}{d} = \frac{d \cdot d}{1 \cdot d} = \frac{d}{1}$.

Combining these, we have

$$\frac{40c^3d^2}{16c^5d} = \frac{40}{16} \cdot \frac{c^3}{c^5} \cdot \frac{d^2}{d} = \frac{5}{2} \cdot \frac{1}{c^2} \cdot \frac{d}{1} = \frac{5d}{2c^2}.$$

We can't simplify $\frac{5d}{2c^2}$ any further, since neither the 5 nor the d in the numerator can cancel with anything in the denominator. $\square$

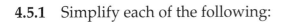

4.5.1 Simplify each of the following:

(a) $\frac{36}{27}$ (b) $\frac{256}{304}$ (c) $\frac{4800}{12000}$ (d) $\frac{1260}{1008}$

4.5.2 Compute each of the following. Express your answer in simplest form.

(a) $\frac{24}{80} \cdot \frac{28}{49}$ (c) $\left(-\frac{84}{125}\right) \cdot \frac{100}{63}$

(b) $\frac{88}{34} \div \frac{44}{51}$ (d) $\frac{400}{39} \div \frac{1300}{9}$

4.5.3 Simplify the following fractions, assuming that a, b, m, and p are nonzero:

(a) $\dfrac{4a^3b}{2ab}$ (b) $\dfrac{8m^7p^{12}}{12m^5p^{15}}$

4.5.4 Express the product $\frac{3}{4} \cdot \frac{4}{5} \cdot \frac{5}{6} \cdot \frac{6}{7} \cdot \frac{7}{8} \cdot \frac{8}{9} \cdot \frac{9}{10} \cdot \frac{10}{11} \cdot \frac{11}{12}$ in simplest form.

4.5.5 Evaluate $\frac{42x^3y^6}{35x^2y^6}$ when $x = \frac{5}{4}$ and $y = \frac{2012}{2013}$. **Hints:** 65

4.6 Comparing Fractions

In this section, we reverse our fraction simplification strategies from the previous section to compare values of fractions.

Problems

Problem 4.34: Which is greater, $\frac{3}{5}$ or $\frac{4}{5}$?

Problem 4.35: In this problem, we determine which is greater, $\frac{3}{5}$ or $\frac{7}{10}$.

(a) What fraction with denominator 10 is equal to $\frac{3}{5}$?

(b) Which is greater, $\frac{3}{5}$ or $\frac{7}{10}$?

Problem 4.36:

(a) Which is greater, $\frac{5}{7}$ or $\frac{8}{11}$?

(b) Which is greater, $\frac{5}{6}$ or $\frac{7}{9}$?

Problem 4.37: Which is greater, $\frac{2}{7}$ or $\frac{2}{5}$?

Problem 4.38: Which is greater, $-\frac{17}{14}$ or $-\frac{41}{35}$?

Problem 4.39: Which is greater, $\frac{541}{539}$ or $\frac{399}{401}$?

Problem 4.34: Which is greater, $\frac{3}{5}$ or $\frac{4}{5}$?

Solution for Problem 4.34: We can see that $\frac{4}{5}$ is greater than $\frac{3}{5}$ by considering the number line. To locate both fractions on the number line, we divide the number line between 0 and 1 into 5 equal pieces. Since $\frac{3}{5}$ is at the right end of the 3rd piece and $\frac{4}{5}$ is at the right end of the 4th piece, we conclude that $\frac{4}{5}$ is to the right of $\frac{3}{5}$.

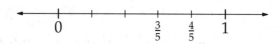

Therefore, $\frac{4}{5}$ is greater than $\frac{3}{5}$. $\square$

In general, if two fractions have the same positive denominator, then the fraction with the greater numerator is the greater of the two fractions.

Problem 4.35: Which is greater, $\frac{3}{5}$ or $\frac{7}{10}$?

Solution for Problem 4.35: We know how to compare two fractions that have the same denominator, so it would be convenient if we could express the two fractions with the same denominator. To do so, we use our fraction simplification strategy from Section 4.5 in reverse. Multiplying $\frac{3}{5}$ by 1 doesn't change the value of the fraction, so we multiply $\frac{3}{5}$ by $\frac{2}{2}$, which equals 1, to express $\frac{3}{5}$ with 10 as the denominator:

$$\frac{3}{5} = \frac{3}{5} \cdot \frac{2}{2} = \frac{3 \cdot 2}{5 \cdot 2} = \frac{6}{10}.$$

Since 7 is greater than 6, we know that $\frac{7}{10}$ is greater than $\frac{6}{10}$, so $\frac{7}{10}$ is greater than $\frac{3}{5}$. $\square$

We often leave out the "multiplying by 1" step when writing a fraction with a new denominator. Instead, we go straight to multiplying the numerator and denominator by the same factor:

$$\frac{3}{5} = \frac{3 \cdot 2}{5 \cdot 2} = \frac{6}{10}.$$

When we write multiple fractions with the same denominator, we say that we write the fractions with a **common denominator**.

Problem 4.36:
(a) Which is greater, $\frac{5}{7}$ or $\frac{8}{11}$?
(b) Which is greater, $\frac{5}{6}$ or $\frac{7}{9}$?

Solution for Problem 4.36:

(a) We know how to compare fractions that have the same denominator. Unfortunately, neither of our denominators in this part is a multiple of the other. So, we change both denominators to make them the same. When writing two fractions with a common denominator, we can always use the product of the fractions' denominators as the common denominator. Writing each fraction with $7 \cdot 11$ as the denominator gives

$$\frac{5}{7} = \frac{5 \cdot 11}{7 \cdot 11} = \frac{55}{77}, \qquad \frac{8}{11} = \frac{8 \cdot 7}{11 \cdot 7} = \frac{56}{77}.$$

Since $\frac{56}{77}$ is greater than $\frac{55}{77}$, we know that $\frac{8}{11}$ is greater than $\frac{5}{7}$.

(b) Once again, we can use the product of the denominators as our common denominator. Writing each fraction with $6 \cdot 9$ as the denominator gives

$$\frac{5}{6} = \frac{5 \cdot 9}{6 \cdot 9} = \frac{45}{54}, \qquad \frac{7}{9} = \frac{7 \cdot 6}{9 \cdot 6} = \frac{42}{54}.$$

Since $\frac{45}{54}$ is greater than $\frac{42}{54}$, we know that $\frac{5}{6}$ is greater than $\frac{7}{9}$.

Thinking back to Section 3.5, we realize that we could have used a smaller common denominator. The common denominator must be a multiple of both 6 and 9. The least common multiple of 6 and 9 is 18, so we can write both $\frac{5}{6}$ and $\frac{7}{9}$ with a denominator of 18:

$$\frac{5}{6} = \frac{5 \cdot 3}{6 \cdot 3} = \frac{15}{18}, \qquad \frac{7}{9} = \frac{7 \cdot 2}{9 \cdot 2} = \frac{14}{18}.$$

Once again, we see that $\frac{5}{6}$ is greater than $\frac{7}{9}$.

□

The **least common denominator** of two or more fractions is the least common multiple of their denominators. In part (a) of Problem 4.36, the least common denominator is 77, while in part (b), the least common denominator is 18.

Problem 4.37: Which is greater, $\frac{2}{7}$ or $\frac{2}{5}$?

Solution for Problem 4.37: The least common denominator of $\frac{2}{7}$ and $\frac{2}{5}$ is 35. Writing both fractions with this denominator gives

$$\frac{2}{7} = \frac{2}{7} \cdot \frac{5}{5} = \frac{10}{35}, \qquad \frac{2}{5} = \frac{2}{5} \cdot \frac{7}{7} = \frac{14}{35},$$

so we see that $\frac{2}{5}$ is greater than $\frac{2}{7}$.

We also could have considered the number line. To locate $\frac{2}{7}$ on the number line, we split the number line between 0 and 1 into 7 equal pieces, and $\frac{2}{7}$ is at the right end of the 2nd piece. Similarly, to locate $\frac{2}{5}$ on the number line, we split the number line between 0 and 1 into 5 equal pieces, and $\frac{2}{5}$ is at the right end of the 2nd piece. We make larger pieces when we make 5 pieces than we do when we make 7 pieces, so $\frac{2}{5}$ is farther from 0 than $\frac{2}{7}$ is from 0. Therefore, $\frac{2}{5}$ is greater than $\frac{2}{7}$. $\square$

In general, if two positive fractions have the same numerator, then the fraction with the smaller denominator is the greater fraction.

Problem 4.38: Which is greater, $-\frac{17}{14}$ or $-\frac{41}{35}$?

Solution for Problem 4.38: Before we even start thinking about common denominators, we note that the numbers in this problem are negative. So, we first have to think about how comparing negative numbers is different from comparing positive numbers. When comparing two positive numbers, the number that is farthest from 0 is the greater number. When comparing two negative numbers, this is reversed! The number closest to 0 is the greater number. For example, -2 is greater than -10.

Now, we're ready to compare the fractions by finding a common denominator. The least common multiple of 14 and 35 is 70, so we write each fraction with 70 as the denominator:

$$-\frac{17}{14} = -\frac{17 \cdot 5}{14 \cdot 5} = -\frac{85}{70}, \qquad -\frac{41}{35} = -\frac{41 \cdot 2}{35 \cdot 2} = -\frac{82}{70}.$$

Since $-\frac{82}{70}$ is closer to 0, it is the greater of these two negative numbers. Therefore, $-\frac{41}{35}$ is greater than $-\frac{17}{14}$. $\square$

Problem 4.39: Which is greater, $\frac{541}{539}$ or $\frac{399}{401}$?

Solution for Problem 4.39: Writing these fractions with a common denominator looks like a pain. Fortunately, we don't have to! Since the numerator of $\frac{541}{539}$ is greater than its denominator, the fraction $\frac{541}{539}$ is greater than 1. Meanwhile, the numerator of $\frac{399}{401}$ is less than its denominator, so $\frac{399}{401}$ is less than 1. Putting these together, $\frac{541}{539}$ must be greater than $\frac{399}{401}$. $\square$

Exercises

4.6.1 In each of the following pairs of numbers, which number is *smaller*?

(a) $\frac{3}{2}$, $\frac{7}{5}$ (b) $\frac{1}{2}$, $-\frac{3}{4}$ (c) $-\frac{2}{5}$, $-\frac{3}{5}$

4.6.2 For each of the following lists of numbers, arrange the numbers in decreasing order (from largest to smallest).

(a) $\frac{1}{2}$, $\frac{3}{4}$, $\frac{5}{12}$ 　　　　　(b) $\frac{3}{4}$, $\frac{2}{3}$, $\frac{5}{8}$ 　　　　　(c) $-\frac{5}{4}$, -3, $\frac{5}{2}$, $-\frac{13}{3}$

4.6.3 Which one of these numbers is less than its reciprocal?

$$-2, \quad -1, \quad 0, \quad 1, \quad 2$$

(Source: AMC 8)

4.6.4 Which number is greater, $\frac{3}{2011}$ or $\frac{3}{2012}$?

4.6.5 Which number is greater, $\frac{19}{30}$ or $\frac{22}{35}$?

4.6.6 Which number is greater, $\frac{506}{101}$ or $\frac{509}{102}$?

4.7 Adding and Subtracting Fractions

We've found fractions on the number line. We multiplied them and divided them. We raised them to powers and compared them to each other. Now, we're ready to add and subtract them. In Section 1.7, we learned that division by a number distributes over addition and subtraction. In other words, if c is not zero, then:

$$(a + b) \div c = (a \div c) + (b \div c),$$
$$(a - b) \div c = (a \div c) - (b \div c).$$

Writing these relationships in terms of fractions, we have the following:

> **Important:** **Division by a number distributes over addition:** If c is not zero, then
> $$\frac{a+b}{c} = \frac{a}{c} + \frac{b}{c}.$$
>
> **Division by a number distributes over subtraction:** If c is not zero, then
> $$\frac{a-b}{c} = \frac{a}{c} - \frac{b}{c}.$$

We'll start with a warning.

> **WARNING!!** To multiply fractions, we multiply the numerators and multiply the denominators. We do **NOT** add fractions by simply adding the numerators and adding the denominators.

For an example why we do not add fractions by adding the numerators and adding the denominators, consider the sum

$$\frac{1}{2} + \frac{1}{2}.$$

If we add the numerators and add the denominators, we get $\frac{1+1}{2+2}$, which equals $\frac{2}{4}$. Simplifying $\frac{2}{4}$ gives $\frac{1}{2}$. But obviously the sum $\frac{1}{2} + \frac{1}{2}$ does not equal $\frac{1}{2}$. The sum of two halves is 1! We can see this by using the "division by a number distributes over addition" rule, which tells us that $\frac{a}{c} + \frac{b}{c} = \frac{a+b}{c}$ when c is nonzero:

$$\frac{1}{2} + \frac{1}{2} = \frac{1+1}{2} = \frac{2}{2} = 1.$$

We also can visualize the sum on the number line. To add $\frac{1}{2} + \frac{1}{2}$, we start at $\frac{1}{2}$ and go to the right a distance of $\frac{1}{2}$, which brings us to 1 on the number line:

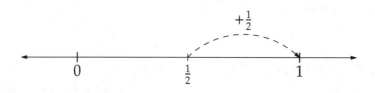

Problems

Problem 4.40: Evaluate each of the following in simplest form:

(a) $\frac{3}{7} + \frac{2}{7}$

(b) $\frac{7}{10} + \frac{9}{10}$

Problem 4.41: Evaluate each of the following in simplest form:

(a) $\frac{17}{18} - \frac{5}{18}$

(b) $-\frac{29}{24} + \frac{23}{24}$

Problem 4.42: Evaluate each of the following in simplest form:

(a) $\frac{1}{3} + \frac{2}{9}$

(b) $\frac{1}{2} - \frac{3}{8}$

Problem 4.43: Evaluate each of the following in simplest form:

(a) $\frac{1}{3} + \frac{1}{4}$

(b) $\frac{15}{24} - \frac{900}{1400}$

(c) $-\frac{2}{3} + 6$

(d) $\frac{6}{5} - \frac{9}{4} + \frac{7}{6}$

Problem 4.44: Megan puts $\frac{3}{4}$ cup of sugar in an empty bowl. When she's not looking, her son takes $\frac{1}{2}$ cup of sugar from the bowl. When Megan notices that some sugar has been removed, she adds another $\frac{2}{3}$ cup of sugar to the bowl. How much sugar is now in the bowl?

Problem 4.45: Jake spends $\frac{1}{5}$ of his year-end bonus on a television and $\frac{1}{3}$ of the bonus on a computer. After these two purchases, he has $735 of his bonus remaining. In this problem, we determine what Jake's bonus was.

(a) What total fraction of Jake's bonus did he spend?

(b) What fraction of Jake's bonus remains?

(c) What was the amount of Jake's bonus?

Problem 4.46: What is the integer closest to $\frac{87}{88} + \frac{24}{23}$?

Problem 4.40: Evaluate each of the following in simplest form:

(a) $\frac{3}{7} + \frac{2}{7}$ (b) $\frac{7}{10} + \frac{9}{10}$

Solution for Problem 4.40:

(a) Because division by a number distributes over addition, we have

$$\frac{3}{7} + \frac{2}{7} = \frac{3+2}{7} = \frac{5}{7}.$$

We can also visualize the relationship on the number line. We start at $\frac{3}{7}$ and move to the right by $\frac{2}{7}$:

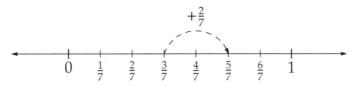

(b) Once again, the denominators are the same, so we can use the distributive property:

$$\frac{7}{10} + \frac{9}{10} = \frac{7+9}{10} = \frac{16}{10} = \frac{8 \cdot 2}{5 \cdot 2} = \frac{8}{5}.$$

□

Problem 4.41: Evaluate each of the following in simplest form:

(a) $\frac{17}{18} - \frac{5}{18}$ (b) $-\frac{29}{24} + \frac{23}{24}$

Solution for Problem 4.41:

(a) The denominators are the same, so we can apply the distributive property:

$$\frac{17}{18} - \frac{5}{18} = \frac{17-5}{18} = \frac{12}{18} = \frac{2}{3}.$$

Again, this makes sense. We take 5 eighteenths away from 17 eighteenths, and we have $17 - 5 = 12$ eighteenths remaining. On the number line, we start at $\frac{17}{18}$ and move to the left by $\frac{5}{18}$:

(b) Here, we have to be careful with the minus sign:

$$-\frac{29}{24} + \frac{23}{24} = \frac{-29}{24} + \frac{23}{24} = \frac{-29 + 23}{24} = \frac{-6}{24} = -\frac{6}{24} = -\frac{1}{4}.$$

□

We've seen that fraction addition and subtraction when the denominators are the same is simply an application of the distributive property. If c is nonzero, we have

$$\frac{a}{c} + \frac{b}{c} = \frac{a+b}{c}, \qquad \frac{a}{c} - \frac{b}{c} = \frac{a-b}{c}.$$

But what if the denominators aren't the same?

Problem 4.42: Evaluate each of the following in simplest form:

(a) $\frac{1}{3} + \frac{2}{9}$ 　　　　　　　　　　　(b) $\frac{1}{2} - \frac{3}{8}$

Solution for Problem 4.42:

(a) We know how to handle fraction addition when the denominators are the same, so let's write the fractions with a common denominator. Since 9 is a multiple of 3, we can write the fractions with a common denominator of 9:

$$\frac{1}{3} + \frac{2}{9} = \frac{1 \cdot 3}{3 \cdot 3} + \frac{2}{9} = \frac{3}{9} + \frac{2}{9} = \frac{3+2}{9} = \frac{5}{9}.$$

(b) We write both fractions with a common denominator of 8:

$$\frac{1}{2} - \frac{3}{8} = \frac{1 \cdot 4}{2 \cdot 4} - \frac{3}{8} = \frac{4}{8} - \frac{3}{8} = \frac{4-3}{8} = \frac{1}{8}.$$

□

Problem 4.43: Evaluate each of the following in simplest form:

(a) $\frac{1}{3} + \frac{1}{4}$ 　　　　　　　　　　　(c) $-\frac{2}{3} + 6$

(b) $\frac{15}{24} - \frac{900}{1400}$ 　　　　　　　　(d) $\frac{6}{5} - \frac{9}{4} + \frac{7}{6}$

Solution for Problem 4.43:

(a) To make the denominators of these fractions the same, we'll have to change the denominators of both fractions. The least common multiple of the denominators (3 and 4) is 12. Writing both fractions with 12 as the denominator gives

$$\frac{1}{3} = \frac{1 \cdot 4}{3 \cdot 4} = \frac{4}{12}, \qquad \frac{1}{4} = \frac{1 \cdot 3}{4 \cdot 3} = \frac{3}{12}.$$

We can add these fractions easily: $\frac{1}{3} + \frac{1}{4} = \frac{4}{12} + \frac{3}{12} = \frac{7}{12}$.

(b) Before trying to find a common denominator, we notice that both $\frac{15}{24}$ and $\frac{900}{1400}$ can be simplified.

> **Concept:** When performing arithmetic with fractions, it's often useful to simplify the fractions first.

We have $\frac{15}{24} = \frac{5 \cdot 3}{8 \cdot 3} = \frac{5}{8}$ and $\frac{900}{1400} = \frac{9 \cdot 100}{14 \cdot 100} = \frac{9}{14}$, so we can simplify the given expression to $\frac{5}{8} - \frac{9}{14}$. The least common multiple of 8 and 14 is 56. Writing $\frac{5}{8}$ and $\frac{9}{14}$ with 56 as the denominator gives

$$\frac{5}{8} = \frac{5 \cdot 7}{8 \cdot 7} = \frac{35}{56}, \qquad \frac{9}{14} = \frac{9 \cdot 4}{14 \cdot 4} = \frac{36}{56}.$$

So, we have $\frac{5}{8} - \frac{9}{14} = \frac{35}{56} - \frac{36}{56} = -\frac{1}{56}$.

(c) We know how to add and subtract fractions, and we know how to add and subtract integers. But how do we combine a fraction with an integer? Any number equals itself divided by 1, so we have $6 = 6 \div 1 = \frac{6}{1}$.

> **Concept:** We can think of an integer as a fraction with 1 as the denominator.

Writing 6 as $\frac{6}{1}$, our problem becomes $-\frac{2}{3} + \frac{6}{1}$. Now we can treat it just like the others we have solved. Using 3 as our common denominator, we have

$$-\frac{2}{3} + \frac{6}{1} = \frac{-2}{3} + \frac{18}{3} = \frac{-2 + 18}{3} = \frac{16}{3}.$$

(d) *Solution 1: Two fractions at a time.* We start with the first two fractions. The least common multiple of 5 and 4 is 20, so we write the first two fractions with 20 as the denominator:

$$\frac{6}{5} = \frac{6 \cdot 4}{5 \cdot 4} = \frac{24}{20}, \qquad \frac{9}{4} = \frac{9 \cdot 5}{4 \cdot 5} = \frac{45}{20}.$$

So, we have $\frac{6}{5} - \frac{9}{4} = \frac{24}{20} - \frac{45}{20} = -\frac{21}{20}$. Therefore,

$$\frac{6}{5} - \frac{9}{4} + \frac{7}{6} = -\frac{21}{20} + \frac{7}{6}.$$

The least common denominator of $\frac{21}{20}$ and $\frac{7}{6}$ is the least common multiple of 20 and 6, which is 60. Writing both fractions with this denominator gives

$$-\frac{21}{20} + \frac{7}{6} = -\frac{21 \cdot 3}{20 \cdot 3} + \frac{7 \cdot 10}{6 \cdot 10} = -\frac{63}{60} + \frac{70}{60} = \frac{-63 + 70}{60} = \frac{7}{60}.$$

Solution 2: All three fractions at once. We find a common denominator of all three fractions. The least common multiple of 5, 4, and 6 is 60, so we write each fraction with 60 as the denominator:

$$\frac{6}{5} = \frac{6 \cdot 12}{5 \cdot 12} = \frac{72}{60}, \qquad \frac{9}{4} = \frac{9 \cdot 15}{4 \cdot 15} = \frac{135}{60}, \qquad \frac{7}{6} = \frac{7 \cdot 10}{6 \cdot 10} = \frac{70}{60}.$$

This gives us $\frac{6}{5} - \frac{9}{4} + \frac{7}{6} = \frac{72}{60} - \frac{135}{60} + \frac{70}{60} = \frac{72-135+70}{60} = \frac{7}{60}$.

□

> **Important:** To add or subtract fractions, write the fractions with a common denominator, and then apply the fact that division by a number distributes over addition and subtraction.

Problem 4.44: Megan puts $\frac{3}{4}$ cup of sugar in an empty bowl. When she's not looking, her son takes $\frac{1}{2}$ cup of sugar from the bowl. When Megan notices that some sugar has been removed, she adds another $\frac{2}{3}$ cup of sugar to the bowl. How much sugar is now in the bowl?

Solution for Problem 4.44: After her son takes $\frac{1}{2}$ cup, there is $\frac{3}{4} - \frac{1}{2}$ cup of sugar in the bowl. Subtracting, we find that there is $\frac{3}{4} - \frac{1}{2} = \frac{3}{4} - \frac{2}{4} = \frac{1}{4}$ cup in the bowl. Then, Megan adds another $\frac{2}{3}$ cup, so there is $\frac{1}{4} + \frac{2}{3}$ cup in the bowl. Adding these fractions gives

$$\frac{1}{4} + \frac{2}{3} = \frac{1 \cdot 3}{4 \cdot 3} + \frac{2 \cdot 4}{3 \cdot 4} = \frac{3}{12} + \frac{8}{12} = \frac{11}{12}$$

cup of sugar in the bowl.

We also could have combined all three fractions at once. After Megan's two additions and her son's subtraction, the number of cups in the bowl is $\frac{3}{4} - \frac{1}{2} + \frac{2}{3}$. The least common denominator of these three fractions is 12, and the number of cups in the bowl is

$$\frac{3}{4} - \frac{1}{2} + \frac{2}{3} = \frac{9}{12} - \frac{6}{12} + \frac{8}{12} = \frac{9-6+8}{12} = \frac{11}{12}.$$

□

Problem 4.45: Jake spends $\frac{1}{5}$ of his year-end bonus on a television and $\frac{1}{3}$ of the bonus on a computer. After these two purchases, he has \$735 of his bonus remaining. How much was Jake's bonus?

Solution for Problem 4.45: If we can figure out what fraction of Jake's bonus the remaining $735 represents, then we can figure out how much his bonus was. The total fraction of his bonus that he spent on the television and the computer was

$$\frac{1}{5} + \frac{1}{3} = \frac{3}{15} + \frac{5}{15} = \frac{8}{15}.$$

He started with 1 whole bonus and spent $\frac{8}{15}$ of the bonus, so $1 - \frac{8}{15}$ is the fraction of his bonus that remains. Since $1 - \frac{8}{15} = \frac{15}{15} - \frac{8}{15} = \frac{7}{15}$, the $735 he has left is $\frac{7}{15}$ of his original bonus.

We present two ways to finish from here:

Method 1: Fraction division. Since $\frac{7}{15}$ of his bonus is $735, his bonus is the number that goes in the box in the equation:

$$\frac{7}{15} \cdot \boxed{} = \$735.$$

So, we divide to find that the original bonus was

$$\$735 \div \frac{7}{15} = \$735 \cdot \frac{15}{7} = \frac{\$735 \cdot 15}{7} = \frac{\$735}{7} \cdot 15 = \$105 \cdot 15 = \$1575.$$

Method 2: Clever scaling. 7 fifteenths of Jake's bonus is $735, so 1 fifteenth of his bonus is $735 \div 7 = \$105$. We can think of this $105 as one of 15 equal pieces of his bonus, so his whole bonus was $15 \cdot (\$105) = \$1575$. □

Problem 4.46: What is the integer closest to $\frac{87}{88} + \frac{24}{23}$?

Solution for Problem 4.46: Rather than cranking through our process for adding fractions, we remember that fractions are numbers. The number $\frac{87}{88}$ is just a tiny bit less than 1 and $\frac{24}{23}$ is just a tiny bit more than 1. So, we expect their sum to be very close to 2. We find that

$$\frac{87}{88} + \frac{24}{23} = \left(1 - \frac{1}{88}\right) + \left(1 + \frac{1}{23}\right) = 2 + \frac{1}{23} - \frac{1}{88}.$$

Since $\frac{1}{23}$ is greater than $\frac{1}{88}$, we know that $2 + \frac{1}{23} - \frac{1}{88}$ is between 2 and $2 + \frac{1}{23}$. So, the integer closest to $\frac{87}{88} + \frac{24}{23}$ is 2. □

Exercises ▶

4.7.1 Compute each of the following. Express each answer in simplest form.

(a) $\frac{2}{3} + \frac{3}{4}$

(b) $\frac{9}{8} - \frac{11}{12}$

(c) $\frac{3100}{2700} + \frac{55}{66} - \frac{888}{999}$

(d) $2^{-1} + 3^{-1}$

(e) $\frac{24}{16} + \frac{15}{9} - \frac{7}{6}$

(f) $\frac{8}{2 - \frac{2}{3}}$

(g) $\frac{3}{4} + 6 - \frac{7}{2}$

(h) $\dfrac{\frac{2}{3} + \frac{5}{6}}{\frac{3}{4} - \frac{1}{2}}$

4.7.2 What is the reciprocal of $\frac{1}{2} + \frac{1}{5}$?

4.7.3 How much greater is $\frac{2003}{25} + 25$ than $\frac{2003+25}{25}$? *(Source: MOEMS)*

4.7.4 Compute each of the following sums in simplest form:

(a) $\frac{1}{1\cdot 2} + \frac{1}{2\cdot 3}$.

(b) $\frac{1}{1\cdot 2} + \frac{1}{2\cdot 3} + \frac{1}{3\cdot 4}$.

(c) $\frac{1}{1\cdot 2} + \frac{1}{2\cdot 3} + \frac{1}{3\cdot 4} + \frac{1}{4\cdot 5}$.

(d) $\frac{1}{1\cdot 2} + \frac{1}{2\cdot 3} + \frac{1}{3\cdot 4} + \frac{1}{4\cdot 5} + \frac{1}{5\cdot 6}$.

4.7.5 Express $\frac{2}{3} \cdot \frac{4}{5} + \frac{2}{3} \cdot \frac{11}{10}$ in simplest form.

4.7.6 What is the sum of the reciprocals of the positive divisors of 12? Express your answer as a fraction in simplest form.

4.7.7

(a) What number must we add to $\frac{3}{10}$ to get $\frac{7}{15}$?

(b) What number must we subtract $\frac{5}{9}$ from to get $\frac{1}{6}$?

(c) What number must we subtract from $\frac{5}{6}$ to get $\frac{1}{10}$?

4.7.8 At Clover View Junior High, one half of the students go home on the school bus. One fourth go home by automobile. One tenth go home on their bicycles. The rest walk home. What fraction of the students walk home? *(Source: AMC 8)*

4.7.9 Consider the sum $\frac{1}{4} + \frac{1}{4}$. We have $\frac{1}{4} + \frac{1}{4} = \frac{2}{4} = \frac{1}{2}$. Notice that the sum, when written in simplest form, has a smaller denominator than either of the two fractions we originally added. Find two fractions in simplest form with *different denominators* such that the sum of the fractions, written in simplest form, has a smaller denominator than either of the original two fractions.

4.8 Mixed Numbers

On a construction site, you'll probably never hear something like, "Trim thirty-seven fourths inches off this!" After all, how long is $\frac{37}{4}$ inches? What you'll probably hear instead is "Trim nine and a quarter inches off this!" For most people, a length of "nine and a quarter inches" is much easier to understand than "thirty-seven fourths inches."

We have a special name for mixes of an integer and a fraction like "nine and a quarter." We call these **mixed numbers**, and we write them with the integer immediately followed by the fraction, with no space between. The integer in a mixed number is called the **integer part** and the fraction is the **fractional part**. So, in the mixed number $9\frac{1}{4}$, the 9 is the integer part and the $\frac{1}{4}$ is the fractional part. The fractional part of a mixed number is between 0 and 1.

So, the mixed number "nine and a quarter" is written $9\frac{1}{4}$, and this stands for $9 + \frac{1}{4}$.

WARNING!! The number $9\frac{1}{4}$ is not $9 \cdot \frac{1}{4}$.
☢

When asked a question in terms of mixed numbers, we usually answer as a mixed number rather than as a fraction.

Problems ▶

Problem 4.47: Convert $4\frac{2}{5}$ to a fraction.

Problem 4.48:

(a) Convert $\frac{7}{2}$ to a mixed number.

(b) Convert $\frac{137}{12}$ to a mixed number.

Problem 4.49: Express each of the following as a mixed number or as the negation of a mixed number.

(a) $7 + \frac{1}{3}$

(b) $7 - \frac{1}{3}$

(c) $-7 - \frac{1}{3}$

(d) $-7 + \frac{1}{3}$

Problem 4.50:

(a) What is $5\frac{3}{5} + 6\frac{1}{5}$?

(b) What is $4\frac{2}{3} + 8\frac{2}{3}$?

(c) What is $8\frac{2}{5} - 3\frac{1}{5}$?

(d) What is $6\frac{4}{7} - 8\frac{2}{7}$?

Problem 4.51:

(a) What is $12\frac{2}{3} + 9\frac{1}{2}$?

(b) What is $18\frac{1}{2} - 6\frac{5}{6}$?

Problem 4.52:

(a) What is $3 \cdot 4\frac{3}{5}$?

(b) What is $\frac{4}{5} \cdot 2\frac{1}{2}$?

(c) What is $7\frac{1}{3} \div 2$?

Problem 4.53: Between what two consecutive integers is $\frac{1603}{80} - \frac{62}{7}$?

Problem 4.54: Jenna has outgrown her pants and gives them to her sister. The legs of the pants were $25\frac{1}{4}$ inches long, but her sister wears pants in which the legs are $22\frac{1}{2}$ inches long. By how many inches will her sister have to reduce the legs of the pants to make them fit?

Problem 4.47: Convert $4\frac{2}{5}$ to a fraction.

Solution for Problem 4.47: Writing $4\frac{2}{5}$ as $4 + \frac{2}{5}$, we have

$$4\frac{2}{5} = 4 + \frac{2}{5} = \frac{20}{5} + \frac{2}{5} = \frac{22}{5}.$$

$\square$

Problem 4.48:

(a) Convert $\frac{7}{2}$ to a mixed number.

(b) Convert $\frac{137}{12}$ to a mixed number.

Solution for Problem 4.48:

(a) We must write $\frac{7}{2}$ as an integer plus a fraction between 0 and 1. We know that $\frac{6}{2}$ is an integer, so we write

$$\frac{7}{2} = \frac{6}{2} + \frac{1}{2} = 3 + \frac{1}{2} = 3\frac{1}{2}.$$

(b) Most occurrences of mixed numbers involve fractions with small denominators, so usually a little number sense is all we need to perform conversions between fractions and mixed numbers. But for fractions involving larger numbers, we can turn to division.

The integer part of the mixed number must be as large as possible without being greater than $\frac{137}{12}$. To find this integer, we divide: 137 divided by 12 has a quotient of 11 and a remainder of 5. But what is the fractional part of our mixed number? To see how the remainder of our division tells us the fractional part of the mixed number, we turn to the number line.

To locate $\frac{137}{12}$ on the number line, we divide the number line between each pair of consecutive integers into 12 equal pieces. If we start counting from 0, the number $\frac{137}{12}$ is at the right end of the 137th of these pieces.

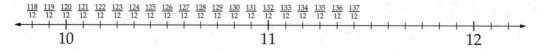

The quotient of our division is the final integer we pass while counting out these pieces, and the remainder tells us how many pieces we must go past 11 to reach $\frac{137}{12}$. So, we have $\frac{137}{12} = \frac{132}{12} + \frac{5}{12} = 11 + \frac{5}{12} = 11\frac{5}{12}$.

$\square$

In general, to convert a fraction to a mixed number, we divide the denominator into the numerator to find a quotient and remainder. The quotient is the integer part of the mixed number. The denominator of the fractional part of the mixed number is the same as the denominator of the original fraction, and the numerator of the fractional part is the remainder of our division.

> **Problem 4.49:** Express each of the following as a mixed number or as the negation of a mixed number.
>
> (a) $7 + \frac{1}{3}$ (b) $7 - \frac{1}{3}$ (c) $-7 - \frac{1}{3}$ (d) $-7 + \frac{1}{3}$

Solution for Problem 4.49:

(a) By the definition of a mixed number, we have $7 + \frac{1}{3} = 7\frac{1}{3}$.

(b) We can take 1 from 7 to write $7 - \frac{1}{3}$ as the sum of an integer and a fraction between 0 and 1:

$$7 - \frac{1}{3} = 6 + \left(1 - \frac{1}{3}\right) = 6 + \frac{2}{3} = 6\frac{2}{3}.$$

We can also use the number line to see that $7 - \frac{1}{3} = 6\frac{2}{3}$:

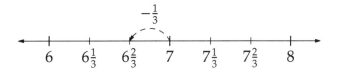

Going left by $\frac{1}{3}$ from 7 takes us to $6\frac{2}{3}$, so $7 - \frac{1}{3} = 6\frac{2}{3}$.

(c) We can distribute a negation to write $-(x + y)$ as $-x - y$. Here, we go in the other direction:

$$-7 - \frac{1}{3} = -\left(7 + \frac{1}{3}\right) = -\left(7\frac{1}{3}\right) = -7\frac{1}{3}.$$

> **WARNING!!** In a negation of a mixed number, the negation applies to both the integer and the fraction. So, for example,
>
> $$-7\frac{1}{3} = -\left(7\frac{1}{3}\right) = -\left(7 + \frac{1}{3}\right) = -7 - \frac{1}{3}.$$

We can also visualize $-7 - \frac{1}{3}$ on the number line:

Going left by $\frac{1}{3}$ from -7 takes us to $-7\frac{1}{3}$, so $-7 - \frac{1}{3} = -7\frac{1}{3}$.

(d) This one's a bit tricky. We'll start with the same strategy as in part (c):

$$-7 + \frac{1}{3} = -\left(7 - \frac{1}{3}\right).$$

We have $7 - \frac{1}{3} = 6\frac{2}{3}$ from part (b), so

$$-7 + \frac{1}{3} = -\left(7 - \frac{1}{3}\right) = -\left(6\frac{2}{3}\right) = -6\frac{2}{3}.$$

As in part (c), we can also use the number line to visualize $-7 + \frac{1}{3}$:

Going right by $\frac{1}{3}$ from -7 takes us to $-6\frac{2}{3}$, so $-7 + \frac{1}{3} = -6\frac{2}{3}$.

$\Box$

Problem 4.50:
(a) What is $5\frac{3}{5} + 6\frac{1}{5}$?
(b) What is $4\frac{2}{3} + 8\frac{2}{3}$?
(c) What is $8\frac{2}{5} - 3\frac{1}{5}$?
(d) What is $6\frac{4}{7} - 8\frac{2}{7}$?

Solution for Problem 4.50:

(a) Since $5\frac{3}{5} = 5 + \frac{3}{5}$ and $6\frac{1}{5} = 6 + \frac{1}{5}$, we can add the integer parts and the fractional parts separately:

$$5\frac{3}{5} + 6\frac{1}{5} = \left(5 + \frac{3}{5}\right) + \left(6 + \frac{1}{5}\right) = (5 + 6) + \left(\frac{3}{5} + \frac{1}{5}\right) = 11 + \frac{4}{5} = 11\frac{4}{5}.$$

(b) Again, we add the integer parts and the fractional parts separately:

$$4\frac{2}{3} + 8\frac{2}{3} = (4 + 8) + \left(\frac{2}{3} + \frac{2}{3}\right) = 12 + \frac{4}{3}.$$

We can write $12 + \frac{4}{3}$ as a mixed number by first writing $\frac{4}{3}$ as the mixed number $1\frac{1}{3}$:

$$12 + \frac{4}{3} = 12 + \frac{3}{3} + \frac{1}{3} = 12 + 1\frac{1}{3} = 13\frac{1}{3}.$$

We could have also thought about this problem in steps, adding $8\frac{2}{3}$ to $4\frac{2}{3}$ by first adding 8 and then adding $\frac{2}{3}$. Adding 8 to $4\frac{2}{3}$ gives $12\frac{2}{3}$. Adding $\frac{2}{3}$ to $12\frac{2}{3}$ is easy to visualize on the number line as taking two steps of length $\frac{1}{3}$ to the right of $12\frac{2}{3}$. The first step takes us to 13 and the second to $13\frac{1}{3}$.

(c) We handle subtraction just like addition. We work with the integers and fractions separately. We have to be careful about our signs though:

$$8\frac{2}{5} - 3\frac{1}{5} = \left(8 + \frac{2}{5}\right) - \left(3 + \frac{1}{5}\right) = 8 + \frac{2}{5} - 3 - \frac{1}{5}.$$

Grouping the integers and grouping the fractions gives

$$8 + \frac{2}{5} - 3 - \frac{1}{5} = (8 - 3) + \left(\frac{2}{5} - \frac{1}{5}\right) = 5 + \frac{1}{5} = 5\frac{1}{5}.$$

We could have also thought about this problem in steps, much as we tackled the previous part. To subtract $3\frac{1}{5}$ from $8\frac{2}{5}$, we subtract 3 first, and then subtract $\frac{1}{5}$ from the result. Subtracting 3 from $8\frac{2}{5}$ gives $5\frac{2}{5}$, and subtracting $\frac{1}{5}$ from this gives $5\frac{1}{5}$.

(d) Since $8\frac{2}{7}$ is greater than $6\frac{4}{7}$, the result in this problem is negative. So, we'll have to be particularly careful about signs.

Working with the integers and fractions separately gives

$$6\frac{4}{7} - 8\frac{2}{7} = 6 + \frac{4}{7} - 8 - \frac{2}{7} = (6 - 8) + \left(\frac{4}{7} - \frac{2}{7}\right) = -2 + \frac{2}{7} = -1\frac{5}{7}.$$

(If you don't see why $-2 + \frac{2}{7}$ equals $-1\frac{5}{7}$, review Problem 4.49.)

See if you can also compute $6\frac{4}{7} - 8\frac{2}{7}$ by subtracting $8\frac{2}{7}$ from $6\frac{4}{7}$ in two steps, as we did in the previous two parts.

$\square$

Problem 4.51:

(a) What is $12\frac{2}{3} + 9\frac{1}{2}$?

(b) What is $18\frac{1}{2} - 6\frac{5}{6}$?

Solution for Problem 4.51:

(a) We have $12 + 9 = 21$ and $\frac{2}{3} + \frac{1}{2} = \frac{4}{6} + \frac{3}{6} = \frac{7}{6} = 1\frac{1}{6}$, so

$$12\frac{2}{3} + 9\frac{1}{2} = (12 + 9) + \left(\frac{2}{3} + \frac{1}{2}\right) = 21 + 1\frac{1}{6} = 22\frac{1}{6}.$$

(b) Again, we work with the integers and the fractions separately. Since $\frac{1}{2} - \frac{5}{6} = \frac{3}{6} - \frac{5}{6} = -\frac{2}{6} = -\frac{1}{3}$, we have

$$18\frac{1}{2} - 6\frac{5}{6} = 18 + \frac{1}{2} - 6 - \frac{5}{6} = (18 - 6) + \left(\frac{1}{2} - \frac{5}{6}\right) = 12 - \frac{1}{3} = 11\frac{2}{3}.$$

□

Problem 4.52:

(a) What is $3 \cdot 4\frac{3}{5}$?

(b) What is $\frac{4}{5} \cdot 2\frac{1}{2}$?

(c) What is $7\frac{1}{3} \div 2$?

Solution for Problem 4.52:

(a) *Solution 1: Convert the mixed number to a fraction.* We know how to multiply fractions, so we write $4\frac{3}{5}$ as $4 + \frac{3}{5} = \frac{20}{5} + \frac{3}{5} = \frac{23}{5}$. We then have

$$3 \cdot 4\frac{3}{5} = 3 \cdot \frac{23}{5} = \frac{69}{5}.$$

Dividing 69 by 5 gives a quotient of 13 and remainder of 4, so $3 \cdot 4\frac{3}{5} = \frac{69}{5} = 13\frac{4}{5}$.

Solution 2: Use the distributive property. We have

$$3 \cdot 4\frac{3}{5} = 3\left(4 + \frac{3}{5}\right) = 3 \cdot 4 + 3 \cdot \frac{3}{5} = 12 + \frac{9}{5} = 12 + 1\frac{4}{5} = 13\frac{4}{5}.$$

> **Concept:** There's not a "right way" to work with fractions and mixed numbers. Choose the approaches you're most comfortable with, and feel free to use different strategies for different types of problems.

(b) Writing $2\frac{1}{2}$ as $2 + \frac{1}{2} = \frac{4}{2} + \frac{1}{2} = \frac{5}{2}$ gives us $\frac{4}{5} \cdot 2\frac{1}{2} = \frac{4}{5} \cdot \frac{5}{2} = \frac{4}{2} \cdot \frac{5}{5} = 2.$

(c) Since $7\frac{1}{3} = 7 + \frac{1}{3} = \frac{21}{3} + \frac{1}{3} = \frac{22}{3}$, we have $7\frac{1}{3} \div 2 = \frac{22}{3} \div 2 = \frac{22}{3} \cdot \frac{1}{2} = \frac{11}{3} = 3\frac{2}{3}.$

□

Problem 4.53: Between what two consecutive integers is $\frac{1603}{80} - \frac{62}{7}$?

Solution for Problem 4.53: Rather than finding a common denominator and subtracting, we get a sense for how large $\frac{1603}{80}$ and $\frac{62}{7}$ are by thinking of them as mixed numbers.

> **Concept:** We often communicate fractions greater than 1 as mixed numbers. We do so because mixed numbers are better than fractions for giving people a sense of how large a number is.

Since $1600 = 80 \cdot 20$, we see that $\frac{1603}{80} = 20\frac{3}{80}$. We also have $\frac{62}{7} = 8\frac{6}{7}$, so

$$\frac{1603}{80} - \frac{62}{7} = 20\frac{3}{80} - 8\frac{6}{7}.$$

So, we are subtracting a number that is a little less than 9 from a number that is a little more than 20. We therefore know that the difference is greater than 11, and we expect that the difference is less than 12. To make sure the difference is less than 12, we note that

$$20\frac{3}{80} - 8\frac{6}{7} = 20 + \frac{3}{80} - \left(9 - \frac{1}{7}\right) = 20 - 9 + \frac{3}{80} + \frac{1}{7} = 11 + \frac{3}{80} + \frac{1}{7}.$$

Both $\frac{3}{80}$ and $\frac{1}{7}$ are less than $\frac{1}{2}$, so $11 + \frac{3}{80} + \frac{1}{7}$ is between 11 and 12. Therefore, $\frac{1603}{80} - \frac{62}{7}$ is between 11 and 12. □

Problem 4.54: Jenna has outgrown her pants and gives them to her sister. The legs of the pants were $25\frac{1}{4}$ inches long, but her sister wears pants in which the legs are $22\frac{1}{2}$ inches long. By how many inches will her sister have to reduce the legs of the pants to make them fit?

Solution for Problem 4.54: Jenna's sister needs the legs to be $22\frac{1}{2}$ inches long, but the legs are currently $25\frac{1}{4}$ inches. So, the pants are $25\frac{1}{4} - 22\frac{1}{2}$ inches too long. We subtract the integer parts and the fractional parts separately:

$$25\frac{1}{4} - 22\frac{1}{2} = (25 - 22) + \left(\frac{1}{4} - \frac{1}{2}\right) = 3 + \left(\frac{1}{4} - \frac{2}{4}\right) = 3 + \left(-\frac{1}{4}\right) = 2\frac{3}{4}.$$

So, the pants must be reduced by $2\frac{3}{4}$ inches. □

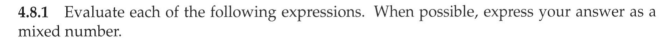

Exercises

4.8.1 Evaluate each of the following expressions. When possible, express your answer as a mixed number.

(a) $4\frac{7}{8} - 1\frac{3}{4}$

(b) $3\frac{1}{3} - 7\frac{2}{9}$

(c) $19\frac{3}{20} - 9\frac{13}{15}$

(d) $18 - \left(6\frac{1}{2} + 5\frac{1}{3}\right)$

(e) $5\frac{5}{12} \cdot 24$

(f) $1\frac{1}{2} \cdot \left(6\frac{2}{3} - 4\frac{4}{9}\right)$

(g) $5\frac{1}{3} + 2\frac{1}{3} \div 3\frac{1}{2}$

(h) $3\frac{2}{3} \div \left(-6\frac{7}{8}\right)$

4.8.2 Find the largest integer that is smaller than the sum $2\frac{1}{2} + 3\frac{1}{3} + 4\frac{1}{4} + 5\frac{1}{5} + 6\frac{1}{6}$.

4.8.3 Evaluate $(7a^2 - 11a + 3)(3a - 4)$ for $a = 1\frac{1}{3}$.

4.8.4 Peggy weighed $136\frac{3}{4}$ pounds before basketball season and $131\frac{7}{8}$ pounds after the season. How many pounds did she lose during the season? *(Source: MATHCOUNTS)*

4.8.5 I have two recipes for cake. The first recipe calls for $2\frac{1}{2}$ cups of flour and the second calls for $3\frac{1}{3}$ cups of flour. How much flour do I need to make three of each cake?

4.8.6 Out of each hour of TV programming, $6\frac{1}{2}$ minutes are allocated to commercials. What fraction of each hour is dedicated to television programs? *(Source: MATHCOUNTS)*

4.9 Summary

Definition: If a is a number and b is a nonzero number, then the **fraction** $\frac{a}{b}$ equals $a \div b$. In the fraction $\frac{a}{b}$, the **numerator** is a and the **denominator** is b.

A fraction is in **simplest form** if its numerator and denominator have no positive common divisor besides 1.

We perform multiplication, division, and exponentiation with fractions according to the following rules:

- **Multiplication of fractions.** If b and d are nonzero, then $\frac{a}{b} \cdot \frac{c}{d} = \frac{ac}{bd}$.

- **Reciprocation.** If a and b are nonzero, the reciprocal of $\frac{a}{b}$ is $\frac{b}{a}$, so $\left(\frac{a}{b}\right)^{-1} = \frac{b}{a}$.

- **Division by a fraction.** If b, c, and d are nonzero, then $\frac{a}{b} \div \frac{c}{d} = \frac{a}{b} \cdot \frac{d}{c} = \frac{ad}{bc}$.

- **Exponentiation.** If a and b are nonzero, and n is an integer, then $\left(\frac{a}{b}\right)^{n} = \frac{a^{n}}{b^{n}}$.

- **Negation in exponent.** If a and b are nonzero, and n is an integer, then $\left(\frac{a}{b}\right)^{-n} = \left(\frac{b}{a}\right)^{n}$.

We perform fraction addition and subtraction by writing the fractions with a **common denominator**, and then applying the distributive property. That is, if c is nonzero, we have

$$\frac{a}{c} + \frac{b}{c} = \frac{a+b}{c} \qquad \text{and} \qquad \frac{a}{c} - \frac{b}{c} = \frac{a-b}{c}.$$

We sometimes write the sum of a positive integer and a fraction between 0 and 1 as a **mixed number**, which consists of the integer immediately followed by the fraction. For example, $3 + \frac{1}{3}$ can be written as $3\frac{1}{3}$.

4.55 Evaluate each of the following in simplest form.

(a) $\frac{3}{14} + \frac{5}{7} - \frac{1}{21}$

(e) $\left(\frac{3}{4}\right)^3$

(i) $\frac{50-(-3)^3}{\left(\frac{2}{7}\right)^{-1}}$

(b) $\frac{64}{96} - \frac{63}{84}$

(f) $\left(\frac{18}{27}\right)^{-4}$

(j) $\left(5\frac{1}{3} - 2\frac{1}{4}\right) + \left(5\frac{1}{4} - 3\frac{1}{3}\right)$

(c) $\frac{36}{48} \cdot \frac{44}{66} \cdot \frac{16}{56}$

(g) $6\left(\frac{7}{12} - \frac{2}{3} + \frac{1}{4}\right)$

(k) $\left(-1\frac{1}{4}\right)^2$

(d) $\frac{27\cdot14\cdot35}{42\cdot9\cdot28\cdot24}$

(h) $\frac{31+71+111}{1+3+5} \cdot \frac{5+15+25}{111+71+31}$

(l) $6\left(11\frac{2}{3} + 4\frac{1}{2}\right)$

4.56 Evaluate $\frac{3+x(3+2x)-3^2}{x-5+x^2}$ when $x = -4$.

4.57 What is the value of $\frac{1}{2} \cdot 4 \cdot \frac{1}{8} \cdot 16 \cdot \frac{1}{32} \cdot 64 \cdot \frac{1}{128} \cdot 256$?

4.58 Find the value of $\frac{1}{6}$ of $\frac{2}{7}$ of $\frac{1}{2}$ of 168.

4.59 A woman begins her work at 10:20 a.m. and estimates that it will take $5\frac{9}{10}$ hours to finish. At what time does she expect to finish? *(Source: MATHCOUNTS)*

4.60 Which number is greater, 99 or $99 \div \frac{101}{102}$?

4.61 What is the sum $2\frac{1}{5} + 3\frac{1}{3} + 5\frac{1}{2}$?

4.62 What is the product $\frac{3}{2} \times \frac{4}{3} \times \frac{5}{4} \times \cdots \times \frac{2012}{2011}$?

4.63 Simplify $\frac{\frac{1}{2} \cdot \frac{2}{3} \cdot \frac{3}{4}}{\frac{6}{8} \cdot \frac{6}{9} \cdot \frac{1}{2}}$.

4.64 Kory pays $\frac{1}{3}$ of his income in tax. He then spends $\frac{4}{5}$ of what remains after tax, and places the rest into a savings account. What fraction of his income does he put in his savings account?

4.65 Find the value of $\frac{xy}{7x+3y}$ when $x = \frac{3}{7}$ and $y = \frac{4}{3}$.

4.66 For each of the following lists of numbers, arrange the numbers in increasing order (from smallest to largest).

(a) $\frac{3}{8}, \frac{7}{16}, -\frac{13}{32}, \frac{23}{64}$

(b) $\frac{9}{7}, \frac{5}{4}, \frac{14}{11}$

(c) $\frac{199}{400}, \frac{100}{199}, \frac{1}{2}$

4.67 Which integer is closest to the quotient $\frac{725}{60} \div \frac{25}{6}$?

4.68 Compute $2\left(1 - \frac{1}{2}\right) + 3\left(1 - \frac{1}{3}\right) + 4\left(1 - \frac{1}{4}\right) + \cdots + 10\left(1 - \frac{1}{10}\right)$. *(Source: AMC 8)*

4.69 Sam purchased $3\frac{1}{4}$ pounds of cheese. He used half of the purchased cheese for a casserole and $\frac{1}{4}$ pound for sandwiches. Express as a mixed number the number of pounds of cheese he has left. *(Source: MATHCOUNTS)*

4.70 List every fraction that satisfies all four of the following conditions:

(i) The fraction is in simplest form.

(ii) The fraction is greater than $\frac{1}{6}$.

(iii) The reciprocal of the fraction is an integer.

(iv) The numerator of the fraction is positive.

4.71 Evaluate $\frac{3}{19} \cdot 95 - \frac{3}{19} \cdot 57$.

4.72 Simplify the product $\frac{15}{42}\left(-\frac{63}{55}\right)\left(\frac{3}{2}\right)^{-2}\left(\frac{11}{2}\right)^{2}$.

4.73 Maya starts with 400 pennies. She then gives $\frac{3}{5}$ of her pennies to her brother Mitch, and then gives $\frac{3}{4}$ of her remaining pennies to her mother. How many pennies does Maya have left?

4.74 Express as a fraction in simplest form: $\frac{9}{5}\left(3\frac{1}{3} \cdot \frac{1}{4} - \frac{10}{12} \cdot \frac{1}{8}\right)$.

4.75 Express as a single fraction: $\frac{7}{19} \cdot \frac{13}{44} + \frac{7}{19} \cdot \frac{19}{44} + \frac{7}{19} \cdot \frac{25}{44} + \frac{7}{19} \cdot \frac{31}{44}$. *(Source: MOEMS)*

4.76 Which is greater, $99 \cdot 2\frac{1}{49}$ or 200?

4.77 The reciprocals of what three different positive integers have sum equal to 1?

4.78 If $12\frac{2}{3}$ feet of steel tubing are needed to make one kitchen stool, how many feet of tubing are needed to make 300 stools? *(Source: MATHCOUNTS)*

4.79 The reciprocal of 5 plus the reciprocal of 7 is the reciprocal of what mixed number?

Challenge Problems

4.80 Solve each of the following problems without writing anything.

(a) Which is greater, $\frac{23}{44}$ or $\frac{33}{64}$? **Hints:** 90

(b) Which is greater, $\frac{52}{53}$ or $\frac{97}{98}$?

4.81 Evaluate in simplest form: $\dfrac{\left(\frac{6}{5}\right)^{3}\left(\frac{25}{36}\right)^{4}}{\left(\frac{5}{6}\right)^{4}}$.

4.82 Two-fifths of the students in Central Middle School are boys. One-third of the girls have blond hair and one-quarter of the boys have blond hair.

(a) What fraction of the students in Central Middle School have blond hair? **Hints:** 42

(b) If 36 of the students in Central Middle School have blond hair, then how many students total does Central Middle School have?

4.83 Find the sum of the reciprocals of all the positive factors of 30. Express your answer as a fraction in simplest form.

4.84 Compute $\frac{2+4+6+\cdots+36}{3+6+9+\cdots+54}$.

4.85 Find the number halfway between $-2\frac{5}{6}$ and $\frac{3}{5}$ on the number line. **Hints:** 158, 148

4.86 Two 600 ml pitchers contain vinegar. One pitcher is $\frac{1}{3}$ full and the other pitcher is $\frac{2}{5}$ full. Oil is added to fill each pitcher completely, and then both pitchers are poured into one large container. What fraction of the mixture in the large container is vinegar? *(Source: AMC 8)*

4.87★ I climb half the steps in a staircase. Next I climb one-third of the remaining steps. Then I climb one-eighth of the rest and stop to catch my breath. What is the least possible number of steps in the staircase? *(Source: MOEMS)*

4.88★ For each of the following, write the expression in simplest form, then square the result, and finally subtract 2. Notice anything interesting?

(a) $1 + \dfrac{1}{2 + \frac{1}{2}}$

(b) $1 + \dfrac{1}{2 + \frac{1}{2+\frac{1}{2}}}$

(c) $1 + \dfrac{1}{2 + \frac{1}{2+\frac{1}{2+\frac{1}{2}}}}$

4.89★ Loki, Moe, Nick, and Ott are good friends. Ott had no money, but the others did. Moe gave Ott one-fifth of his money, Loki gave Ott one-fourth of his money, and Nick gave Ott one-third of his money. Each gave Ott the same amount of money. What fractional part of the group's money does Ott now have? *(Source: AMC 8)* **Hints:** 58, 120

4.90

(a) Find two different positive integers whose reciprocals sum to $\frac{1}{2}$.

(b) Find two different positive integers whose reciprocals sum to $\frac{1}{3}$.

(c) Find two different positive integers whose reciprocals sum to $\frac{1}{4}$.

(d) Find two different positive integers whose reciprocals sum to $\frac{1}{5}$.

(e) Find two different positive integers whose reciprocals sum to $\frac{1}{6}$.

(f)★ Let n be a positive integer. Find two different positive integers (in terms of n) whose reciprocals sum to $\frac{1}{n}$.

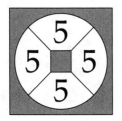 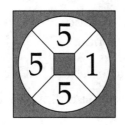 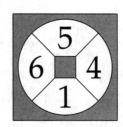 

The human mind has never invented a labor-saving machine equal to algebra. – Unknown

CHAPTER **5**

Equations and Inequalities

5.1 Expressions

When we combine numbers or variables using mathematical operations, we form a mathematical **expression**. For example, the following are all expressions:

$$2 + 7 - 3 \qquad 3 + x - 6 \qquad x^2 - 3x + 9$$

A **term** is a product of a number and a variable raised to some power. We say that the number in a term is the **coefficient** of the power of the variable. For example, in the expression $6x^2 + 3x$, the terms are $6x^2$ and $3x$, the coefficient of x^2 is 6, and the coefficient of x is 3. A number by itself is a term as well, so in the expression $3x + 7$, both $3x$ and 7 are terms. A term that is just a number by itself is called a **constant** or **constant term**.

Two one-variable expressions with the same variable are **equivalent** if they are equal for every value of the variable for which at least one of the expressions is defined. For example, the expressions

$$x + 7 \qquad \text{and} \qquad 7 + x$$

are equivalent, as are the expressions

$$\frac{1}{t} \qquad \text{and} \qquad \frac{2-1}{t}.$$

We say that we **simplify** an expression when we write it as an equivalent expression with as few terms as possible, and write each term as simply as possible. For example, the expression $t \cdot t + 1 + 2 \cdot 4$ can be simplified to $t^2 + 9$, but the expression $x + 7$ is already simplified.

Problems ▶

Problem 5.1:

(a) Are $-x + 6$ and $6 - x$ equivalent?

(b) Are $t + 1$ and $t - 1$ equivalent?

(c) Are $\frac{12x}{4}$ and $3x$ equivalent?

(d) Are $\frac{r^2}{r}$ and r equivalent?

Problem 5.2:

(a) Jeremy has 5 packs of gum and Shannon has 6 packs of gum. Suppose each pack of gum has x pieces of gum. Write an expression for the number of pieces of gum Jeremy has. Write an expression for the number of pieces of gum Shannon has. Write two different expressions that each equal the total number of pieces of gum the two of them have together.

(b) Simplify the expression $5x + 6x$.

Problem 5.3: Allison has three boxes of chocolate and five extra pieces of chocolate. Atlas has four boxes of chocolate and eight extra pieces of chocolate. Suppose each box of chocolate has x pieces of chocolate.

(a) Write an expression for the total number of pieces Allison has.

(b) Write an expression for the total number of pieces Atlas has.

(c) Write an expression for the total number of pieces they have together.

(d) Simplify the expression $(3x + 5) + (4x + 8)$.

(e) Simplify the expression $(5r - 6) + (4r + 1) + (9 - 3r)$.

Problem 5.4:

(a) Expand the product $7(y + 2)$.

(b) Simplify the expression $6r + 2(4 - 3r)$.

(c) Simplify the expression $5(z - 3) + 3(7 - 2z)$.

Problem 5.5:

(a) Yao Ming is 7 feet, 6 inches tall. Earl Boykins is 5 feet, 5 inches tall. How much taller is Yao Ming than Earl Boykins?

(b) Simplify the expression $(7x + 6) - (5x + 5)$.

(c) Simplify the expression $(8a - 3) - 2(3 - 5a)$.

Problem 5.6:

(a) Simplify $\dfrac{10t}{6} + \dfrac{12t}{9}$.

(b) Simplify $-\dfrac{2x}{3} + \dfrac{5x}{7}$.

Problem 5.7:

(a) Express $\dfrac{a}{2} + \dfrac{6a - 5}{4}$ as a single fraction.

(b) Express $\dfrac{2x + 7}{6} - \dfrac{9 - 2x}{9}$ as a single fraction.

Problem 5.1:

(a) Are $-x + 6$ and $6 - x$ equivalent?

(b) Are $t + 1$ and $t - 1$ equivalent?

(c) Are $\frac{12x}{4}$ and $3x$ equivalent?

(d) Are $\frac{r^2}{r}$ and r equivalent?

Solution for Problem 5.1:

(a) By the commutative property of addition, we have $-x + 6 = 6 + (-x) = 6 - x$, so $-x + 6$ and $6 - x$ are equivalent.

(b) If $t = 1$, then $t + 1 = 2$ and $t - 1 = 0$. Because there is a value of t for which $t + 1$ and $t - 1$ are not equal, the two expressions are not equivalent.

(c) We can use our rules for multiplying fractions to simplify the expression $\frac{12x}{4}$ as follows:

$$\frac{12x}{4} = \frac{12}{4} \cdot \frac{x}{1} = 3 \cdot x = 3x.$$

Therefore, $\frac{12x}{4}$ and $3x$ are equivalent.

(d) At first we might think that we can always simplify $\frac{r^2}{r}$ as follows:

$$\frac{r^2}{r} = \frac{r \cdot r}{r \cdot 1} = \frac{r}{r} \cdot \frac{r}{1} = 1 \cdot r = r.$$

This makes it appear that $\frac{r^2}{r}$ and r are equivalent. However, we must be careful; when $r = 0$, the expression $\frac{r^2}{r}$ is not defined, but the expression r is simply 0. So, the expressions $\frac{r^2}{r}$ and r are *not* equal when $r = 0$. Since there is a value of r for which $\frac{r^2}{r}$ and r are not equal, these two expressions are not equivalent.

$\square$

Problem 5.2:

(a) Jeremy has 5 packs of gum and Shannon has 6 packs of gum. Suppose each pack of gum has x pieces of gum. Write an expression for the number of pieces of gum Jeremy has. Write an expression for the number of pieces of gum Shannon has. Write two different expressions that each equal the total number of pieces of gum the two of them have together.

(b) Simplify the expression $5x + 6x$.

Solution for Problem 5.2:

(a) If each pack has x pieces and Jeremy has 5 packs, then he has $5x$ pieces total. Similarly, Shannon's packs have $6x$ pieces total. Together, Jeremy and Shannon have $5x + 6x$ total pieces of gum.

 Instead of counting Jeremy's pieces and Shannon's pieces separately, suppose we count the number of packs they have together before counting the pieces. Together, they have $5 + 6 = 11$ packs, and each pack has x pieces, so they have $11x$ pieces total.

(b) In part (a), we counted Jeremy's and Shannon's pieces separately and found that there are $5x + 6x$ pieces. When we combined their packs before counting the pieces, we found that there are $11x$ pieces. So, we must have $5x + 6x = 11x$.

 We can use the distributive property to show why expressions $5x + 6x$ and $11x$ are equivalent:

$$5x + 6x = 5 \cdot x + 6 \cdot x = (5 + 6) \cdot x = 11x.$$

$\square$

We can extend our work in Problem 5.2 to simplify longer sums (and differences) of terms in which the variable part of each term is the same. For example, we have

$$3x + x + 6x - 2x = (3 + 1 + 6 - 2)x = 8x.$$

We're now ready to add more complicated expressions.

Problem 5.3: Allison has three boxes of chocolate and five extra pieces of chocolate. Atlas has four boxes of chocolate and eight extra pieces of chocolate. Suppose each box of chocolate has x pieces of chocolate.

(a) Write an expression for the total number of pieces Allison has.

(b) Write an expression for the total number of pieces Atlas has.

(c) Write an expression for the total number of pieces they have together.

(d) Simplify the expression $(3x + 5) + (4x + 8)$.

(e) Simplify the expression $(5r - 6) + (4r + 1) + (9 - 3r)$.

Solution for Problem 5.3:

(a) Each of Allison's 3 boxes has x pieces of chocolate, so the boxes contain $3x$ pieces in total. She has 5 extra pieces, giving her a total of $3x + 5$ pieces of chocolate.

(b) Atlas's 4 boxes of chocolate have x pieces each, for a total of $4x$ pieces in boxes. Including his extra 8 pieces, Atlas has $4x + 8$ pieces of chocolate.

(c) Together, Allison and Atlas have $3 + 4 = 7$ boxes of chocolate. These boxes each have x pieces, for a total of $7x$ pieces of chocolate in boxes. Allison and Atlas together have $5 + 8 = 13$ extra pieces. Combining the boxes and the extras gives us $7x + 13$ pieces.

(d) Since Allison has $3x + 5$ pieces of chocolate, Atlas has $4x + 8$ pieces, and together they have $7x + 13$ pieces, we know that

$$(3x + 5) + (4x + 8) = 7x + 13.$$

Fortunately, we don't have to think about boxes of chocolate any time we want to simplify expressions like $(3x + 5) + (4x + 8)$. We can add $3x + 5$ and $4x + 8$ by grouping the x terms and grouping the constants:

$$\begin{aligned}
(3x + 5) + (4x + 8) &= 3x + 5 + 4x + 8 \\
&= 3x + 4x + 5 + 8 \\
&= (3x + 4x) + (5 + 8) \\
&= 7x + 13.
\end{aligned}$$

Manipulations like this show why the "obvious" commutative and associative properties of addition are so important. It's these properties that allow us to group the x terms and group the constants when we add $3x + 5$ and $4x + 8$.

(e) We group the terms with r and we group the constants:

$$\begin{aligned}
(5r - 6) + (4r + 1) + (9 - 3r) &= 5r - 6 + 4r + 1 + 9 - 3r \\
&= 5r + 4r - 3r - 6 + 1 + 9 \\
&= (5r + 4r - 3r) + (-6 + 1 + 9) \\
&= 6r + 4.
\end{aligned}$$

> **WARNING!!** We have to keep careful track of our signs when rearranging a group of numbers that we are adding and subtracting. When we rearrange
>
> $$5r - 6 + 4r + 1 + 9 - 3r$$
>
> to
>
> $$5r + 4r - 3r - 6 + 1 + 9,$$
>
> we are careful not to mistakenly change the signs of any terms.

□

When we add $(5r - 6) + (4r + 1) + (9 - 3r)$ to get $6r + 4$, we say we are **combining like terms**, because we are combining all the r terms into one term ($5r + 4r - 3r$ simplifies to $6r$), and we are combining all the constants into one term ($-6 + 1 + 9$ simplifies to 4).

Problem 5.4:

(a) Expand the product $7(y + 2)$.

(b) Simplify the expression $6r + 2(4 - 3r)$.

(c) Simplify the expression $5(z - 3) + 3(7 - 2z)$.

Solution for Problem 5.4: We can use the distributive property with variables in the same way that we do with numbers.

(a) $7(y + 2) = 7 \cdot y + 7 \cdot 2 = 7y + 14$.

(b) First, we expand $2(4 - 3r)$ with the distributive property:

$$6r + 2(4 - 3r) = 6r + 2 \cdot 4 - 2 \cdot 3r = 6r + 8 - 6r.$$

Next, we combine like terms:

$$6r + 8 - 6r = 6r - 6r + 8 = 0 + 8 = 8.$$

The $6r$ and $-6r$ canceled out! The original expression simplifies to 8. So, no matter what value of r we choose, the expression $6r + 2(4 - 3r)$ equals 8.

(c) First, we use the distributive property to expand our two products. We are careful to keep track of the negative signs:

$$5(z - 3) + 3(7 - 2z) = 5 \cdot z - 5 \cdot 3 + 3 \cdot 7 - 3 \cdot (2z)$$
$$= 5z - 15 + 21 - 6z.$$

Now we can combine like terms (and watch out for sign errors) to find

$$5z - 15 + 21 - 6z = 5z - 6z - 15 + 21 = (5 - 6)z + 6 = -1z + 6 = -z + 6.$$

□

The distributive property also helps us subtract one expression from another.

Problem 5.5:

(a) Yao Ming is 7 feet, 6 inches tall. Earl Boykins is 5 feet, 5 inches tall. How much taller is Yao Ming than Earl Boykins?

(b) Simplify the expression $(7x + 6) - (5x + 5)$.

(c) Simplify the expression $(8a - 3) - 2(3 - 5a)$.

Solution for Problem 5.5:

(a) We could find both of the heights in inches, but we can find the difference in their heights more quickly by subtracting the feet and inches separately. Yao is taller than Boykins by $7 - 5 = 2$ feet and $6 - 5 = 1$ inch. We're basically using the distributive property to help subtract two expressions:

$$(7 \text{ feet} + 6 \text{ inches}) - (5 \text{ feet} + 5 \text{ inches}) = 7 \text{ feet} + 6 \text{ inches} - 5 \text{ feet} - 5 \text{ inches}$$
$$= (7 \text{ feet} - 5 \text{ feet}) + (6 \text{ inches} - 5 \text{ inches})$$
$$= 2 \text{ feet} + 1 \text{ inch}.$$

(b) We have

$$(7x + 6) - (5x + 5) = (7x + 6) - 5x - 5$$
$$= 7x - 5x + 6 - 5$$
$$= 2x + 1.$$

(c) We have

$$(8a - 3) - 2(3 - 5a) = 8a - 3 - 2(3) - 2(-5a)$$
$$= 8a - 3 - 6 + 10a$$
$$= 8a + 10a - 3 - 6$$
$$= 18a - 9.$$

□

Problem 5.6:

(a) Simplify $\dfrac{10t}{6} + \dfrac{12t}{9}$.

(b) Simplify $-\dfrac{2x}{3} + \dfrac{5x}{7}$.

Solution for Problem 5.6:

(a) First, we simplify both fractions. We have $\frac{10t}{6} = \frac{10}{6} \cdot \frac{t}{1} = \frac{5}{3}t$, and $\frac{12t}{9} = \frac{12}{9} \cdot \frac{t}{1} = \frac{4}{3}t$. So, we have

$$\frac{10t}{6} + \frac{12t}{9} = \frac{5}{3}t + \frac{4}{3}t = \left(\frac{5}{3} + \frac{4}{3}\right)t = \left(\frac{9}{3}\right)t = 3t.$$

(b) We have

$$-\frac{2x}{3} + \frac{5x}{7} = -\frac{2}{3}x + \frac{5}{7}x = \left(-\frac{2}{3} + \frac{5}{7}\right)x.$$

Writing $-\frac{2}{3}$ and $\frac{5}{7}$ with a common denominator gives

$$\left(-\frac{2}{3} + \frac{5}{7}\right)x = \left(-\frac{14}{21} + \frac{15}{21}\right)x = \left(\frac{1}{21}\right)x = \frac{x}{21}.$$

We also could have written $-\frac{2x}{3}$ and $\frac{5x}{7}$ with a common denominator in the very beginning. Writing both fractions with 21 as the denominator gives

$$-\frac{2x}{3} = -\frac{2x}{3} \cdot \frac{7}{7} = -\frac{14x}{21}, \qquad \frac{5x}{7} = \frac{5x}{7} \cdot \frac{3}{3} = \frac{15x}{21}.$$

Therefore, we have

$$-\frac{2x}{3} + \frac{5x}{7} = -\frac{14x}{21} + \frac{15x}{21} = \frac{-14x}{21} + \frac{15x}{21} = \frac{-14x + 15x}{21} = \frac{x}{21}.$$

Notice that we are careful to keep the negative sign in the $-14x$ in the numerator when we combine the fractions.

$\square$

Now that we can handle fractions combined with variables, let's take a look at more complicated expressions with fractions.

Problem 5.7:

(a) Express $\dfrac{a}{2} + \dfrac{6a - 5}{4}$ as a single fraction.

(b) Express $\dfrac{2x + 7}{6} - \dfrac{9 - 2x}{9}$ as a single fraction.

Solution for Problem 5.7:

(a) The least common denominator of the fractions is 4. Writing $\frac{a}{2}$ with a denominator of 4 gives

$$\frac{a}{2} = \frac{a}{2} \cdot \frac{2}{2} = \frac{2a}{4}.$$

We then have

$$\frac{a}{2} + \frac{6a - 5}{4} = \frac{2a}{4} + \frac{6a - 5}{4} = \frac{2a + 6a - 5}{4} = \frac{8a - 5}{4}.$$

(b) The least common denominator of the fractions is 18. Writing both fractions with this denominator gives

$$\frac{2x + 7}{6} = \frac{2x + 7}{6} \cdot \frac{3}{3} = \frac{(2x + 7)(3)}{(6)(3)} = \frac{6x + 21}{18},$$
$$\frac{9 - 2x}{9} = \frac{9 - 2x}{9} \cdot \frac{2}{2} = \frac{(9 - 2x)(2)}{(9)(2)} = \frac{18 - 4x}{18}.$$

Now, we subtract:

$$\frac{2x + 7}{6} - \frac{9 - 2x}{9} = \frac{6x + 21}{18} - \frac{18 - 4x}{18} = \frac{6x + 21 - (18 - 4x)}{18}.$$

The key thing to note here is how we treat the subtraction of the second numerator. We subtract the entire numerator, $18 - 4x$, so the numerator in the combined fraction is $6x + 21 - (18 - 4x)$, not $6x + 21 - 18 - 4x$. Make sure you see the difference between these! Finally, we distribute in the numerator and we finish:

$$\frac{6x + 21 - (18 - 4x)}{18} = \frac{6x + 21 - 18 + 4x}{18} = \frac{(6x + 4x) + (21 - 18)}{18} = \frac{10x + 3}{18}.$$

□

Exercises

5.1.1 Simplify each of the following:

(a) $2r + 3r - 7r$

(b) $3y - 2y + 7y - 9y$

(c) $6 - t + 3t - 4 + 2t$

(d) $-5z + \frac{3}{2} - 2 + 3z$

(e) $-\frac{x}{2} + x + \frac{x}{3}$

(f) $5 - \frac{5}{2}r + 7 - \frac{7}{3}r$

5.1.2 Simplify each of the following:

(a) $7(x - 2) + 5(2x + 3)$

(b) $4(3a - 4) - 6(2a - 1)$

(c) $-3(1 + 3t) - (t + 3)(1 + 4)$

(d) $-5(22 - 31y) + 22(4y + 3)$

5.1.3 Simplify each of the following:

(a) $\dfrac{12 - 4c}{4} + \dfrac{27 + 18c}{3}$

(b) $\dfrac{1}{2}(6 - 4y) + \dfrac{3}{2}(6y + 4)$

(c) $3r + 7 - \dfrac{24 - 16r}{8}$

(d) $\dfrac{x - 7}{3} - \dfrac{5 - x}{2}$

5.1.4 Are the expressions $(2/x)/4$ and $2/(x/4)$ equivalent?

5.1.5 The expression $3x + 4x$ can be simplified to $7x$. Can the expression $3x + 4y$ be simplified similarly?

5.1.6 The expression $x + x$ can be simplified to $2x$.

(a) Can the expression $x^2 + x^2$ be simplified similarly?

(b) Can the expression $x^2 + x$ be simplified similarly?

5.2 Solving Linear Equations I

An **equation** states that two quantities are equal. The most basic type of equation comes from arithmetic. For example,

$$2 + 6 = 3 + 5.$$

You've already seen many examples of this sort of equation.

So far in this book, nearly every equation with variables has been used to say that two expressions are equivalent, such as

$$a + b = b + a.$$

In this section, we introduce equations with a variable such that the equation is true for only some values of the variable. Unfortunately, we use the same symbol, "=", to mean that two expressions are equivalent and to write equations that are only true for some values of a variable.

For example, the equation $x + 3 = 9$ does not tell us that $x + 3$ is 9 for all values of x. If $x = 3$, then $x + 3$ is 6, not 9, so the equation $x + 3 = 9$ is not true when $x = 3$. However, if $x = 6$, then $x + 3$ is 9, so the equation $x + 3 = 9$ is true when $x = 6$. The **solutions** to an equation are the values of the variables that make the equation true. So, $x = 6$ is a solution to $x + 3 = 9$.

We say that we **solve** an equation when we find all values of the variable that make the equation true. The two most important tactics we use to solve equations are:

1. *We can replace any expression with an equivalent expression.* For example, in the equation

$$5x - 4x + 3 = 14,$$

   we can simplify the left-hand side to $x + 3$, so the equation becomes

$$x + 3 = 14.$$

2. *We can perform the same mathematical operation to both sides of the equation.* For example, starting with the equation $x + 3 = 14$, we can subtract 3 from both sides of the equation to get

$$x + 3 - 3 = 14 - 3.$$

   Simplifying both sides of the equation then gives $x = 11$, and we have found the solution to the equation. Looking back to the original equation, $5x - 4x + 3 = 14$, we see that when we have $x = 11$, we get $5 \cdot 11 - 4 \cdot 11 + 3 = 14$, which is indeed a true equation.

> **Important:** If you add, subtract, multiply, or divide the expression on one side of the equation by something, then you have to do the same to the expression on the other side of the equation.

We often solve equations with one variable by performing operations on both sides of the equation and simplifying expressions until the variable is alone on one side of the equation. When we do this, we say that we **isolate** the variable.

In this section, we focus on solving **linear equations**. An equation is a linear equation if every term in the equation is a constant term or is a constant times the first power of the variable. So,

$$2x + 4x - 5 = 3 - 6x \qquad \text{and} \qquad 2y + 7 = 3 - 2y$$

are linear equations. The equations

$$x^2 = 36 \qquad \text{and} \qquad \frac{2}{y^3 - 5} = 19$$

are not linear equations.

 Problems

Problem 5.8: Consider the equation $x - 12 = 289$. We will solve this equation in several different ways.

(a) Use your understanding of numbers to find a value of x that makes the equation true.

(b) Use the number line to find a value of x that makes the equation true.

(c) What number can be added to both sides of the equation to give an equation in which x is alone on the left side?

(d) Use part (c) to solve the equation.

Problem 5.9: Solve the following equations:

(a) $x - 4\frac{2}{3} = 2\frac{4}{5}$

(b) $4 - 5\frac{1}{5} = 2x + 3 - x + 3\frac{1}{5}$

Problem 5.10: Consider the equation $31x = 713$.

(a) By what number can we divide both sides of the equation to give an equation in which x is alone on the left side?

(b) Solve the equation.

Problem 5.11: Solve the following equations:

(a) $5t = -13$

(b) $24 = -75y$

(c) $\dfrac{u}{7} = \dfrac{3}{14}$

(d) $-\dfrac{2r}{9} = \dfrac{8}{15}$

Problem 5.8: Solve the equation $x - 12 = 289$.

Solution for Problem 5.8: We present three different solutions.

Inspection. The equation means that 12 less than x equals 289. Since 289 is 12 less than x, we know that x must be 12 more than 289. Therefore, x equals $289 + 12$, which is 301.

Number Line. If we consider the number line, the equation $x - 12 = 289$ tells us that 289 is 12 steps to the left of x. This means that x is 12 steps to the right of 289, so x is $289 + 12 = 301$.

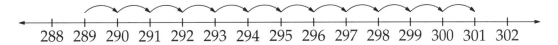

Algebra. To solve the equation, we manipulate it until it reads $x =$ (some number). Therefore, we must get x alone on one side of the equation. To do so, we eliminate the -12 on the left side by adding 12 to both sides of the equation:

$$\begin{array}{rl} x - 12 = & 289 \\ + 12 = & +12 \\ \hline x \quad\ = & 301 \end{array}$$

We have therefore isolated x on the left side of the equation. We can now see that the solution to the equation $x - 12 = 289$ is $x = 301$.

Whichever method we use to solve the equation, we can check our answer by substituting our solution, $x = 301$, back in to the original equation, $x - 12 = 289$, to get $301 - 12 = 289$. This equation is true, so our solution works. □

Perhaps you noticed that each of our three solution approaches comes down to the same key step, adding 12 to 289 to get our answer. The first uses words, the second uses pictures, the third uses algebra. While logic and pictures are sometimes helpful in solving equations, algebraic manipulations are by far the most generally useful tools to solve equations. Try using algebra to solve the following equations.

Problem 5.9: Solve the following equations:

(a) $x - 4\frac{2}{3} = 2\frac{4}{5}$

(b) $4 - 5\frac{1}{5} = 2x + 3 - x + 3\frac{1}{5}$

Solution for Problem 5.9:

(a) We isolate x by adding $4\frac{2}{3}$ to both sides:

$$\begin{array}{rl} x - 4\frac{2}{3} = & 2\frac{4}{5} \\ + 4\frac{2}{3} = & +4\frac{2}{3} \\ \hline x \qquad = & 2\frac{4}{5} + 4\frac{2}{3} \end{array}$$

We finish by adding the mixed numbers on the right side:

$$x = 2\frac{4}{5} + 4\frac{2}{3} = 2 + 4 + \frac{4}{5} + \frac{2}{3} = 6 + \frac{12}{15} + \frac{10}{15} = 6 + \frac{22}{15} = 6 + 1\frac{7}{15} = 7\frac{7}{15}.$$

This example shows how algebra can help keep our work organized and simple. If we take a logic or picture approach, the fractions might lead to confusion. The algebraic approach makes it very clear how to find the answer.

(b) We start by simplifying both sides of the equation. The left side is simply $4 - 5\frac{1}{5} = -1\frac{1}{5}$. On the right side, we combine the two variable terms and combine the two constants:

$$2x + 3 - x + 3\frac{1}{5} = (2x - x) + \left(3 + 3\frac{1}{5}\right) = x + 6\frac{1}{5}.$$

Now our equation is

$$-1\frac{1}{5} = x + 6\frac{1}{5}$$

To solve this equation, we isolate x by subtracting $6\frac{1}{5}$ from both sides:

$$\begin{array}{r} -1\frac{1}{5} = x + 6\frac{1}{5} \\ -6\frac{1}{5} = \quad -6\frac{1}{5} \\ \hline -7\frac{2}{5} = x \end{array}$$

We typically write the variable first when communicating the solution. The solution to the original equation is $x = -7\frac{2}{5}$.

□

> **Concept:** Isolate, isolate, isolate. The key to solving most equations is to get the variable alone on one side of the equation.

Addition and subtraction are not the only tools we can use to solve linear equations.

Problem 5.10: Solve the equation $31x = 713$.

Solution for Problem 5.10: We divide both sides of the equation by 31. This leaves x alone on the left:
$$\frac{31x}{31} = \frac{713}{31}.$$
Since $31x/31 = x$ and $713/31 = 23$, we have $x = 23$. □

In this solution we used division to change the coefficient of x from 31 to 1. We could also have viewed this as multiplying both sides of the equation by the reciprocal of the coefficient of $31x$ to give $\frac{1}{31} \cdot 31x = \frac{1}{31} \cdot 713$. The $\frac{1}{31}$ and 31 cancel on the left, and we have $x = \frac{713}{31} = 23$.

Problem 5.11: Solve the following equations:

(a) $5t = -13$

(b) $24 = -75y$

(c) $\dfrac{u}{7} = \dfrac{3}{14}$

(d) $-\dfrac{2r}{9} = \dfrac{8}{15}$

Solution for Problem 5.11:

(a) We isolate t by dividing both sides of the equation by 5:

$$\frac{5t}{5} = \frac{-13}{5}.$$

Since $\frac{5t}{5}$ simplifies to t, we have $t = -\frac{13}{5}$ as our solution.

(b) We divide both sides by -75:

$$\frac{24}{-75} = \frac{-75y}{-75},$$

so $\frac{24}{-75} = y$. We usually write the variable first, so we can write this equation as

$$y = \frac{24}{-75}.$$

We finish by simplifying the right-hand side:

$$y = \frac{24}{-75} = -\frac{24}{75} = -\frac{8}{25}.$$

Therefore, the solution is $y = -\frac{8}{25}$.

We can check our answer by substituting $y = -\frac{8}{25}$ in the original equation. We see that $-75 \cdot \left(-\frac{8}{25}\right)$ does equal 24, so our answer is correct.

> **Important:** When solving an equation, we can check our answer by substituting our answer back into the original equation. If the original equation is not satisfied by our answer, then we probably made a mistake and should solve the equation again.

(c) To get rid of the 7 in the denominator on the left side, we multiply both sides by 7:

$$7\left(\frac{u}{7}\right) = 7\left(\frac{3}{14}\right).$$

We have $7\left(\frac{u}{7}\right) = \frac{7u}{7} = u$ and $7\left(\frac{3}{14}\right) = \frac{3}{2}$, so the equation above simplifies to $u = \frac{3}{2}$.

(d) At first, it might look like we can't isolate r with one step. But if we write $-\frac{2r}{9}$ as $\left(-\frac{2}{9}\right)r$, we have

$$\left(-\frac{2}{9}\right)r = \frac{8}{15}.$$

Now, we can isolate r by multiplying both sides of the equation by the reciprocal of the coefficient of r. The reciprocal of $-\frac{2}{9}$ is $-\frac{9}{2}$, and multiplying both sides of the equation by $-\frac{9}{2}$ gives

$$\left(-\frac{9}{2}\right)\left(-\frac{2}{9}\right)r = \left(-\frac{9}{2}\right)\frac{8}{15}.$$

The product of a number and its reciprocal is 1, so the left side simplifies to r, as planned. We therefore have

$$r = \left(-\frac{9}{2}\right)\frac{8}{15} = -\frac{9}{2} \cdot \frac{8}{15} = -\frac{12}{5}.$$

Checking our work, we find that when $r = -\frac{12}{5}$, we have

$$-\frac{2r}{9} = -\frac{2(-12/5)}{9} = -\frac{-24/5}{9} = -\left(-\frac{24}{5 \cdot 9}\right) = \frac{24}{45} = \frac{8}{15}.$$

So, the equation is indeed satisfied when $r = -\frac{12}{5}$.

$\square$

Exercises

5.2.1 Solve each of the following equations:

(a) $t + 235 = 137$

(b) $a + \frac{7}{9} = \frac{-2}{9}$

(c) $-6\frac{1}{10} = -14 + c$

(d) $-2y + 2\frac{3}{5} + 3y = 1\frac{7}{10}$

5.2.2 Solve each of the following equations:

(a) $-7y = 343$

(b) $16x = 3\frac{1}{3}$

(c) $\frac{x}{5} = \frac{6}{7}$

(d) $-\frac{5y}{2} = -\frac{14}{15}$

5.2.3 Solve the equation $5\frac{1}{4} - y = 19\frac{3}{4}$.

5.2.4 Solve the equation $\frac{x-3}{7} = 2$.

5.2.5 Solve the equation $3(r - 7) = 24$.

5.2.6★ Find the value of c such that $x = 2$ is a solution to the equation $\frac{x}{c} = 3$.

5.3 Solving Linear Equations II

Problems

Problem 5.12: In this problem, we solve the equation $8t + 9 = 65$.

(a) Isolate the $8t$ by subtracting an appropriate constant from both sides.

(b) Solve the resulting equation for t.

Problem 5.13: In this problem, we solve the equation $7j - 4 + 3j = 6 + 2j - 4j - 8$.

(a) Simplify both sides of the equation by combining like terms.

(b) Add an expression to both sides of your equation from part (a) to give an equation in which no variables are on the right-hand side.

(c) Solve the equation resulting from part (b).

(d) Check your answer! Substitute your value of j into the original equation. If it doesn't work, then do the problem again.

Problem 5.14: Solve the following equations:

(a) $8k - 13\frac{2}{5} = -12\frac{1}{25}$

(b) $4(t - 7) = 3(2t + 3)$

(c) $\dfrac{2r - 7}{9} = 3$

(d) $\dfrac{3x + 4}{5} = \dfrac{2x - 8}{7}$

Problem 5.15: Solve the following equations:

(a) $\dfrac{9}{5} - \dfrac{2x}{3} = \dfrac{6x}{5} + \dfrac{7}{3}$

(b) $\dfrac{4 - 7t}{6} = \dfrac{t}{8} + 2$

Problem 5.16:

(a) Find all values of w that satisfy $5w + 3 - 2w = w - 8 + 2w - 3$.

(b) Find all values of z that satisfy $2z - 8 - 5z = 2 - 3z - 10$.

Problem 5.17: For what value of c do the equations $2y - 5 = 17$ and $cy - 8 = 36$ have the same solution for y?

In the last section, we used addition and subtraction to solve some equations, and used multiplication and division to solve others. To solve most linear equations, however, we'll have to use a combination of these tactics.

Problem 5.12: Solve the equation $8t + 9 = 65$.

Solution for Problem 5.12: This equation doesn't look exactly like any of the equations we already know how to solve. It may not be obvious immediately how to isolate t. However, we can isolate $8t$ by subtracting 9 from both sides:

$$\begin{array}{rl} 8t + 9 &= 65 \\ -9 &= -9 \\ \hline 8t &= 56 \end{array}$$

Now we have an equation we know how to solve! We divide both sides by 8 to find $t = 7$.

We can check our work by substituting this value for t back into our original equation. We find that $8(7) + 9 = 65$, so our answer works.

We didn't have to add first when we solved this equation. We could have divided first:

$$\frac{8t + 9}{8} = \frac{65}{8}.$$

We can then distribute on the left side. Since

$$\frac{8t + 9}{8} = \frac{8t}{8} + \frac{9}{8} = t + \frac{9}{8},$$

we have

$$t + \frac{9}{8} = \frac{65}{8}.$$

We then subtract $\frac{9}{8}$ from both sides of this equation to get $t = \frac{65}{8} - \frac{9}{8} = \frac{56}{8} = 7$, as before. $\square$

The equation in Problem 5.12 is not exactly like any of the equations we solved in the previous section. However, we were still able to solve it with the same tools.

Concept: When solving an equation that isn't exactly like an equation you have solved before, try to manipulate it into a form you already know how to deal with.

See if you can apply this strategy to the following problem.

Problem 5.13: Solve the equation $7j - 4 + 3j = 6 + 2j - 4j - 8$.

Solution for Problem 5.13: Our first step is to simplify both sides of the equation. By grouping like terms, the left-hand side of the original equation becomes

$$7j - 4 + 3j = (7j + 3j) - 4 = 10j - 4.$$

The right-hand side of the original equation becomes

$$6 + 2j - 4j - 8 = (2j - 4j) + (6 - 8) = -2j - 2.$$

Combining these results simplifies the original equation to

$$10j - 4 = -2j - 2.$$

We haven't solved any equations in which the variable appears on both sides. We know how to handle an equation if the variable only appears on one side. So, we add $2j$ to both sides to eliminate the variable from the right-hand side:

$$\begin{array}{rcl} 10j - 4 & = & -2j - 2 \\ +\, 2j & = & +2j \\ \hline 12j - 4 & = & -2 \end{array}$$

Now we have an equation we know how to solve! We add 4 to both sides to get $12j = 2$. We then divide by 12 to find $j = \frac{2}{12} = \frac{1}{6}$. $\square$

We now have another strategy for solving linear equations.

> **Concept:** If the variable appears on both sides of the equation, we can use addition and subtraction to get all terms with the variable on the same side of the equation.

Similarly, we use addition and subtraction to get all the constant terms on the other side of the equation.

Here's a little more practice.

> **Problem 5.14:** Solve the following equations:
>
> (a) $8k - 13\frac{2}{5} = -12\frac{1}{25}$
>
> (b) $4(t - 7) = 3(2t + 3)$
>
> (c) $\dfrac{2r - 7}{9} = 3$
>
> (d) $\dfrac{3x + 4}{5} = \dfrac{2x - 8}{7}$

Solution for Problem 5.14:

(a) Adding $13\frac{2}{5}$ to both sides leaves the variable term on the left while putting all the constant terms on the right:

$$8k = -12\frac{1}{25} + 13\frac{2}{5}.$$

Simplifying the right-hand side gives $-12\frac{1}{25} + 13\frac{2}{5} = (-12 + 13) + \left(-\frac{1}{25} + \frac{2}{5}\right) = 1\frac{9}{25}$, so we now have

$$8k = 1\frac{9}{25}.$$

Multiplying both sides by $\frac{1}{8}$ (which is the same as dividing both sides by 8) gives

$$k = \frac{1}{8} \cdot 1\frac{9}{25} = \frac{1}{8} \cdot \frac{34}{25} = \frac{34}{200} = \frac{17}{100}.$$

(b) First, we use the distributive property to expand both sides:

$$4 \cdot t - 4 \cdot 7 = 3 \cdot 2t + 3 \cdot 3.$$

Simplifying both sides gives

$$4t - 28 = 6t + 9.$$

Next, we get all the terms with t on one side of the equation and all the constants on the other side. Subtracting $4t$ from both sides gives $-28 = 2t + 9$. Subtracting 9 from both sides gives $-37 = 2t$. Finally, dividing both sides by 2 gives $t = -\frac{37}{2}$.

(c) First, make sure you see why adding 7 to $\frac{2r-7}{9}$ doesn't "cancel the -7." This is because $\frac{2r-7}{9} + 7$ equals $\frac{2r}{9} - \frac{7}{9} + 7$, which is $\frac{2r}{9} + \frac{56}{9}$. There's still a constant term; the $\frac{2r}{9}$ term is not yet isolated.

Since $\frac{2r-7}{9}$ equals $\frac{2r}{9} - \frac{7}{9}$, we add $\frac{7}{9}$ to both sides of

$$\frac{2r}{9} - \frac{7}{9} = 3$$

to eliminate the constant on the left side and isolate $\frac{2r}{9}$. Doing so gives us

$$\frac{2r}{9} = 3 + \frac{7}{9} = \frac{34}{9}.$$

Multiplying both sides of $\frac{2r}{9} = \frac{34}{9}$ by $\frac{9}{2}$ gives $r = \frac{34}{9} \cdot \frac{9}{2} = 17$.

We could have avoided fractions entirely by multiplying both sides of $\frac{2r-7}{9} = 3$ by 9 on the first step to get $9 \cdot \frac{2r-7}{9} = 27$. Since

$$9 \cdot \frac{2r - 7}{9} = \frac{9(2r - 7)}{9} = \frac{9}{9}(2r - 7) = 2r - 7,$$

the 9's cancel on the left side of $9 \cdot \frac{2r-7}{9} = 27$ to leave $2r - 7 = 27$. Adding 7 to both sides gives $2r = 34$, so $r = 17$, as before.

Checking our answer, we find that if $r = 17$, then $\frac{2r-7}{9} = \frac{2\cdot17-7}{9} = \frac{27}{9} = 3$, as required.

(d) We start by getting rid of the fractions. We eliminate the denominator on the right by multiplying both sides by 7:

$$7 \cdot \frac{3x + 4}{5} = 7 \cdot \frac{2x - 8}{7}.$$

The 7's on the right-hand side cancel, because

$$7 \cdot \frac{2x - 8}{7} = \frac{7 \cdot (2x - 8)}{7} = \frac{7}{7} \cdot \frac{2x - 8}{1} = 2x - 8.$$

So, we can write $7 \cdot \frac{3x+4}{5} = 7 \cdot \frac{2x-8}{7}$ as

$$\frac{7(3x + 4)}{5} = 2x - 8.$$

Next, we multiply both sides by 5 to cancel the 5 in the denominator on the left-hand side:

$$5 \cdot \frac{7(3x + 4)}{5} = 5(2x - 8).$$

The 5's on the left cancel, and we are left with

$$7(3x + 4) = 5(2x - 8).$$

Expanding both sides gives

$$7(3x) + 7(4) = 5(2x) - 5(8).$$

Simplifying both sides gives $21x + 28 = 10x - 40$, and now we're in familiar territory. Subtracting $10x$ from both sides gives $11x + 28 = -40$. Subtracting 28 from both sides gives $11x = -68$. Dividing both sides by 11 gives $x = -\frac{68}{11}$.

$\square$

Notice that multiplying both sides of

$$\frac{3x + 4}{5} = \frac{2x - 8}{7}$$

by the denominators of both fractions gave us

$$7(3x + 4) = 5(2x - 8).$$

Rather than performing these multiplications as two separate steps, we will often perform both at once. Multiplying both sides of the original equation by 5 and by 7 gives

$$5 \cdot 7 \cdot \frac{3x + 4}{5} = 5 \cdot 7 \cdot \frac{2x - 8}{7}.$$

The 5 on the left cancels with the 5 in the denominator on the left, and the 7 on the right cancels with the 7 in the denominator on the right, leaving

$$7(3x + 4) = 5(2x - 8).$$

We call this process **cross-multiplying**.

Our last example above showed another way to simplify working with equations:

> **Concept:** If you don't like dealing with fractions, you can eliminate fractions from a linear equation by multiplying both sides of the equation by a constant that cancels the denominators of the fractions.

Let's practice this strategy.

Problem 5.15: Solve the following equations:

(a) $\dfrac{9}{5} - \dfrac{2x}{3} = \dfrac{6x}{5} + \dfrac{7}{3}$

(b) $\dfrac{4 - 7t}{6} = \dfrac{t}{8} + 2$

Solution for Problem 5.15:

(a) Let's get rid of the fractions right away. We multiply both sides of the equation by 3 to cancel the denominators that are 3, and multiply by 5 to cancel the denominators that are 5. Therefore, we can take care of both at once by multiplying by $3 \cdot 5 = 15$. Using the distributive property to expand, the left-hand side becomes

$$\begin{aligned}
15\left(\frac{9}{5} - \frac{2x}{3}\right) &= 15 \cdot \frac{9}{5} - 15 \cdot \frac{2x}{3} \\
&= \frac{15}{5} \cdot 9 - \frac{15}{3} \cdot 2x \\
&= 27 - 5 \cdot 2x \\
&= 27 - 10x.
\end{aligned}$$

Multiplying the right-hand side of the original equation by 15 gives

$$\begin{aligned}
15\left(\frac{6x}{5} + \frac{7}{3}\right) &= 15 \cdot \frac{6x}{5} + 15 \cdot \frac{7}{3} \\
&= \frac{15}{5} \cdot 6x + \frac{15}{3} \cdot 7 \\
&= 3 \cdot 6x + 5 \cdot 7 \\
&= 18x + 35.
\end{aligned}$$

Combining this with our simplified left-hand side gives

$$27 - 10x = 18x + 35.$$

We add $10x$ to both sides to get $27 = 28x + 35$. We subtract 35 from both sides to get $-8 = 28x$ and divide by 28 to find $x = -\frac{8}{28} = -\frac{2}{7}$.

(b) We might start by multiplying both sides by $6 \cdot 8$ to cancel both denominators. However, since $\text{lcm}[6, 8] = 24$, we can cancel both denominators by multiplying both sides by 24 instead of 48:

$$24\left(\frac{4 - 7t}{6}\right) = 24\left(\frac{t}{8} + 2\right).$$

Multiplying on the left-hand side and distributing on the right gives

$$\frac{24(4 - 7t)}{6} = 24 \cdot \frac{t}{8} + 24 \cdot 2,$$

so

$$\frac{24}{6}(4 - 7t) = \frac{24}{8}t + 48.$$

Dividing gives $4(4 - 7t) = 3t + 48$. No more fractions! Expanding the left-hand side gives us $16 - 28t = 3t + 48$. Adding $28t$ to both sides and subtracting 48 from both sides gives $-32 = 31t$. Dividing by 31 gives us $t = -\frac{32}{31}$.

$\square$

So far, all the equations we have solved have had exactly one solution. This isn't always the case!

Problem 5.16:

(a) Find all values of w that satisfy $5w + 3 - 2w = w - 8 + 2w - 3$.

(b) Find all values of z that satisfy $2z - 8 - 5z = 2 - 3z - 10$.

Solution for Problem 5.16:

(a) We first simplify both sides. This gives us

$$3w + 3 = 3w - 11.$$

When we next try to get all the w terms on one side by subtracting $3w$ from both sides, we have

$$3 = -11.$$

Uh-oh! What happened to the w's? They all canceled. Worse yet, we are left with an equation that can clearly never be true, since 3 cannot ever equal -11!

Since the equation $3 = -11$ can never be true, we know that the original equation can never be true either. That is, the original equation is not true for any value of w. We can see why when we look back to the equation $3w + 3 = 3w - 11$. The left-hand side is 14 greater than the right-hand side, no matter what value of w we use.

We conclude that there are no solutions to the original equation.

(b) Once again, we simplify both sides of the equation, which gives

$$-3z - 8 = -3z - 8.$$

Since both sides of the equation simplify to the same expression, we see that the equation is *always* true! No matter what value of z we choose, the equation will always be true. Therefore, all values of z satisfy the given equation.

$\square$

We see now that some linear equations have no solutions, and others that are satisfied by every value of the variable in the equation.

> **Important:** If a linear equation can be manipulated into an equation that is
> never true (such as $3 = -11$), then there are no solutions to the
> equation.
>
> If the two sides of an equation are equivalent, such as in the equa-
> tion $-3z - 8 = -3z - 8$, then all possible values of the variable
> are solutions to the original equation. Similarly, if a linear equa-
> tion can be manipulated into an equation in which both sides are
> identical, then all possible values of the variable are solutions to
> the original equation. (The one exception to this is if one of the
> manipulations is multiplying both sides by 0, which is a pretty
> silly thing to do to a linear equation!)

Problem 5.17: For what value of c do the equations $2y - 5 = 17$ and $cy - 8 = 36$ have the same solution for y?

Solution for Problem 5.17: We know how to handle the first equation, so let's start there. By solving the first equation for y, we can find the value of y that must satisfy both equations. Adding 5 to both sides of $2y - 5 = 17$ gives $2y = 22$. Dividing by 2 then gives $y = 11$. This value of y must also satisfy $cy - 8 = 36$. So, when we substitute $y = 11$ into $cy - 8 = 36$, we must have a true equation. This substitution gives

$$11c - 8 = 36.$$

Now that we have a linear equation for c, we can find c. Adding 8 to both sides gives $11c = 44$. Dividing by 11 then gives $c = 4$. $\square$

> **Extra!** *Archimedes will be remembered when Aeschylus is forgotten, because languages die*
> ⟫⟫⟫⟫ *and mathematical ideas do not. "Immortality" may be a silly word, but probably a*
> *mathematician has the best chance of whatever it may mean.* –G. H. Hardy

 **Exercises** ▶

5.3.1 Solve the following equations:

(a) $2x + 5 = 11$

(b) $\frac{1}{3} = -1\frac{1}{2} - 6a$

(c) $-7t + 19 = 61$

5.3.2 Solve the following equations:

(a) $3y + 9 = 2y + 1$

(b) $5x - 3 - x = 14 - 3x + 11$

(c) $1000a + 218 = 998a + 232$

5.3.3 If $3x - 2 = 11$, then what is the value of $6x + 5$?

5.3.4 Solve the following equations:

(a) $\frac{2}{3}t + \frac{4}{5} = -\frac{1}{2}$

(b) $\frac{1}{2}(z + 3) = \frac{1}{3}(z - 7)$

(c) $\frac{4x}{7} - \frac{1}{2} = -\frac{3}{4} - \frac{2x}{5}$

5.3.5 Solve $\dfrac{2x + 7}{5} = -\dfrac{1 - 3x}{8}$.

5.3.6 Solve the following equations:

(a) $2(z + 3) - 5(6 - z) = 8(3z + 3) - 4(1 - 2z)$

(b) $\dfrac{m + 11}{3} + \dfrac{m - 2}{6} = \dfrac{2m - 1}{12}$

(c) $\dfrac{p - 2}{4} = \dfrac{2p - 3}{8}$

5.4 Word Problems

Most word problems can be solved using the following general method:

1. Read the problem carefully. Wait, I didn't say that loud enough:

Read the problem carefully!

2. Convert the words to math.

3. Solve the math.

4. Convert your answer back to words.

5. Check your answer (and check to be sure that you answered the question that was asked).

 **Problems**

Problem 5.18: Seven more than twice what number equals thirty-five?

Problem 5.19: Six plus half of a number equals four plus one-third of the same number. What is the number?

Problem 5.20: When you add 12 to a number and then divide the sum by 13, you get the same result as when you subtract 13 from the number and then divide the difference by 12. What is the number? *(Source: MATHCOUNTS)*

Problem 5.21: My sister and I are buying a television for our room. Because I am older, I will pay $45 more than my sister. If the television costs $299, then how much does my sister have to pay?

Problem 5.22: I bought a new comic book at the Comic Book Shoppe and paid entirely using quarters. If I had instead paid using only dimes, I would have needed 9 more coins. How much did the comic book cost?

Problem 5.23: A garage has 17 cars and motorcycles. Altogether, there are 56 wheels. How many of each type of vehicle are there?

Problem 5.24: Three years ago, I was two-thirds as old as I will be eight years from now. How old am I now?

Problem 5.25: In slurfball, a fizzle is worth 2 points and a globbo is worth 5 points. Kumquare and the Wazzits recently played for the Intergalactic Slurfball Championship. During the game, Kumquare scored eight more fizzles than the Wazzits, but scored five fewer globbos than the Wazzits. Together the two teams scored 93 points total. What was the final score?

Problem 5.18: Seven more than twice what number equals thirty-five?

Solution for Problem 5.18: The first step in turning many word problems into math is assigning a variable to an unknown quantity. Here, we let x be the unknown number. Now, we can rewrite the problem as

Seven more than twice x equals thirty-five.

We can write "Seven more than twice x" as $7 + 2x$, so we can rewrite the problem as

$7 + 2x$ *equals thirty-five.*

Now, it's clear how to write this as an equation:

$$7 + 2x = 35.$$

Subtracting 7 from both sides gives $2x = 28$, and dividing both sides by 2 gives $x = 14$.

Checking our answer, we see that seven more than twice 14 does indeed equal 35. Therefore, the desired number is 14. □

Problem 5.19: Six plus half of a number equals four plus one-third of the same number. What is the number?

Solution for Problem 5.19: We again start by assigning a variable, x, to the unknown number. This makes our problem:

Six plus half of x equals four plus one-third of x.

Converting this sentence into an equation gives

$$6 + \frac{1}{2}x = 4 + \frac{1}{3}x.$$

Subtracting $\frac{1}{3}x$ from both sides gives

$$6 + \frac{1}{2}x - \frac{1}{3}x = 4,$$

so $6 + \frac{1}{6}x = 4$. Subtracting 6 from both sides gives $\frac{1}{6}x = -2$. Multiplying both sides by 6 gives $x = -12$.

We finish by checking our answer. Six plus half of -12 equals 0. Four plus one-third of -12 also equals 0. So, the number is -12. □

Problem 5.20: When you add 12 to a number and then divide the sum by 13, you get the same result as when you subtract 13 from the number and then divide the difference by 12. What is the number? *(Source: MATHCOUNTS)*

Solution for Problem 5.20: Let's mix it up a little bit. We'll use n for the number this time. We'll also go straight from the words in the problem to the equation:

$$\frac{12 + n}{13} = \frac{n - 13}{12}.$$

Concept: When you write an equation to represent a problem, take a moment to check that your equation does correctly represent the problem before solving the equation.

Multiplying both sides by 12 and by 13 to cancel the denominators gives

$$12(12 + n) = 13(n - 13).$$

Expanding both sides gives

$$144 + 12n = 13n - 169.$$

Subtracting $12n$ from both sides gives $144 = n - 169$. Adding 169 to both sides gives $n = 313$.

Checking our answer, we see that adding 12 to 313 and dividing the sum by 13 gives 25. Subtracting 13 from 313 and then dividing the difference by 12 also gives 25. So, the desired number is indeed 313. □

Of course, you won't often be confronted with problems written in terms of "a number" you must find. Instead, you'll usually be seeking a more meaningful unknown quantity.

Problem 5.21: My sister and I are buying a television for our room. Because I am older, I will pay $45 more than my sister. If the television costs $299, then how much does my sister have to pay?

Solution for Problem 5.21: We don't know how much I pay or how much my sister pays. To which of these quantities should we assign a variable?

Concept: When assigning a variable in a problem with multiple unknown quantities, we usually assign the variable to the unknown quantity we care most about.

We wish to know how much my sister pays, so let s be the number of dollars she pays. We then express how much I pay in terms of my sister's variable.

Concept: We can often express multiple unknown quantities in terms of the same variable.

Since I pay $45 more than my sister does, I must pay $s + 45$ dollars. Together, we spend $299, so we must have

$$(s + 45) + s = 299.$$

Simplifying the left side gives $2s + 45 = 299$. Subtracting 45 from both sides gives $2s = 254$. Dividing both sides by 2 gives $s = 127$. Therefore, my sister pays $127.

Checking our answer, I must pay $127 + $45 = $172. Combining this with the $127 my sister pays gives $172 + $127 = $299, as expected. □

Sometimes it isn't immediately obvious what quantity the variable should represent in a problem.

Problem 5.22: I bought a new comic book at the Comic Book Shoppe and paid entirely using quarters. If I had instead paid using only dimes, I would have needed 9 more coins. How much did the comic book cost?

Solution for Problem 5.22: At first, it looks like we should assign a variable to the cost of the comic book. But it's not immediately clear how we'd relate that to the information about the numbers of quarters and dimes.

> **Concept:** Sometimes you might not find a way to use your first choice for assigning a variable to make an equation. If assigning a variable to the quantity you seek doesn't seem to work, try assigning a variable to a quantity you have information about. This is especially true when you can relate this quantity to what you seek.

We know something about the number of quarters I paid. Also, if we find the number of quarters I paid, then we can figure out how much the comic book costs. So, let q be the number of quarters I paid. In order to pay with dimes, I would have needed $q+9$ dimes. Both q quarters and $q + 9$ dimes must equal the price of the comic book. Since q quarters is $25q$ cents, and $q + 9$ dimes is $10(q + 9)$ cents, we must have

$$25q = 10(q + 9).$$

Expanding the right side gives $25q = 10q + 90$. Subtracting $10q$ from both sides gives $15q = 90$, and dividing by 15 gives $q = 6$. Therefore, I paid 6 quarters for the comic book, which means the comic book cost \$1.50. To check our answer, we note that $6 + 9 = 15$ dimes is also \$1.50. $\square$

Problem 5.23: A garage has 17 cars and motorcycles. Altogether, there are 56 wheels. How many of each type of vehicle are there?

Solution for Problem 5.23: Let c be the number of cars. Since there are 17 cars and motorcycles total, there are $17 - c$ motorcycles. Since each car has 4 wheels and each motorcycle has 2 wheels, the total number of wheels is $4c + 2(17 - c)$. Therefore, we must have

$$4c + 2(17 - c) = 56.$$

Expanding the product on the left gives $4c + 34 - 2c = 56$, and simplifying gives $2c + 34 = 56$. Subtracting 34 from both sides gives $2c = 22$, so $c = 11$. This means that there are 11 cars and $17 - 11 = 6$ motorcycles. Checking, we find that 11 cars and 6 motorcycles together have $11 \cdot 4 + 6 \cdot 2 = 56$ wheels.

We also might have solved this problem with a little clever insight. If all 17 vehicles were motorcycles, then there are $17 \cdot 2 = 34$ wheels total. That's $56 - 34 = 22$ wheels too few! Each time we replace a motorcycle with a car, the number of wheels increases by 2. So, if we start with 17 motorcycles, which together have 22 wheels too few, then we need to replace $22/2 = 11$ motorcycles with 11 cars in order to have 56 wheels total. $\square$

Problem 5.24: Three years ago, I was two-thirds as old as I will be eight years from now. How old am I now?

Solution for Problem 5.24: Let my age now be n. Three years ago, my age was $n - 3$, and eight years from now, my age will be $n + 8$. What's wrong with this next step:

Bogus Solution: Converting the words in the problem to an equation gives
$$\frac{2}{3}(n - 3) = n + 8.$$

We set the equation up incorrectly. The problem tells us that

My age three years ago = two-thirds my age eight years from now.

Since my age three years ago is $n - 3$, and my age eight years from now is $n + 8$, we have the equation
$$n - 3 = \frac{2}{3}(n + 8).$$
Multiplying both sides by 3 gives $3(n-3) = 2(n+8)$. Expanding both sides gives $3n-9 = 2n+16$. Subtracting $2n$ from both sides gives $n - 9 = 16$, and adding 9 to both sides gives $n = 25$. Therefore, I'm 25 years old now.

Checking, we see that three years ago I was 22, and eight years from now I'll be 33. Since $\frac{2}{3}(33) = 22$, our answer is correct. $\square$

In our Bogus Solution to Problem 5.24, we started with the equation $\frac{2}{3}(n-3) = n+8$. Suppose we hadn't realized that we wrote the wrong equation, and proceeded to solve the equation. Multiplying both sides by 3 to get rid of the fraction gives
$$3 \cdot \frac{2}{3}(n - 3) = 3(n + 8),$$
so $2(n - 3) = 3(n + 8)$. Expanding both sides gives $2n - 6 = 3n + 24$. Subtracting $2n$ from both sides gives $-6 = n + 24$, and subtracting 24 from both sides gives $-30 = n$. Clearly this is ridiculous; my age can't be negative! This is a strong clue that we made an error somewhere and we need to check our work.

WARNING!! Always take a moment to consider whether or not your final answer makes sense.

Problem 5.25: In slurfball, a fizzle is worth 2 points and a globbo is worth 5 points. Kumquare and the Wazzits recently played for the Intergalactic Slurfball Championship. During the game, Kumquare scored eight more fizzles than the Wazzits, but scored five fewer globbos than the Wazzits. Together the two teams scored 93 points total. What was the final score?

Solution for Problem 5.25: Once again, it isn't obvious what quantity a variable should represent. We do know that the two teams together scored 93 points. So, if we let Kumquare's score be k, then the Wazzits' score was $93 - k$. But how will we build an equation?

What else do we know about the scores of the teams? Kumquare scored eight more fizzles, which is $8 \cdot 2 = 16$ points, than the Wazzits. But Kumquare scored five fewer globbos, which is $5 \cdot 5 = 25$ points, than the Wazzits. So, altogether, Kumquare scored 9 fewer points than the Wazzits. Since Kumquare scored k points, the Wazzits' scored $k + 9$ points. We now have two expressions for the same quantity, the Wazzits' score, so we can write an equation setting these expressions equal:

$$k + 9 = 93 - k.$$

> **Concept:** If you find two different expressions that represent the same quantity, then you have an equation.

Adding k and subtracting 9 from both sides of $k + 9 = 93 - k$ gives $2k = 84$. Dividing by 2 gives $k = 42$, which means Kumquare scored 42 points and the Wazzits scored $42 + 9 = 51$ points. So, the final score was the Wazzits 51 points and Kumquare 42 points. $\square$

A key step in our solution to Problem 5.25 was assigning a variable to Kumquare's score even though it wasn't immediately clear how doing so would lead to an equation.

> **Concept:** Do something! Don't wait until you see how to build an equation to assign variables and start thinking algebraically. You may not get to the solution immediately, but you'll almost certainly do better by trying something than by not trying anything.

Exercises

5.4.1 Kellie thinks of a number, then doubles the number, and then multiplies the result by 3. If her final number is 65 more than her original number, then what was her original number?

5.4.2 If I add 5 to $\frac{1}{3}$ of a number, the result is $\frac{1}{2}$ of the number. What is the number? *(Source: MOEMS)*

5.4.3 One of my dogs is 25 pounds heavier than the other and the two together weigh 137 pounds. How much does the heavier dog weigh?

5.4.4 What integer is tripled when nine is added to three-fourths of it? *(Source: MATH-COUNTS)*

5.4.5 The sum of the ages of three children is 32. The age of the oldest is twice the age of the youngest. The two older children differ by three years. What is the age of the youngest child? *(Source: MOEMS)*

5.4.6   If the sum of six consecutive even integers is 282, then what is the largest of the integers?

5.4.7   Bobby's Bike Shack orders tires each week for its two-wheel bikes and three-wheel bikes. They order tires for all 47 of their bikes this week. If they ordered 112 tires, how many two-wheel bikes does the Bike Shack have?

5.4.8★   In Problem 5.22, we solved this problem:

> I bought a new comic book at the Comic Book Shoppe and paid entirely using quarters. If I had instead paid using only dimes, I would have needed 9 more coins. How much did the comic book cost?

We first considered assigning a variable to the cost of the comic book, but instead found a solution by assigning a variable to the number of quarters I used to buy the comic book. However, it is possible to find the solution by assigning a variable to the cost of the comic book. How? **Hints:** 113

5.4.9★   The Phillies won 3 of their first 21 games. How many games in a row after these 21 games do the Phillies have to win in order to have won exactly $\frac{3}{5}$ of the games they have played?

5.5   Inequalities

So far we've primarily dealt with expressions that are equal. In this section, we deal with expressions that are *not* equal. If we know that one expression is greater than another, we can write an **inequality** to show this relationship. For example,

$$2 + 7 > 5.$$

The > symbol means "greater than," so $2 + 7 > 5$ tells us that $2 + 7$ is greater than 5. We could also write this relationship with 5 on the left side:

$$5 < 2 + 7.$$

The < symbol means "less than," so $5 < 2 + 7$ tells us that 5 is less than $2 + 7$.

Both of the inequalities above are **strict inequalities**, since one side must be larger than the other. We can also write **nonstrict inequalities**, in which one side is greater than or equal to the other. The ≥ symbol means "greater than or equal to," so

$$2 + 7 \geq 9$$

means $2 + 7$ is greater than or equal to 9. Similarly, the ≤ symbol means "less than or equal to."

Just as with equations, we can include variables in inequalities, such as:

$$x > 5.$$

This tells us that x is greater than 5. For example, x could be 6 or $118\frac{1}{2}$, but could not be -2. We can graph the values of x that satisfy the inequality on the number line, as shown below:

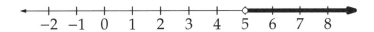

We draw an open circle at 5 on the number line to indicate that $x = 5$ is not a valid solution to the inequality $x > 5$. (It is not a valid solution because 5 is not greater than 5.) We bold the portion of the number line that corresponds to values of x that satisfy the inequality. Note that we bold the arrow on the positive end of the number line. This indicates that all the numbers beyond the arrow in that direction are also solutions to the inequality.

Just as we use an open circle to mark the end point of a strict inequality like $x > 5$, we use a closed circle to mark an end point of a nonstrict inequality. So, we can graph the solutions to $y \leq 3$ on the number line as shown below:

Problem 5.26:

(a) Manute is taller than Michael. Michael is taller than Mugsy. Is Manute taller than Mugsy?

(b) If $a > b$ and $b > c$, then is $a > c$?

(c) If $a > b$ and $b < c$, then do we know which of a or c is larger?

Problem 5.27:

(a) Bill Gates has more money than Warren Buffett. If they each win a 100-million-dollar lottery, then will Bill Gates still have more money than Warren Buffett? What if they each give 100 million dollars to the Art of Problem Solving Foundation? Then who will have more money?

(b) Suppose $x > y$. Explain why $x + 5 > y + 5$ and $x - 5 > y - 5$.

(c) Suppose $x > y$ and $a > b$. Explain why $x + a > y + b$.

(d) Note that $7 > 5$ and $3 > 2$, and that $7 + 2 > 5 + 3$. Is it always true that if $x > y$ and $a > b$, then $x + b > y + a$?

Problem 5.28: In this problem, we investigate what happens when we multiply both sides of an inequality by a positive number. Suppose that $x > y$.

(a) Must we always have $3x > 3y$?

(b) Must we always have $\frac{2}{3}x > \frac{2}{3}y$?

(c) Must we always have $ax > ay$ for any positive number a?

Problem 5.29: In this problem, we investigate what happens when we multiply both sides of an inequality by a negative number. Suppose that $x > y$.

(a) Which is greater, $-2x$ or $-2y$?

(b) If $b < 0$, then which is greater, bx or by?

Problem 5.30: In each of the following parts, describe the values of the variable that make the inequality true, and graph those values on the number line.

(a) $-2 < r \le 4$ (b) $2x + 7 < -3$ (c) $3(5 - 2y) \ge 2y - 9$

Problem 5.31: My town has two cell phone providers. The provider DontTalkMuch charges $80 per month, plus 1 dollar per hour. The provider TalkLots charges $20 per month, plus 4 dollars per hour. How much do you have to use your phone in a month in order for DontTalkMuch's deal to be better for you?

Problem 5.32: I have 308 baseball cards. Tommy has 532 baseball cards. Starting tomorrow, Tommy will give each of his four closest friends, including me, one baseball card each from his collection every day. How many cards will I have on the first day that I have more cards than Tommy has?

Problem 5.26:

(a) Manute is taller than Michael. Michael is taller than Mugsy. Is Manute taller than Mugsy?

(b) If $a > b$ and $b > c$, then is $a > c$?

(c) If $a > b$ and $b < c$, then do we know which of a or c is larger?

Solution for Problem 5.26:

(a) Because Manute is taller than Michael, Manute is taller than everyone who is shorter than Michael. Since Mugsy is one of the people who is shorter than Michael, we know that Manute is taller than Mugsy, too.

(b) This is essentially the same as the first part. Because a is larger than b and b is larger than c, we know that a is larger than c. So, $a > c$.

    We can also see this on the number line. Since $a > b$, a is to the right of b. Since $b > c$, b is to the right of c. Putting these together, a is to the right of c, so $a > c$. An example is shown below.

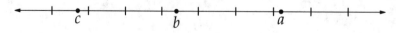

We can put the inequalities $a > b$ and $b > c$ together in a single statement,

$$a > b > c.$$

We sometimes call such a combination of inequalities an **inequality chain**.

(c) If $a > b$ and $c > b$, then we don't know how to relate a and c! For example, suppose $b = 2$. If we have $a = 3$ and $c = 4$ ($3 > 2, 4 > 2$), then $c > a$ ($4 > 3$). However, if we have $a = 4$ and $c = 3$ ($4 > 2, 3 > 2$), then we get $c < a$ ($3 < 4$).

☐

> **Important:** If $a > b$ and $b > c$, then $a > c$.
> Similarly, if $a \geq b$ and $b \geq c$, then $a \geq c$.

Problem 5.27:

(a) Bill Gates has more money than Warren Buffett. If they each win a 100-million-dollar lottery, then will Bill Gates still have more money than Warren Buffett? What if they each give 100 million dollars to the Art of Problem Solving Foundation? Then who will have more money?

(b) Suppose $x > y$. Explain why $x + 5 > y + 5$ and $x - 5 > y - 5$.

(c) Suppose $x > y$ and $a > b$. Explain why $x + a > y + b$.

(d) Note that $7 > 5$ and $3 > 2$, and that $7 + 2 > 5 + 3$. Is it always true that if $x > y$ and $a > b$, then $x + b > y + a$?

Solution for Problem 5.27:

(a) If they each win 100 million dollars, then each of them will have the same increase in the amount of money they have. So, the difference between the amount of money each has will stay the same. Specifically, Gates will still have more money than Buffett.

Similarly, if they each donate 100 million dollars to the Art of Problem Solving Foundation (a very fine idea, we think), then each of them will have their wealth changed by the same amount. So, the difference between the amount of money Gates has and the amount of money Buffett has will stay the same, which means Gates would still have more money than Buffett after their donations.

(b) Since $x > y$, we know that x is to the right of y on the number line. When we add 5 to each, we move 5 steps to the right of each on the number line. In other words, $x + 5$ is 5 to the right of x, and $y + 5$ is 5 to the right of y.

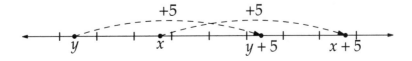

Since x is to the right of (larger than) y, we know $x + 5$ is to the right of $y + 5$. Therefore, we have $x + 5 > y + 5$.

Subtraction is moving left on the number line. Just as with addition, moving 5 units to the left of x and y will leave us with $x - 5 > y - 5$.

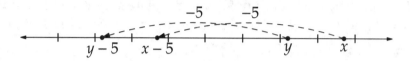

Similarly, we can add or subtract any number to both sides of an inequality.

> **Important:** If $x > y$, then $x + a > y + a$ for any number a.
> If $x \geq y$, then $x + a \geq y + a$ for any number a.
> In other words, we can add the same quantity to both sides of an inequality, just like we can add the same quantity to both sides of an equation.

(c) We'll use another Bill Gates and Warren Buffett example to get a sense for what this part is telling us. Suppose that Bill starts with more money than Warren has. Then, imagine they both win a contest in which Bill wins more money than Warren wins. Since Bill started with more money than Warren, and then Bill's money increased by more than Warren's increased, Bill must end with more money than Warren.

Returning to the problem, we are given $x > y$ and $a > b$. From the previous part, we know that adding a to both sides of $x > y$ gives

$$x + a > y + a.$$

So, if we show that $y + a > y + b$, then we will know that $x + a$ is also greater than $y + b$. We are given $a > b$, and adding y to both sides of $a > b$ gives us the inequality

$$y + a > y + b.$$

Therefore, we have $x + a > y + a$ and $y + a > y + b$, so $x + a > y + b$.

> **Important:** If $x > y$ and $a > b$, then $x + a > y + b$.
> If $x \geq y$ and $a \geq b$, then $x + a \geq y + b$.
> In other words, if we have two inequalities, then the sum of the larger sides of the inequalities is greater than the sum of the smaller sides of the inequalities.

(d) No! It is not always true that $x + b > y + a$ if $x > y$ and $a > b$. For example, note that $9 > 8$ and $5 > 2$, but $9 + 2$ is not greater than $8 + 5$. If all we know is that $x > y$ and $a > b$, we cannot tell which of $x + b$ and $y + a$ is greater (they could even be equal).

□

We've tackled addition and subtraction; let's try multiplication and division.

Problem 5.28: In this problem, we investigate what happens when we multiply both sides of an inequality by a positive number. Suppose that $x > y$.

(a) Must we always have $3x > 3y$?

(b) Must we always have $\frac{2}{3}x > \frac{2}{3}y$?

(c) Must we always have $ax > ay$ for any positive number a?

Solution for Problem 5.28:

(a) Earlier, we saw that if $x > y$ and $a > b$, then $x + a > y + b$. Therefore, adding $x > y$ to another copy of $x > y$ gives $x + x > y + y$, so $2x > 2y$. Similarly, adding $2x > 2y$ and $x > y$ gives $3x > 3y$.

(b) Unfortunately, we can't use the same process we used in part (a).

We need to prove something about products. One thing we know about products and inequalities is that the product of two positive numbers is greater than 0. So, let's see if we can use that.

We already have one positive number, $\frac{2}{3}$. Because $x > y$, we can subtract y from (or add $-y$ to) both sides of the inequality to get $x - y > 0$. So, we have another positive number, $x - y$. The product of the positive numbers $\frac{2}{3}$ and $x - y$ must be positive, so we have

$$\frac{2}{3}(x - y) > 0.$$

Expanding the left side gives $\frac{2}{3}x - \frac{2}{3}y > 0$, and adding $\frac{2}{3}y$ to both sides gives $\frac{2}{3}x > \frac{2}{3}y$.

(c) We can use the same steps as in the previous part. Subtracting y from both sides of $x > y$ gives $x - y > 0$. The product of the two positive numbers a and $x - y$ must be positive:

$$a(x - y) > 0.$$

Expanding the left side gives $ax - ay > 0$, and adding ay to both sides gives $ax > ay$.

$\square$

Now we have some rules for multiplying inequalities by positive numbers.

Important: If $x > y$ and $a > 0$, then $ax > ay$.
If $x \geq y$ and $a > 0$, then $ax \geq ay$.
In other words, we can multiply both sides of an inequality by the same positive number, just like we can multiply both sides of an equation by the same positive number.

These rules take care of division, too, since dividing by a number is the same as multiplying by its reciprocal. For example, if $x > y$, then $\frac{x}{2} > \frac{y}{2}$, since dividing by 2 is the same as multiplying by $\frac{1}{2}$. However, the rules above only hold for multiplying (or dividing) by a *positive* number. We have to be careful when dealing with negative numbers.

Problem 5.29: In this problem, we investigate what happens when we multiply both sides of an inequality by a negative number. Suppose that $x > y$.

(a) Which is greater, $-2x$ or $-2y$?

(b) If $b < 0$, then which is greater, bx or by?

Solution for Problem 5.29:

(a) To get a feel for the problem, we experiment. If we start with

$$7 > 5,$$

we get $(-2) \cdot 7 = -14$ and $(-2) \cdot 5 = -10$, so, since $-14 < -10$, we have

$$(-2) \cdot 7 < (-2) \cdot 5.$$

If we start with

$$11 > -6,$$

we get $(-2) \cdot 11 = -22$ and $(-2) \cdot (-6) = 12$, so, since $-22 < 12$, we have

$$(-2) \cdot 11 < (-2) \cdot (-6).$$

Our experiments suggest that when we multiply both sides of an inequality by -2, we must *reverse the inequality sign*.

We do know what happens when we multiply both sides of an inequality by a positive number. So, instead of starting by multiplying both sides of $x > y$ by -2, we start by multiplying both sides by positive 2. This gives us $2x > 2y$. But we want to compare $-2x$ and $-2y$. So we subtract $2y$ from both sides of $2x > 2y$ to get $2x - 2y > 0$, and then we subtract $2x$ from both sides to get $-2y > -2x$. Since $-2y > -2x$, we have $-2x < -2y$.

We also could have used a similar argument to the one we used to show that if $x > y$, then $\frac{2}{3}x > \frac{2}{3}y$. There, we started by subtracting y from both sides of $x > y$ to get $x - y > 0$. Then, we noted that the product of two positive numbers must be positive, so $\frac{2}{3}(x - y) > 0$. Suppose we instead multiply $x - y$ by -2. The product of a positive and a negative number is negative, so $-2(x - y) < 0$. Expanding the left-hand side gives $-2x - (-2y) < 0$, so $-2x < -2y$.

We conclude that if

$$x > y,$$

then

$$-2x < -2y.$$

(b) We expect that multiplying both sides of $x > y$ by any negative number b will result in reversing the direction of the inequality. To see why this is true, we look back to our work when multiplying an inequality by a positive number.

> **Concept:** Considering similar problems that you know how to solve can help you solve new problems.

Our key step in investigating multiplying an inequality by a positive number was noticing that the product of two positive numbers is positive. To use this fact, we subtracted y from both sides of $x > y$ to get $x - y > 0$. Next, we noted that multiplying $x - y$, which is positive, by a positive number gives a positive result. What if we instead multiply $x - y$ by a negative number? The product of a positive number and a negative number must be negative. So, the product of the positive number $x - y$ and the negative number b is negative:

$$b(x - y) < 0.$$

Expanding the left side gives $bx - by < 0$. Adding by to both sides give $bx < by$, as expected. So, when we multiply both sides of

$$x > y$$

by a negative number b we *reverse the inequality sign* and have

$$bx < by.$$

$\square$

We now know how to multiply an inequality by a negative number:

> **Important:** If we multiply an inequality by a negative number, we must reverse the direction of the inequality. That is, if $x > y$ and $a < 0$, then $ax < ay$. Similarly, if $x \geq y$ and $a < 0$, then $ax \leq ay$.

As with our rules for multiplying by a positive number, these rules take care of division, since dividing by a number is the same as multiplying by its reciprocal. So, for example, if we have $x > y$, then $\frac{x}{-2} < \frac{y}{-2}$, since dividing by -2 is the same as multiplying by $-\frac{1}{2}$.

> **WARNING!!** Be careful when multiplying or dividing an inequality by a negative number or by an expression that could be negative.

Now that we know how to work with inequalities, let's turn to solving inequalities that have variables. Solving an equation with a variable means finding what values of the variable make the equation true. Similarly, solving an inequality that has a variable means describing exactly what values of the variable make the inequality true.

Problem 5.30: In each of the following parts, describe the values of the variable that make the inequality true, and graph those values on the number line.

(a) $-2 < r \leq 4$ (b) $2x + 7 < -3$ (c) $3(5 - 2y) \geq 2y - 9$

Solution for Problem 5.30:

(a) The inequality states that r must be larger than -2 and less than or equal to 4. We particularly note that $r = 4$ satisfies $-2 < r \leq 4$, but $r = -2$ does not. We graph the solutions on the number line below:

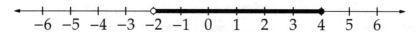

Notice that we use an open circle at -2 to indicate that -2 is not a solution, and we use a closed circle at 4 to show that 4 is a solution.

(b) We know how to describe the solutions to an inequality in which the variable is alone on one side of the inequality and a constant is on the other side. So, we try to isolate x using the rules we have learned in this section for working with inequalities. We start by subtracting 7 from both sides, which gives $2x < -10$. Dividing both sides by 2 gives $x < -5$. So, the original inequality is satisfied by all values of x that are less than -5. We graph these solutions on the number line below:

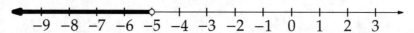

(c) We start by expanding the product on the left side with the distributive property. This gives

$$15 - 6y \geq 2y - 9.$$

Subtracting $2y$ from both sides gives $15 - 8y \geq -9$. Subtracting 15 from both sides gives $-8y \geq -24$. Our next step is dividing both sides by -8 to isolate y, but we have to be careful. When we divide both sides of an inequality by a negative number, we must reverse the direction of the inequality symbol. So, dividing $-8y \geq -24$ by -8 gives $y \leq 3$, not $y \geq 3$. We graph the solutions on the number line below:

$\square$

When we solve an inequality, we obviously can't test all of the possible answers in the way that we can check our answer to an equation. For example, in part (c) of the previous problem, we found that all values of y for which $y \leq 3$ are solutions to $3(5 - 2y) \geq 2y - 9$. We certainly can't test every single value that's less than or equal to 3. But we can test a few, just to make sure. For example, $y = 0$ does satisfy the original inequality, since $3(5 - 2 \cdot 0) \geq 2 \cdot 0 - 9$. Also, when $y = 3$, both sides of $3(5 - 2y) \geq 2y - 9$ equal -3, so the inequality is satisfied. Meanwhile, $y = 5$ does not satisfy the original inequality, since $3(5 - 2 \cdot 5) = -15$ and $2 \cdot 5 - 9 = 1$.

These quick checks are particularly helpful at catching errors with signs or with the direction of the inequality. Suppose we had gotten the direction of the inequality wrong and finished with $y \geq 3$, or made a sign error and finished with $y \leq -3$. The quick checks we just did would have revealed that we made a mistake somewhere.

> **Problem 5.31:** My town has two cell phone providers. The provider DontTalkMuch charges $80 per month, plus 1 dollar per hour. The provider TalkLots charges $20 per month, plus 4 dollars per hour. How much do you have to use your phone in a month in order for DontTalkMuch's deal to be better for you?

Solution for Problem 5.31: The cost of each provider depends on the number of hours of usage per month. So, we start by letting h be the number of hours of phone usage per month. DontTalkMuch charges $80 per month plus $1 for each of the h hours, for a total of $80 + h$ dollars per month. TalkLots charges $20 per month plus $4 for each of the h hours, for a total of $20 + 4h$ dollars per month.

We seek the values of h for which DontTalkMuch costs less than TalkLots. Therefore, we must have

$$80 + h < 20 + 4h.$$

Subtracting h and 20 from both sides gives $60 < 3h$. Dividing by 3 gives $20 < h$. Therefore, DontTalkMuch offers the better deal whenever you talk more than 20 hours in a month. □

> **Problem 5.32:** I have 308 baseball cards. Tommy has 532 baseball cards. Starting tomorrow, Tommy will give each of his four closest friends, including me, one baseball card each from his collection every day. How many cards will I have on the first day that I have more cards than Tommy has?

Solution for Problem 5.32: Each day Tommy gives away cards, I gain 1 card. So, after he has given away cards on d days, I have $308 + d$ cards. Each day Tommy gives away cards, he loses 4 cards, so he has given away $4d$ cards after d days. This leaves him with $532 - 4d$ cards. We wish to know when I will have more cards, so we want to know when

$$308 + d > 532 - 4d.$$

Adding $4d$ to both sides, and subtracting 308 from both sides, gives $5d > 224$. Dividing both sides by 5 gives $d > \frac{224}{5}$. Since $\frac{224}{5} = 44\frac{4}{5}$, we have $d > 44\frac{4}{5}$.

Tommy can't give away cards a fractional number of times, so the smallest that d can be is 45. So, the first time I'll have more cards than Tommy is just after he has given away cards 45 times. At that point, I will have $308 + 45 = 353$ cards and he will have $532 - 4 \cdot 45 = 352$ cards. Therefore, I will have 353 cards the first time I have more cards than Tommy has. □

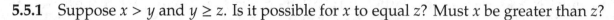

Exercises

5.5.1 Suppose $x > y$ and $y \geq z$. Is it possible for x to equal z? Must x be greater than z?

5.5.2 In each of the following parts, describe the values of the variable that make the inequality true, and graph those values on the number line.

(a) $7 \geq t > 4$ (b) $3x - 41 \leq 2x - 37$ (c) $14 - 7y < 4 - 2y$

5.5.3 Half of my favorite number is greater than the sum of 6 and my favorite number. What are the possible values of my number?

5.5.4

(a) Which is greater, $\dfrac{1}{2}$ or $\dfrac{1}{3}$?

(b) Which is greater, $\dfrac{1}{5}$ or $\dfrac{1}{8}$?

(c) Which is greater, $\dfrac{1}{1/2}$ or $\dfrac{1}{1/3}$?

(d) Suppose a and b are positive and $a > b$. Which is greater, $\dfrac{1}{a}$ or $\dfrac{1}{b}$?

(e) Suppose a and b are negative and $a > b$. Which is greater, $\dfrac{1}{a}$ or $\dfrac{1}{b}$?

(f) Suppose a is positive and b is negative and $a > b$. Which is greater, $\dfrac{1}{a}$ or $\dfrac{1}{b}$?

5.5.5 Suppose that x and y are positive and $x > y$. Explain why we must have $x^2 > y^2$.

5.5.6 At the end of Week 3 of my baseball team's season, our record is 5 wins and 7 losses. Each week after that, we win 3 games and lose 1 game. At the end of which week will my team have first won at least twice as many games total this season as it has lost?

5.6 Summary

In this chapter, we learned how to solve **one-variable linear equations**. By "solving" an equation, we mean finding all values of the variable for which the equation is true. The "one-variable" in "one-variable linear equation" means that only one variable appears in the equation, though it may appear multiple times. The "linear" means that every term in the equation is a constant term or is a constant times the first power of the variable.

We say that we **solve** an equation when we find all values of the variable that make the equation true. The two most important tactics we use to solve equations are:

1. *We can replace any expression with an equivalent expression.* For example, in the equation

$$5x - 4x + 3 = 14,$$

we can simplify the left-hand side to $x + 3$, so the equation becomes

$$x + 3 = 14.$$

2. *We can perform the same mathematical operation to both sides of the equation.* For example, starting with the equation $x + 3 = 14$, we can subtract 3 from both sides of the equation to get

$$x + 3 - 3 = 14 - 3.$$

Simplifying both sides of the equation then gives $x = 11$, and we have found the solution to the equation. Looking back to the original equation, $5x - 4x + 3 = 14$, we see that when we have $x = 11$, we get $5 \cdot 11 - 4 \cdot 11 + 3 = 14$, which is indeed a true equation.

> **Important:** When solving an equation, we can check our answer by substituting it back into the original equation. If the original equation is not satisfied by our answer, then we made a mistake.

> **Important:** If a linear equation can be manipulated into an equation that is never true (such as $-1 = -5$), then there are no solutions to the equation. Similarly, if a linear equation can be manipulated into an equation that is always true (such as $4r + 5 = 4r + 5$), then all possible values of the variable are solutions to the original equation.

We can often solve word problems by turning them into linear equations.

> **Important:** The key to solving word problems is converting the words into the language of mathematics. To do so, assign a variable to be a quantity you seek. Then, try to build an equation to solve for that variable.

> **WARNING!!** When solving a word problem, define your variable clearly and use it exactly as you've defined it.

The statement $x > y$ means that x is greater than y. Similarly, $x < y$ means that x is less than y. Both $x > y$ and $x < y$ are **inequalities**. More specifically, they are strict inequalities, because in both cases we cannot have $x = y$.

We can also write nonstrict inequalities, such as $x \geq y$, which means that x is greater than or equal to y. Similarly, $x \leq y$ means that x is less than or equal to y.

Important: Here are several useful rules regarding ways in which we can manipulate inequalities:

- If $a > b$ and $b > c$, then $a > c$.

- If $x > y$, then $x + c > y + c$ for any number c. If we also have $a > b$, then $x + a > y + b$.

- If $x > y$ and $a > 0$, then $xa > ya$.

Important: If we multiply or divide an inequality by a negative number, we must reverse the direction of the inequality. For example, if $x > y$ and $a < 0$, then $xa < ya$.

Similar rules hold for nonstrict inequalities. For example, if $a \geq b$ and $b \geq c$, then $a \geq c$.

WARNING!! Inequality rules that work when all the variables are positive don't always work when some of the variables are negative! Be careful when dealing with negative numbers (or expressions that can be negative) in inequalities.

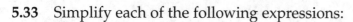

REVIEW PROBLEMS

5.33 Simplify each of the following expressions:

(a) $4(2 - 3r) - \dfrac{1}{2}(4 + 24r)$

(b) $\dfrac{24x}{21} + \dfrac{35x}{49} - \dfrac{x}{2}$

(c) $3y + \dfrac{y - 8}{2} + \dfrac{6y}{4}$

(d) $\dfrac{20z - 1}{3} - \dfrac{8z + 4}{12}$

5.34 Solve each of the following equations:

(a) $133 + w = -5$

(b) $3y - 12\dfrac{7}{8} = y + 3\dfrac{1}{4}$

(c) $\dfrac{2}{3}t = -18$

(d) $168 + 76a = 53a + 65a$

(e) $4r - 5 = 7 - 3r + 3(2 - r)$

(f) $6 - 4(2 - 3x) = 74 - 2(3 - x)$

(g) $\dfrac{z}{3} - 4 = \dfrac{2z - 9}{6}$

(h) $\dfrac{3p + 4}{7} = \dfrac{2p - 7}{4}$

(i) $\dfrac{12y - 8}{6} + \dfrac{9y + 1}{3} = 5\left(y - \dfrac{1}{5}\right)$

(j) $3(4 - 2x) - x(7 - 4) = \dfrac{x}{7} - \dfrac{2x}{3}$

5.35 For what value of t does $\dfrac{t/4}{16} = \dfrac{1}{6}$?

5.36 Solve for x: $\dfrac{1}{10^1} + \dfrac{1}{10^2} + \dfrac{1}{10^3} + \dfrac{1}{10^4} + \dfrac{1}{10^5} + \dfrac{1}{10^6} = \dfrac{x}{10^6}$. *(Source: MATHCOUNTS)*

5.37

(a) What is the value of $\dfrac{x-2}{2x+7}$ when $x = 0$?

(b) What is the value of $\dfrac{x-2}{2x+7}$ when $x = -3$?

(c) What is the value of $\dfrac{x-2}{2x+7}$ when $x = \dfrac{1}{2}$?

(d) For what value of x can we not determine a value of the expression $\dfrac{x-2}{2x+7}$? **Hints:** 41

5.38 Billie solved the equation $2y - 7 = y/3 + 9$ and found $y = 7$. She then shakes her head and starts over. How did she know so quickly that she made a mistake?

5.39 If $2 - 7g = 23$, then what is $\dfrac{g+7}{g+4}$?

5.40 For what value of x does $\dfrac{8}{x} = -3$?

5.41 If $\dfrac{2}{3} = \dfrac{x}{24} = \dfrac{84}{y}$, then what is $x + y$? *(Source: AMC 8)*

5.42 Six more than double a number equals twelve less than half the number. What is the number?

5.43 Tom multiplied a number by $2\frac{1}{2}$ correctly and got 50 as an answer. However, he was supposed to have divided the number by $2\frac{1}{2}$. What answer should he have found? *(Source: MOEMS)*

5.44 Jay had 60 tickets he could turn in at the end of the year for extra-credit points he had earned during the year. Some tickets were worth two points and others were worth five points. If he was entitled to a total of 231 extra-credit points, how many two-point tickets did he have?

5.45 If I give my sister 5 dollars, then we will have the same amount of money. If instead she gives me 8 dollars, then I'll have twice as much money as she has. How much money does she have?

5.46 From a certain apple tree, Jenny picked $\frac{1}{4}$ of the apples and Lenny picked $\frac{1}{3}$ of the apples. Penny picked the rest of the apples. If Lenny picked 7 more apples than Jenny did, how many apples did Penny pick? *(Source: MOEMS)*

5.47 The five members of the computer club decided to buy a used computer, dividing up the cost equally. Later, three new members joined the club and agreed to pay their fair share of the purchase price. This resulted in a saving of $15 for each of the original five members. What was the price of the used computer? *(Source: MOEMS)*

5.48   A road crew took three days to pave a road. On the first day they paved $\frac{2}{5}$ of the road, and on the second day they paved $\frac{1}{3}$ of the road. On the last day, they paved 1500 yards. How many yards long is the road?

5.49   The manager of a company planned to distribute a $50 bonus to each employee from the company fund, but the fund contained $5 less than what was needed. Instead, the manager gave each employee a $45 bonus and kept the remaining $95 in the company fund. How much money was in the company fund before any bonuses were paid? *(Source: AMC 8)*

5.50   My teacher gave me a number and told me to subtract 5 from the number and then multiply the result by 8. Unfortunately, I wasn't really listening. I thought she told me to subtract 8 first and then multiply the result by 5. I did those computations correctly, and came up with 70 as my answer. What is the correct answer to the question my teacher actually asked me?

5.51   Determine whether each of the following statements is true or false. If it is true, explain why it is true. If it is false, provide an example that shows the statement is false.

(a) If $a \leq b$ and $b \leq c$, then $a < c$.

(b) If $a \geq b \geq a$, then $a = b$.

(c) If $a > b$, then $ac > bc$.

(d) If $a > b$ and $c \leq 0$, then $ac \leq bc$.

(e) If $x + a \geq y + a$, then $x \geq y$.

(f) If $x + a \geq y + b$, then $x \geq y$ and $a \geq b$.

5.52   Suppose that $a > b > c > d$.

(a) Must we have $a + c > b + d$?

(b) Must we have $a + d > b + c$?

(c) Must we have $ac > bd$?

(d) Must we have $ab > cd$?

5.53   In each of the following parts, describe the values of the variable that make the inequality true, and graph those values on the number line.

(a) $-2\frac{1}{10} < k < 4\frac{1}{2}$

(b) $9t + 5 - 12t \geq 7 + 3t + 10$

(c) $\frac{3}{4}(3 - x) \leq -\frac{2}{3}(2 + x)$

5.54

(a) What values of x satisfy $2 - 3x \geq 6x - 3 - 9x$?

(b) What values of x satisfy $9 + 2x - 5x \geq -x + 12 - 2x$?

5.55 Terry finds a pile of money with at least \$500. If she puts \$100 of the pile in her left pocket, gives away $\frac{2}{3}$ of the rest of the pile, and then puts the remaining money from the pile in her right pocket, she'll have more money than if she instead gave away \$500 of the original pile and kept the rest. What are the possible values of the original pile of money?

Challenge Problems

5.56 Solve for x: $\dfrac{6\frac{1}{4}}{2\frac{1}{2}} = \dfrac{1\frac{1}{2}}{x}$. *(Source: MATHCOUNTS)* **Hints:** 38

5.57 What values of n satisfy the inequality $\dfrac{1}{n} \geq 6$?

5.58 Kayla adds the same number to both the numerator and denominator of the fraction $\frac{1}{10}$. Her resulting fraction equals $\frac{2}{3}$. What number did she add to both the numerator and denominator of her original fraction?

5.59 Douglas writes down his favorite number, which is a two-digit positive integer. He then turns the number into a three-digit number by writing a 7 at the end of his favorite number. This new number is 385 more than Douglas's favorite number. What is Douglas's favorite number? **Hints:** 140

5.60 Solve for p: $\dfrac{5}{6} = \dfrac{n}{72} = \dfrac{m+n}{84} = \dfrac{p-m}{120}$. *(Source: MATHCOUNTS)* **Hints:** 99

5.61 Suppose that x is nonzero.

(a) Express $\dfrac{1}{x} + \dfrac{3}{x}$ as a single fraction.

(b) Express $\dfrac{5}{4x} - \dfrac{2}{2x}$ as a single fraction.

(c) Express $\dfrac{7}{16x} - \dfrac{3}{10x}$ as a single fraction.

5.62 Solve the equation $\dfrac{1}{z-1} + \dfrac{5}{3} = \dfrac{3}{z-1}$. **Hints:** 55

5.63 Find all values of t for which $(12 - t)^2 = (3 + 2t)^2$. **Hints:** 77

5.64 For what integers a and b do we have $a = 2b + 21$ and $a = b - 28$? **Hints:** 9

5.65 For what number c does the equation $7y + 3c = 9y + 12 - 2y + 3$ have infinitely many solutions for y?

5.66 Paula can't quite read the board in her math class. She writes down the equation she reads on the board as $2x - 7 = 23$. She correctly solves the equation she wrote down, but is surprised to hear the teacher say the answer is 5 less than the answer Paula found. When Paula asks the teacher to check her work, the teacher says that Paula copied the coefficient of x incorrectly (but copied everything else correctly). What should the coefficient of x have been? **Hints:** 111

5.67★ Graph on a number line the values of x that satisfy $7 + x \geq 2x + 3 > 12 - x$. **Hints:** 26

5.68★ Graph on the number line all values of x that satisfy $\dfrac{2x + 2}{x + 7} \geq 0$. **Hints:** 132

5.69★ A number x is twice its reciprocal. What is x^6? *(Source: MATHCOUNTS)* **Hints:** 146

5.70

(a) Find the value of n for which $\dfrac{1}{2} = \dfrac{1}{3} + \dfrac{1}{n}$.

(b) Find the value of n for which $\dfrac{1}{3} = \dfrac{1}{4} + \dfrac{1}{n}$.

(c) Find the value of n for which $\dfrac{1}{4} = \dfrac{1}{5} + \dfrac{1}{n}$.

(d) Find the value of n for which $\dfrac{1}{1000} = \dfrac{1}{1001} + \dfrac{1}{n}$.

(e)★ Evaluate the sum $\dfrac{1}{1 \cdot 2} + \dfrac{1}{2 \cdot 3} + \dfrac{1}{3 \cdot 4} + \cdots + \dfrac{1}{99 \cdot 100}$. **Hints:** 97

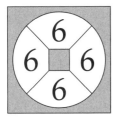 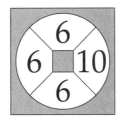 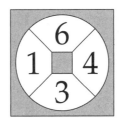 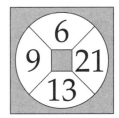

Decimals have a point. – Unknown

CHAPTER **6**
_____

Decimals

In Chapter 4, we explored one way to represent non-integer numbers: fractions. In this chapter, we'll explore another way: decimals.

6.1 Arithmetic with Decimals

Our method of writing integers is based on powers of tens (probably because we have 10 fingers). It's sometimes called the **base 10** system. For example, the number 572 literally means "5 hundreds and 7 tens and 2 ones." We can write this number in terms of powers of 10 as

$$572 = 500 + 70 + 2$$
$$= (5 \cdot 100) + (7 \cdot 10) + (2 \cdot 1)$$
$$= (5 \cdot 10^2) + (7 \cdot 10^1) + (2 \cdot 10^0).$$

Don't forget that $a^0 = 1$ for any number a, so $10^0 = 1$ is also a power of 10.

Decimals involve extending this "powers of 10" idea to non-integer numbers. We use a **decimal point** to separate a number into a part that's an integer and a part that's between 0 and 1. For example, the number 29.17 is equal to $29 + 0.17$, where 29 is a integer and 0.17 is between 0 and 1. (The "0" in "0.17" is not necessary—we could just write .17 without the zero—but including the 0 makes the number easier to read.) We read 29.17 to mean "2 tens and 9 ones and 1 tenth and 7 hundredths," where a tenth is $\frac{1}{10}$ and a hundredth is $\frac{1}{100}$. Since $\frac{1}{10} = 10^{-1}$ and

$\frac{1}{100} = \frac{1}{10^2} = 10^{-2}$, we can also write 29.17 in terms of powers of 10 as

$$29.17 = 20 + 9 + 0.1 + 0.07$$
$$= (2 \cdot 10) + (9 \cdot 1) + (1 \cdot 0.1) + (7 \cdot 0.01)$$
$$= (2 \cdot 10^1) + (9 \cdot 10^0) + (1 \cdot 10^{-1}) + (7 \cdot 10^{-2}).$$

Problems

Problem 6.1: Compute the following quantities:

(a) $2.6 + 3.1$

(b) $13.9 + 2.37$

(c) $0.002 + 0.4$

(d) $123.8 + 5.2$

(e) $3 - 0.27$

(f) $0.135 - 0.28$

Problem 6.2: Compute the following quantities:

(a) $2.59 \cdot 100$

(b) $36.7 \div 1000$

(c) $0.0028 \cdot 1000$

Problem 6.3: Compute the following quantities:

(a) $3.1 \cdot 5$

(b) $2.9 \cdot 1.3$

(c) $0.002 \cdot 0.003$

(d) $0.11 \cdot 0.15$

(e) $0.48 \div 0.06$

(f) $0.48 \div 0.6$

(g) $0.001 \div 0.0001$

(h) $100 \div 0.25$

Problem 6.4: List the following numbers from greatest to least:

$$0.5, 0.505, 0.55, 0.555, 0.06, 0.6, 0.65, 0.56, 0.005$$

Problem 6.5: Compute the following quantities:

(a) $(0.2)^2$

(b) $(1.7)^2$

(c) $1/(0.2)$

(d) $(0.03)^3$

Addition and subtraction of decimals is straightforward—we just need to be sure that the decimal points line up properly.

Problem 6.1: Compute the following quantities:

(a) $2.6 + 3.1$

(b) $13.9 + 2.37$

(c) $0.002 + 0.4$

(d) $123.8 + 5.2$

(e) $3 - 0.27$

(f) $0.135 - 0.28$

Solution for Problem 6.1:

(a) You probably already know how to add these numbers (and may even be able to add them in your head!), but just to be clear let's see exactly how this works.

We can write the two numbers that we're adding in terms of powers of 10:

$$2.6 + 3.1 = \big((2 \cdot 10^0) + (6 \cdot 10^{-1})\big) + \big((3 \cdot 10^0) + (1 \cdot 10^{-1})\big).$$

The commutative and associative properties of addition let us rearrange these products, so that the two products with 10^0 are together and the two products with 10^{-1} are together:

$$2.6 + 3.1 = \big((2 \cdot 10^0) + (3 \cdot 10^0)\big) + \big((6 \cdot 10^{-1}) + (1 \cdot 10^{-1})\big).$$

Now we factor:

$$2.6 + 3.1 = (2 + 3) \cdot 10^0 + (6 + 1) \cdot 10^{-1} = 5 \cdot 10^0 + 7 \cdot 10^{-1}.$$

Writing this last quantity as a decimal, we see that $2.6 + 3.1 = 5.7$.

Of course, this is a lot of work for a fairly simple idea. The digits in the ones place (2 and 3) get added and their sum (5) is in the ones place of the sum. The digits in the tenths place (6 and 1) get added and their sum (7) is in the tenths place of the sum. But this is exactly what we do when we add integers: the digits in the ones place get added and their sum goes in the ones place, the digits in the tens place get added and their sum goes in the tens place, and so on. We're just extending this idea—that digits in the same decimal place get added together—to the right of the decimal point.

$$\begin{array}{r} 2.6 \\ +\,3.1 \\ \hline 5.7 \end{array}$$

> **Concept:** When adding decimals, we add digits that are in the same decimal place. (Tens to tens, ones to ones, tenths to tenths, and so on.)

(b) Ones digits get added to ones digits, tenths digits get added to tenths digits, hundredths digits get added to hundredths digits, and so on. There is a minor issue with the fact that 13.9 doesn't appear to have a hundredths digit, whereas 2.37 does have a 7 as its hundredths digit. However, we know that $13.9 = 13.90$, so in fact 13.9 has an (unwritten) 0 as its hundredths digit. If we write that hidden 0, then we get the sum shown above at right. Notice how the decimal points are "lined up" in the sum.

$$\begin{array}{r} 13.90 \\ +\,2.37 \\ \hline \end{array}$$

Usually we don't write unnecessary 0's in the sum, as shown to the right. We have the (unwritten) 0 in the hundredths place of 13.9 added to the 7 in the hundredths place of 2.37 to give a 7 in the hundredths place of the sum.

$$\begin{array}{r} 13.9 \\ +\ 2.37 \\ \hline 16.27 \end{array}$$

Also note that the 9 that's the tenths digit in 13.9 gets added to the 3 that's the tenths digit in 2.37. This sums to 12 tenths, so we place a 2 in the tenths digit of the sum, and carry the extra 10 tenths over as a 1 in the ones digit (just like we carry when adding integers). Thus, the ones digit in our sum is $3 + 2 + 1$ (from the carry) $= 6$.

(c) We add as shown to the right. Notice that the hidden 0's in the hundredths and thousandths digits of 0.4 are part of the addition.

$$\begin{array}{r} 0.002 \\ +0.4 \\ \hline 0.402 \end{array}$$

> **Important:** We often have to think about the extra hidden 0's that are present in decimals, even if they are not written down.

(d) Here we see that the sum of the two decimals gives us .0 to the right of the decimal point, so that our sum is in fact an integer. We usually don't write the .0 part in our final answer, and instead just write $123.8 + 5.2 = 129$.

$$\begin{array}{r} 123.8 \\ +\ \ 5.2 \\ \hline 129.0 \end{array}$$

(e) Subtraction is essentially the same as addition. However, it is usually easier to explicitly write down the hidden 0's that we need, because it makes the subtraction a bit easier to compute. In particular, the first step of our subtraction is to subtract the 7 in the hundredths digit of 0.27 from the 0 in the hundredths digit of 3. As you know, this requires regrouping (or borrowing) a 10 from the 0 in the tenths digit of 3, and this in turn requires regrouping (or borrowing) a 10 from the 3 in the ones digit of 3.

$$\begin{array}{r} 3.00 \\ -0.27 \\ \hline 2.73 \end{array}$$

(f) The number that we are subtracting (0.280) is larger than the number that we are subtracting from (0.135), so the subtraction results in a negative decimal. Thus, just as with integers, we actually compute $0.28 - 0.135$ and then take its negation to get our answer. This calculation is shown at right, and our answer is

$$\begin{array}{r} 0.280 \\ -0.135 \\ \hline 0.145 \end{array}$$

$$0.135 - 0.28 = -(0.28 - 0.135) = -0.145.$$

Again, just like in part (e), writing the hidden 0 in the thousandths digit of 0.28 makes the subtraction a bit easier to compute.

□

Multiplying or dividing by a power of 10 is also pretty easy. We usually think of multiplying or dividing by a power of 10 as "moving the decimal point," as we see in the following examples:

Problem 6.2: Compute the following quantities:

(a) $2.59 \cdot 100$ (b) $36.7 \div 1000$ (c) $0.0028 \cdot 1000$

Solution for Problem 6.2:

(a) You may already know the quick way to compute this product. But in case you don't, and to see why the quick way works, let's first write the whole product in terms of powers of 10 (note that we'll also write the 100 as a power of 10):

$$2.59 \cdot 100 = \left((2 \cdot 10^0) + (5 \cdot 10^{-1}) + (9 \cdot 10^{-2})\right) \cdot 10^2.$$

Now we use the distributive property to move the 10^2 term inside the large parentheses.

$$2.59 \cdot 100 = \left((2 \cdot 10^0) \cdot 10^2\right) + \left((5 \cdot 10^{-1}) \cdot 10^2\right) + \left((9 \cdot 10^{-2}) \cdot 10^2\right).$$

We then use the associative property on each product in the above sum to group the powers of 10 together:

$$2.59 \cdot 100 = \left(2 \cdot (10^0 \cdot 10^2)\right) + \left(5 \cdot (10^{-1} \cdot 10^2)\right) + \left(9 \cdot (10^{-2} \cdot 10^2)\right).$$

Next, we use what we know about exponents to combine the powers of 10:

$$2.59 \cdot 100 = (2 \cdot 10^2) + (5 \cdot 10^1) + (9 \cdot 10^0).$$

Finally, we write the right side of this last equation as a decimal number:

$$2.59 \cdot 100 = 259.$$

That's a lot of work for a pretty simple computation. What's essentially going on is that multiplying by $100 = 10^2$ increases the exponent of each power of 10 by 2. But this means that each digit gets moved 2 positions to the left of where it starts. Specifically, the 2 that was originally in the units (10^0) position gets moved to the hundreds (10^2) position; the 5 that was originally in the tenths (10^{-1}) position gets moved to the tens (10^1) position; and the 9 that was originally in the hundredths (10^{-2}) position gets moved to the units (10^0) position.

We can also think of multiplying by $100 = 10^2$ as "moving the decimal point 2 places to the right," as follows:

$$2.59 \quad \rightarrow \quad 259.$$

> **Concept:** Multiplying by 10^n means moving each digit n positions to the left. We can also think of this as moving the decimal point n places to the right.

(b) Again, let's first be long-winded and perform the entire computation in terms of powers of 10. We know that $1000 = 10^3$, and we know that dividing by 10^3 is the same as multiplying by 10^{-3}. That is,

$$36.7 \div 1000 = 36.7 \cdot \frac{1}{1000} = 36.7 \cdot \frac{1}{10^3} = 36.7 \cdot 10^{-3}.$$

Now we write 36.7 in terms of powers of 10:

$$36.7 \div 1000 = \big((3 \cdot 10^1) + (6 \cdot 10^0) + (7 \cdot 10^{-1})\big) \cdot 10^{-3}.$$

The distributive property lets us multiply each term of the sum by 10^{-3}:

$$36.7 \div 1000 = \big((3 \cdot 10^1) \cdot 10^{-3}\big) + \big((6 \cdot 10^0) \cdot 10^{-3}\big) + \big((7 \cdot 10^{-1}) \cdot 10^{-3}\big).$$

We can now use the associative property of multiplication to group the powers of 10 together:

$$36.7 \div 1000 = \big(3 \cdot (10^1 \cdot 10^{-3})\big) + \big(6 \cdot (10^0 \cdot 10^{-3})\big) + \big(7 \cdot (10^{-1} \cdot 10^{-3})\big).$$

Next, we combine the powers of 10:

$$36.7 \div 1000 = (3 \cdot 10^{-2}) + (6 \cdot 10^{-3}) + (7 \cdot 10^{-4}).$$

Finally, we write our answer as a decimal, with a 3 as the hundredths digit (since it multiplies 10^{-2}), a 6 as the thousandths digit (since it multiplies 10^{-3}), and a 7 as the ten-thousandths digit (since it multiplies 10^{-4}):

$$36.7 \div 1000 = 0.0367.$$

Notice the "extra" 0 that we have to write as the tenths digit of our answer.

When doing the above computation, we used the fact that dividing by a power of 10 is the same as multiplying by a power of 10. (In this example, dividing by 10^3 was the same as multiplying by 10^{-3}.) So it makes sense that we can also think of division in terms of "moving the digits" or "moving the decimal point," just like multiplication. Specifically, in this example, we are dividing by $1000 = 10^3$, so all digits get moved 3 positions to the right, which is the same as the decimal point getting moved 3 places to the left:

$$36.7 \quad \rightarrow \quad 0.0367$$

The decimal point that was immediately to the right of the 6 gets moved three places to the left. Notice that we need to add a 0 in front of the 3 in order to move the decimal point three places. Also, note that each digit ends up three positions to the right of where it started before the division.

> **Concept:** Dividing by 10^n means moving each digit n positions to the right. We can also think of this as moving the decimal point n places to the left.

(c) Multiplying by $1000 = 10^3$ moves the decimal point 3 places to the right (or, equivalently, moves all digits 3 positions to the left), so

$$0.0028 \cdot 1000 = 0002.8.$$

This is sort of the opposite of part (b): we now have extra zeros that we don't need, so we just write the answer as 2.8.

□

Multiplication and division of decimals are a bit more complicated. We have to be especially careful about where the decimal point ends up in the result.

Problem 6.3: Compute the following quantities:

(a) $3.1 \cdot 5$

(b) $2.9 \cdot 1.3$

(c) $0.002 \cdot 0.003$

(d) $0.11 \cdot 0.15$

(e) $0.48 \div 0.06$

(f) $0.48 \div 0.6$

(g) $0.001 \div 0.0001$

(h) $100 \div 0.25$

Solution for Problem 6.3:

(a) We can expand the decimal by powers of 10, and then use the distributive property:

$$3.1 \cdot 5 = (3 + 0.1) \cdot 5 = (3 \cdot 5) + (0.1 \cdot 5) = 15 + 0.5 = 15.5.$$

This approach was pretty straightforward for this example, but this is not how we typically multiply decimals. A more typical process, which works better for harder examples, is:

- Write each quantity as an integer times a power of 10,
- Multiply the integers and the powers of 10 separately, and
- Rewrite the product as a decimal.

For example, we would compute $3.1 \cdot 5$ as

$$\begin{aligned}
3.1 \cdot 5 &= (31 \cdot 10^{-1}) \cdot (5 \cdot 10^0) \\
&= (31 \cdot 5) \cdot (10^{-1} \cdot 10^0) \\
&= 155 \cdot 10^{-1} \\
&= 15.5.
\end{aligned}$$

Normally, we wouldn't go to so much trouble for a simple example, but this procedure will help with the more complicated examples that follow.

(b) We use the procedure described in part (a) above:

$$\begin{aligned}
2.9 \cdot 1.3 &= (29 \cdot 10^{-1}) \cdot (13 \cdot 10^{-1}) \\
&= (29 \cdot 13) \cdot (10^{-1} \cdot 10^{-1}) \\
&= 377 \cdot 10^{-2} \\
&= 3.77.
\end{aligned}$$

As a check, note that our multiplication is taking the number 1.3 and nearly tripling it (since 2.9 is just a bit less than 3). So we expect our answer to be slightly less than 3.9, and indeed 3.77 fits the bill. This gives us reassurance that the decimal point is in the correct spot.

> **Concept:** If possible, perform a quick check at the end of a computation, to see if your answer is reasonable.

(c) Here we know that the answer will have the digit 6 (since $6 = 2 \cdot 3$); the only issue is where the decimal point is located. Explicitly writing the powers of 10 makes it less likely that you'll make a mistake:

$$(0.002) \cdot (0.003) = (2 \cdot 10^{-3}) \cdot (3 \cdot 10^{-3}) = 6 \cdot 10^{-6} = 0.000006.$$

Alternatively, you can also think of the computation as

$$0.002 \cdot 0.003 = 2 \cdot 0.001 \cdot 3 \cdot 0.001 = (2 \cdot 3) \cdot 0.001 \cdot 0.001.$$

We compute $2 \cdot 3 = 6$. Then, multiplying by the first factor of 0.001 moves the decimal point 3 places to the left, and multiplying by the second factor of 0.001 moves the decimal point another 3 places to the left. So our answer is 6 with the decimal point moved a total of $3 + 3 = 6$ places to the left, which is 0.000006.

(d) We have

$$
\begin{aligned}
0.11 \cdot 0.15 &= (11 \cdot 10^{-2}) \cdot (15 \cdot 10^{-2}) \\
&= (11 \cdot 15) \cdot (10^{-2} \cdot 10^{-2}) \\
&= 165 \cdot 10^{-4} \\
&= 0.0165.
\end{aligned}
$$

We could also compute this product as

$$0.11 \cdot 0.15 = (11 \cdot 0.01) \cdot (15 \cdot 0.01) = (11 \cdot 15) \cdot (0.01 \cdot 0.01).$$

We compute $11 \cdot 15 = 165$, then move the decimal point to the left a total of $2 + 2 = 4$ places (2 places for each factor of 0.01). Thus the answer is 0.0165.

As a check, note that both original numbers (0.11 and 0.15) are between 0.1 and 0.2, so our product should be between $(0.1)^2 = 0.01$ and $(0.2)^2 = 0.04$. The answer 0.0165 is indeed between 0.01 and 0.04, so we can be confident the decimal point is in the correct place.

> **Concept:** There are many processes for multiplying decimals. Use the method that works best for you for any particular problem. The most common mistake when multiplying decimals is placing the decimal point in an incorrect location in the product. Whenever it's reasonably possible, double-check your answer to be sure that you have correctly placed the decimal point.

(e) We can use a similar process with division: we write each number as an integer times a power of 10, and then group the integers together and the powers of 10 together. In this problem, we have

$$0.48 \div 0.06 = (48 \cdot 10^{-2}) \div (6 \cdot 10^{-2})$$
$$= (48 \div 6) \cdot (10^{-2} \div 10^{-2})$$
$$= 8 \cdot 10^{0}$$
$$= 8.$$

We could also write the division as a fraction, and multiply by a suitable power of 10 to make both numerator and denominator an integer. Using this method, our computation is:

$$\frac{0.48}{0.06} = \frac{0.48 \cdot 10^2}{0.06 \cdot 10^2} = \frac{48}{6} = 8.$$

(f) This is almost the same as part (e), but the number that we are dividing by in this part is 10 times the number we are dividing by in part (e). So since we are now dividing by a number that is 10 times as large, our answer to this part should be our answer from part (e) divided by 10, or $8 \div 10 = 0.8$. We can check this by computing using powers of 10:

$$0.48 \div 0.6 = (48 \cdot 10^{-2}) \div (6 \cdot 10^{-1})$$
$$= (48 \div 6) \cdot (10^{-2} \div 10^{-1})$$
$$= 8 \cdot 10^{-1}$$
$$= 0.8.$$

As a computation using fractions, this is

$$\frac{0.48}{0.6} = \frac{0.48 \cdot 10^2}{0.6 \cdot 10^2} = \frac{48}{60} = \frac{8}{10} = 0.8.$$

(g) We can write this directly as a power of 10:

$$0.001 \div 0.0001 = 10^{-3} \div 10^{-4} = 10^{-3-(-4)} = 10^{1} = 10.$$

Alternatively, we might recognize that 0.001 is 10 times 0.0001, since moving the decimal point in 0.0001 one place to the right gives 0.001.

(h) Using fractions we have

$$\frac{100}{0.25} = \frac{100 \cdot 10^2}{0.25 \cdot 10^2} = \frac{10000}{25} = 400.$$

A simpler solution is to recognize that $0.25 = \frac{25}{100} = \frac{1}{4}$, so $100 \div 0.25 = 100 \div \frac{1}{4} = 100 \cdot 4 = 400$. (If you don't see why $0.25 = \frac{1}{4}$, we will discuss converting decimals to fractions in Section 6.3.)

$\square$

Problem 6.4: List the following numbers from greatest to least:

$$0.5, 0.505, 0.55, 0.555, 0.06, 0.6, 0.65, 0.56, 0.005$$

Solution for Problem 6.4: All the numbers in the list are between 0 and 1, so we start comparing them by looking at the first digit after the decimal point. We can group the numbers by their tenths digits: all those with tenths digit 6 are larger than all those with tenths digit 5, which are all larger than all those with tenths digit 0:

$$\{0.6, 0.65\} \quad \text{larger than} \quad \{0.5, 0.505, 0.55, 0.555, 0.56\} \quad \text{larger than} \quad \{0.06, 0.005\}$$

Within each group, we then compare hundredths digits. We have to keep in mind that if a hundredths digit is not present, then it is 0. For example, $0.65 > 0.6$, because they have equal tenths digits, and the hundredths digit of 0.65 (which is 5) is greater than the hundredths digit of 0.6 (which is 0). If the numbers agree in both the tenths digit and the hundredths digit (like 0.55 and 0.555), we then look at the thousandths digit (so that $0.555 > 0.55$). In the end, the numbers get arranged as

$$0.65 > 0.6 > 0.56 > 0.555 > 0.55 > 0.505 > 0.5 > 0.06 > 0.005.$$

Another way to approach this problem is to write some of the hidden zeros in the decimals, so that all the decimals are the same length. That is, we rewrite our original list as

$$0.500, 0.505, 0.550, 0.555, 0.060, 0.600, 0.650, 0.560, 0.005.$$

Now it's straightforward to arrange these numbers in numerical order:

$$0.650 > 0.600 > 0.560 > 0.555 > 0.550 > 0.505 > 0.500 > 0.060 > 0.005,$$

and removing the unnecessary zeros gives us our answer. $\square$

Problem 6.5: Compute the following quantities:

(a) $(0.2)^2$ (b) $(1.7)^2$ (c) $1/(0.2)$ (d) $(0.03)^3$

Solution for Problem 6.5:

(a) As with multiplication, we generally find it easiest to raise a decimal to a power if we first write the decimal as the product of an integer and a power of 10. So, we compute

$$(0.2)^2 = (2 \cdot 10^{-1})^2 = 2^2 \cdot (10^{-1})^2 = 4 \cdot 10^{-2} = 0.04.$$

We also could have written the decimal as a fraction:

$$(0.2)^2 = \left(\frac{2}{10}\right)^2 = \frac{4}{100} = 0.04.$$

(b) As in part (a), we compute:

$$(1.7)^2 = (17 \cdot 10^{-1})^2 = 17^2 \cdot (10^{-1})^2 = 289 \cdot 10^{-2} = 2.89.$$

As a check, note that 1.7 is between 1 and 2, so $(1.7)^2$ should be between $1^2 = 1$ and $2^2 = 4$, and indeed $1 < 2.89 < 4$.

(c) Reciprocals of decimals can be a little tricky. We can use the same method as from parts (a) and (b), remembering that taking a reciprocal is the same as raising to the -1 power.

$$1/(0.2) = (0.2)^{-1} = (2 \cdot 10^{-1})^{-1} = 2^{-1} \cdot (10^{-1})^{-1} = \frac{1}{2} \cdot 10^1 = \frac{1}{2} \cdot 10 = 5.$$

We can check this using fractions: note that $0.2 = \frac{2}{10} = \frac{1}{5}$, so $1/(0.2) = 1/(\frac{1}{5}) = 5$.

(d) We can cube a decimal using the same computation as in the previous parts:

$$(0.03)^3 = (3 \cdot 10^{-2})^3 = 3^3 \cdot (10^{-2})^3 = 27 \cdot 10^{-6} = 0.000027.$$

$\square$

Exercises

6.1.1 Arrange the following numbers from smallest to largest:

$$0.99, 0.9099, 0.9, 0.909, 0.9009.$$

6.1.2 Which nonzero digit of 0.54321, when changed to a 9, gives the largest number?

6.1.3 Compute the following quantities:

(a) $0.4 + 0.02 + 0.006$

(b) $0.92 + 0.093$

(c) $1.28 - 0.377$

(d) $8 - 1.001$

(e) $0.0006 - 0.002$

(f) $1.1 - 0.11 + 0.011$

6.1.4 Compute the following quantities:

(a) $23.879 \cdot 100$

(b) $2 \div 10^5$

(c) $1.6 \div 400$

(d) $0.0031 \cdot 10^6$

(e) $3.6 \div 0.09$

(f) $1.01 \cdot 3.03$

6.1.5 Evaluate $(250+25+2.5+0.25+0.025) \div (50+5+0.5+0.05+0.005)$. *(Source: MATHCOUNTS)*

6.1.6 Let x be the number

$$0.\underbrace{0000\ldots00001}_{\text{5000 zeros}},$$

where there are 5000 zeros after the decimal point before the 1. Arrange the following numbers in order from least to greatest:

$$2+x, 2-x, 2x, \frac{2}{x}, \frac{x}{2}.$$

6.1.7 Betty used a calculator to find the product $0.075 \cdot 2.56$. She forgot to enter the decimal points. The calculator showed 19200. If Betty had entered the decimal points correctly, what would the answer have been? *(Source: AMC 8)*

6.1.8 Which of the following numbers is equal to $1000 \cdot 1993 \cdot 0.1993 \cdot 10$:

$$1.993 \cdot 10^3; \ 1993.1993; \ (199.3)^2; \ 1{,}993{,}001.993; \ \text{or} \ (1993)^2?$$

(Source: AMC 8)

6.1.9 If $0.0481 \cdot 10^{-4} = 4.81 \cdot N$, what is N? *(Source: MATHCOUNTS)*

6.1.10★ Curt mistakenly multiplied a number by 10 when he should have divided the number by 10. The answer he found was 33.66 more than the answer he should have found. Find the original number. *(Source: MOEMS)* **Hints:** 130, 159

6.2 Rounding

When we **round** an integer to a particular power of 10, we mean that we approximate our number by the closest number that's a multiple of our chosen power of 10. For example, the number 16,392 is nearer to 16,000 than to 17,000, so 16,392 rounds to the nearest thousand as 16,000. Similarly, 16,392 rounds to the nearest hundred as 16,400, because 16,392 is closer to 16,400 than to 16,300.

We always round to the nearest whole multiple of the power of 10 that we're rounding to. If a number is exactly halfway between two whole multiples of the power of 10 that we're rounding to, then we always pick the larger one. For example, the number 2,500 gets rounded to the nearest thousand as 3,000, even though 2,500 is equally close to 2,000 and 3,000.

We can also round decimals. The simplest sort of rounding for a decimal is to round it to the nearest integer. Remember that 1 is a power of 10, since $1 = 10^0$, so rounding to an integer is essentially "rounding to a multiple of 1." For example, 2.18 rounds to the nearest integer as 2, and 5.891 rounds to the nearest integer as 6.

We can also round a decimal to the nearest tenth, nearest hundredth, or to any decimal place that we choose. For instance, 3.419 rounds to the nearest tenth to 3.4 or to the nearest hundredth as 3.42. We also sometimes say that 3.419 rounds to 3.4 "to one decimal place" or rounds to 3.42 "to two decimal places." Again, if a number is exactly halfway between the two nearest multiples of the power of 10 that we're rounding to, we always pick the larger one. For example, 11.35 rounded to the nearest tenth is 11.4, even though 11.35 is exactly halfway between 11.3 and 11.4.

We often round numbers in our everyday life because it's usually easier for us to think about "round" numbers rather than exact numbers. For example, the high temperature today might be 78.39 degrees, but the weather forecast will probably just say "high of 78" and your mom might tell you that it's "about 80 degrees." Another common use of rounding is with large numbers that are hard to measure exactly. For example, according to the 2010 census, the population of Los Angeles is 3,792,621 people, but it is silly to think that this number can be exactly measured. It is more meaningful, and easier to process, if we round and say that the population of Los Angeles is about 3.8 million people.

We also use rounding to simplify or check calculations. For instance, if you wanted to multiply 2,049 and 6,892, we could instead multiply the numbers rounded to the nearest thousand, 2,000 and 7,000. This multiplication is just

$$2,000 \cdot 7,000 = (2 \cdot 1,000) \cdot (7 \cdot 1,000) = (2 \cdot 7) \cdot (1,000 \cdot 1,000) = 14 \cdot 1,000,000 = 14,000,000.$$

So we expect that $2,049 \cdot 6,892$ should be close to 14,000,000. (In fact it is 14,121,708.)

Problem 6.6:

(a) Round 697 to the nearest hundred.

(b) Round −2,712 to the nearest thousand.

(c) Round 1.651 to the nearest tenth.

(d) Round 0.00282 to the nearest thousandth.

(e) Round 0.03 to the nearest tenth.

(f) Round 0.1972 to the nearest hundredth.

(g) Round −2.35 to the nearest tenth.

(h) Round 1.995 to the nearest hundredth.

Problem 6.7:
(a) Round 4.73, 4.739, and 4.7395 each to the nearest tenth.

(b) When rounding a positive number to the nearest tenth, which digit determines whether the number you round to is larger or smaller than the original number?

Problem 6.8: Suppose you are told that the number x rounds to 2.7 when rounded to the nearest tenth. What can you conclude about x?

Problem 6.9: Suppose your friend tells you that $5,192 \cdot 7,832$ equals 51,663,744. Is this reasonable? Why or why not?

Problem 6.6:

(a) Round 697 to the nearest hundred.

(b) Round −2,712 to the nearest thousand.

(c) Round 1.651 to the nearest tenth.

(d) Round 0.00282 to the nearest thousandth.

(e) Round 0.03 to the nearest tenth.

(f) Round 0.1972 to the nearest hundredth.

(g) Round −2.35 to the nearest tenth.

(h) Round 1.995 to the nearest hundredth.

Solution for Problem 6.6:

(a) 697 is closer to 700 than to 600, so 697 rounded to the nearest hundred is 700.

(b) −2,712 is closer to −3,000 than to −2,000, so −2,712 rounded to the nearest thousand is −3,000. Note also that 2,712 rounded to the nearest thousand is 3,000. Is it true that $-x$ always rounds in the same way as x? (By the time we finish all the parts of this problem, we'll know the answer.)

(c) 1.651 is slightly closer to 1.7 than to 1.6. We can tell because 1.65 is exactly halfway between them, and 1.651 is a little bit larger than 1.65. So 1.65 rounded to the nearest tenth is 1.7.

(d) 0.00282 is closer to 0.003 than to 0.002, so 0.00282 rounded to the nearest thousandth is 0.003.

(e) 0.03 is closer to 0 than to 0.1, so 0.03 rounded to the nearest tenth is 0. Many people would write the answer as 0.0 to emphasize that it is rounded to the tenths decimal place, but of course 0 and 0.0 are the same number.

(f) 0.1972 is closer to 0.20 than to 0.19, so 0.1972 rounded to the nearest hundredth is 0.2. Again, many would write this as 0.20 to emphasize that we are worried about the hundredths digit.

(g) −2.35 is exactly halfway between −2.3 and −2.4, so by rule, it rounds to the greater number, or −2.3. Note that 2.35, by the same rule, would round to 2.4, so here is an example of a number x for which x and $-x$ round differently.

(h) 1.995 is exactly halfway between 1.99 and 2, so by rule, it rounds to the larger quantity, which is 2. Often we would write this as 2.00 (that is, write the "unnecessary" 0's in the tenths and hundredths digits) to emphasize the fact that we've rounded to the nearest hundredth.

□

Problem 6.7:

(a) Round 4.73, 4.739, and 4.7395 each to the nearest tenth.

(b) When rounding a positive number to the nearest tenth, which digit determines whether the number you round to is larger or smaller than the original number?

Solution for Problem 6.7:

(a) Each of these numbers is between 4.7 and 4.8, and is closer to 4.7 than to 4.8 because each is less than 4.75. Therefore, each rounded to the nearest tenth is 4.7.

(b) Part (a) suggests that only the hundredths digit matters when rounding to the nearest tenth, because even adding a digit of 9 to go from 4.73 to 4.739 doesn't change the fact that we round down. Indeed, any number of the form 4.7D, where D is one of the digits 0, 1, 2, 3, or 4, will satisfy

$$4.7 \leq 4.7D < 4.75.$$

(Here we write 4.7D not to mean 4.7 multiplied by D, but instead to mean the number with 4 as the units digit, 7 as the tenths digit, and D as the hundredths digit.) Moreover, adding additional digits after the D will still keep the number below 4.75. So any number of the form 4.7D..., where D is one of the digits 0, 1, 2, 3, or 4, is rounded down to the nearest tenth to 4.7. (Actually, there is one technical exception to this rule, which we will discuss in Section 6.4.)

On the other hand, if D is one of the digits 5, 6, 7, 8, or 9, then the number 4.7D satisfies

$$4.75 \leq 4.7D < 4.8,$$

and adding additional digits after the D will still keep the number between 4.75 and 4.8. So 4.7D..., where D is one of the digits 5, 6, 7, 8, or 9, is rounded up to the nearest tenth to 4.8. This also suggests why we round 4.75 up to 4.8, even though it is exactly halfway between 4.7 and 4.8: it makes "look at the hundredths digit" a consistent rule for rounding positive numbers to the nearest tenth.

□

Problem 6.8: Suppose you are told that the number x rounds to 2.7 when rounded to the nearest tenth. What can you conclude about x?

Solution for Problem 6.8: We know that x rounds to 2.7 if x is closer to 2.7 than to any other multiple of 0.1. This can only happen if x is between 2.6 and 2.7, or if x is between 2.7 and 2.8.

If x is between 2.6 and 2.7, then it rounds up to 2.7 only if it is halfway between (that is, if $x = 2.65$) or greater. So $2.65 \leq x < 2.7$.

If x is between 2.7 and 2.8, then it rounds down to 2.7 only if it is less than halfway between. So $2.7 < x < 2.75$.

And, of course, we could have $x = 2.7$ to begin with. Putting all these cases together, we conclude that $2.65 \leq x < 2.75$. □

One use of rounding is as a quick check of the validity of a solution to a lengthy computation, as in the following example:

Problem 6.9: Suppose your friend tells you that $5{,}192 \cdot 7{,}832$ equals $51{,}663{,}744$. Is this reasonable? Why or why not?

Solution for Problem 6.9: The following argument is not quite good enough:

> **Bogus Solution:** 5,192 rounded to the nearest thousand is 5,000, and 7,832 rounded to the nearest thousand is 8,000. Since 1 thousand times 1 thousand is 1 million, the product of the two given numbers rounds, to the nearest million, as
>
> $$5{,}000 \cdot 8{,}000 = (5 \cdot 10^3) \cdot (8 \cdot 10^3) = (5 \cdot 8) \cdot 10^6 = 40 \cdot 10^6 = 40{,}000{,}000.$$
>
> But my friend's answer rounded to the nearest million is 52,000,000, so it cannot be correct.

This is the right idea, but not quite precise enough. It is not necessarily true that the product xy rounds in the same way that the product of x rounded and y rounded do. For example, 6 and 7 each round to the nearest ten as 10, but their product $6 \cdot 7 = 42$ does not round to the nearest hundred as $10 \cdot 10 = 100$, since 42 rounded to the nearest hundred is 0.

But we can still use thousands to make an estimate of the product. We note that

$$5{,}000 \; < \; 5{,}192 \; < \; 6{,}000,$$
$$7{,}000 \; < \; 7{,}832 \; < \; 8{,}000.$$

So the product of 5,192 and 7,832 must be between the product of the lower estimates and the product of the higher estimates. That is,

$$(5{,}000)(7{,}000) < (5{,}192)(7{,}832) < (6{,}000)(8{,}000),$$

which means that the product is between 35,000,000 and 48,000,000. But the answer given is larger than 48 million, so it cannot be correct. □

Exercises

6.2.1 Round 28.2508 to

(a) the nearest ten.

(b) the nearest tenth.

(c) the nearest hundredth.

6.2.2 Round −0.155 to

(a) the nearest integer.

(b) the nearest tenth.

(c) the nearest hundredth.

6.2.3 Round 7.6397 to the nearest thousandth.

6.2.4 Find a number x such that x rounded to the nearest tenth is 1.8, x rounded to the nearest hundredth is 1.82, and x rounded to the nearest thousandth is 1.819.

6.2.5 The fraction $\dfrac{401}{.205}$ is closest to which of the following numbers:

$$.2, \ 2, \ 20, \ 200, \ \text{or } 2000\,?$$

(Source: AMC 8)

6.3 Decimals and Fractions

We have two ways to express a number that is not an integer: as a fraction or as a decimal. Since we may want to use the same number in more than one format, we need to be able to convert numbers back and forth between fractions and decimals.

 **Problems**

Problem 6.10: Our goal is to write 0.2 as a fraction.

(a) Write 0.2 in terms of a power of 10.

(b) Write the power of 10 from part (a) as a fraction.

(c) Write 0.2 as a fraction.

Problem 6.11: Write the following decimals as fractions:

(a) 0.8   (c) 0.04   (e) −1.72

(b) 0.5   (d) 0.125   (f) 2.5625

Problem 6.12: Write the following fractions as decimals:

(a) $\dfrac{1}{2}$ (c) $\dfrac{29}{100}$ (e) $-\dfrac{11}{20}$

(b) $\dfrac{3}{5}$ (d) $\dfrac{7}{8}$ (f) $\dfrac{19}{32}$

Problem 6.13: Write 12.3456 as a fraction in simplest form.

Problem 6.14: Find the reciprocal of 2.5 (express your answer as a decimal).

Problem 6.10: Our goal is to write 0.2 as a fraction.

(a) Write 0.2 in terms of a power of 10.

(b) Write the power of 10 from part (a) as a fraction.

(c) Write 0.2 as a fraction.

Solution for Problem 6.10:

(a) The 2 is in the tenths digit, so $0.2 = 2 \cdot 10^{-1}$.

(b) We have $10^{-1} = \dfrac{1}{10^1} = \dfrac{1}{10}$.

(c) Our decimal equals $0.2 = 2 \cdot 10^{-1} = 2 \cdot \dfrac{1}{10} = \dfrac{2}{10} = \dfrac{1}{5}$.

$\square$

That's really all there is to it! We express our decimal in terms of powers of 10, write the powers of 10 as fractions, and combine the resulting expression into a single fraction.

Here are a few more to practice on:

Problem 6.11: Write the following decimals as fractions:

(a) 0.8

(b) 0.5

(c) 0.04

(d) 0.125

(e) −1.72

(f) 2.5625

Solution for Problem 6.11:

(a) We have

$$0.8 = 8 \cdot 10^{-1} = 8 \cdot \frac{1}{10} = \frac{8}{10} = \frac{4}{5}.$$

This makes perfect sense: 0.8 is read aloud as "eight tenths." The digit 8 is in the tenths place of 0.8, and the equivalent fraction is $\frac{8}{10}$.

(b) We have

$$0.5 = 5 \cdot 10^{-1} = \frac{5}{10} = \frac{1}{2}.$$

We could also notice that 0.5 is exactly halfway between 0 and 1, so $0.5 = \frac{1}{2}$.

(c) We have $0.04 = 4 \cdot 10^{-2} = \frac{4}{100} = \frac{1}{25}$.

(d) We can expand this decimal and convert each part of the expansion to a fraction, then add:

$$0.125 = (1 \cdot 10^{-1}) + (2 \cdot 10^{-2}) + (5 \cdot 10^{-3})$$
$$= \frac{1}{10} + \frac{2}{100} + \frac{5}{1000}$$
$$= \frac{100}{1000} + \frac{20}{1000} + \frac{5}{1000} = \frac{100 + 20 + 5}{1000} = \frac{125}{1000} = \frac{125}{8 \cdot 125} = \frac{1}{8}.$$

However, it is easier to perform this computation if we write the decimal as an integer times a power of 10, as $0.125 = 125 \cdot 0.001 = 125 \cdot 10^{-3}$. Then, we immediately have

$$0.125 = 125 \cdot 10^{-3} = \frac{125}{1000} = \frac{125}{8 \cdot 125} = \frac{1}{8}.$$

(e) We'll use the technique from part (d):

$$-1.72 = -172 \cdot 0.01 = -\frac{172}{100} = -\frac{43}{25}.$$

(f) We have $2.5625 = 2\frac{5625}{10000}$. Since $\frac{5625}{10000} = \frac{9 \cdot 625}{16 \cdot 625} = \frac{9}{16}$, we have

$$2.5625 = 2\frac{5625}{10000} = 2\frac{9}{16} = \frac{41}{16}.$$

□

We also need to be able to convert fractions to decimals. To do this, we try to write our fraction with a denominator that is a power of 10.

Problem 6.12: Write the following fractions as decimals:

(a) $\frac{1}{2}$ (c) $\frac{29}{100}$ (e) $-\frac{11}{20}$

(b) $\frac{3}{5}$ (d) $\frac{7}{8}$ (f) $\frac{19}{32}$

Solution for Problem 6.12:

(a) We can do this directly by converting the denominator to a power of 10:

$$\frac{1}{2} = \frac{5}{10} = 5 \cdot \frac{1}{10} = 0.5.$$

(b) This is also pretty easy to write with the denominator as a power of 10:

$$\frac{3}{5} = \frac{6}{10} = 0.6.$$

(c) The denominator is already a power of 10:

$$\frac{29}{100} = 29 \cdot \frac{1}{100} = 29 \cdot 0.01 = 0.29.$$

(d) This one is a little trickier. To get the denominator to be a power of 10, we want to find the smallest power of 10 that is a multiple of 8. Since $8 = 2^3$ and $10^3 = 2^3 \cdot 5^3$, we can multiply the numerator and denominator of the fraction by $5^3 = 125$ to get

$$\frac{7}{8} = \frac{7 \cdot 125}{8 \cdot 125} = \frac{875}{1000} = 875 \cdot 0.001 = 0.875.$$

(e) Multiplying the numerator and denominator by 5 will do the trick:

$$-\frac{11}{20} = -\frac{55}{100} = -55 \cdot 0.01 = -0.55.$$

(f) Since $32 = 2^5$, we can multiply by $5^5 = 3125$ to get 10^5 in the denominator.

$$\frac{19}{32} = \frac{19 \cdot 3125}{10^5} = 59375 \cdot 10^{-5} = 0.59375.$$

$\square$

Some fractions, such as $\frac{1}{3}$, cannot be written as an equivalent fraction with an integer numerator and a denominator that's a power of 10. We will see how to convert these fractions to decimals in Section 6.4.

Problem 6.13: Write 12.3456 as a fraction in simplest form.

Solution for Problem 6.13: Since moving the decimal point 4 places to the right gives us the integer 123456, we know that $123456 = 12.3456 \cdot 10^4$. Thus, dividing by 10^4, we can write the decimal as

$$12.3456 = \frac{123456}{10^4}.$$

Clearly 123456 is not a multiple of 5, but we can try to cancel all four of the powers of 2 in the denominator by seeing if 16 is a factor of 123456. Indeed, we have $123456 = 16 \cdot 7716$, so the fraction simplifies as

$$12.3456 = \frac{123456}{10^4} = \frac{2^4 \cdot 7716}{2^4 \cdot 5^4} = \frac{7716}{5^4} = \frac{7716}{625}.$$

$\square$

Problem 6.14: Find the reciprocal of 2.5 (express your answer as a decimal).

Solution for Problem 6.14: It's usually easier to find reciprocals of fractions than of decimals, so let's first convert 2.5 to a fraction:

$$2.5 = \frac{25}{10} = \frac{5}{2}.$$

Its reciprocal is then $\frac{2}{5}$, and as a decimal this is $\frac{2}{5} = \frac{4}{10} = 0.4$. (As a check, note that $(2.5)(0.4) = 1$.)
□

Exercises

6.3.1 Express each of the following as a decimal:

(a) $\dfrac{2}{25}$

(b) $\dfrac{5}{16}$

(c) $-\dfrac{11}{4}$

(d) $\dfrac{81}{1000}$

(e) $\dfrac{17}{40}$

(f) $\dfrac{3}{10000}$

6.3.2 Express $\dfrac{2}{10} + \dfrac{4}{100} + \dfrac{6}{1000}$ as a decimal. *(Source: AMC 8)*

6.3.3 Express each of the following decimals as a fraction in simplest form:

(a) -0.7

(b) 0.0138

(c) 0.375

(d) 1.11

(e) 0.002

(f) 2.6

6.3.4 Express the product $8 \times .25 \times 2 \times .125$ as a fraction. *(Source: AMC 8)*

6.3.5 Express the reciprocal of 3.2 as a fraction. *(Source: MATHCOUNTS)*

6.3.6 How many eighths are in 5.75? *(Source: MATHCOUNTS)*

6.3.7★ A ball is dropped from a height of 3 meters. On its first bounce it rises to a height of 2 meters. It keeps falling and bouncing to $\frac{2}{3}$ of the height it reached in the previous bounce. On which bounce will it first not rise to a height of 0.5 meters? *(Source: AMC 8)*

6.3.8★ On a calculator Julian divided x into y and got the answer 1.0625. Both x and y were positive integers less than 50, but he can't remember what they were. What is the sum of all possible values of x and y? *(Source: MATHCOUNTS)* **Hints:** 106

6.4 Repeating Decimals

Many fractions (like $\frac{1}{2}$ or $\frac{3}{100}$) are easily converted to decimals ($\frac{1}{2} = 0.5$ and $\frac{3}{100} = 0.03$). But other fractions, even though they are simple in fraction form, are more difficult to write as decimals. We'll start with the most basic example.

Let's investigate how we would go about writing $\frac{1}{3}$ as a decimal.

Problem 6.15:

(a) Round $\frac{1}{3}$ to the nearest tenth.

(b) Round $\frac{1}{3}$ to the nearest hundredth.

(c) Does this pattern continue? When will it stop?

(d) Is it possible to write $\frac{1}{3}$ as a decimal? If so, how? If not, why not?

Solution for Problem 6.15:

(a) We can try to write $\frac{1}{3}$ with a denominator of 10:

$$\frac{1}{3} = \frac{1 \cdot \frac{10}{3}}{3 \cdot \frac{10}{3}} = \frac{\frac{10}{3}}{10} = \frac{3\frac{1}{3}}{10}.$$

So we see that $\frac{1}{3} = \frac{3\frac{1}{3}}{10}$ is between $\frac{3}{10}$ and $\frac{4}{10}$, and is closer to $\frac{3}{10}$. Therefore, $\frac{1}{3}$ rounds (to the nearest tenth) to 0.3.

Another way to see this is to note that $\frac{1}{3} = \frac{10}{30}$, so we have the inequality

$$\frac{9}{30} < \frac{10}{30} < \frac{12}{30}.$$

But $\frac{9}{30} = \frac{3}{10}$ and $\frac{12}{30} = \frac{4}{10}$, hence

$$\frac{3}{10} < \frac{1}{3} < \frac{4}{10}.$$

Thus $\frac{1}{3}$ is between 0.3 and 0.4. Furthermore, since 10 is closer to 9 than to 12, we know that $\frac{10}{30}$ is closer to $\frac{9}{30}$ than to $\frac{12}{30}$, and hence $\frac{1}{3}$ is closer to 0.3 than to 0.4. Thus, $\frac{1}{3}$ rounds (to the nearest tenth) to 0.3.

(b) We write $\frac{1}{3}$ with a denominator of 100:

$$\frac{1}{3} = \frac{1 \cdot \frac{100}{3}}{3 \cdot \frac{100}{3}} = \frac{\frac{100}{3}}{100} = \frac{33\frac{1}{3}}{100}.$$

So we see that $\frac{1}{3} = \frac{33\frac{1}{3}}{100}$ is between $\frac{33}{100}$ and $\frac{34}{100}$, and is closer to $\frac{33}{100}$. Therefore, $\frac{1}{3}$ rounds (to the nearest hundredth) to 0.33.

(c) The pattern seems clear, but we could do one more decimal place to be sure. If we want to round $\frac{1}{3}$ to the nearest thousandth, we can write $\frac{1}{3}$ with a denominator of 1000:

$$\frac{1}{3} = \frac{1 \cdot \frac{1000}{3}}{3 \cdot \frac{1000}{3}} = \frac{\frac{1000}{3}}{1000} = \frac{333\frac{1}{3}}{1000}.$$

So we see that $\frac{1}{3} = \frac{333\frac{1}{3}}{1000}$ is between $\frac{333}{1000}$ and $\frac{334}{1000}$, and is closer to $\frac{333}{1000}$. Therefore, $\frac{1}{3}$ rounds (to the nearest thousandth) to 0.333.

As our previous computations show, we expect to get a 3 in every decimal place to the right of the decimal point. For example, $\frac{1}{3}$ rounded to the nearest millionth is 0.333333. In fact, when we round $\frac{1}{3}$ to the nearest 10^{-n} (where n is a positive integer), we get n 3's to the right of the decimal point. This is because

$$\frac{1}{3} = \frac{\overbrace{33\ldots33}^{n\,3\text{'s}}\frac{1}{3}}{\underbrace{100\ldots0}_{n\,0\text{'s}}},$$

so that $\frac{1}{3}$ is always between $\frac{33\ldots33}{100\ldots0}$ and $\frac{33\ldots34}{100\ldots0}$ and is closer to $\frac{33\ldots33}{100\ldots0}$. Therefore, $\frac{1}{3}$ rounds to $0.333\ldots3$, where there are n 3's to the right of the decimal point.

(d) At first glance, it seems as though it is impossible to write $\frac{1}{3}$ as a decimal, since $\frac{1}{3}$ is always between $0.33\ldots33$ and $0.33\ldots34$ no matter how many decimal places we look at. But all this means is that we can't write $\frac{1}{3}$ as a *finite* decimal. We can write $\frac{1}{3}$ as the *infinite* decimal

$$\frac{1}{3} = 0.333\ldots.$$

The 3's to the right of the decimal point never end—they go on forever!

You may find this quite strange. But there are at least a couple of different explanations for why it makes sense that $\frac{1}{3}$ is equal to an infinite decimal.

Explanation 1: some algebra. We set $x = 0.333\ldots$ (that is, x is the number that has infinitely many 3's to the right of the decimal point), and we'll show that $x = \frac{1}{3}$. When we multiply x by 10, we move the decimal point 1 place to the right, so $10x = 3.333\ldots$. Now watch what happens when we subtract x from $10x$:

$$\begin{aligned} 10x &= 3.333\ldots \\ -\quad\ x &= 0.333\ldots \\ \hline (10x - x) &= 3 \end{aligned}$$

All of the 3's to the right of the decimal point cancel when we subtract, and we are left with just $10x - x = 3$, so $9x = 3$. Dividing by 9 gives $x = \frac{3}{9} = \frac{1}{3}$. So we have shown that

$$\frac{1}{3} = x = 0.333\ldots.$$

Explanation 2: long division. We remember that $\frac{1}{3} = 1 \div 3$, so we attempt to perform long division to compute $1 \div 3$. Of course, this seems a little silly at first, because we know that $1 \div 3$ gives a quotient of 0 and a remainder of 1. It's more interesting if we first write 1 itself as an infinite decimal:

$$1 = 1.000\ldots,$$

that is, 1 is equal to 1 with infinitely many 0's after the decimal point. We can then perform the long division $1.000\ldots \div 3$:

$$
\begin{array}{r}
.333 \\
3 \overline{\smash{\big)}\ 1.000} \\
0.9 \\
\overline{0.10} \\
0.09 \\
\overline{0.010} \\
0.009 \\
\overline{0.001}
\end{array}
$$

The above calculation shows that 3 divides into 1.000 giving quotient 0.333 and remainder 0.001. We can see that this long division will never end! At every step we'll be dividing 3 into 10, giving a quotient of 3 and remainder of 1, and then when we drop down another 0 from $1.000\ldots$ we'll be dividing 3 into 10 again, giving a quotient of 3 and remainder of 1, and then... it never ends! We can never get 3 to divide evenly at any step of the long division, so we'll get a quotient of $0.333\ldots$ going on forever.

□

So we see that the simple fraction $\frac{1}{3}$ cannot be written as a decimal with only finitely many digits, but instead is the infinite decimal $0.333\ldots$. This is called a **repeating decimal**, because the digit 3 repeats forever. Decimals that do not repeat forever, like 0.5 and 0.67676, are called **terminating decimals** or **finite decimals**.

We have a symbol that we use to write repeating decimals:

$$\frac{1}{3} = 0.333\ldots = 0.\overline{3}.$$

The bar over the 3 indicates that the 3 repeats forever. We can have decimals in which more than one digit repeats—for example

$$0.2\overline{79} = 0.279797979\ldots,$$

where we have a single "2" followed by a "79" that repeats forever. (We'll see in the problems below how to deal with this sort of repeating decimal.)

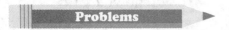
Problems

Problem 6.16: Write the following as repeating decimals:

(a) $\dfrac{5}{9}$ (b) $\dfrac{37}{90}$ (c) $\dfrac{1}{7}$ (d) $\dfrac{19}{11}$

Problem 6.17: Write the following as fractions in simplest form:

(a) $0.\overline{2}$ (b) $0.\overline{51}$ (c) $0.2\overline{8}$ (d) $5.00\overline{25}$

Problem 6.18:

(a) When we convert the fractions

$$\frac{1}{2}, \frac{1}{3}, \frac{1}{4}, \frac{1}{5}, \frac{1}{6}, \frac{1}{7}, \frac{1}{8}, \frac{1}{9}, \frac{1}{10},$$

to decimal form, which of them have finite decimals, and which of them have infinitely repeating decimals?

(b) Suppose $n \geq 2$ is a positive integer. Is there an easy way to tell if the decimal form of $\frac{1}{n}$ is finite or infinitely repeating?

Problem 6.19: What is the 100th digit to the right of the decimal point in the decimal representation of $\frac{3}{7}$?

Problem 6.20: What simpler number does $0.\overline{9}$ equal?

Problem 6.16: Write the following as repeating decimals:

(a) $\frac{5}{9}$ (b) $\frac{37}{90}$ (c) $\frac{1}{7}$ (d) $\frac{19}{11}$

Solution for Problem 6.16:

(a) We use long division to compute $\frac{5}{9}$, by dividing 9 into $5.000\ldots$ as shown at right. But we only have to do one step: we immediately get a remainder of 5, so every later step of the division will be the same as the first step. Thus, we conclude that $\frac{5}{9} = 0.555\ldots = 0.\overline{5}$.

$$\begin{array}{r} .5\ldots \\ 9\,\overline{)5.0\ldots} \\ 4.5 \\ \hline 0.5 \end{array}$$

We can check this answer with a little algebra. Let $x = 0.\overline{5}$. Then multiplying x by 10 moves the decimal point one place to the right, so that $10x = 5.\overline{5}$. Subtracting our original x from $10x$ gives

$$10x - x = 5.\overline{5} - 0.\overline{5} = (5 + 0.\overline{5}) - 0.\overline{5} = 5.$$

In other words, the repeating decimal canceled out! Since $10x - x = 9x$, we're left with just $9x = 5$, and hence $x = \frac{5}{9}$.

In fact, if n is any nonzero digit (that is, if $1 \leq n \leq 9$), then

$$\frac{n}{9} = 0.\overline{n}.$$

For example, $\frac{2}{9} = 0.222\ldots = 0.\overline{2}$. The computation is essentially the same as the above long division. We can also check with algebra as we did above. We let $x = 0.\overline{n}$. Multiplying by

10 moves the decimal point one place to the right, so that $10x = n.\overline{n}$. Then we subtract:

$$10x - x = n.\overline{n} - 0.\overline{n} = n + 0.\overline{n} - 0.\overline{n} = n,$$

so $10x - x = n$. This gives us $9x = n$, so $x = \frac{n}{9}$. (This leads to a somewhat weird situation when n is 9, which we will discuss in Problem 6.20.)

(b) Since we know how to work with a denominator of 9 (from part (a)), we can try to write $\frac{37}{90}$ using some fraction with a denominator of 9. One way to achieve this is

$$\frac{37}{90} = \frac{37}{9} \cdot \frac{1}{10} = \frac{37}{9} \cdot 0.1.$$

So we just need to write the decimal for $\frac{37}{9}$, and then move the decimal point one place to the left. We can't immediately use the result from part (a), because 37 isn't a digit from 1 to 9. But $\frac{37}{9} = 4\frac{1}{9}$, and from part (a) we know that $\frac{1}{9} = 0.\overline{1}$. So $\frac{37}{9} = 4.\overline{1}$, and thus we conclude that

$$\frac{37}{90} = 4.\overline{1} \cdot 0.1 = 0.4\overline{1} = 0.4111\ldots.$$

(c) We attempt to compute $\frac{1}{7}$ by dividing 7 into the infinite decimal $1.000\ldots$. The first few steps are shown to the right. When we get to the remainder of 1 at the bottom, we see that we will begin to repeat, for if we were to continue the computation, the next step would be to divide the 7 into a 1 (followed by infinitely many 0's) at the bottom. But this is exactly the same as the first step. Thus, we know that the string of digits 142857 will repeat forever, and hence

$$\frac{1}{7} = 0.\overline{142857}.$$

```
            .142857...
        7 ) 1.000000...
            0.7
            ‾‾‾‾‾
            0.30
            0.28
            ‾‾‾‾‾
            0.020
            0.014
            ‾‾‾‾‾
            0.0060
            0.0056
            ‾‾‾‾‾
            0.00040
            0.00035
            ‾‾‾‾‾‾
            0.000050
            0.000049
            ‾‾‾‾‾‾
            0.000001
```

We can check this answer using algebra as in part (a). Let $x = 0.\overline{142857}$. Then multiplying by $10^6 = 1,000,000$ moves the decimal point 6 places to the right, so that $10^6 \cdot x = 142857.\overline{142857}$. Subtracting our original x from this gives

$$\begin{array}{r} 10^6 x = 142857.142857\ldots \\ - \quad x = 0.142857\ldots \\ \hline 10^6 x - x = 142857. \end{array}$$

So we have $(10^6 - 1)x = 142857$. Thus, $x = \frac{142857}{10^6 - 1}$, but it just so happens that

$$10^6 - 1 = 999999 = 7 \cdot 142857$$

(check it if you don't believe me!), and hence the fraction simplifies as

$$x = \frac{142857}{999999} = \frac{142857}{7 \cdot 142857} = \frac{1}{7}.$$

> **Sidenote:** The decimal representations of fractions with denominator 7 are somewhat magical. We have
>
> $$\frac{1}{7} = 0.\overline{142857}, \qquad \frac{2}{7} = 0.\overline{285714},$$
>
> $$\frac{3}{7} = 0.\overline{428571}, \qquad \frac{4}{7} = 0.\overline{571428},$$
>
> $$\frac{5}{7} = 0.\overline{714285}, \qquad \frac{6}{7} = 0.\overline{857142}.$$
>
> It's the same numbers in each decimal, and in the same order, just starting at a different digit in each. See if you can figure out why this happens!

(d) We divide 11 into 19 as shown at right. The 8 we get as remainder in the last line at right is a repetition of the 8 that we have as remainder after the first step of the long division, so we know the decimal will repeat at that point. Thus, we conclude that $\frac{19}{11} = 1.\overline{72}$.

$$
\begin{array}{r}
1.72\ldots \\
11\,\overline{)\,19.00\ldots} \\
11. \\
\hline
8.0 \\
7.7 \\
\hline
0.30 \\
0.22 \\
\hline
0.08
\end{array}
$$

Again, we can check this using algebra. Let $x = 1.\overline{72}$, so that multiplying by 100 (to move the decimal point 2 places to the right) gives $100x = 172.\overline{72}$. Subtracting gives

$$100x - x = 172.\overline{72} - 1.\overline{72} = 171.$$

Thus $99x = 171$, so $x = \dfrac{171}{99} = \dfrac{19 \cdot 9}{11 \cdot 9} = \dfrac{19}{11}$, as expected.

☐

Problem 6.17: Write the following as fractions in simplest form:

(a) $0.\overline{2}$ (b) $0.\overline{51}$ (c) $0.2\overline{8}$ (d) $5.00\overline{25}$

Solution for Problem 6.17:

(a) From our work in Problem 6.16(a), you may immediately recognize that $0.\overline{2} = \frac{2}{9}$. However, if you don't recognize this right away, we can compute it using a little bit of algebra.

Let $x = 0.\overline{2}$. Then multiplying by 10 moves the decimal point one place to the right, so that $10x = 2.\overline{2}$. Subtracting x from $10x$ will cancel all the repeating decimals, leaving us with $10x - x = 2.\overline{2} - 0.\overline{2} = 2$. This gives us $9x = 2$, and dividing by 9 gives $x = \frac{2}{9}$.

(b) Again, the strategy is to use a little algebra to make the repeating decimals cancel when we subtract. We let $x = 0.\overline{51}$. To preserve the repeating decimal to the right of the decimal point after multiplication, we'll need to multiply by the power of 10 that moves the decimal point 2 places to the right (to the start of the next repeating block of "51"). Thus, we want to multiply by 100, to get $100x = 51.\overline{51}$. Now we subtract:

$$
\begin{array}{r}
100x = 51.5151\ldots \\
-\quad x = 0.5151\ldots \\
\hline
100x - x = 51.
\end{array}
$$

Simplifying the left-hand side gives $99x = 51$, and hence $x = \frac{51}{99} = \frac{17}{33}$.

(c) *Solution 1: use a little algebra.* Let $x = 0.2\overline{8}$. Multiplying by 10 gives $10x = 2.\overline{8}$. Now be careful! Don't make the following mistake:

> **Bogus Solution:** Subtracting x from $10x$ will cancel the repeating decimal, so $10x - x = 2$, hence $9x = 2$ and $x = \frac{2}{9}$.

This is not what happens. The repeating decimal does cancel, but the 8 in the tenths digit of $2.\overline{8}$ does not cancel with the 2 in the tenths digit of $0.2\overline{8}$. The correct subtraction is

$$10x - x = 2.\overline{8} - 0.2\overline{8} = 2.8\overline{8} - 0.2\overline{8} = 2.8 - 0.2 = 2.6.$$

Hence $9x = 2.6$, so $x = \dfrac{2.6}{9} = \dfrac{26}{90} = \dfrac{13}{45}$.

Solution 2: use the fact from Problem 6.16(a). We'd like to use our fact from Problem 6.16(a) that $0.\overline{n} = \frac{n}{9}$ for any digit $1 \le n \le 9$. But this only works when the decimal begins repeating immediately after the decimal point. So, we have to manipulate $0.2\overline{8}$ a little bit first:

$$0.2\overline{8} = 2.\overline{8} \cdot 0.1 = (2 + 0.\overline{8}) \cdot 0.1.$$

Now we can use the conversion $0.\overline{8} = \frac{8}{9}$ to finish the computation:

$$0.2\overline{8} = \left(2 + \frac{8}{9}\right) \cdot \frac{1}{10} = \frac{26}{9} \cdot \frac{1}{10} = \frac{26}{90} = \frac{13}{45}.$$

(d) Again, we'll use some algebra. Let $x = 5.00\overline{25}$. Since the repeating part of the decimal is a block of 2 digits, we'll need to move the decimal point 2 places in order to get cancellation. So we multiply by 100 to get $100x = 500.\overline{25}$. Then

$$100x - x = 500.\overline{25} - 5.00\overline{25} = 500.25\overline{25} - 5.00\overline{25} = 500.25 - 5.00 = 495.25.$$

Thus $99x = 495.25$, and hence we get

$$x = \frac{495.25}{99} = \frac{49525}{9900} = \frac{1981 \cdot 25}{396 \cdot 25} = \frac{1981}{396}.$$

As a check, note that $\frac{1981}{396} = 5\frac{1}{396}$, so our answer is slightly more than 5, as expected. As a further check, note that $5.0025 = 5\frac{1}{400}$, so that $5.00\overline{25} = 5\frac{1}{396}$ makes sense—0.0025 is slightly smaller than $0.00\overline{25}$, and $\frac{1}{400}$ is slightly smaller than $\frac{1}{396}$.

$\square$

Problem 6.18:

(a) When we convert the fractions

$$\frac{1}{2}, \frac{1}{3}, \frac{1}{4}, \frac{1}{5}, \frac{1}{6}, \frac{1}{7}, \frac{1}{8}, \frac{1}{9}, \frac{1}{10},$$

to decimal form, which of them have finite decimals, and which of them have infinitely repeating decimals?

(b) Suppose $n \geq 2$ is a positive integer. Is there an easy way to tell if the decimal form of $\frac{1}{n}$ is finite or infinitely repeating?

Solution for Problem 6.18:

(a) Most of these we have already computed in one of the previous problems. The others we will leave for you to check on your own.

$$\frac{1}{2} = 0.5 \qquad \frac{1}{3} = 0.\overline{3} \qquad \frac{1}{4} = 0.25$$

$$\frac{1}{5} = 0.2 \qquad \frac{1}{6} = 0.1\overline{6} \qquad \frac{1}{7} = 0.\overline{142857}$$

$$\frac{1}{8} = 0.125 \qquad \frac{1}{9} = 0.\overline{1} \qquad \frac{1}{10} = 0.1$$

Those with denominator 2, 4, 5, 8, or 10 are finite, and those with denominator 3, 6, 7, or 9 are infinitely repeating.

(b) We can think about how we compute the decimal form of $\frac{1}{n}$ using long division: we divide n into $1.000\ldots$. If this process stops at some point, we get a finite decimal; if this process repeats forever, then we get an infinitely repeating decimal.

What does it mean that the process stops? It means that n divides evenly into $1.00\ldots0$ after some *finite* number of zeros. But this means that n is a divisor of $100\ldots0$ for some finite number of zeros; that is, n is a divisor of 10^k for some positive integer k.

But how can this occur—when is n a divisor of 10^k? It's exactly when the prime factorization of n is included in the prime factorization of 10^k. We can compute the prime factorization of 10^k as

$$10^k = (2 \cdot 5)^k = 2^k \cdot 5^k.$$

Thus, for n to be a divisor of 10^k, we see that n can have only 2 or 5 (or both) as primes its prime factorization. Hence, $\frac{1}{n}$ is a finite decimal if n has only 2 or 5 (or both) in its prime factorization. If n has any other prime in its prime factorization, then $\frac{1}{n}$ is an infinitely repeating decimal.

Indeed, we see that 2, 4, 5, 8, and 10 from our list in part (a) all have only 2 or 5 as prime factors, and that 3, 6, 7, and 9 have some prime factor other than 2 and 5 (namely, 3, 6, and 9 all have 3 as a prime factor, and 7 has 7 as a prime factor). □

With a little more number theory (a bit beyond what we learned in Chapter 3), we can extend part (b) to any fraction in simplest form, not just fractions with 1 as the numerator:

> **Important:** Let a and b be positive integers with $b > 1$. If the fraction $\frac{a}{b}$
> ⚠ is in simplest form, then its decimal form is finite if b only has
> prime factors 2 or 5 (or both). Otherwise, the decimal form of $\frac{a}{b}$ is
> infinitely repeating.

Problem 6.19: What is the 100th digit to the right of the decimal point in the decimal representation of $\frac{3}{7}$?

Solution for Problem 6.19: From the sidenote in Problem 6.16(c), we know that $\frac{3}{7} = 0.\overline{428571}$. In particular, the decimal repeats in blocks of 6 digits. That means that the 1st, 7th, 13th, etc. digits of the decimal are 4, the 2nd, 8th, 14th, etc. digits of the decimal are 2, and so on. Also, every block ends on a digit that is a multiple of 6 positions to the right of the decimal point; that is, the 6th, 12th, 18th, etc. are all at the end of a 6-digit block and hence are the digit 1.

So how can we tell which digit is the 100th? We need to know what position of the 6-digit block corresponds to the 100th digit. We see that $6 \cdot 16 = 96$, so 100 is 4 more than a multiple of 6. Thus, to get to the 100th digit, we have 16 complete 6-digit blocks that use up 96 digits, and the 100th digit is the 4th digit of the next block. Hence the digit we want is 5. □

Problem 6.20: What simpler number does $0.\overline{9}$ equal?

Solution for Problem 6.20: We can repeat our computation from Problem 6.16(a). Let $x = 0.\overline{9}$. Multiplying by 10 moves the decimal point 1 place to the right, so $10x = 9.\overline{9}$. We then subtract to get

$$10x - x = 9.\overline{9} - 0.\overline{9},$$

then the decimal parts cancel and we are left with $10x - x = 9$, so $9x = 9$, and hence $x = 1$. Thus, we conclude that
$$0.\overline{9} = 1.$$
We can also see this using the fact that $\frac{1}{3} = 0.\overline{3}$. Multiplying by 3, we get

$$0.\overline{9} = 3 \cdot 0.\overline{3} = 3 \cdot \frac{1}{3} = 1.$$

□

Despite the above evidence, some people still have a hard time believing that $0.\overline{9}$ and 1 are the same number. They are! If you still don't believe it, ask yourself: what number could possibly be between $0.\overline{9}$ and 1? There can't be any such number, because all of the digits of $0.\overline{9}$ are already 9, so there's no room to have a bigger number less than 1: we can't increase any digit (because they're all already 9) and we can't add more digits (because it's already an infinite decimal).

> **Important:**
>
> $$0.\overline{9} = 1.$$

> **Sidenote:** We've seen that every fraction converts to either a finite decimal or an infinite repeating decimal. But what about decimals that are infinite but not repeating? These numbers do exist: they are called **irrational numbers**. (By contrast, any number that can be written as a fraction with integer numerator and denominator is called a **rational number**.) Perhaps the most famous example of an irrational number is the number π:
>
> $$\pi = 3.1415926535\ldots.$$
>
> (You've probably already heard of π; we'll define π in Chapter 11.) The digits of π do not repeat and have no apparent pattern. You will also see some examples of irrational numbers in Chapter 9. Together, the rational and irrational numbers make up the **real numbers**— every point on the number line is a real number, and every real number is a point on the number line.

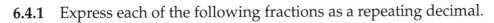

Exercises

6.4.1 Express each of the following fractions as a repeating decimal.

(a) $\dfrac{2}{11}$ (c) $\dfrac{1}{30}$ (e) $\dfrac{71}{90}$

(b) $\dfrac{21}{11}$ (d) $\dfrac{5}{33}$ (f) $\dfrac{118}{55}$

6.4.2 What is the 14th digit to the right of the decimal point in the decimal representation of $\frac{1}{13}$?

6.4.3 Find the smallest positive integer x so that the fraction $\dfrac{1}{10+x}$ has a finite decimal. *(Source: MATHCOUNTS)*

6.4.4 Express each of the following repeating decimals as a fraction in simplest form.

(a) $0.\overline{7}$ (d) $0.\overline{45}$ (g) $0.3\overline{6}$

(b) $0.\overline{12}$ (e) $0.\overline{912}$ (h) $0.0\overline{9}$

(c) $0.\overline{16}$ (f) $0.00\overline{1}$ (i) $2.\overline{02}$

6.4.5 Arrange the following numbers from smallest to largest:

$$1.2345, 1.234\overline{5}, 1.23\overline{45}, 1.2\overline{345}, 1.\overline{2345}.$$

6.4.6 By how much does $0.\overline{63}$ exceed 0.63? Express your answer as a fraction.

6.4.7 Express $\dfrac{.\overline{48}}{.\overline{15}}$ as a mixed number.

6.5 Summary

We use decimals in our base 10 system in order to write numbers that are not integers. Arithmetic with decimals is mostly the same as arithmetic with integers, except that we have to be careful about where the decimal point goes in our computations. In particular, multiplying and dividing by powers of 10 are easy with decimals—we just move the decimal point—so we can express numbers in terms of powers of 10 to help us with arithmetic computations.

We often round numbers to the nearest multiple of a power of 10. One reason that we round is that round numbers are simpler to deal with. Another reason is for a quick check of a complicated calculation.

Every fraction can be written either as a finite decimal or as an infinite repeating decimal. If the denominator of a fraction in simplest form has only 2 or 5 (or both) as prime factors, then we can rewrite the fraction as a fraction with a denominator that's a power of 10; this will give us a finite decimal. Otherwise, if the denominator of the fraction has a prime factor other than 2 or 5, then the fraction can be expressed as a repeating decimal. A frequently appearing example of a repeating decimal is $\frac{n}{9} = 0.\overline{n}$ where n is any digit from 1 to 9. An important special case of this is $0.\overline{9} = 1$.

REVIEW PROBLEMS

6.21 Arrange the following numbers from smallest to largest: $0.97, 0.979, 0.9709, 0.907, 0.9089$.

6.22 Compute the following quantities:

(a) $8.97 + 0.254$

(b) $0.27 - 1.006$

(c) $0.902 \cdot 10000$

(d) $25.5 \div 0.05$

(e) $0.025 \cdot 0.042$

(f) $(0.11)^3$

6.23 The product $100 \times 33.67 \times 3.367 \times 1000$ is equal to the square of what positive number?

6.24 What is the value of $\frac{6}{.3} + \frac{.3}{.06}$? *(Source: MOEMS)*

6.25 By how much does 3.5 exceed its reciprocal? Express your answer as a fraction. *(Source: MATHCOUNTS)*

6.26 Compute $\frac{(.2)^3}{(.02)^2}$. *(Source: AMC 8)*

6.27 Nanette rounds 10.68494 to the nearest hundredth. Duane rounds 10.68494 to the nearest integer. What is the positive difference between their two answers? Express your answer as a fraction. *(Source: MATHCOUNTS)*

6.28 It costs 2.5¢ to copy a page. How many pages can you copy for \$20? *(Source: MATH-COUNTS)*

6.29 Express each of the following fractions as a decimal:

(a) $\frac{11}{8}$

(c) $\frac{7}{15}$

(e) $\frac{25}{33}$

(b) $\frac{10}{7}$

(d) $\frac{39}{20}$

(f) $\frac{4}{21}$

6.30 What is the 100th digit to the right of the decimal point in the decimal form of $\frac{4}{37}$? *(Source: AMC 8)*

6.31 Express each of the following repeating decimals as a fraction in simplest form.

(a) $0.\overline{6}$

(c) $0.0\overline{8}$

(e) $0.3\overline{21}$

(b) $0.\overline{97}$

(d) $0.\overline{36}$

(f) $0.46\overline{9}$

Challenge Problems

6.32 Express the sum $\frac{1}{2} + \frac{.1}{2} + \frac{1}{.2}$ as a decimal. *(Source: MOEMS)*

6.33 A positive number is written in **scientific notation** if it is written in the form $a \cdot 10^b$, where a is a number with $1 \leq a < 10$ and b is an integer. For example, 38100 is written in scientific notation as $3.81 \cdot 10^4$, and 0.025 is written in scientific notation as $2.5 \cdot 10^{-2}$.

(a) Explain why every positive number can be written in scientific notation.

(b) Write the product $(3 \cdot 10^5) \cdot (4 \cdot 10^6)$ in scientific notation.

(c) Write the quotient $(3 \cdot 10^2) \div (5 \cdot 10^{-3})$ in scientific notation.

(d) If a positive integer n is expressed in scientific notation as $a \cdot 10^b$, how many digits does n have when written out?

6.34 What is the smallest positive integer k such that $\frac{k}{660}$ can be expressed as a terminating decimal?

6.35 Suppose that x is a repeating decimal of the form $0.\overline{K}$, where K is a n-digit number (for some positive integer n). For example, if $K = 238$, then $n = 3$ and $x = 0.\overline{238}$. Show that x equals K divided by the n-digit number consisting of all 9's. That is,

$$x = 0.\overline{K} = \frac{K}{\underbrace{9\ldots9}_{n \text{ nines}}}.$$

6.36

(a) How many digits are in the decimal expansion of 10^{30}?

(b)⋆ How many digits are in the decimal expansion of 2^{30}? **Hints:** 2

(c)⋆ How many digits are in the decimal expansion of 5^{30}? **Hints:** 161

6.37⋆ How many positive integers less than 100 have reciprocals with terminating decimal representations? *(Source: MATHCOUNTS)*

6.38⋆

(a) Compute the infinite sum

$$\frac{7}{10} + \frac{7}{100} + \frac{7}{1000} + \frac{7}{10000} + \cdots.$$

(b) Compute the infinite sum

$$\frac{6}{10} + \frac{3}{100} + \frac{6}{1000} + \frac{3}{10000} + \cdots,$$

where the numerators of the terms alternate between 6 and 3.

(c) Compute the infinite sum

$$\frac{1}{3} + \frac{1}{9} + \frac{1}{27} + \frac{1}{81} + \cdots,$$

where the denominators of the terms increase by a factor of 3. **Hints:** 75, 133

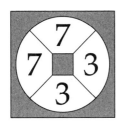 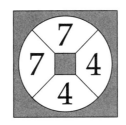 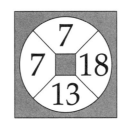 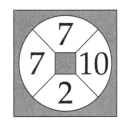

I continued to do arithmetic with my father, passing proudly through fractions to decimals. I eventually arrived at the point where so many cows ate so much grass, and tanks filled with water in so many hours—I found it quite enthralling. – Agatha Christie

CHAPTER 7

Ratios, Conversions, and Rates

In this chapter we will discuss:

- **ratios** that compare two or more quantities,

- **conversion factors** that we use to convert measurements from one unit to another (for example, from inches to yards), and

- **rates** that measure how a quantity changes over time.

These ideas are all related—in fact, the last two (conversions and rates) can be thought of as special cases of ratios.

7.1 What is a Ratio?

A **ratio** is used to compare the *relative* quantities of (usually) two groups or items of data.

A simple example should give you an idea of what we mean. Suppose a certain science class has 10 girls and 7 boys. We would say that the **ratio** of girls to boys in the class is 10 to 7. We can write this in a few different ways:

$$10 \text{ to } 7, \quad 10 : 7, \quad 10/7.$$

The notation 10 : 7 is the most commonly used when writing, and is usually spoken "10 to 7."

The key concept to remember is that the ratio only compares the two quantities—it doesn't tell us anything about the amount of the quantities. For example, suppose that you know that in a history class, the ratio of girls to boys is 2 : 3. All this tells you is that for every 2 girls, there are 3 boys. There might be 2 girls and 3 boys in the class, or there might be 10 girls and 15 boys in the class, or there might be 200 girls and 300 boys in the class (in a very large classroom!). All you know is that if there are $2n$ girls, then there are $3n$ boys, but you don't know what n is.

> **Concept:** A ratio gives a *relative* comparison of two quantities. It doesn't tell
> you anything about the total amount of the quantities.

Ratios behave a lot like fractions. They are usually written in **simplest form** as a ratio of two positive integers with no common factor larger than 1. To change our example, suppose that we're now considering a math class with 12 girls and 6 boys. We could write that the ratio of girls to boys is 12 to 6 or 12 : 6. However, we could also divide the students into 6 identical groups, where each group has 2 girls and 1 boy. This means that the ratio of girls to boys is 2 : 1 in each group, but since all the groups are the same, the overall ratio of girls to boys is also 2 : 1. We therefore have 12 : 6 = 2 : 1.

We typically reduce to simplest form by dividing the greatest common factor from each part of the ratio. So to continue our example, since the greatest common factor of 12 and 6 is 6, the ratio of girls to boys is $\frac{12}{6}$ to $\frac{6}{6}$, or 2 to 1. This also makes sense if we use fraction notation:

$$12/6 = 2/1.$$

In words this means that for every 2 girls there is 1 boy. This process of reducing the ratio to simplest form is also called **simplifying** the ratio.

> **Definition:** To **simplify** a ratio means to write it as a ratio of integers with no common
> factor larger than 1.

Problems

Problem 7.1: Simplify the following ratios:

(a) 2 : 10

(b) 9 : 6

(c) $\frac{1}{2} : \frac{1}{3}$

(d) $2\frac{1}{3} : 1\frac{4}{9}$

(e) 1.4 : 2.4

Problem 7.2: The ratio of cats to dogs in a pet shop is 2 : 5. If there are 25 dogs in the shop, then how many cats are there?

Problem 7.3: Mrs. Miller's class has a ratio of girls to boys of 4 : 3. If there are 35 students in the class, then how many of them are girls?

Problem 7.4: A 10-foot length of rope is cut into two pieces whose lengths are in the ratio 1 : 4. What is the length of the longer piece? *(Source: MATHCOUNTS)*

Problem 7.5: My aunt's candy jar has 56 pieces of candy. She only has butterscotch and jelly beans, and the ratio of butterscotch to jelly beans is 5 : 2. I like jelly beans more, and I want to add some jelly beans so that the ratio of butterscotch to jelly beans is 2 : 1. How many jelly beans should I add?

Problem 7.1: Simplify the following ratios:

(a) $2 : 10$

(b) $9 : 6$

(c) $\frac{1}{2} : \frac{1}{3}$

(d) $2\frac{1}{3} : 1\frac{4}{9}$

(e) $1.4 : 2.4$

Solution for Problem 7.1:

(a) The greatest common factor of 2 and 10 is 2. So, we divide both parts of the ratio by 2, and we get

$$2 : 10 = \frac{2}{2} : \frac{10}{2} = 1 : 5.$$

Therefore the simplified ratio is $1 : 5$. We can also see this using fractions, since $\frac{2}{10} = \frac{1}{5}$.

(b) The greatest common factor of 9 and 6 is 3, so we divide both parts of the ratio by 3, and we get

$$9 : 6 = \frac{9}{3} : \frac{6}{3} = 3 : 2.$$

As fractions, this is the same as $\frac{9}{6} = \frac{3}{2}$.

(c) To write $\frac{1}{2} : \frac{1}{3}$ as a ratio of positive integers, we need to multiply both parts of the ratio by some number that will cancel both denominators. The number we need is the least common multiple of the two denominators, which is 6. This gives us

$$\frac{1}{2} : \frac{1}{3} = \left(\frac{1}{2} \cdot 6\right) : \left(\frac{1}{3} \cdot 6\right) = 3 : 2.$$

As a fraction, this simplification is equivalent to

$$\frac{\frac{1}{2}}{\frac{1}{3}} = \frac{\frac{1}{2} \cdot 6}{\frac{1}{3} \cdot 6} = \frac{3}{2}.$$

(d) It is usually easier to work with mixed numbers by first converting them to fractions. So we start by writing $2\frac{1}{3} = 2 + \frac{1}{3} = \frac{6}{3} + \frac{1}{3} = \frac{7}{3}$ and $1\frac{4}{9} = 1 + \frac{4}{9} = \frac{9}{9} + \frac{4}{9} = \frac{13}{9}$, making our ratio

$$2\frac{1}{3} : 1\frac{4}{9} = \frac{7}{3} : \frac{13}{9}.$$

Then, multiplying by 9 will remove the denominators, giving us

$$2\frac{1}{3} : 1\frac{4}{9} = \frac{7}{3} : \frac{13}{9} = \left(\frac{7}{3} \cdot 9\right) : \left(\frac{13}{9} \cdot 9\right) = 21 : 13.$$

This is a ratio of two positive integers with no common factor (other than 1), so we're done.

(e) We can first write the ratio as a ratio of integers by multiplying by 10:

$$1.4 : 2.4 = 14 : 24.$$

Then, 14 and 24 have greatest common factor 2, so we divide by 2 to finish the simplification:

$$1.4 : 2.4 = 14 : 24 = \frac{14}{2} : \frac{24}{2} = 7 : 12.$$

□

Problem 7.2: The ratio of cats to dogs in a pet shop is $2 : 5$. If there are 25 dogs in the shop, then how many cats are there?

Solution for Problem 7.2: The ratio $2 : 5$ means that for every 2 cats, there are 5 dogs. Naturally, this also means that for every 5 dogs, there are 2 cats. The latter way of thinking about this ratio seems more useful, since we are told how many dogs there are and we want to figure out how many cats there are.

There are 25 dogs in the shop. We can think of this as 5 groups of 5 dogs each. Each group of 5 dogs has a corresponding group of 2 cats. So in the shop, there are 5 groups of 2 cats each, for a total of $5 \cdot 2 = 10$ cats.

Another way to think about this problem is to let c be the number of cats in the shop.

Concept: It often helps to assign a variable to an unknown quantity. Also, pick your variable names to help you remember what they represent, like c for "cats."

Since the ratio of cats to dogs in the shop is $2 : 5$, we have the equation

$$c : 25 = 2 : 5.$$

We can make the second ratio look like the first one by multiplying the parts of the second ratio by 5, giving

$$c : 25 = 2 : 5 = (2 \cdot 5) : (5 \cdot 5) = 10 : 25.$$

Comparing the first and last ratios above tells us that $c = 10$, so there are 10 cats in the shop. Indeed, we can check that $10 : 25 = 2 : 5$. $\square$

Setting two ratios equal, such as $c : 25 = 2 : 5$ in Problem 7.2, is an example of a **proportion**. We will cover proportions in more detail in Section 7.3.

Problem 7.3: Mrs. Miller's class has a ratio of girls to boys of $4 : 3$. If there are 35 students in the class, then how many of them are girls?

Solution for Problem 7.3: At first, it seems like we may not have enough information to solve this problem—the ratio tells us a relationship between girls and boys, but we're not given the number of girls or the number of boys. Instead, we're just told the total number of students.

However, we can use the given ratio to construct a new ratio: the ratio of girls to the total number of students. We know that the $4 : 3$ girls-to-boys ratio means that for every 4 girls, there are 3 boys. So this means that for every 4 girls, there are $4 + 3 = 7$ *total* students (girls and boys), and thus the ratio of girls to all students is $4 : 7$.

Let g be the number of girls in the class. Since there are 35 students in the class, we have

$$4 : 7 = g : 35.$$

Multiplying the parts of the first ratio by 5 gives

$$20 : 35 = g : 35,$$

so $g = 20$ and there are 20 girls.

Another way to think of this is that girls make up $\frac{4}{4+3} = \frac{4}{7}$ of the total number of students, and boys make up $\frac{3}{4+3} = \frac{3}{7}$ of the total number of students. As a check, notice that $\frac{4}{7} + \frac{3}{7} = \frac{7}{7} = 1$, so girls and boys together make up all of the students. $\square$

> **Important:** Suppose we are using a ratio to compare two quantities that together make up a group (such as girls and boys in a class). If the two quantities are in the ratio $a : b$, then the first quantity makes up $\dfrac{a}{a+b}$ of the whole, and the second quantity makes up $\dfrac{b}{a+b}$ of the whole.

Try using this method in the next problem:

Problem 7.4: A 10-foot length of rope is cut into two pieces whose lengths are in the ratio $1 : 4$. What is the length of the longer piece? *(Source: MATHCOUNTS)*

Solution for Problem 7.4: When we cut the rope, it will consist of two pieces that together make up the whole rope. Since the pieces have lengths in ratio $1 : 4$, the shorter piece will make up

$\frac{1}{1+4} = \frac{1}{5}$ of the original length, and the longer piece will make up $\frac{4}{1+4} = \frac{4}{5}$ of the original length. The longer piece is $\frac{4}{5}$ of a 10-foot rope, so its length is

$$\frac{4}{5} \cdot (10 \text{ feet}) = \left(\frac{4}{5} \cdot 10\right) \text{ feet} = 8 \text{ feet.}$$

□

> **Problem 7.5:** My aunt's candy jar has 56 pieces of candy. She only has butterscotch and jelly beans, and the ratio of butterscotch to jelly beans is 5 : 2. I like jelly beans more, and I want to add some jelly beans so that the ratio of butterscotch to jelly beans is 2 : 1. How many jelly beans should I add?

Solution for Problem 7.5: We start by figuring out how many pieces of each type of candy are in the jar. For practice, we'll show the two main methods.

Method 1: Use a variable. Since the ratio of butterscotch to jelly beans is 5 : 2, we know that there are $5n$ pieces of butterscotch and $2n$ jelly beans for some n. We also know that there are 56 pieces total. So $5n + 2n = 56$, which means $7n = 56$. Dividing by 7 gives us $n = 8$, so there are $5(8) = 40$ pieces of butterscotch and $2(8) = 16$ jelly beans in the jar.

Method 2: Parts of the whole. The butterscotch and the jelly beans are the only candies in the jar, and they have ratio 5 : 2. Therefore, we know that butterscotch makes up $\frac{5}{5+2} = \frac{5}{7}$ of the total candy and that jelly beans make up $\frac{2}{5+2} = \frac{2}{7}$ of the total candy. Thus, since there are 56 pieces total, there are $\frac{5}{7} \cdot 56 = 40$ pieces of butterscotch and $\frac{2}{7} \cdot 56 = 16$ jelly beans.

Next, we want the final ratio of butterscotch to jelly beans to be 2 : 1. There are 40 pieces of butterscotch, and that won't change after we add jelly beans, so we want the new total amount j of jelly beans to be such that $40 : j = 2 : 1$. You can probably see right away that we must have $j = 20$, but if not, we can always compute it by multiplying both parts of the 2 : 1 ratio by 20 so that the first part of the ratio equals 40, like this:

$$2 : 1 = (2 \cdot 20) : (1 \cdot 20) = 40 : 20.$$

This must equal $40 : j$, so we must have $j = 20$.

We conclude that I want the jar to have 20 jelly beans. It starts with 16 jelly beans, so I need to add $20 - 16 = 4$ jelly beans to the jar. □

Exercises

7.1.1 Simplify the following ratios:

(a) $20 : 8$

(b) $6^3 : 8^3$

(c) $\frac{3}{5} : \frac{1}{10}$

(d) $100 : 500$

(e) $2\frac{1}{4} : 3\frac{5}{8}$

(f) $672 : 0$

7.1.2   There are 10 boys in a class of 25 students. What is the ratio of girls to boys?

7.1.3   Gear A makes 2 revolutions for every 5 revolutions gear B makes. If gear A makes 36 revolutions in 1 minute, then how many revolutions does gear B make in 1 minute? *(Source: MATHCOUNTS)*

7.1.4   The ratio of girls to boys participating in intramural volleyball at Ashland Middle School is 7 to 4. There are 42 girls in the program. What is the total number of participants? *(Source: MATHCOUNTS)*

7.1.5   Two numbers are in the ratio 3 : 8. Their sum is 44. What is the greater of the two numbers?

7.1.6   An 8-inch-long submarine sandwich is cut into two pieces whose lengths are in the ratio of 7 to 5. How long is the shorter piece?

7.1.7   A father left 280 acres of land to be divided among his sons Al and Bob in the ratio 4 : 3, respectively. How many acres should Al receive? *(Source: MATHCOUNTS)*

7.1.8   Two positive numbers are in the ratio of 4 : 9. Their difference is 30. What is the sum of the two numbers?

7.1.9   The ratio of teachers to students in a particular school is 1 to 11. The ratio of female students to the total number of students is 4 to 9. If there are 396 female students, then how many teachers are there? *(Source: MATHCOUNTS)*

7.1.10★   The ratio of losses to wins for Kyle's team is 3 to 2. If the team had played the same number of games, but had won twice as many of its games, then what would the ratio of losses to wins have been? *(Source: MATHCOUNTS)* **Hints:** 95

7.1.11★   The ratio of pennies to dimes in a jar is 2 : 5 and there are a total of 245 pennies and dimes in the jar. How many pennies should be added to make the ratio of pennies to dimes be 3 : 7?

7.2   Multi-way Ratios

A ratio is a handy gadget for comparing two quantities. But it's also useful for comparing *more* than two quantities. For example, suppose a pet store has 4 dogs, 5 cats, and 11 goldfish. We would say that the numbers of dogs, cats, and goldfish are in the ratio of 4 : 5 : 11. Since 4, 5, and 11 have no common factors, we cannot simplify this ratio any further. If a different (more exotic) pet store had 9 geckos, 12 iguanas, and 21 snakes, then we would say that the numbers of geckos, iguanas, and snakes are in the ratio of 9 : 12 : 21. But now, since 3 is a common factor of 9, 12, and 21, we can divide each term of the ratio by 3, to say that the numbers of geckos, iguanas, and snakes are in the ratio of

$$9 : 12 : 21 = \frac{9}{3} : \frac{12}{3} : \frac{21}{3} = 3 : 4 : 7.$$

Just as with a two-way ratio, a multi-way ratio only gives you information about the *relative* quantities of the items—it doesn't tell you anything about the total number of items. For example, if you know that a third pet store has hamsters, guinea pigs, and rabbits in the ratio $1 : 2 : 5$, all you know is that for every hamster, there are 2 guinea pigs and 5 rabbits. There might be 1 hamster, 2 guinea pigs, and 5 rabbits, or there might be 6 hamsters, 12 guinea pigs, and 30 rabbits; more generally, there are n hamsters, $2n$ guinea pigs, and $5n$ rabbits for some number n.

Although the multiple parts of a multi-way ratio may at first look confusing, they're really not that much different from a two-way ratio, as we will see in the following problems.

Problems

Problem 7.6: Simplify the following ratios:

(a) $5 : 15 : 10$

(b) $6 : 10 : 9$

(c) $8 : 32 : 4 : 8$

(d) $\frac{1}{2} : \frac{1}{3} : \frac{2}{3}$

(e) $3\frac{1}{3} : 4\frac{1}{4} : 5\frac{1}{5}$

Problem 7.7: A bowling tournament pays out prizes to the top 3 players in the ratio $5 : 2 : 1$. If the total prize money is $1,000, then how much does the first-place winner receive?

Problem 7.8: Sam wants to bake a cake that requires butter, flour, sugar, and milk in the ratio $1 : 6 : 2 : 1$. Sam has $\frac{1}{2}$ cup of sugar. How much of the other ingredients does he need?

Problem 7.9: Jamal needs three gallons of a mix that is two parts blue paint, three parts white paint, and one part red paint. How many gallons of red paint will he need? *(Source: MATHCOUNTS)*

Problem 7.10: I have blots, bleets, and blits in a bag. The ratio of the number of blots to the number of bleets is $3 : 4$. The ratio of the number of bleets to the number of blits is $5 : 6$. What is the ratio of the number of blots to the number of blits?

Just as with a two-part ratio, to **simplify** a multi-way ratio means to write the ratio using integers with no common factor larger than 1. So, the ratio

$$6 : 4 : 8$$

is not simplified because each part is a multiple of 2, while the ratio

$$\frac{1}{2} : \frac{1}{3} : \frac{2}{3}$$

is not simplified because the parts are not integers.

Problem 7.6: Simplify the following ratios:

(a) $5 : 15 : 10$

(b) $6 : 10 : 9$

(c) $8 : 32 : 4 : 8$

(d) $\frac{1}{2} : \frac{1}{3} : \frac{2}{3}$

(e) $3\frac{1}{3} : 4\frac{1}{4} : 5\frac{1}{5}$

Solution for Problem 7.6:

(a) The greatest common factor of 5, 15, and 10 is 5, so we divide each part of the ratio by 5:

$$5 : 15 : 10 = \frac{5}{5} : \frac{15}{5} : \frac{10}{5} = 1 : 3 : 2.$$

(b) It is a little more difficult to see what the greatest common factor of 6, 10, and 9 is. We can get a little more insight by factoring each number:

$$6 = 2 \cdot 3, \ 10 = 2 \cdot 5, \ 9 = 3 \cdot 3.$$

Now we can see that there is no factor greater than 1 that is common to all three numbers, so the ratio $6 : 10 : 9$ is already simplified.

(c) We notice that 4 divides all the terms of the ratio, so we have

$$8 : 32 : 4 : 8 = \frac{8}{4} : \frac{32}{4} : \frac{4}{4} : \frac{8}{4} = 2 : 8 : 1 : 2.$$

(d) We handle fractions a little bit differently: now we want to find a number we can multiply each term by so that each becomes a integer. This is usually the least common denominator of the fractions. In the ratio $\frac{1}{2} : \frac{1}{3} : \frac{2}{3}$, the common denominator is 6, so we multiply:

$$\frac{1}{2} : \frac{1}{3} : \frac{2}{3} = \left(\frac{1}{2} \cdot 6\right) : \left(\frac{1}{3} \cdot 6\right) : \left(\frac{2}{3} \cdot 6\right) = 3 : 2 : 4.$$

(e) Mixed numbers only look more complicated—they're really just the same as fractions. We normally find them easier to work with if we convert them to fractions:

$$3\frac{1}{3} : 4\frac{1}{4} : 5\frac{1}{5} = \frac{10}{3} : \frac{17}{4} : \frac{26}{5}.$$

Then, as in part (d) above, we multiply by the least common denominator, which in this example is $3 \cdot 4 \cdot 5 = 60$, to convert the ratio to integers:

$$\frac{10}{3} : \frac{17}{4} : \frac{26}{5} = \left(\frac{10}{3} \cdot 60\right) : \left(\frac{17}{4} \cdot 60\right) : \left(\frac{26}{5} \cdot 60\right) = 200 : 255 : 312.$$

$\square$

Just as with a two-way ratio, we can think of a multi-way ratio in terms of "parts of the whole," as in the next problem.

Problem 7.7: A bowling tournament pays out prizes to the top 3 players in the ratio $5 : 2 : 1$. If the total prize money is $1,000, then how much does the first-place winner receive?

Solution for Problem 7.7: The $5 : 2 : 1$ ratio means that for every $5 the winner gets, the second-place player gets $2 and the third-place player gets $1. In other words, for every $5 that the winner gets, a total of $5 + $2 + $1 = $8 is paid out. Therefore, the winner gets $\frac{5}{8}$ of the total money paid out. Since the total prize money is $1,000, and the winner gets $\frac{5}{8}$ of the total, he gets $\frac{5}{8} \cdot \$1,000 = \$625$. $\square$

In Problem 7.7, we saw that a ratio of $5 : 2 : 1$ led to the first quantity being $\frac{5}{5+2+1} = \frac{5}{8}$ of the whole. In the same way, the second-place winner gets $\frac{2}{5+2+1} = \frac{2}{8} = \frac{1}{4}$ of the prize money, and the third-place winner gets $\frac{1}{5+2+1} = \frac{1}{8}$ of the prize money.

> **Concept:** In a multi-part ratio, you can often think of each term as a "part of the whole." That is, you add all the terms in the ratio to get the "whole," and then each individual term makes up part of that whole.

> **WARNING!!** Again, remember that ratio is a *relative* concept. The ratio only tells you the fraction of the whole that each part represents—it doesn't tell you anything about how much the total or each part is.

Going back to Problem 7.7, the ratio itself only tells us that the first-place winner gets $\frac{5}{8}$ of the money. The ratio doesn't tell us exactly how much the winner gets. It is only with the additional information about the total prize money that we can compute the actual money the winner receives.

Problem 7.8: Sam wants to bake a cake that requires butter, flour, sugar, and milk in the ratio $1 : 6 : 2 : 1$. Sam has $\frac{1}{2}$ cup of sugar. How much of the other ingredients does he need?

Solution for Problem 7.8: We'll present three different methods for solving this problem.

Method 1: Convert the ratio to match the given quantity. The given ratio of butter to flour to sugar to milk is $1 : 6 : 2 : 1$. But we only have $\frac{1}{2}$ cup of sugar, so we convert the ratio so that $\frac{1}{2}$ appears in the "sugar" position. Since the given ratio has a 2 in that position, we need to divide each term of the ratio by 4:

$$1 : 6 : 2 : 1 = \frac{1}{4} : \frac{6}{4} : \frac{2}{4} : \frac{1}{4} = \frac{1}{4} : \frac{3}{2} : \frac{1}{2} : \frac{1}{4}.$$

Now we can just read from the ratio the quantities of the other ingredients that correspond to $\frac{1}{2}$ cup of sugar: $\frac{1}{4}$ cup of butter, $\frac{3}{2}$ cup of flour, and $\frac{1}{4}$ cup of milk.

Method 2: Use separate two-part ratios. We can break up the multi-way ratio into several separate two-part ratios, where each ratio compares some ingredient to sugar. For example, the ratio of butter to sugar is $1:2$—this is just a ratio consisting of the butter and sugar terms from the original 4-part ratio.

> **Concept:** We can remove terms from a multi-way ratio to get a simpler ratio that only compares some of the quantities from the original ratio.

Since the butter and sugar are in ratio $1:2$, we know that there is half as much butter as sugar. We have $\frac{1}{2}$ cup of sugar, so the amount of butter is $\frac{1}{2} \cdot \frac{1}{2} = \frac{1}{4}$ cup.

Similarly, the ratio of flour to sugar is $6:2 = 3:1$, so there is three times as much flour as sugar. Thus, since there is $\frac{1}{2}$ cup of sugar, there are $3 \cdot \frac{1}{2} = \frac{3}{2}$ cups of flour. Finally, the ratio of sugar to milk is $2:1$, so there is $\frac{1}{2} \cdot \frac{1}{2} = \frac{1}{4}$ cup of milk.

Method 3: Compute the total. We can use the "parts of the whole" way of thinking with our 4-part ratio. The sugar is $\frac{2}{1+6+2+1} = \frac{2}{10} = \frac{1}{5}$ of the entire ingredients, and we have $\frac{1}{2}$ cup of sugar. Thus the total quantity of ingredients is $\frac{1}{2} \div \frac{1}{5} = \frac{5}{2}$ cups.

Now we can use the "parts of the whole" to compute the other ingredient amounts. The butter is $\frac{1}{10}$ of the whole, so there is $\frac{1}{10} \cdot \frac{5}{2} = \frac{5}{20} = \frac{1}{4}$ cup of butter. Next, the flour is $\frac{6}{10} = \frac{3}{5}$ of the whole, so there are $\frac{3}{5} \cdot \frac{5}{2} = \frac{3}{2}$ cups of flour. Finally, the milk is $\frac{1}{10}$ of the whole, so there is $\frac{1}{10} \cdot \frac{5}{2} = \frac{1}{4}$ cup of milk. $\square$

> **Concept:** None of the techniques from Problem 7.8 are "right" or "wrong." Ratios are best approached with flexible thinking. Ratios can be interpreted in many different ways, and you should use the method that you feel most comfortable with, or the method that appears to work best for the particular problem that you're working on.

Problem 7.9: Jamal needs three gallons of a mix that is two parts blue paint, three parts white paint, and one part red paint. How many gallons of red paint will he need? *(Source: MATHCOUNTS)*

Solution for Problem 7.9: Since we are given the total amount and we want to find the amount of one of the parts, the "parts of the whole" method will probably work best. The given ratio is $2:3:1$ of blue : white : red, and the total is 3 gallons. So the red paint is $\frac{1}{2+3+1} = \frac{1}{6}$ of the whole, and thus Jamal needs $\frac{1}{6} \cdot 3 = \frac{1}{2}$ gallon of red paint. $\square$

Problem 7.10: I have blots, bleets, and blits in a bag. The ratio of the number of blots to the number of bleets is 3 : 4. The ratio of the number of bleets to the number of blits is 5 : 6. What is the ratio of the number of blots to the number of blits?

Solution for Problem 7.10: Let's make a little chart of the data we're given:

$$\text{blots : bleets} \qquad \text{bleets : blits}$$
$$3 : 4 \qquad\qquad 5 : 6$$

We'd be able to compare blits and blots if the number of bleets in the above two ratios were equal. So let's make them equal! We can do this by multiplying the parts of the first ratio by 5 and the parts of the second ratio by 4:

$$\text{blots : bleets} \qquad \text{bleets : blits}$$
$$15 : 20 \qquad\qquad 20 : 24$$

Aha—now we can write it as a 3-way ratio of blots to bleets to blits.

$$\text{blots : bleets : blits}$$
$$15 : 20 : 24$$

The problem asked us for the relationship between blots and blits, and we can read this information from our 3-way ratio. We see that blots and blits are in the ratio 15 : 24, which can be simplified as

$$\text{blots : blits} = 15 : 24 = \frac{15}{3} : \frac{24}{3} = 5 : 8.$$

$\square$

Exercises

7.2.1 A log whose length is 60 inches is cut into three pieces in the ratio 1 : 3 : 5. What is the number of inches in the length of the shortest piece?

7.2.2 Three numbers have ratio 1 : 2 : 3, and their sum is 48. What is the greatest of these three numbers?

7.2.3 Purple paint is made with a 16 : 3 : 1 ratio of white paint : blue paint : red paint. How much white paint is needed in order to make one gallon of purple paint? *(Source: MATHCOUNTS)*

7.2.4 Three friends, Akira, Bruno, and Carmela, pooled their money to start a lemonade stand. Akira contributed $25, Bruno contributed $20, and Carmela contributed $35. After a month, their lemonade stand had earned $2,000, and they want to distribute this money in the same ratio as the money that was invested. How many dollars will Bruno receive?

7.2.5 The top four winners in a golf tournament share the prize money in the ratio 9 : 5 : 2 : 1. If the top prize winner receives $45,000, then how much prize money is awarded in total?

7.2.6   Alex owns three times as many brown shoes as red shoes, twice as many black shoes as brown shoes, and four times as many white shoes as red shoes. What is the ratio of the number of white shoes to the number of black shoes he owns? *(Source: MATHCOUNTS)*

7.2.7★   Three siblings have a gift of $169 to split in the ratio of $\frac{1}{2} : \frac{1}{3} : \frac{1}{4}$. What is the greatest number of dollars that any of the siblings will receive? *(Source: MATHCOUNTS)* **Hints:** 135

7.3   Proportions

Whenever we have two ratios that are equal, we have a **proportion**. The most common usage of proportion is when we have two changing quantities that are related in such a way that their ratio doesn't change.

For example, suppose that Mario's secret recipe for chocolate milk uses 8 ounces of milk and 2 ounces of chocolate syrup, and produces a 10-ounce glass of chocolate milk. The ratio of milk to chocolate syrup is 8 : 2, or 4 : 1. If Mario wants to make a big pitcher of chocolate milk for 6 people, then he will need $6 \cdot 8 = 48$ ounces of milk and $6 \cdot 2 = 12$ ounces of chocolate syrup, so the ratio of milk to chocolate syrup is 48 : 12, which is still 4 : 1. No matter what quantity of chocolate milk that we want, the ratio of milk to chocolate syrup will always be 4 : 1. We say that the milk and chocolate syrup are **proportional** or **in proportion**.

> **Problems** ▶

Problem 7.11: Charlotte is planning a vacation to Europe. The exchange rate is 1 dollar equals 0.6 euros, or \$1 = €0.60. If Charlotte wants to have €300 for her trip, then how many dollars does she need to convert?

Problem 7.12: A recipe calls for $2\frac{1}{2}$ cups of flour and 4 eggs. If only 3 eggs are used, then how many cups of flour should be used? *(Source: MATHCOUNTS)*

Problem 7.13: Sadie is 3 feet tall and at 6 p.m. in Sunnytown, Sadie casts an 8-foot shadow. Nick is 5 feet tall. How long is his shadow at 6 p.m. in Sunnytown?

Problem 7.14: My map of upstate New York has the scale $\frac{1}{4}$ inch = 5 miles. If Buffalo and Albany are 13 inches apart on my map, then how far apart are the cities?

Problem 7.15: Sylvia is an architect designing a new building. The building will be 30 feet tall, and the windows will each be 8 feet high. Sylvia draws blueprints for the building on which the building is 8 inches tall. How tall are the windows on Sylvia's blueprints?

Problem 7.16: My wallet-size photo of my pet cat Snookums is 3 cm wide and 5 cm tall. If I want a larger photo to put on my wall, and I want the area of the photo to be 135 square centimeters, then how many centimeters wide should the larger photo be?

Problem 7.11: Charlotte is planning a vacation to Europe. The exchange rate is 1 dollar equals 0.6 euros, or \$1 = €0.60. If Charlotte wants to have €300 for her trip, then how many dollars does she need to convert?

Solution for Problem 7.11: Since \$1 equals €0.60, the ratio between an equal amount of dollars and euros is 1 : 0.6, which simplifies to 5 : 3. We let x be the number of dollars that equals €300, which is what we want to find. Then as a proportion we have

$$5 : 3 = x : 300,$$

which gives $\frac{5}{3} = \frac{x}{300}$. We can solve for x as $x = 300 \cdot \frac{5}{3} = 500$. Hence, Charlotte must convert \$500 in order to receive €300. □

Problem 7.12: A recipe calls for $2\frac{1}{2}$ cups of flour and 4 eggs. If only 3 eggs are used, then how many cups of flour should be used? *(Source: MATHCOUNTS)*

Solution for Problem 7.12: There are two primary methods we can use.

Method 1: Set up a proportion by equating ratios. Because the recipe calls for $2\frac{1}{2}$ cups of flour and 4 eggs, we know that the ratio of flour to eggs should always equal $2\frac{1}{2} : 4$. If we only have 3 eggs, then we need an amount of flour so that the ratio of flour to eggs still equals $2\frac{1}{2} : 4$. This means that if we have x cups of flour to go with our 3 eggs, we must have

$$2\frac{1}{2} : 4 = x : 3.$$

We solve this by writing the equation with fractions:

$$\frac{2\frac{1}{2}}{4} = \frac{x}{3}.$$

Multiplying both sides of this equation by 12 gives $3 \cdot \left(2\frac{1}{2}\right) = 4x$. So $\frac{15}{2} = 4x$, and dividing by 4 gives $\frac{15}{8} = x$. Therefore we need $\frac{15}{8} = 1\frac{7}{8}$ cups of flour.

Method 2: Scale the quantities. Because we only have 3 eggs and the recipe calls for 4 eggs, we are only using $\frac{3}{4}$ of the recipe amount. In order for the ratio of flour to eggs to remain constant, we also need to use $\frac{3}{4}$ of the recipe amount of flour. Therefore, the amount of flour that we need is

$$\frac{3}{4} \cdot 2\frac{1}{2} = \frac{3}{4} \cdot \frac{5}{2} = \frac{15}{8} = 1\frac{7}{8}$$

cups. □

In the next problem, we use the geometric fact that at any given time, the length of an object is proportional to the length of its shadow. (This is based on the geometric concept of **similarity**, which you will learn when you take a geometry course.)

Problem 7.13: Sadie is 3 feet tall and at 6 p.m. in Sunnytown, Sadie casts an 8-foot shadow. Nick is 5 feet tall. How long is his shadow at 6 p.m. in Sunnytown?

Solution for Problem 7.13: The information about Sadie tells us that the length of an object (or person) and the length of its shadow are proportional in the ratio 3 : 8. If Nick's shadow has length x, then the ratio 5 : x must equal the ratio 3 : 8. Therefore, $\frac{5}{x} = \frac{3}{8}$, and multiplying both sides by $8x$ gives $40 = 3x$, so $x = \frac{40}{3} = 13\frac{1}{3}$. Thus, Nick's shadow is $13\frac{1}{3}$ feet long. □

Problem 7.14: My map of upstate New York has the scale $\frac{1}{4}$ inch = 5 miles. If Buffalo and Albany are 13 inches apart on my map, then how far apart are the cities?

Solution for Problem 7.14: A map's scale is another example of a proportion—it tells us that the ratio of the distance on the map to the distance in the real world is constant. For my map, this ratio is

$$\frac{1}{4} \text{ inch} : 5 \text{ miles.}$$

Multiplying by 4 simplifies this ratio to 1 inch : 20 miles, so that 1 inch on the map corresponds to 20 miles in real life. Thus, the 13 inches on the map between Buffalo and Albany means that the cities are $13 \cdot 20 = 260$ miles apart. □

Problem 7.15: Sylvia is an architect designing a new building. The building will be 30 feet tall, and the windows will each be 8 feet high. Sylvia draws blueprints for the building on which the building is 8 inches tall. How tall are the windows on Sylvia's blueprints?

Solution for Problem 7.15: We start with the ratio

$$\text{building height : window height} = 30 \text{ feet} : 8 \text{ feet} = 30 : 8 = 15 : 4.$$

Thus, on the blueprints, we must have the same ratio between the heights of the building and the window. So if the window height on the blueprints is x inches, then we have

$$15 : 4 = 8 : x,$$

so that $\frac{15}{4} = \frac{8}{x}$. Multiplying both sides of this equation by $4x$ gives $15x = 32$, so $x = \frac{32}{15} = 2\frac{2}{15}$. Therefore, the windows are $2\frac{2}{15}$ inches tall on the blueprints. □

Problem 7.16: My wallet-size photo of my pet cat Snookums is 3 cm wide and 5 cm tall. If I want a larger photo to put on my wall, and I want the area of the photo to be 135 square centimeters, then how many centimeters wide should the larger photo be?

Solution for Problem 7.16: The assumption in this problem is that no matter what the size, the picture will always have the same shape. More precisely, this means that the ratio of width to height will remain constant. Since the wallet-size photo has width 3 cm and height 5 cm, the ratio of width to height will always be 3 : 5. But we're given neither the width nor the height of the larger photo: we're only given the area. So how do we set up a proportion?

The proportion tells us that the width is $3x$ cm and the height is $5x$ cm for some number x. This means that the area is $(3x) \cdot (5x) = 15x^2$ square centimeters. If I want a larger photo with area 135 square centimeters, then we must have $15x^2 = 135$, or $x^2 = 135/15 = 9$. Therefore, $x = 3$. So my larger photo will be $3x = 3(3) = 9$ cm wide (and $5x = 5(3) = 15$ cm high). □

Exercises

7.3.1 A ream of paper containing 500 sheets is 5 cm thick. How many sheets of this type of paper would there be in a stack 7.5 cm high? *(Source: AMC 8)*

7.3.2 An American traveling in Japan wishes to exchange American money (dollars, symbol $) for Japanese money (yen, symbol ¥). If the exchange rate is $1 = ¥80, then how many dollars will the traveler need to purchase ¥10,000?

7.3.3 Alexia designed a logo 2 inches wide and 1.5 inches tall to be used on her school's website. The school wants the logo to appear on the website as 8 inches wide. How tall will the logo be on the website if it is enlarged proportionally? *(Source: MATHCOUNTS)*

7.3.4 A bank has two flagpoles next to each other. If the taller 30-foot pole (flying the U.S. flag) casts a shadow of 20 feet, and the shorter flagpole (flying the state flag) casts a shadow of 15 feet, then how tall is the shorter flagpole?

7.3.5 If $\frac{1}{4}$ inch on a map represents 50 miles, then what is the number of miles represented by $2\frac{7}{8}$ inches?

7.3.6 A draftsperson makes a scale drawing of a 100 meter × 30 meter building, where 1 centimeter represents 2.5 meters. How many centimeters are in the smaller dimension of the drawing of the building? *(Source: MATHCOUNTS)*

7.3.7 Twelve friends met for dinner at Oscar's Overstuffed Oyster House, and each ordered one meal. The portions were so large, there was enough food for 18 people. If they share, then how many meals should they have ordered to have just enough food for the 12 of them? *(Source: AMC 8)*

7.3.8★ For every 3° rise in temperature, the volume of a certain gas expands by 4 cubic centimeters. If the volume of the gas is 24 cubic centimeters when the temperature is 32°, then what was the volume of the gas when the temperature was 20°? *(Source: AMC 8)*

7.4 Conversions

There is a special type of ratio that is useful for converting between different units of measurement. Let's illustrate how this works with a simple example.

We know that there are 12 inches in a foot and there are 3 feet in a yard. Suppose you want to use this information to compute the number of inches in a yard. Of course, you can probably do this problem in your head, or you may even have the answer memorized. But let's carefully work through two methods that we can use to solve the problem. These methods will help us work through harder conversion problems, where the answer is not so obvious.

Method 1: Set up ratios. We'll use a method similar to Problem 7.10 (the problem with the blits and bleets and blots). We can write ratios to express the relationships between the units:

$$\text{inches} : \text{feet} \qquad \text{feet} : \text{yards}$$
$$12 : 1 \qquad\qquad 3 : 1$$

We'd like to combine this into a 3-way ratio relating all three units. To do that, we need the "feet" amount in both 2-way ratios to match. The easiest way to do this is to multiply both parts of the first ratio by 3:

$$\text{inches} : \text{feet} \qquad \text{feet} : \text{yards}$$
$$36 : 3 \qquad\qquad 3 : 1$$

Now we can write it as a 3-way ratio:

$$\text{inches} : \text{feet} : \text{yards} = 36 : 3 : 1$$

Removing the "feet" gives us a ratio of inches : yards = 36 : 1, so there are 36 inches in a yard.

Method 2: Use conversion factors. If we write the ratios from Method 1 as fractions, then we have what are called **conversion factors**. To help us keep track of what's going on, we'll write the units as part of the fraction. So we'd write

$$\frac{12 \text{ inches}}{1 \text{ feet}} \quad \text{and} \quad \frac{3 \text{ feet}}{1 \text{ yards}}.$$

(For consistency, we usually write all units in plural, so we write the weird-looking "1 feet" instead of "1 foot.") Multiplying the conversion factors together will cancel the "feet" and leave us with a conversion factor relating inches to yards:

$$\frac{12 \text{ inches}}{1 \text{ feet}} \cdot \frac{3 \text{ feet}}{1 \text{ yards}} = \frac{36 \text{ inches}}{1 \text{ yards}}.$$

So there are 36 inches in a yard.

Compare the two methods used above. They're really the same thing! The conversion factors from Method 2 are just a convenient way for us to keep track of the ratios from Method 1.

There are two key ideas to keep in mind when using conversion factors. First,

> **Concept:** Think of conversion factors as fractions that are equal to 1.

For example, we know that there are 12 inches in a foot, so we think of

$$12 \text{ inches} = 1 \text{ feet}.$$

In other words, the quantities "12 inches" and "1 feet" are *equal quantities,* so it makes sense to write them equal to each other in an equation. Going one step further, this then makes the fraction

$$\frac{12 \text{ inches}}{1 \text{ feet}} = 1.$$

The right way to think about this is as a fraction with equal numerator and denominator, so of course it is equal to 1. Also, we can just as easily write its reciprocal too:

$$\frac{1 \text{ feet}}{12 \text{ inches}} = 1.$$

Our second key idea about conversion factors is:

> **Concept:** We multiply conversion factors together to cancel units.

We see this concept if we revisit our earlier computation:

$$\frac{12 \text{ inches}}{1 \text{ feet}} \cdot \frac{3 \text{ feet}}{1 \text{ yards}} = \frac{36 \text{ inches}}{1 \text{ yards}}.$$

All we're doing is multiplying two fractions on the left that are each equal to 1, so naturally (since $1 \cdot 1 = 1$) the quantity on the right side of the equation is also equal to 1. But we also notice that the "feet" units cancel. You might see this more clearly if we put in some missing steps in the above calculation:

$$\frac{12 \text{ inches}}{1 \text{ feet}} \cdot \frac{3 \text{ feet}}{1 \text{ yards}} = \frac{(12 \text{ inches}) \cdot (3 \text{ feet})}{(1 \text{ feet}) \cdot (1 \text{ yards})} = \frac{(12 \cdot 3)(\text{inches} \cdot \cancel{\text{feet}})}{(1 \cdot 1)(\cancel{\text{feet}} \cdot \text{ yards})} = \frac{36 \text{ inches}}{1 \text{ yards}}.$$

The beauty of this is that it helps us prevent mistakes. For example, if we incorrectly tried to combine conversion factors as:

$$\frac{12 \text{ inches}}{1 \text{ feet}} \cdot \frac{1 \text{ yards}}{3 \text{ feet}} = \frac{4(\text{inches} \cdot \text{ yards})}{1(\text{feet} \cdot \text{ feet})},$$

we see that the units don't cancel properly, so we probably made a mistake somewhere.

Conversion factors make it easy to convert units. For example, suppose we want to convert the length "6 yards" into inches. We know that a conversion factor is just a fraction that equals 1, and multiplying "6 yards" by 1 doesn't change the length. Therefore, we have

$$6 \text{ yards} = (6 \text{ yards}) \cdot 1 = (6 \text{ yards}) \cdot \frac{36 \text{ inches}}{1 \text{ yards}}.$$

But now the units nicely cancel, and we can finish the computation:

$$6 \text{ yards} = (6 \text{ yards}) \cdot \frac{36 \text{ inches}}{1 \text{ yards}} = \frac{6 \cdot 36 \text{ inches}}{1} = 216 \text{ inches}.$$

Notice how the "yards" units cancelled, and we are left with just the "inches" units, as we want. Therefore, 6 yards is equal to 216 inches.

Problems

Problem 7.17: How many yards equals 90 inches?

Problem 7.18: A tablespoon is half of a fluid ounce, a cup is 8 fluid ounces, and a gallon is 16 cups. How many tablespoons are in a gallon?

Problem 7.19: Will took $1,000 on his trip to Japan, where the exchange rate between dollars and yen is $1 = ¥90. He spent ¥45,000 on his hotel room and ¥11,250 on meals and souvenirs. How much money (in dollars) did he have remaining at the end of his trip?

Problem 7.20: The density of water is approximately 8.3 pounds per gallon, and there are 4 quarts in a gallon. How much does 7 quarts of water weigh?

Problem 7.21: An inch is approximately 2.5 centimeters. Approximately how many square centimeters are in a square inch?

Problem 7.17: How many yards equals 90 inches?

Solution for Problem 7.17: We discovered above that 1 yard is equal to 36 inches. To convert 90 inches into yards, we start with the quantity "90 inches" and multiply by the appropriate conversion factors until we get something with the units "yards." In this case, it's easy: we just need a conversion factor with inches in the denominator (to cancel the inches in our initial quantity) and yards in the numerator (so we'll be left with yards). Our calculation is:

$$90 \text{ inches} = 90 \text{ inches} \cdot \frac{1 \text{ yards}}{36 \text{ inches}} = \frac{90}{36} \text{ yards} = 2.5 \text{ yards}.$$

Thus, 90 inches is the same as 2.5 yards. □

> **Concept:** The reason the calculation in Problem 7.17 works is that the conversion factor is equal to 1. That is, because 1 yards = 36 inches, the fraction $\frac{1 \text{ yards}}{36 \text{ inches}}$ is equal to 1. Therefore, multiplying 90 inches by this fraction is the same as multiplying by 1, and hence the length does not change.

Problem 7.18: A tablespoon is half of a fluid ounce, a cup is 8 fluid ounces, and a gallon is 16 cups. How many tablespoons are in a gallon?

Solution for Problem 7.18: We want to convert "1 gallon" into some number of tablespoons. But we don't have a single gallons-to-tablespoons conversion factor. Instead, we have to use the multiple conversion factors that we are given in the problem statement. First, we show a step-by-step solution.

We first convert gallons to cups. We don't really need a "conversion factor" for this, since we can just read this data from the problem statement:

$$1 \text{ gallon} = 16 \text{ cups}.$$

Next, we convert cups to ounces, using the cups-to-ounces conversion:

$$1 \text{ gallon} = 16 \text{ cups} = 16 \text{ cups} \cdot \frac{8 \text{ ounces}}{1 \text{ cups}} = (16 \cdot 8) \text{ ounces} = 128 \text{ ounces}.$$

Finally, we convert ounces to tablespoons (abbreviated tbsp):

$$1 \text{ gallon} = 128 \text{ ounces} = 128 \text{ ounces} \cdot \frac{1 \text{ tbsp}}{\frac{1}{2} \text{ ounces}} = \frac{128}{\frac{1}{2}} \text{ tbsp} = 256 \text{ tbsp}.$$

So there are 256 tablespoons in a gallon.

But conversion factors are nice in that we can use more than one of them at the same time. In particular, we could do the gallon-to-tablespoons conversion all at once:

$$1 \text{ gallon} = 1 \text{ gallon} \cdot \frac{16 \text{ cups}}{1 \text{ gallons}} \cdot \frac{8 \text{ ounces}}{1 \text{ cups}} \cdot \frac{1 \text{ tbsp}}{\frac{1}{2} \text{ ounces}} = \frac{16 \cdot 8}{\frac{1}{2}} \text{ tbsp} = 256 \text{ tbsp}.$$

As long as we are sure that each conversion factor equals 1 (meaning that its numerator and denominator represent the same quantity), and that the units cancel properly, we can line up as many conversion factors as might be necessary to do a complicated conversion. □

We can use conversion factors whenever we wish to compare two different units—they don't necessarily have to be typical "measurements" like length or volume. For example:

Problem 7.19: Will took $1,000 on his trip to Japan, where the exchange rate between dollars and yen is $1 = ¥90. He spent ¥45,000 on his hotel room and ¥11,250 on meals and souvenirs. How much money (in dollars) did he have remaining at the end of his trip?

Solution for Problem 7.19: Method 1: Convert and then convert back. When Will went to Japan, his dollars became:

$$\$1,000 \cdot \frac{¥90}{\$1} = ¥90,000.$$

This is just like any other conversion: notice how the conversion factor $\frac{¥90}{\$1}$ equals 1 because ¥90 equals \$1, and notice how the \$ units cancel leaving us with the desired ¥ units. After his spending, he was left with

$$¥90{,}000 - ¥45{,}000 - ¥11{,}250 = ¥33{,}750.$$

When Will got home, he converted his remaining yen back into dollars:

$$¥33{,}750 \cdot \frac{\$1}{¥90} = \$\frac{33{,}750}{90} = \$375.$$

So Will had \$375 dollars remaining after his trip.

Method 2: Convert just the spending. Rather than convert Will's entire bankroll to yen and then convert it back, we can just figure out how much he spent in dollars. His total spending was ¥45,000 + ¥11,250 = ¥56,250, so in dollars this is

$$¥56{,}250 \cdot \frac{\$1}{¥90} = \$\frac{56{,}250}{90} = \$625.$$

Thus Will spent the equivalent of \$625 on his trip, and had \$1,000 − \$625 = \$375 remaining. □

Problem 7.20: The density of water is approximately 8.3 pounds per gallon, and there are 4 quarts in a gallon. How much does 7 quarts of water weigh?

Solution for Problem 7.20: We want to convert from quarts to pounds. We can use two conversion factors: one for quarts to gallons, and one for gallons to pounds:

$$7 \text{ quarts} = 7 \text{ quarts} \cdot \frac{1 \text{ gallons}}{4 \text{ quarts}} \cdot \frac{8.3 \text{ pounds}}{1 \text{ gallons}} = \frac{7 \cdot 8.3}{4} \text{ pounds} = 14.525 \text{ pounds}.$$

□

Problem 7.21: An inch is approximately 2.5 centimeters. Approximately how many square centimeters are in a square inch?

Solution for Problem 7.21: Method 1: Reason geometrically. A square inch is the area of a square that is 1 inch on each side. But this same square is 2.5 centimeters on each side, so its area is (2.5)(2.5) = 6.25 square centimeters.

Method 2: Use conversion factors. We wish to convert from square inches (written in^2) to square centimeters (written cm^2). So we need to cancel the inches units *twice* and be left with the centimeters units *twice*. Thus, we need to multiply by two conversion factors:

$$1 \text{ in}^2 = 1 \text{ in}^2 \cdot \frac{2.5 \text{ cm}}{1 \text{ in}} \cdot \frac{2.5 \text{ cm}}{1 \text{ in}} = (2.5)(2.5) \text{ cm}^2 = 6.25 \text{ cm}^2.$$

□

| Exercises |

7.4.1 Suppose that one US dollar is worth C$1.25 in Canadian dollars. If I want to buy a C$15 book in Canada, then how many US dollars do I need?

7.4.2 Basketball center Steve Tootall is 7 feet 2 inches in height. What is Steve's height in inches?

7.4.3 Recall that 1 inch is approximately 2.5 centimeters. What is the area, in square centimeters, of a square that is $\frac{1}{2}$ feet long on each side?

7.4.4 There are approximately 28.35 grams in an ounce, and 16 ounces in a pound. How many grams does a quarter-pound hamburger weigh? Round your answer to nearest whole number of grams.

7.4.5 Natalya's secret recipe for peanut butter cookies calls for $2\frac{1}{2}$ cups of flour. Unfortunately, Natalya has lost all of her measuring equipment except for a teaspoon. There are 3 teaspoons in a tablespoon, $\frac{1}{2}$ ounce in a tablespoon, and 8 ounces in a cup. How many teaspoons of flour does Natalya need for her recipe?

7.4.6 1000 meters is 1 kilometer, and 100 hectares is one square kilometer. How many square meters are in 1 hectare?

7.4.7 On the planet Qinbob, the unit of currency is the Ploktar, the unit of weight is the stuun, and the unit of volume is the piquat. The precious liquid *vimwy* is worth 400 Ploktars per stuun and has a density of 20 stuun per piquat. If Aanie has 500 piquat of vimwy, then how many Ploktars is her vimwy worth? **Hints:** 129

7.5 Speed

You are probably already familiar with the idea of **speed**. Speed is a measure of how fast something is moving.

For example, suppose a car is traveling at a constant speed of 40 miles per hour. After 1 hour, it has traveled 40 miles; after 2 hours, it has traveled 80 miles; after 3 hours, it has traveled 120 miles, and so on. Notice that the ratio of distance traveled (in miles) to time traveled (in hours) is always constant:

$$40 : 1 = 80 : 2 = 120 : 3.$$

In general, if the car travels for x hours, it will have traveled $40x$ miles, for a ratio of distance to time of $40x : x = 40 : 1$.

Concept: Speed is the ratio of distance to time.

We can write "speed is the ratio of distance to time" as the equation

$$\text{speed} = \frac{\text{distance}}{\text{time}}.$$

This equation can be rearranged as

$$(\text{speed}) \cdot (\text{time}) = \text{distance}$$

and also as

$$\text{time} = \frac{\text{distance}}{\text{speed}}.$$

The units associated with speed help us remember these equations. For example, the speed of a car (in the U.S.) is usually given in "miles per hour," abbreviated "mph." The word **per** essentially means "divided by," so a speed in miles per hour means to take distance (in miles) and divide by time (in hours). So, for instance, a car that travels 110 miles in 2 hours is traveling at a speed of

$$\frac{110 \text{ miles}}{2 \text{ hours}} = \frac{110}{2} \text{ miles per hour} = 55 \text{ miles per hour}.$$

Similarly, a car that travels at a speed of 70 miles per hour for 2 hours covers a distance of:

$$(70 \text{ miles per hour}) \cdot (2 \text{ hours}) = 140 \text{ miles}.$$

We can also think of speed as a type of conversion factor, one that converts between time and distance. To repeat our previous example, a car that travels at a speed of 70 miles per hour for 2 hours is essentially "converting" the 2 hours of time into a distance, as

$$2 \text{ hours} \cdot \frac{70 \text{ miles}}{1 \text{ hours}} = (2 \cdot 70) \text{ miles} = 140 \text{ miles}.$$

Problems

Problem 7.22:

(a) How far does a car traveling at 75 miles per hour travel in 2.6 hours?

(b) If a truck travels at a constant speed and travels 238 miles in 3.5 hours, then at what speed did the truck travel?

(c) How long will a motorcycle traveling at 80 miles per hour need to travel 420 miles?

Problem 7.23: A freight train travels 1 mile in 1 minute 30 seconds. At this rate, how many miles will the train travel in 1 hour? *(Source: MOEMS)*

Problem 7.24: If you walk for 45 minutes at a rate of 4 mph and then run for 30 minutes at a rate of 10 mph, then how many miles have you gone at the end of one hour and 15 minutes? What was your average speed for the journey? *(Source: AMC 8)*

Problem 7.25: Shelly drove the 50 miles from her home to her office at an average speed of 75 miles per hour. Coming home, she encountered heavy traffic and drove the same 50 miles at an average speed of 50 miles per hour. What was her average speed for the entire 100-mile roundtrip?

Problem 7.26: Ben leaves his house at 7 a.m. and bikes at a constant speed of 15 miles per hour due east. Alisha lives 100 miles due east of Ben, leaves her house at 8 a.m., and bikes at a constant speed of 10 miles per hour due west. At what time do they meet?

Problem 7.27:

(a) On Monday, Yogi and Boo-Boo start at the same place and at the same time on a 400-meter circular track and run in *opposite* directions. Yogi runs at 5 meters per second and Boo-Boo runs at 3 meters per second. In how many seconds will they first meet after starting?

(b) On Tuesday, Yogi and Boo-Boo start at the same place and at the same time on a 400-meter circular track and run in the *same* direction. Yogi runs at 5 meters per second and Boo-Boo runs at 3 meters per second. In how many seconds will they first meet after starting?

The most basic type of speed problem gives you two of the three pieces of data—speed, time, distance—and asks you to compute the third.

Problem 7.22:

(a) How far does a car traveling at 75 miles per hour travel in 2.6 hours?

(b) If a truck travels at a constant speed and travels 238 miles in 3.5 hours, then at what speed did the truck travel?

(c) How long will a motorcycle traveling at 80 miles per hour need to travel 420 miles?

Solution for Problem 7.22: In each of these three types of computation, simply keeping track of the units will show us what to do.

(a) The car travels 75 miles during each hour that it travels, so in 2.6 hours it travels $75 \cdot 2.6 = 195$ miles.

   We can think about the units to see why we should multiply the speed $75 \frac{\text{miles}}{\text{hour}}$ by the time 2.6 hours to get the distance traveled in miles. Multiplying these two allows us to cancel out the "hours":

$$\text{distance} = \text{speed} \cdot \text{time} = \frac{75 \text{ miles}}{1 \text{ hours}} \cdot 2.6 \text{ hours} = (75 \cdot 2.6) \text{ miles} = 195 \text{ miles}.$$

(b) If the truck travels 238 miles at a constant speed in 3.5 hours, then it must travel $\frac{238}{3.5} = 68$ miles in each hour. Therefore, its speed is 68 miles per hour.

   Again, we can think about units to realize that we should divide. Our answer is a speed, so its units should be "miles per hour." Thus, we divide the distance (in miles) by the time (in hours):

$$\text{speed} = \frac{\text{distance}}{\text{time}} = \frac{238 \text{ miles}}{3.5 \text{ hours}} = \frac{238}{3.5} \text{ miles per hour} = 68 \text{ miles per hour}.$$

(c) If a motorcycle covers 80 miles in each hour, then it will cover 420 miles in $\frac{420}{80} = 5.25$ hours.

As with the first two parts, thinking about units can help us see why we divide. Our answer is time, so it should be expressed in "hours." Thus, we have to divide distance (in miles) by speed (in miles per hours) to end up with an answer in terms of hours:

$$\text{time} = \frac{\text{distance}}{\text{speed}} = \frac{420 \text{ miles}}{80 \frac{\text{miles}}{\text{hours}}} = \frac{420}{80} \text{ hours} = 5.25 \text{ hours}.$$

This may be easier to see (and remember) if we write this computation to look more like a conversion factor:

$$420 \text{ miles} \cdot \frac{1 \text{ hours}}{80 \text{ miles}} = \frac{420}{80} \text{ hours} = 5.25 \text{ hours}.$$

□

> **WARNING!!** There's nothing special about "miles" and "hours" in Problem 7.22. Speed can be expressed in any distance unit per any time unit. So it might be given in meters per second, or feet per minute, or light years per fortnight. Just be sure that you keep your units consistent!

> **Problem 7.23:** A freight train travels 1 mile in 1 minute 30 seconds. At this rate, how many miles will the train travel in 1 hour? *(Source: MOEMS)*

Solution for Problem 7.23: One minute 30 seconds is $\frac{3}{2}$ minutes, so the train's speed is

$$\text{speed} = \frac{1 \text{ miles}}{\frac{3}{2} \text{ minutes}} = \frac{2}{3} \frac{\text{miles}}{\text{minute}}.$$

There are 60 minutes in an hour, so the distance traveled in 60 minutes is

$$\text{distance} = (60 \text{ minutes}) \cdot \left(\frac{2}{3} \frac{\text{miles}}{\text{minute}} \right) = 40 \text{ miles}.$$

□

Another way to solve Problem 7.23 is to reason as follows: the number of "1 minute 30 second" intervals in a 60-minute hour is $60/(\frac{3}{2}) = 40$. The train covers a mile in each of these 40 intervals. Therefore the train covers 40 miles in an hour.

Problem 7.24: If you walk for 45 minutes at a rate of 4 mph and then run for 30 minutes at a rate of 10 mph, then how many miles have you gone at the end of one hour and 15 minutes? What was your average speed for the journey? *(Source: AMC 8)*

Solution for Problem 7.24: We can compute the walking distance and running distances separately, then add them. You walk for 45 minutes, which is $\frac{3}{4}$ hours, at a rate of 4 mph, so the walking distance is (4 mph)($\frac{3}{4}$ hours) = 3 miles. You run for 30 minutes, which is $\frac{1}{2}$ hour, at a rate of 10 mph, so the running distance is (10 mph)($\frac{1}{2}$ hour) = 5 miles. So the total distance you cover is $3 + 5 = 8$ miles.

Now we can also compute the average speed for the journey. You covered 8 miles in $\frac{5}{4}$ hours, so your average speed was

$$\frac{8 \text{ miles}}{\frac{5}{4} \text{ hours}} = \frac{8}{\frac{5}{4}} \text{ mph} = \frac{32}{5} \text{ mph} = 6.4 \text{ mph}.$$

$\square$

Problem 7.25: Shelly drove the 50 miles from her home to her office at an average speed of 75 miles per hour. Coming home, she encountered heavy traffic and drove the same 50 miles at an average speed of 50 miles per hour. What was her average speed for the entire 100-mile roundtrip?

Solution for Problem 7.25: You might think:

> **Bogus Solution:** Shelly drove half of her trip at 75 mph and the other half of her trip at 50 mph. Therefore, her average speed is just the average of the speeds from the two halves of the trip, which is $(75 + 50)/2 = 125/2 = 62\frac{1}{2}$ mph.

We cannot average speeds in this way, as we will see when we compute the amount of time the trip takes.

The trip from the home to the office was 50 miles at 75 mph, so it takes

$$\frac{50 \text{ miles}}{75 \text{ mph}} = \frac{2}{3} \text{ hours}.$$

The trip from the office to the home was 50 miles at 50 mph, so it takes 1 hour. Thus, the entire 100-mile trip takes $1\frac{2}{3}$ hours of travel time, and we can compute the average speed to be

$$\frac{100 \text{ miles}}{1\frac{2}{3} \text{ hours}} = \frac{300}{5} \text{ mph} = 60 \text{ mph}.$$

Therefore the average speed of the round-trip journey is 60 miles per hour. $\square$

> **WARNING!!** Speeds do not usually "average" in the way that you might
> expect them to.

> **Sidenote:** There is a relationship between the speeds for the two portions of
> the journey in Problem 7.25. The average speed for the entire trip is
> the **harmonic mean** of the speeds for each half of the trip, given by
>
> $$\frac{2}{\frac{1}{75} + \frac{1}{50}} = \frac{2}{\frac{5}{150}} = \frac{300}{5} = 60.$$
>
> More generally, the harmonic mean of two numbers a and b is
>
> $$\frac{2}{\frac{1}{a} + \frac{1}{b}}.$$
>
> Harmonic mean is another kind of "average" that has many uses in
> advanced mathematics.

Problem 7.26: Ben leaves his house at 7 a.m. and bikes at a constant speed of 15 miles per hour due east. Alisha lives 100 miles due east of Ben, leaves her house at 8 a.m., and bikes at a constant speed of 10 miles per hour due west. At what time do they meet?

Solution for Problem 7.26: There are a couple of different ways we could approach this.

Method 1: Set up an equation. Let t be the time of day in hours—it makes sense to make this our variable since this is what we're trying to find in the problem. We can also imagine the houses as being on the number line, where Ben's house is at 0 and Alisha's house is at 100.

Ben starts cycling at 7 a.m., and he moves right (along our imaginary number line) at 15 miles per hour. So his position at time t is $15(t - 7)$. Alisha starts cycling at 8 a.m., and she moves left at 10 miles per hour. So her position at time t is $100 - 10(t - 8)$. (Note the minus sign in front of the 10, because she is moving to the left.)

They meet when their positions are equal, so at the time that they meet we have

$$15(t - 7) = 100 - 10(t - 8).$$

Expanding this equation gives $15t - 105 = 100 - 10t + 80$, and simplifying gives $25t = 285$. So $t = 285/25 = 11.4$. Therefore, we could say that they meet at 11.4 a.m., but of course this is not how we normally express the time of day. This is $0.4 \cdot 60 = 24$ minutes past 11 a.m., so they meet at 11:24 a.m.

Method 2: Think about how the people are moving relative to each other. We notice that in the first hour (between 7 and 8 a.m.), only Ben is moving, and he covers 15 miles. Therefore, at 8 a.m., the two people are $100 - 15 = 85$ miles apart.

After 8 a.m., since Ben and Alisha cover a combined 25 miles per hour between them, they reduce the distance between them at a rate of 25 miles per hour. They will meet when this distance is reduced all the way to 0. Since they start with 85 miles between them at 8 a.m., and they reduce this distance at a rate of 25 miles per hour, it will take them $85/25 = 3.4$ hours to reduce the distance between them all the way to 0. So they will meet 3.4 hours after 8 a.m., which is 11.4 a.m. as in Method 1. Again, converting to minutes gives $0.4 \cdot 60 = 24$ minutes past 11 a.m., so they meet at 11:24 a.m. □

Method 2 above uses the following important idea:

Concept: When there are two people or objects moving simultaneously, it is often easiest to keep track of the distance between the objects, rather than trying to keep track of the objects separately.

Try this concept in the next problem.

Problem 7.27:

(a) On Monday, Yogi and Boo-Boo start at the same place and at the same time on a 400-meter circular track and run in *opposite* directions. Yogi runs at 5 meters per second and Boo-Boo runs at 3 meters per second. In how many seconds will they first meet after starting?

(b) On Tuesday, Yogi and Boo-Boo start at the same place and at the same time on a 400-meter circular track and run in the *same* direction. Yogi runs at 5 meters per second and Boo-Boo runs at 3 meters per second. In how many seconds will they first meet after starting?

Solution for Problem 7.27:

(a) We can think of Yogi and Boo-Boo as being 400 meters apart at the start, because they have to run a combined 400 meters until they will meet again. They reduce the distance between them at a rate of $5 + 3 = 8$ meters per second. So they will meet after $400/8 = 50$ seconds.

(b) When they run in the same direction, we think of the distance between them as increasing. The rate at which the distance is increasing is the difference in their speeds, which is $5 - 3 = 2$ meters per second. They meet when Yogi "laps" Boo-Boo, meaning when Yogi has increased his lead over Boo-Boo to 400 meters, or an entire lap, and thus Yogi catches Boo-Boo from behind. Since Yogi's lead increases by 2 meters per second, he will catch Boo-Boo after $400/2 = 200$ seconds.

□

Sidenote: Considering how two people or objects move relative to each other is a key concept in solving many problems in physics.

| | Exercises | ▶ |

7.5.1

(a) At 50 miles per hour, how far does a car travel in $2\frac{3}{4}$ hours?

(b) At 60 miles per hour, how long does it take a car to travel 320 miles?

(c) How fast does a car have to travel to go 280 miles in $3\frac{1}{2}$ hours?

7.5.2 On a sunny July day, Mo starts at 10 a.m. in Calgary, at which time her car's odometer reads 27289 kilometers. At 4 p.m. she arrives in Saskatoon, at which time her car's odometer reads 27816 kilometers. (Mo did not need to adjust her clock for a time zone crossing, because in the summer the time in Calgary is the same as the time in Saskatoon.) What was her average speed for the trip?

7.5.3 On a trip, a car traveled 80 miles in an hour and a half, then was stopped in traffic for 30 minutes, and then traveled 100 miles during the next two hours. What was the car's average speed for the 4-hour trip? *(Source: AMC 8)*

7.5.4 Peter had a 12:00 noon appointment that was 60 miles from his home. He drove from his home at an average rate of 40 miles per hour and arrived 15 minutes late. At what time did Peter leave home for the appointment? *(Source: MOEMS)*

7.5.5 I usually walk from home to work. This morning, I walked for 10 minutes until I was halfway to work. I then realized that I would be late if I kept walking. I ran the rest of the way. I run twice as fast as I walk. How many minutes total did it take me to get from home to work?

7.5.6 A train is traveling 1 mile every 75 seconds. If the train continues at this rate, then how far will it travel in two hours?

7.5.7 Jason and Jeremy work together at a juggling-ball factory. Jason lives 25 miles away from the factory and drives at 60 miles per hour. Jeremy lives 35 miles away from the factory and drives at 70 miles per hour. If they leave their houses at the same time, then who arrives at the factory first, and how long is it until the other arrives?

7.5.8 A man drives from his home at 30 miles per hour to a shopping mall that is 20 miles from his home. On the return trip, he encounters heavy traffic and averages 12 miles per hour. To the nearest mile per hour, what is his average speed for the round-trip to and from the mall?

7.5.9 Two dogs run around a circular track 300 feet long in the same direction. One dog runs at a steady rate of 15 feet per second, the other at a steady rate of 12 feet per second. Suppose they start at the same point and time. What is the least number of seconds that will elapse before they are again together? *(Source: MOEMS)*

7.5.10★ A train traveling at 30 miles per hour reaches a tunnel that is 9 times as long as the train. If the train takes 2 minutes to completely clear the tunnel, then how long is the train in feet? (1 mile equals 5280 feet.) *(Source: MOEMS)* **Hints:** 62

7.6 Other Rates

Speed is just a special example of a **rate**. Whenever a quantity changes by a certain amount in a fixed unit of time, we have a rate. The idea of rate is very flexible and can be used in a lot of different situations.

 **Problems**

> **Problem 7.28:** Jason can type at a rate of 40 words per minute. How long will it take him to type a 2,000 word essay?

> **Problem 7.29:** A hose fills a swimming pool at a rate of 0.5 gallons per second. If the pool's capacity is 9,000 gallons, then how many hours does it take for the hose to completely fill an empty pool?

> **Problem 7.30:** Julie wants to give a 45-minute speech, and she speaks 120 words per minute. Her written notes contain 500 words per page. How many pages should she prepare?

> **Problem 7.31:** Rajiv's car has tires that have circumference 75 inches. (The *circumference* of a tire is the distance around the outside of the tire.) How many revolutions will his tires make if Rajiv drives to a store that is $\frac{1}{4}$ mile away? (Assume that the drive is completely straight, and recall that 1 mile is 5,280 feet.)

> **Problem 7.32:** If 5 woodchucks could chuck 50 cords of wood in 4 days, then how many cords of wood could 7 woodchucks chuck in 6 days?

> **Problem 7.33:** Tom can paint Mr. Thatcher's fence in 6 hours, while Huck can paint Mr. Thatcher's fence in 5 hours. If they work together, then how long will it take them to paint the fence?

Just as with speed, the use of the word "per" is likely a signal that we are working with a rate. Also, just as with speed, we can use the units to our advantage when solving problems involving rates.

Here is a basic example:

> **Problem 7.28:** Jason can type at a rate of 40 words per minute. How long will it take him to type a 2,000 word essay?

Solution for Problem 7.28:

Method 1: Direct reasoning. Jason needs to type 2000 words, and for every 40 words that he will type, he will need 1 minute. Therefore, he needs $\dfrac{2000}{40} = 50$ minutes to type the entire 2000 words.

Method 2: Conversion factor. Jason's typing essentially converts "minutes" into "words" and vice versa, so we can use a conversion factor. We need to arrange the data so that the "words" units cancel and we are left with "minutes" units:

$$\text{time} = 2000 \text{ words} \cdot \frac{1 \text{ minutes}}{40 \text{ words}} = \frac{2000}{40} \text{ minutes} = 50 \text{ minutes}.$$

So it takes Jason 50 minutes to type the essay. We can also easily check this answer: if he types for 50 minutes, and he types 40 words per minute, then he will type a total of

$$(50 \text{ minutes}) \cdot \left(40 \frac{\text{words}}{\text{minute}}\right) = (50 \cdot 40) \text{ words} = 2000 \text{ words},$$

as required. □

> **Concept:** Use the units in your mathematical expressions to help you figure out how to use the information in the problem.

Problem 7.29: A hose fills a swimming pool at a rate of 0.5 gallons per second. If the pool's capacity is 9,000 gallons, then how many hours does it take for the hose to completely fill an empty pool?

Solution for Problem 7.29: First, we can compute how many seconds are necessary. This is just a basic conversion problem:

$$\text{time in seconds} = 9000 \text{ gallons} \cdot \frac{1 \text{ seconds}}{0.5 \text{ gallons}} = \frac{9000}{0.5} \text{ seconds} = 18000 \text{ seconds}.$$

We can also convert seconds to hours using conversion factors. This gives

$$18000 \text{ seconds} = (18000 \text{ seconds}) \cdot \frac{1 \text{ minute}}{60 \text{ seconds}} \cdot \frac{1 \text{ hour}}{60 \text{ minutes}} = \frac{18000}{60 \cdot 60} \text{ hours} = 5 \text{ hours}.$$

Thus it will take 5 hours to fill the pool. □

> **Concept:** Unit conversions are just another type of rate. We can work with rates much like we do conversion factors. In particular, use them in mathematical expressions so that the units cancel in the way that you want.

Problem 7.30: Julie wants to give a 45-minute speech, and she speaks 120 words per minute. Her written notes contain 500 words per page. How many pages should she prepare?

Solution for Problem 7.30: We have a couple of different rates here: both the words per minute and the words per page. We could do this as a two-step problem, or use both rates at once.

Method 1: Count words first, then count pages. First, we compute how many words should be in the speech. Julie wants to talk for 45 minutes and she'll use 120 words per minute, so she will speak (45)(120) = 5400 words. Then, we compute the number of pages: 5400 words at 500 words per page will require 5400/500 = 10.8 pages.

Method 2: Do all at once using conversion factors. We write an expression that cancels the units we don't want and leaves the unit we do want:

$$\text{number of pages} = (45 \text{ minutes}) \cdot \frac{120 \text{ words}}{1 \text{ minutes}} \cdot \frac{1 \text{ pages}}{500 \text{ words}} = \frac{45 \cdot 120}{500} \text{ pages} = 10.8 \text{ pages}.$$

□

Problem 7.31: Rajiv's car has tires that have circumference 75 inches. (The *circumference* of a tire is the distance around the outside of the tire.) How many revolutions will his tires make if Rajiv drives to a store that is $\frac{1}{4}$ mile away? (Assume that the drive is completely straight, and recall that 1 mile is 5,280 feet.)

Solution for Problem 7.31: We can set this up as a product of conversion factors:

$$\text{number of revolutions} = \left(\frac{1}{4} \text{ miles}\right) \cdot \frac{5280 \text{ feet}}{1 \text{ miles}} \cdot \frac{12 \text{ inches}}{1 \text{ feet}} \cdot \frac{1 \text{ revolutions}}{75 \text{ inches}}$$
$$= \frac{5280 \cdot 12}{4 \cdot 75} \text{ revolutions}$$
$$= 211.2 \text{ revolutions.}$$

□

Work problems are another particular type of rate problem. Here is a classic (if slightly confusing) example:

Problem 7.32: If 5 woodchucks could chuck 50 cords of wood in 4 days, then how many cords of wood could 7 woodchucks chuck in 6 days?

Solution for Problem 7.32: What information would be most useful? It would be helpful if we knew how much wood 1 woodchuck could chuck in 1 day. Fortunately it is not too difficult to figure this out.

If

5 woodchucks could chuck 50 cords of wood in 4 days,

and since 1 woodchuck chucks $\frac{1}{5}$ as much wood as 5 woodchucks, then we know that

1 woodchuck could chuck 10 cords of wood in 4 days.

Then, since a woodchuck can chuck $\frac{1}{4}$ as much wood in 1 day as she can chuck in 4 days, we conclude that

1 woodchuck could chuck 2.5 cords of wood in 1 day.

Now we use this to answer our problem. If

1 woodchuck could chuck 2.5 cords of wood in 1 day,

then

1 woodchuck could chuck $(6 \cdot 2.5)$ cords of wood in 6 days.

and thus

7 woodchucks could chuck $(6 \cdot 2.5 \cdot 7)$ cords of wood in 6 days.

Thus the answer is $6 \cdot 2.5 \cdot 7 = 105$ cords of wood. □

Problem 7.33: Tom can paint Mr. Thatcher's fence in 6 hours, while Huck can paint Mr. Thatcher's fence in 5 hours. If they work together, then how long will it take them to paint the fence?

Solution for Problem 7.33: Our plan is to determine their work rates, and then add them. In particular, Tom can paint $\frac{1}{6}$ of a fence per hour, and Huck can paint $\frac{1}{5}$ of a fence per hour. So, together they can paint $\frac{1}{6} + \frac{1}{5} = \frac{11}{30}$ of a fence per hour. Therefore, the time to paint the whole fence is

$$\frac{1 \text{ fence}}{\frac{11}{30} \text{ fences per hour}} = \frac{30}{11} \text{ hours} = 2\frac{8}{11} \text{ hours},$$

or a little over 2.7 hours. □

The key step in our solution to Problem 7.33 was considering how much work Tom and Huck each do per hour.

Concept: Work problems can often be solved by considering the amount of work each worker does per unit of time.

Exercises

7.6.1 Casey has to build a 100-foot-long fence. If it takes her 15 minutes to build 1 foot of the fence, then how many hours will it take her to complete the fence?

7.6.2 Phil can type a page of his new novel in 20 minutes. If he writes for 8 hours, then how many pages will he type?

7.6.3 A kangaroo chases a rabbit that starts 150 feet ahead of the kangaroo. For every 12-foot leap of the kangaroo, the rabbit makes a 7-foot leap. How many leaps will the kangaroo have to make to catch up to the rabbit if the two animals always leap at the same time? *(Source: MOEMS)*

7.6.4   Maria buys computer disks at a price of 4 for \$5 and sells them at a price of 3 for \$5. How many computer disks must she sell in order to make a profit of \$100? *(Source: AMC 8)*

7.6.5   At the beginning of a trip, the mileage odometer read 56,200 miles. The driver filled the gas tank with 6 gallons of gasoline. During the trip, the driver filled his tank again with 12 gallons of gasoline when the odometer read 56,560. At the end of the trip, the driver filled the tank again with 20 gallons of gasoline. The odometer read 57,060. To the nearest tenth, what was the car's average miles-per-gallon for the entire trip? *(Source: AMC 8)*

7.6.6   A twelve-hour clock loses 1 minute every hour. Suppose it shows the correct time now. What is the least number of hours from now when it will again show the correct time? *(Source: MOEMS)*

7.6.7   Homer began peeling a pile of 44 potatoes at the rate of 3 potatoes per minute. Four minutes later, Christen joined him and peeled at the rate of 5 potatoes per minute. When they finished, how many potatoes had Christen peeled? *(Source: AMC 8)*

7.6.8   The cold-water faucet of a bath tub can fill the tub in 15 minutes. The drain, when opened, can empty the full tub in 20 minutes. Suppose the tub is empty and the faucet and drain are both opened at the same time. How long will it take to fill the tub? *(Source: MOEMS)*

7.6.9   Roger can shovel his family's driveway in 1 hour. His older sister Alexis can shovel the driveway in $\frac{1}{2}$ hour. If they work together, then how long will it take them to shovel the driveway?

7.6.10   Three water pipes are used to fill a swimming pool. The first pipe alone takes 8 hours to fill the pool, the second pipe alone takes 12 hours to fill the pool, and the third pipe alone takes 24 hours to fill the pool. If all three pipes are opened at the same time, then how long will it take to fill the pool? *(Source: MOEMS)* **Hints:** 17, 117

7.7   Summary

A ratio is used to compare the *relative* quantities of two or more groups or items. However, a ratio only compares the quantities to each other—it doesn't tell us the actual values of the quantities. For example, suppose that you know that a certain history class has a ratio of girls to boys of 2 : 3. All this tells you is that for every 2 girls, there are 3 boys. It doesn't tell you how many boys or girls there are.

> **Concept:**   A ratio gives a *relative* comparison of two quantities. It doesn't tell you anything about the total amount of the quantities.

> **Definition:**   To **simplify** a ratio means to write it as a ratio of integers with no common factor greater than 1.

> **Important:** Suppose we are using a ratio to compare two quantities that together make up a group (such as girls and boys in a class). If the two quantities are in the ratio $a : b$, then the first quantity makes up $\dfrac{a}{a+b}$ of the whole, and the second quantity makes up $\dfrac{b}{a+b}$ of the whole.

Whenever we have two ratios that are equal, we have a **proportion**. The most common usage of proportion is when we have two changing quantities that are related in such a way that their ratio doesn't change.

A commonly used ratio is **speed**, which is the ratio of distance to time. We can write this as an equation as

$$\text{speed} = \frac{\text{distance}}{\text{time}}.$$

This equation can be rearranged as

$$(\text{speed}) \cdot (\text{time}) = \text{distance}$$

and also as

$$\text{time} = \frac{\text{distance}}{\text{speed}}.$$

The units associated with speed help us remember these equations. The word **per** essentially means "divided by," so a speed in miles per hour means to take distance (in miles) and divide by time (in hours).

> **WARNING!!** Speeds do not usually "average" in the way that you might expect them to.

Speed is just a special example of a **rate**. Whenever a quantity changes by a certain amount in a fixed unit of time, we have a rate. Just as with speed, the use of the word "per" is often a signal that we are working with a rate. Also, just as with speed, we can use the units to our advantage when solving problems.

> **Concept:** Pay close attention to units in word problems! Use the units in your mathematical expressions to help you figure out how to use the information in the problem.

Unit conversions are just another type of rate. We can work with rates much like we work with conversion factors. In particular, we use them in mathematical expressions so that the units cancel in the way that we want.

REVIEW PROBLEMS

7.34   The ratio of cats to dogs at the pound is 2 : 3. If there are 18 cats, then how many dogs are there?

7.35   The ratio of boys to girls at a summer camp is 4 to 5. If the total number of students at the camp is 108, then how many boys are at the camp?

7.36   Given that one pound is sixteen ounces, what is the ratio of 1 pound, 4 ounces to 3 pounds, 10 ounces? *(Source: MATHCOUNTS)*

7.37   A board that is 12 meters long is cut into 2 pieces whose lengths have a ratio of 1 : 5. What is the length of the longer piece?

7.38   The ratio of boys to girls in an assembly is 4 to 3. How many students are present if there are 87 girls?

7.39   For every $3 Marisa spends, Andie spends $5. Andie spends $120 more than Marisa does. How many dollars does Andie spend? *(Source: MOEMS)*

7.40   Originally, there are 20 fish in a tank, and each fish is a guppy or an angelfish. The ratio of guppies to angelfish in the tank is 3 : 2. Twenty more fish are added to the tank. Each new fish is either a guppy or an angelfish. The ratio of guppies to angelfish after the fish are added is 2 : 3. How many guppies were added to the tank?

7.41   The four partners in a business decide to split the profits of their company in the ratio 2 : 3 : 3 : 5. If the profit one year is $26,000, then what is the largest amount of profit received by one of the four partners? *(Source: MATHCOUNTS)*

7.42   The statue of Abraham Lincoln in the Lincoln Memorial in Washington, D.C., is 6 meters tall. On the back of the $5 bill, the statue measures 5 millimeters tall. If the Memorial measures 25 mm tall on the back of the $5 bill, and assuming the bill is drawn to scale, then how tall is the actual Memorial in Washington?

7.43   On a map, two mountains are $5\frac{7}{8}$ inches apart. If $\frac{1}{2}$ of an inch on the map represents 80 miles, then how many miles apart are the two mountains?

7.44   A fortnight is 14 days, and a mile is 8 furlongs. If a desert caravan travels 10 miles per day, then how many furlongs does it travel in a fortnight?

7.45   A 3-inch by 5-inch photo is enlarged proportionally such that its smaller dimension is now 1 foot 3 inches. How many inches are in the larger dimension? *(Source: MATHCOUNTS)*

7.46   On my tourist map of Quebec, the distance between the dots representing Montreal and Quebec City is 10 cm. If the scale of the map is $\frac{4}{9}$ mm = 1 km, then how far apart are Montreal and Quebec City? (Note that 10 mm = 1 cm.)

7.47 Dale travels from city A to city B to city C and back to city A. Each city is 120 miles from the other two. Her average rate from city A to city B is 60 mph. Her average rate from city B to city C is 40 mph. Her average rate from city C to city A is 24 mph. What is Dale's average rate for the entire trip, in miles per hour? *(Source: MOEMS)*

7.48 The density of liquid A is 8 pounds per gallon, and the density of liquid B is 6 pounds per gallon. What quantity of liquid B weighs the same as 30 gallons of liquid A?

7.49 Ike's speedometer on his motorcycle is broken. He is riding at a constant speed. He times himself and finds that it takes him 1 minute and 20 seconds to ride 1 mile. How fast is Ike riding in miles per hour?

7.50 Elisa swims laps in the pool. When she first started, she completed 10 laps in 25 minutes. Now she can finish 12 laps in 24 minutes. By how many minutes has she improved her lap time? *(Source: AMC 8)*

7.51 A northbound train from Miami to Jacksonville made the 324-mile journey at an average speed of 50 miles per hour. On its southbound return trip, it made the journey at an average speed of 40 miles per hour. To the nearest tenth of a mile per hour, what was the train's average speed for the 648-mile roundtrip journey?

7.52 Boston is 295 miles from New York City along a certain route. A car starts from Boston at 1:00 PM and travels along the route toward New York at a steady rate of 50 mph. Another car starts from New York at 1:30 PM and travels along this route toward Boston at a steady rate of 40 mph. At what time do the cars pass each other? *(Source: MOEMS)*

7.53 A seasonal pond in my yard has 1000 gallons of water. If water evaporates at the rate of 12.5 gallons per day and no other water is added or removed, then how much water will be in the pond after 30 days?

7.54 Megan has three candles of the same length to provide light. Candle A burns for exactly 72 minutes. Candle B burns twice as fast as candle A. Candle C burns three times as fast as candle B. What is the greatest total number of minutes of light that all three candles can provide? *(Source: MOEMS)*

7.55 Working alone, Jamie can mow her lawn in 75 minutes. If Bob helps her, then the two can mow the lawn in 30 minutes. How long does it take Bob to mow the lawn alone?

7.56 Carlos is going on vacation from Mexico to London, with a brief stop in New York. He forgot to exchange his pesos for British pounds, and must do so in New York. He would like to have 2000 British pounds for his trip. 12.1 Mexican pesos can be exchanged for 1 dollar, and 1 dollar can be exchanged for 0.62 pounds. To the nearest peso, how many pesos will Carlos have to exchange in order to get 2000 British pounds?

7.57 Four short-order cooks can make 24 omelets in 10 minutes. If a diner gets a to-go order for 90 omelets that needs to be ready in 15 minutes, then how many cooks do they need to complete the order on time?

Challenge Problems

7.58 A stack of 45 dimes is divided into three piles in the ratio $\frac{1}{6} : \frac{1}{3} : \frac{1}{4}$. How many dimes are in the pile with the least number of dimes? *(Source: MATHCOUNTS)*

7.59 Five workers together can build a road in 20 days. Suppose every worker works at the same rate. If three workers work on the road for 10 days before eleven more workers join them, then how long total will it take to build the road? **Hints:** 17, 104

7.60 When Paul crossed the finish line of a 60-meter race, he was ahead of Robert by 10 meters and ahead of Sam by 20 meters. Suppose Robert and Sam continue to race to the finish line without changing their rates of speed. By how many meters will Robert beat Sam? *(Source: MOEMS)* **Hints:** 40

7.61 If $4 : x^2 = x : 16$, then what is the value of x? *(Source: MATHCOUNTS)*

7.62 The Big Telescope Company sells circular mirrors. Their largest mirrors have radii of 5 meters and their smallest mirrors have radii of 1 meter. The cost of every mirror is proportional to the cube of the mirror's radius. What is the ratio of the total cost of 25 of the company's smallest mirrors to the cost of one of the company's largest mirrors? *(Source: MATHCOUNTS)*

7.63 Kim was elected class president. She received 3 votes for every 2 that Amy got. No one else ran. However, if 8 of the people who voted for Kim had voted for Amy instead, Kim would have received only 1 vote for every 2 that Amy would have gotten. How many people voted? *(Source: MOEMS)* **Hints:** 81

7.64 When the Slowpoke Marathon began, the ratio of runners to joggers was 2 to 19. If 4200 participants began the race (each either a runner or a jogger, but not both), and 500 joggers dropped out of the race but all the rest of the participants finished, then what was the ratio of runners to joggers among those who finished the race?

7.65 The students in Mrs. Reed's English class are reading the same 760-page novel. Three friends, Alice, Bob, and Chandra, are in the class. Alice reads a page in 20 seconds, Bob reads a page in 45 seconds, and Chandra reads a page in 30 seconds.

(a) If Bob and Chandra both read the whole book, then Bob will spend how many more seconds reading than Chandra?

(b) Chandra and Bob, who each have a copy of the book, decide that they can save time by "team reading" the novel. In this scheme, Chandra will read from page 1 to a certain page and Bob will read from the next page through page 760, finishing the book. When they are through, they will tell each other about the parts they read. What is the last page that Chandra should read so that she and Bob spend the same amount of time reading the novel? **Hints:** 123

(c) Before Chandra and Bob start reading, Alice says she would like to team read with them. If they divide the book into three sections so that each reads for the same length of time, then how many seconds will each have to read?

(Source: AMC 8)

7.66★ Buses from Dallas to Houston leave every hour on the hour. Buses from Houston to Dallas leave every hour on the half hour. The trip from one city to the other takes 5 hours. Assuming the buses travel on the same highway, how many Dallas-bound buses does a Houston-bound bus pass on the highway (not in the station)? *(Source: AMC 8)*

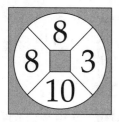 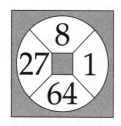 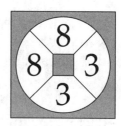 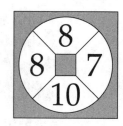

Human beings only use ten percent of their brains. Ten percent! Can you imagine how much we could accomplish if we used the other sixty percent? – Ellen DeGeneres

CHAPTER 8

Percents

8.1 What is a Percent?

A **percent** is really just a special way of writing a fraction. The word "percent" comes from the Latin *per centum*, meaning "per hundred." (This is also related to why the French word for "hundred" is "cent," and why there are 100 cents in a dollar.) When we write a percent, we are really writing a fraction with a hidden denominator of 100. For example:

$$27\% = \frac{27}{100}, \qquad 59\% = \frac{59}{100}, \qquad 80\% = \frac{80}{100} = \frac{4}{5},$$

$$200\% = \frac{200}{100} = 2, \qquad -50\% = \frac{-50}{100} = -\frac{1}{2}, \qquad 0\% = \frac{0}{100} = 0.$$

More generally, we can write

$$x\% = \frac{x}{100}$$

where x is any number. So percents are really nothing new:

> **Concept:** A percent is just a fraction with a hidden denominator of 100.

The usage of the word "per" in "percent" might also make you think of a rate or a ratio. Indeed, we often think about a percent as a ratio of some quantity out of 100. For example, if we say "37% of all teenagers like to play video games," it means that the ratio of teenagers that like to play video games to all teenagers is 37 : 100, or that the fraction of teenagers that like to play video games is $\frac{37}{100}$ of all teenagers.

Like many other concepts in math, percent is a flexible idea and can be used in lots of different situations. Even the word is flexible: many people use the word "percentage" instead of "percent." We prefer "percent," but we will also occasionally use "percentage" so that you get accustomed to seeing it written that way.

 **Problems**

Problem 8.1: Write the following percents as integers, fractions, or mixed numbers.

(a) 19%

(b) 60%

(c) 350%

(d) −95%

(e) −250%

(f) 100%

Problem 8.2: Write the following numbers as percentages.

(a) $\frac{71}{100}$

(b) 1

(c) $\frac{3}{4}$

(d) $\frac{8}{5}$

(e) $-2\frac{1}{10}$

(f) $\frac{1}{3}$

Problem 8.3:

(a) Write 26% as a decimal.

(b) Write 7% as a decimal.

(c) Write 55.2% as a decimal.

(d) Write 246% as a decimal.

(e) Write 0.03% as a decimal.

(f) Write 0.34 as a percent.

(g) Write 0.081 as a percent.

(h) Write −2.19 as a percent.

Problem 8.4:

(a) What is 25% of 200?

(b) What is $22\frac{1}{2}$% of 40?

(c) What is 300% of 15?

(d) What is $\frac{1}{4}$% of 1000?

Problem 8.5:

(a) What percent of 100 is 63?

(b) 40 is what percent of 200?

(c) What percent of 1000 is 2.47?

(d) −12 is what percent of 3?

Problem 8.6:

(a) 80 is 20% of what number?

(b) 2 is −50% of what number?

(c) $\frac{1}{4}$ is 250% of what number?

Problem 8.7: If 20% of x is y, then 35% of x is what percent of y?

Problem 8.1: Write the following percents as integers, fractions, or mixed numbers.

(a) 19%	(c) 350%	(e) −250%
(b) 60%	(d) −95%	(f) 100%

Solution for Problem 8.1:

(a) Remember our key fact: $x\% = \dfrac{x}{100}$. So $19\% = \dfrac{19}{100}$.

(b) Again, we simply start with $60\% = \dfrac{60}{100}$. However, we usually like to write fractions in simplest form. In this case, 60 and 100 are each a multiple of 20, so we can simplify:

$$60\% = \frac{60}{100} = \frac{3 \cdot 20}{5 \cdot 20} = \frac{3}{5}.$$

Another way to think about 60% is to notice that it's a multiple of 10%, and 10% is really easy to deal with:

$$10\% = \frac{10}{100} = \frac{1}{10}.$$

So we can compute

$$60\% = 6 \cdot 10\% = 6 \cdot \frac{1}{10} = \frac{6}{10} = \frac{3}{5}.$$

Concept: Remember, a percent is just a fraction, so all of the things that we can do with fractions, we can do with percents too.

(c) We start with

$$350\% = \frac{350}{100} = \frac{35}{10} = \frac{7}{2}.$$

To write this as a mixed number, we have $\dfrac{7}{2} = 3\dfrac{1}{2}$.

(d) Negative percents are no big deal! We do the same thing as with positive percents:

$$-95\% = \frac{-95}{100} = -\frac{95}{100} = -\frac{19}{20}.$$

(e) This combines the ideas from part (c) and (d). Now we have a percent that is a negative mixed number:

$$-250\% = \frac{-250}{100} = -\frac{25}{10} = -\frac{5}{2} = -2\frac{1}{2}.$$

(f) We have

$$100\% = \frac{100}{100} = \frac{1}{1} = 1.$$

> **Important:**
>
> $$100\% = 1.$$

□

> **Important:** A lot of percents come up so often that you'll probably memorize them. The "quarter" percents are very common:
>
> $$25\% = \frac{25}{100} = \frac{1}{4}, \qquad 50\% = \frac{50}{100} = \frac{1}{2}, \qquad 75\% = \frac{75}{100} = \frac{3}{4}.$$
>
> You should also immediately recognize that $10\% = \frac{10}{100} = \frac{1}{10}$, so any percent that is a multiple of 10% is easy to compute:
>
> $$10\% = 1 \cdot 10\% = \frac{1}{10},$$
> $$20\% = 2 \cdot 10\% = \frac{2}{10} = \frac{1}{5},$$
> $$30\% = 3 \cdot 10\% = \frac{3}{10},$$
>
> and so on.

Let's try going in the other direction—we'll start with a fraction and try to write it as a percent.

Problem 8.2: Write the following numbers as percentages.

(a) $\frac{71}{100}$

(b) 1

(c) $\frac{3}{4}$

(d) $\frac{8}{5}$

(e) $-2\frac{1}{10}$

(f) $\frac{1}{3}$

Solution for Problem 8.2:

(a) Since our fraction is already written with a denominator of 100, it already looks like a percent, and we simply use the percent definition in reverse: $\frac{71}{100} = 71\%$.

(b) We write 1 as a fraction with denominator 100:

$$1 = \frac{100}{100} = 100\%.$$

(c) You might already "know" the percentages for quarters, but if not, they're easy to find—we just need to write our fraction with a denominator of 100. Since $4 \cdot 25 = 100$, we multiply numerator and denominator of $\frac{3}{4}$ by 25:

$$\frac{3}{4} = \frac{3 \cdot 25}{4 \cdot 25} = \frac{75}{100} = 75\%.$$

Another way we can convert fractions to percents is to remember that $100\% = 1$, so we can multiply any number by 100% and not change its value. So we get

$$\frac{3}{4} = \frac{3}{4} \cdot 100\% = \left(\frac{3}{4} \cdot 100\right)\% = \frac{300}{4}\% = 75\%.$$

(d) We write $\frac{8}{5}$ as a fraction with denominator of 100, using the fact that $5 \cdot 20 = 100$:

$$\frac{8}{5} = \frac{8 \cdot 20}{5 \cdot 20} = \frac{160}{100} = 160\%.$$

(e) Mixed numbers are often easiest to work with if we break them up into a sum (or difference) of an integer and a fraction:

$$-2\frac{1}{10} = -2 - \frac{1}{10} = -200\% - 10\% = -210\%.$$

Alternatively, we can write the entire mixed number as a fraction, and then convert the denominator to 100:

$$-2\frac{1}{10} = -\frac{21}{10} = -\frac{210}{100} = -210\%.$$

(f) We can try to write $\frac{1}{3}$ as a fraction with denominator 100:

$$\frac{1}{3} = \frac{x}{100}.$$

Unfortunately, since 100 is not a multiple of 3, there's no way we can have x in the numerator above be a integer. Nonetheless, we can still solve to find that $x = \frac{100}{3}$, so we conclude that $\frac{1}{3} = \frac{100}{3}\%$. This is a somewhat unsatisfying answer, but it's the best we can do with $\frac{1}{3}$. This is also commonly written as a mixed number as $33\frac{1}{3}\%$.

We could also do the conversion to a percent using 100% = 1:

$$\frac{1}{3} = \frac{1}{3} \cdot 100\% = \left(\frac{1}{3} \cdot 100\right)\% = \frac{100}{3}\% = 33\frac{1}{3}\%.$$

> **Concept:** Percents are really nice with fractions whose denominators divide evenly into 100, like 2, 4, or 5. But they're not as nice with fractions whose denominators don't divide evenly into 100, like 3, 6, or 7.

□

One reason that percents are so commonly used is that they are easy to represent using decimals. As we've already seen, decimals are nice because they let us use our familiar base-10 number system to write fractions as well as integers. Since percents are based on 100, we see that 1 percent is equal to 1 hundredth, which we write as

$$1\% = \frac{1}{100} = 0.01.$$

Problem 8.3:

(a) Write 26% as a decimal.

(b) Write 7% as a decimal.

(c) Write 55.2% as a decimal.

(d) Write 246% as a decimal.

(e) Write 0.03% as a decimal.

(f) Write 0.34 as a percent.

(g) Write 0.081 as a percent.

(h) Write −2.19 as a percent.

Solution for Problem 8.3:

(a) We know that $26\% = \frac{26}{100}$, so we can write it as a decimal as $26\% = \frac{26}{100} = 0.26$. Recall that dividing by 100 is the same as moving the decimal point 2 places to the left.

(b) We can write $7\% = \frac{7}{100} = 0.07$.

(c) Here we calculate slightly differently, noting that $1\% = \frac{1}{100} = 0.01$:

$$55.2\% = 55.2 \cdot 1\% = 55.2 \cdot 0.01 = 0.552.$$

(d) Because 246% is greater than 100%, and 100% = 1, our answer should be a decimal that's greater than 1.

$$246\% = \frac{246}{100} = 2.46.$$

(e) It's the same computation that we've already done before in the previous parts:

$$0.03\% = 0.03 \cdot 1\% = 0.03 \cdot 0.01 = 0.0003.$$

Again, we notice that multiplying by 0.01 is the same as moving the decimal point 2 places to the left.

Note that parts (a)–(e) were all essentially the same computation, even though the computation may have been done in different ways in the different parts.

> **Concept:** Don't feel like you "have to" work with percents in any particular way. Use whatever method works best for you. Or, better yet, get comfortable with all the different methods, so that you have lots of flexibility in solving different problems.

(f) Since we move the decimal point 2 positions from the left to convert from a percent to a decimal, it's not too surprising that to convert from a decimal to a percent, we move the decimal point 2 positions to the right: $0.34 = 34\%$. We can also see this by using the "multiply by $100\% = 1$" method:

$$0.34 = 0.34 \cdot 100\% = (0.34 \cdot 100)\% = 34\%.$$

(g) We could write the decimal as a fraction and then change the denominator to 100:

$$0.081 = \frac{81}{1000} = \frac{81/10}{1000/10} = \frac{8.1}{100} = 8.1\%.$$

Or, we could multiply the original decimal by 100%, which moves the decimal point 2 places to the right:

$$0.081 = 0.081 \cdot 100\% = (0.081 \cdot 100)\% = 8.1\%.$$

(h) Nothing changes with a negative percentage—we still move the decimal point 2 places to the right:

$$-2.19 = -2.19 \cdot 100\% = -(2.19 \cdot 100)\% = -219\%.$$

$\square$

We often will want to consider a "percentage of" another quantity. For example, to find "19% of 200" means to find the quantity that is $\frac{19}{100}$ of 200, which is

$$19\% \cdot 200 = \frac{19}{100} \cdot 200 = 19 \cdot 2 = 38.$$

> **Concept:** The word "of" in a word problem usually means multiplication.
> For example, if a carton contains 12 eggs and I take $\frac{1}{3}$ of the eggs in
> the carton, I am taking $\frac{1}{3} \cdot 12 = 4$ eggs. But (like a lot of stuff in this
> book) don't memorize the mantra "*of* means *multiplication*." Instead,
> think about what the words actually mean. Use your knowledge
> and experience to decide how to translate the words into math.

We'll see a lot of uses of this concept in the word problems in Section 8.2, but for now, let's
practice with just the computation.

Problem 8.4:

(a) What is 25% of 200?

(b) What is $22\frac{1}{2}\%$ of 40?

(c) What is 300% of 15?

(d) What is $\frac{1}{4}\%$ of 1000?

Solution for Problem 8.4:

(a) To take a "percent of" a quantity means to multiply that quantity by the percentage. So we
have

$$25\% \text{ of } 200 = 25\% \cdot 200 = \frac{25}{100} \cdot 200 = 25 \cdot 2 = 50.$$

You might also have recognized that $25\% = \frac{1}{4}$, so the answer that we wanted was $\frac{1}{4}$ of 200,
which is $200/4 = 50$.

(b) We can do this in the usual method:

$$22\frac{1}{2}\% \text{ of } 40 = 22\frac{1}{2}\% \cdot 40 = \frac{22\frac{1}{2}}{100} \cdot 40 = \frac{22\frac{1}{2} \cdot 4}{10} = \frac{90}{10} = 9.$$

We could also first write $22\frac{1}{2}\%$ as a common fraction:

$$22\frac{1}{2}\% = \frac{22\frac{1}{2}}{100} = \frac{45}{200} = \frac{9}{40},$$

and then it's easy to see that

$$22\frac{1}{2}\% \text{ of } 40 = \frac{9}{40} \cdot 40 = 9.$$

We could also compute $22\frac{1}{2}\%$ of 40 using decimals:

$$22\frac{1}{2}\% \text{ of } 40 = 0.225 \cdot 40 = 2.25 \cdot 4 = 9.$$

Finally, we could use a clever little trick to get rid of the fractional percentage. We can multiply the percent by any number we like, so long as we divide the other quantity by the same number. In our example, this would work like this:

$$22\frac{1}{2}\% \text{ of } 40 = 22\frac{1}{2}\% \cdot 40 = \left(22\frac{1}{2}\% \cdot 2\right) \cdot (40/2) = 45\% \cdot 20 = \frac{45}{100} \cdot 20 = \frac{45}{5} = 9.$$

Notice that we multiplied and divided by 2 in the same step, so that the quantity didn't change.

(c) Nothing changes just because we have a percent that's greater than 1:

$$300\% \text{ of } 15 = 300\% \cdot 15 = 3 \cdot 15 = 45.$$

(d) Nothing really changes here either:

$$\frac{1}{4}\% \text{ of } 1000 = \frac{1}{4}\% \cdot 1000 = \frac{\frac{1}{4}}{100} \cdot 1000 = \frac{1}{4} \cdot 10 = \frac{5}{2} = 2\frac{1}{2}.$$

You might find it easier to first compute 1% of 1000, which is 10, and then multiply by $\frac{1}{4}$.

□

We can also do this sort of problem in reverse: we start with the answer and we have to figure out the percent.

Problem 8.5:

(a) What percent of 100 is 63?   (c) What percent of 1000 is 2.47?

(b) 40 is what percent of 200?   (d) −12 is what percent of 3?

Solution for Problem 8.5:

(a) We need to write 63 as some percent of 100. In other words, we need to solve

$$63 = x\% \text{ of } 100 = \frac{x}{100} \cdot 100.$$

The 100's cancel on the right side, so $x = 63$, and we see clearly that 63 is 63% of 100.

Alternatively, we can think of the percent as a ratio out of 100. So we are asking: what ratio out of 100 equals 63 out of 100? Naturally, the answer is 63. Another way of stating this is that we are trying to solve

$$\frac{63}{100} = x\%.$$

By definition, this means $x = 63$, so the answer is 63%.

(b) Be careful—this is not worded in the same way as part (a)!

> **Concept:** Always read the problem carefully! It's a big waste of effort to solve the wrong problem.

We want to express 40 as some percent of 200, so we want

$$40 = x\% \text{ of } 200 = \frac{x}{100} \cdot 200.$$

This simplifies to $40 = 2x$, so $x = 20$, and 40 is 20% of 200. We can check this result:

$$20\% \cdot 200 = \frac{1}{5} \cdot 200 = 40,$$

so indeed 20% of 200 is 40.

We can also approach this problem using ratios. We want to take the ratio 40 to 200 and write it as a ratio of some number to 100. That is, we are trying to solve

$$\frac{40}{200} = x\% = \frac{x}{100}.$$

Again, we see $x = 20$, so the answer is 20%.

(c) As a ratio, we want to solve

$$\frac{2.47}{1000} = x\% = \frac{x}{100}.$$

Thus we divide the numerator and denominator of the fraction on the left by 10, and we see $x = 0.247$. So the answer is 0.247%.

Alternatively, we want

$$2.47 = x\% \text{ of } 1000 = \frac{x}{100} \cdot 1000.$$

This simplifies as $2.47 = 10x$, so $x = \frac{2.47}{10} = 0.247$. Thus, 2.47 is 0.247% of 1000.

(d) Negative numbers don't really change the way that we approach the problem. We want to solve

$$-12 = x\% \text{ of } 3 = \frac{x}{100} \cdot 3.$$

Dividing both sides by 3, we see that we need $\frac{x}{100} = -4$, which makes $x = -400$. So -12 is -400% of 3.

□

Problem 8.6:

(a) 80 is 20% of what number?

(b) 2 is -50% of what number?

(c) $\frac{1}{4}$ is 250% of what number?

Solution for Problem 8.6:

(a) We want the number x that satisfies $80 = 20\% \cdot x$. But we know that $20\% = \frac{2}{10} = \frac{1}{5}$. Hence, $80 = \frac{1}{5}x$, and thus $x = 5 \cdot 80 = 400$. Indeed, as a check, we see that $20\% \cdot 400 = \frac{1}{5} \cdot 400 = 80$.

(b) We know that $-50\% = -\frac{1}{2}$, so we want the number that 2 is $-\frac{1}{2}$ of. That is, we need to solve $2 = -\frac{1}{2}x$. Multiplying both sides by -2 gives $-4 = x$, so the answer is -4. Indeed, we check that $-50\% \cdot -4 = (-\frac{1}{2}) \cdot (-4) = 2$.

(c) We solve $\frac{1}{4} = 250\% \cdot x$. But $250\% = 200\% + 50\% = 2 + \frac{1}{2} = \frac{5}{2}$, so $\frac{1}{4} = \frac{5}{2} \cdot x$. Thus,

$$x = \frac{1}{4} \div \frac{5}{2} = \frac{1}{4} \cdot \frac{2}{5} = \frac{1}{10}.$$

$\square$

Problem 8.7: If 20% of x is y, then 35% of x is what percent of y?

Solution for Problem 8.7: Since $20\% = \frac{1}{5}$, the phrase "20% of x is y" can be written as an equation as $\frac{1}{5} \cdot x = y$. This means that $x = 5y$.

The quantity we want is 35% of x, which is $\frac{7}{20}x$. But we also know that $x = 5y$, and we can substitute:

$$\frac{7}{20}x = \frac{7}{20} \cdot 5y = \left(\frac{7}{20} \cdot 5\right)y = \frac{7}{4}y.$$

Therefore, 35% of x is $\frac{7}{4}y$. Since $\frac{7}{4} = \frac{175}{100} = 175\%$, we know that 35% of x is 175% of y.

We could also determine the answer without doing as much algebra, as follows: we start with $20\% \cdot x = y$. To get to 35%, we have

$$35\% \cdot x = (20\% + 15\%) \cdot x = 20\% \cdot x + 15\% \cdot x.$$

We know that the first term ($20\% \cdot x$) on the right above is y. We can also see that the second term ($15\% \cdot x$) is $\frac{3}{4}y$, since 15% is $\frac{3}{4}$ of 20%. So $35\% \cdot x = 20\% \cdot x + 15\% \cdot x = y + \frac{3}{4}y = \frac{7}{4}y$. As before, $\frac{7}{4} = 175\%$, so 35% of x is 175% of y. $\square$

Exercises

8.1.1 Write the following percents as fractions, integers, or mixed numbers:

(a) 37%

(b) 80%

(c) 250%

(d) −25%

(e) −200%

(f) 1810%

8.1.2 Write the following numbers as percents:

(a) $\frac{33}{50}$ (c) $3\frac{1}{4}$ (e) 0   (g) $\frac{2}{7}$

(b) $\frac{2}{5}$ (d) $-2\frac{3}{8}$ (f) -192.5 (h) 0.319

8.1.3 Compute the following numbers:

(a) 30% of 200   (e) 15% of 380

(b) 55% of 120   (f) -100% of 617

(c) 225% of 16   (g) 0% of 2,827,192

(d) -80% of 35   (h) $\frac{1}{5}\%$ of 2000

8.1.4

(a) What percent is 20 of 80?   (d) What percent is $\frac{1}{2}$ of 5?

(b) What percent of 30 is -60?   (e) What percent of $\frac{5}{6}$ is $\frac{2}{3}$?

(c) What percent of 17 is 51?   (f) What percent is 7 of -35?

8.1.5

(a) 11 is 20% of what number?   (c) 3 is -40% of what number?

(b) $\frac{2}{3}$ is 30% of what number?   (d) $\frac{1}{7}$ is $\frac{1}{2}\%$ of what number?

8.1.6 Which is greater, $\frac{7}{9}$ of 180 or 75% of 200? *(Source: MATHCOUNTS)*

8.1.7 What is the sum of 60% of 75 and 75% of 60? *(Source: MATHCOUNTS)*

8.1.8 Express in simplest form: 40% of 70% of 10.

8.1.9★ Two percent of half a number is 5. What is the number? *(Source: MATHCOUNTS)*

8.2 Word Problems

Because percents are used frequently in the real world, they show up a lot in word problems. Word problems involving percents are really no different than any other sort of word problem. The important steps to remember are:

> **Concept:**
> - Read the problem carefully!
>
> - Convert the words to mathematics.
>
> - Solve the mathematical problem.
>
> - Write your answer in terms of the word problem, and make sure that it makes sense.

Here are several word problems involving percents:

Problem 8.8: Stephanie bought a new computer that cost $800. Where Stephanie lives, the sales tax is 7%. How much sales tax does Stephanie have to pay for her computer?

Problem 8.9: Rajiv has 4 blue shirts, 5 black shirts, and 6 white shirts. What percent of his shirts are white?

Problem 8.10: If a school has 300 girls and 200 boys, what percent of the students are girls?

Problem 8.11: An athlete's target heart rate is 80% of the theoretical maximum heart rate. The maximum heart rate, in beats per minute, is found by subtracting the athlete's age, in years, from 220. What is the target heart rate of an athlete who is 26 years old? (Round to the nearest beat per minute.) *(Source: AMC 8)*

Problem 8.12: All of the students in Mr. Sato's History class took an exam. Each student either passed or failed. 85% of the students passed and 3 students failed. How many students are in the class?

Problem 8.13: Patti takes 200 flowers to her middle school to sell on Valentine's Day. She first sells 30% of the flowers to 6th grade students. She then sells 40% of the remaining flowers to 7th grade students. Finally, she sells 50% of the remaining flowers to 8th grade students. How many flowers does she have left?

Problem 8.14: A 100-milliliter bottle of salad dressing initially consists of 80% oil and 20% vinegar. 40% of the dressing is used, and then 4 milliliters of vinegar are added to the bottle. What percentage of the mixture is now vinegar?

Problem 8.8: Stephanie bought a new computer that cost $800. Where Stephanie lives, the sales tax rate is 7%. How much sales tax does Stephanie have to pay for her computer?

Solution for Problem 8.8: This is a very common "real world" use of percents. Most U.S. states have **sales tax** that gets added to many purchases, and these sales taxes are almost always expressed as a percent of the purchase price. The seller (such as a store or restaurant) simply multiplies the sales tax rate by the purchase price to determine the amount of tax due. As an equation:

Sales tax due = (Purchase price) · (Sales tax rate).

In our problem, the item being purchased—a computer—has a price of $800, and the sales tax rate is 7%. So we compute:

$$\text{Sales tax due} = \$800 \cdot 7\% = \$800 \cdot \frac{7}{100} = \frac{\$800 \cdot 7}{100} = \$8 \cdot 7 = \$56.$$

Thus, Stephanie must pay $56 in sales tax.□

> **Sidenote:** Another common percent that is used in restaurants is for tipping. In North America, it is typical to tip 15% of the total bill to one's waiter or waitress. For example, if two people spend a total of $60 on their meal, they would pay an additional $60 · 15% = $60 · $\frac{15}{100}$ = $9 as a tip to their server. In fancier restaurants, the tip rate might be 18% or even 20%.
>
> Since 7% or 8% is a common sales tax rate in the U.S., an easy way to compute approximately how much to tip is to double the sales tax. Think about why this works!

Problem 8.9: Rajiv has 4 blue shirts, 5 black shirts, and 6 white shirts. What percent of his shirts are white?

Solution for Problem 8.9: Rajiv has 6 white shirts and 4 + 5 + 6 = 15 shirts total. So, the percent of his shirts that are white is

$$\frac{6}{15} = \frac{2}{5} = \frac{40}{100} = 40\%.$$

□

Problem 8.10: If a school has 300 girls and 200 boys, what percent of the students are girls?

Solution for Problem 8.10: Avoid the following common mistake:

> **Bogus Solution:** There are 300 girls and 200 boys, so the percent of girls is
>
> $$\frac{300}{200} = \frac{150}{100} = 150\%.$$

This "answer" is clearly incorrect: the percent of girls must be between 0% (no girls) and 100% (all girls). The correct solution is that we must compute the percentage of girls from the *total* number of students.

The school has $300 + 200 = 500$ total students, so the percent of the students who are girls is

$$\frac{300}{500} = \frac{3}{5} = \frac{60}{100} = 60\%.$$

□

Problem 8.11: An athlete's target heart rate is 80% of the theoretical maximum heart rate. The maximum heart rate, in beats per minute, is found by subtracting the athlete's age, in years, from 220. What is the target heart rate of an athlete who is 26 years old? (Round to the nearest beat per minute.) *(Source: AMC 8)*

Solution for Problem 8.11: This is a 2-step problem. First, we have to find the athlete's maximum heart rate. Second, we have to find the target heart rate.

To find the maximum heart rate, we simply follow the directions in the problem: we subtract the athlete's age of 26 from 220, to get $220 - 26 = 194$. This is the maximum heart rate for a 26-year-old.

Then, we are told that the target heart rate is 80% of the maximum heart rate. So to find the target heart rate, we multiply the maximum heart rate by 80%:

$$80\% \cdot 194 = \frac{4}{5} \cdot 194 = \frac{776}{5}.$$

But that's not the answer—the problem asked us to round to the nearest beat per minute. So we must round $\frac{776}{5}$ to the nearest integer. We can compute $\frac{776}{5} = 155.2$, and the nearest integer to 155.2 is 155. Alternatively, we can note that the nearest multiple of 5 to 776 is 775, so the answer is $\frac{775}{5} = 155$ beats per minute. □

Problem 8.12: All of the students in Mr. Sato's History class took an exam. Each student either passed or failed. 85% of the students passed and 3 students failed. How many students are in the class?

Solution for Problem 8.12: What bit of information do we need to answer this problem?

> **Concept:** When deciding how to proceed with a problem, ask yourself: "What information do I need to be able to solve the problem?" Then see if you can find that information.

We know that 3 students failed, and it would be nice to know what percent of the total that is. But we *do* know that! Since the entire class is 100% of the students, and 85% of the students passed, we know that $100\% - 85\% = 15\%$ of the students failed. So 3 students equals 15% of the total number of students in the class.

Let's set n to be the number of students in the class, so that we can write an equation for n.

> **Concept:** When trying to find an unknown quantity, it is often useful to assign a variable to that quantity, so that you can write an equation.

Since 3 students is 15% of the class, we have the equation

$$3 = (15\%)n = \frac{15n}{100}.$$

Multiplying $3 = \frac{15n}{100}$ by 100 gives $300 = 15n$, and dividing by 15 gives $20 = n$. Therefore, there are 20 students in the class.

To check our answer, we note that if 3 students failed, then $20 - 3 = 17$ passed. This must be 85% of all students, and indeed 85% of 20 students totals $85\% \cdot 20 = \frac{85}{100} \cdot 20 = \frac{85}{5} = 17$ students. $\square$

Problem 8.13: Patti takes 200 flowers to her middle school to sell on Valentine's Day. She first sells 30% of the flowers to 6th grade students. She then sells 40% of the remaining flowers to 7th grade students. Finally, she sells 50% of the remaining flowers to 8th grade students. How many flowers does she have left?

Solution for Problem 8.13: Our role in this problem is as an accountant. We need to keep track of her sales during the day.

First, she sells 30% of her original 200 flowers to the 6th grade students. We compute $30\% \cdot 200 = \frac{3}{10} \cdot 200 = 60$, so she sells 60 flowers. This means she has $200 - 60 = 140$ remaining.

Next, she sells 40% of her 140 remaining flowers to the 7th grade students. We compute $40\% \cdot 140 = \frac{2}{5} \cdot 140 = 56$, so she sells 56 flowers. This means she has $140 - 56 = 84$ remaining.

Next, she sells 50% of her 84 remaining flowers to the 8th grade students. We compute $50\% \cdot 84 = \frac{1}{2} \cdot 84 = 42$, so she sells 42 flowers. This means she has $84 - 42 = 42$ remaining.

So she ends the day with 42 flowers.

We could actually solve this problem in one calculation, by keeping track of how many flowers she *keeps* at each step. We use the fact that, at each step, the percents of the flowers she sells and the flowers she keeps must sum to 100%. So we know she keeps 70% of the flowers after the 6th grade sales, then 60% of the remaining flowers after the 7th grade sales, and then 50% of the remaining flowers after the 8th grade sales. So, at the end of the day, she keeps

$$50\% \text{ of } 60\% \text{ of } 70\% \text{ of } 200 = 50\% \cdot 60\% \cdot 70\% \cdot 200 = \frac{1}{2} \cdot \frac{3}{5} \cdot \frac{7}{10} \cdot 200 = \frac{21}{100} \cdot 200 = 42$$

flowers. $\square$

Problem 8.14: A 100-milliliter bottle of salad dressing initially consists of 80% oil and 20% vinegar. 40% of the dressing is used, and then 4 milliliters of vinegar are added to the bottle. What percentage of the mixture is now vinegar?

Solution for Problem 8.14: As in the previous problem, our best approach is to keep track of how the various quantities change.

We start by using 40% of the original 100 ml of dressing, which means that 60% remains. That gives us 60 ml of dressing left in the bottle. Since the composition of the dressing hasn't changed (only the amount has changed), we still have 80% oil and 20% vinegar. This means that we have

$$80\% \cdot 60\,\text{ml} = 48\,\text{ml of oil} \quad \text{and} \quad 20\% \cdot 60\,\text{ml} = 12\,\text{ml of vinegar.}$$

Next, we add the additional 4 ml of vinegar. After this, we still have 48 ml of oil, but we have 12 + 4 = 16 ml of vinegar, and the total amount of dressing is 48 + 16 = 64 ml. Therefore, the percent of the dressing that is vinegar is

$$\frac{16}{64} = \frac{1}{4} = 25\%.$$

It is no surprise that the new vinegar percentage of 25% is higher than the original percentage of 20% vinegar: since we have added vinegar (but not oil), the percent of vinegar relative to the total should be larger. □

Exercises

8.2.1 What percent of the 5 × 5 square to the right is shaded?

8.2.2 At a meeting there were 4 parents, 28 students, and 8 teachers. What percent of people at the meeting were students? *(Source: MATHCOUNTS)*

8.2.3 In the Arborian State Senate, 35 of the 50 state senators are female. What percent of the state senators are male?

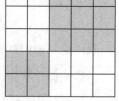

8.2.4 Rhonda the Realtor makes a 6% commission on each property she sells.

(a) If Rhonda sells a $270,000 house, then how much commission does she make?

(b) If Rhonda sells a condo and receives a commission of $15,000, then how much did the condo sell for?

8.2.5 Tori's mathematics test had 75 problems: 10 arithmetic, 30 algebra, and 35 geometry problems. Although she answered 70% of the arithmetic, 40% of the algebra, and 60% of the geometry problems correctly, she did not pass the test because she got less than 60% of the problems right. How many more questions would she have needed to answer correctly to earn a 60% passing grade? *(Source: AMC 8)*

8.2.6 A mixture of 30 liters of paint is 25% red tint, 30% yellow tint, and 45% water. Five liters of yellow tint are added to the original mixture. What is the percent of yellow tint in the new mixture? *(Source: AMC 8)*

8.2.7 When my car's gas tank is 80% empty, it contains 3 gallons of gas. How many gallons of gas does it contain when it is 80% full?

8.2.8 Peter and Emily played Go Fish against each other many times last January. Emily won 65% of the time, and Peter won the other 7 games. (There were no ties.) How many games did Emily win?

8.2.9 The Fighting Tomatoes, a minor-league baseball team, won 30 of their first 50 games. How many of the remaining 40 games must the Tomatoes win so that they will have won exactly 70% of their games at the end of the season?

8.2.10★ The table to the right gives the percent of students in each grade at West Parkville and East Parkville elementary schools. West Parkville has 100 students and East Parkville has 200 students. In the two schools combined, what percent of the students are in grade 6?

Grade	West	East
6th	30%	45%
7th	40%	25%
8th	30%	30%

8.2.11★ 500 students at Euclid University took a math exam. 75% of the students passed the exam. Suppose instead only 10% of the students had *failed* the exam. How many *more* passing grades would there have been? (The exam is either passed or failed.) *(Source: MOEMS)*

8.3 Percent Increase and Decrease

Percents are commonly used to describe an increase or decrease of some quantity. For example, you've probably seen ads for "20% off!" or read a news story about gas prices "rising 5%." In these situations, we take a percent times the original quantity and add or subtract the result to get a new quantity.

For example, the quantity that is "a 30% increase from 400" is computed by first computing 30% of 400:

$$30\% \text{ of } 400 = 30\% \cdot 400 = \frac{3}{10} \cdot 400 = 120,$$

and then adding this increase to our original 400 to get $400 + 120 = 520$. We could also compute this quantity by realizing that "a 30% increase from 400" means that we are adding 30% of 400 to our original 400. But our original 400 is 100% of 400, so after adding another 30% of 400 we will have a total of 130% of 400. Therefore,

a 30% increase from 400

is the same quantity as

130% of 400.

Then we can compute:

$$130\% \text{ of } 400 = 130\% \cdot 400 = \frac{13}{10} \cdot 400 = 13 \cdot 40 = 520.$$

Problems

Problem 8.15: Compute the following quantities:

(a) a 25% increase from 60

(b) 40% more than $\frac{1}{2}$

(c) a 30% decrease from 132

(d) 60% less than 95

(e) a 300% increase from 8

Problem 8.16: Describe the percent increase or decrease given by the following changing quantities:

(a) an increase from 100 to 130

(b) a change from 60 to 210

(c) a change from 8129 to 16258

(d) a decrease from 80 to 20

(e) a change from $\frac{2}{3}$ to $\frac{1}{6}$

(f) a change from 3.8 to 9.5

(g) a change from 271 to 0

Problem 8.17: In 2009, Heart & Sole Shoe Company sold 15 million pairs of shoes. In 2010, they increased advertising, and they sold 20% more shoes than in 2009. How many pairs of shoes did they sell in 2010?

Problem 8.18: An iZest computer (made by Lemon Computer Co.) has a retail price of $600. Jim's House of Electronics is having a "20%-off sale," in which all items are discounted to 20% less than retail. Abigail also has a coupon for 30% off the sale price of any Lemon computer. How much does Abigail have to pay for a new iZest?

Problem 8.19:

(a) In 2005 the population of Cedar Falls was 16,000. In 2010, the population was 20,000. By what percent did the population increase from 2005 to 2010?

(b) In 2015 the population is projected to decrease by 25% from its 2010 level. What is the projected population in 2015?

Problem 8.20: Wendy's stock in GloboSuperOmni Corp is worth $500 at the start of January. In each month, the stock goes up 10% in value. What is the stock worth at the end of March?

Problem 8.15: Compute the following quantities:

(a) a 25% increase from 60

(b) 40% more than $\frac{1}{2}$

(c) a 30% decrease from 132

(d) 60% less than 95

(e) a 300% increase from 8

Solution for Problem 8.15:

(a) We know that 25% = $\frac{1}{4}$, so 25% of 60 is

$$25\% \cdot 60 = \frac{1}{4} \cdot 60 = 15.$$

Therefore, a 25% increase from 60 means that we increase 60 by 15, so the answer is $60 + 15 = 75$.

Alternatively, we could note that a 25% increase from 60 is the same as 100%+25% = 125% of 60, so our answer is

$$125\% \cdot 60 = 1.25 \cdot 60 = 75.$$

(b) We know that 40% = $\frac{4}{10} = \frac{2}{5}$, so 40% of $\frac{1}{2}$ is $\frac{2}{5} \cdot \frac{1}{2} = \frac{1}{5}$. Thus, 40% more than $\frac{1}{2}$ means that we add $\frac{1}{5}$ to $\frac{1}{2}$, which is

$$\frac{1}{2} + \frac{1}{5} = \frac{5}{10} + \frac{2}{10} = \frac{7}{10}.$$

(c) 30% is the same as $\frac{3}{10}$, so 30% of 132 is

$$\frac{3}{10} \cdot 132 = \frac{396}{10} = 39.6.$$

Thus, we have to decrease 132 by 39.6, giving an answer of $132 - 39.6 = 92.4$.

An alternative approach is to realize that removing 30% of a quantity will leave us with $100\% - 30\% = 70\%$ of the quantity remaining. That is, 30% less than 132 is the same as 70% of 132. So, our answer is

$$70\% \text{ of } 132 = 70\% \cdot 132 = \frac{7}{10} \cdot 132 = \frac{924}{10} = 92.4.$$

(d) We know that 60% = $\frac{3}{5}$, so 60% of 95 equals

$$\frac{3}{5} \cdot 95 = 3 \cdot \frac{95}{5} = 3 \cdot 19 = 57.$$

Thus the answer is $95 - 57 = 38$.

Also, as in part (c), we could have instead computed $100\% - 60\% = 40\%$ of 95:

$$60\% \text{ less than } 95 = 40\% \text{ of } 95 = \frac{40}{100} \cdot 95 = \frac{2}{5} \cdot 95 = 2 \cdot 19 = 38.$$

(e) Even though the percent that we're increasing by is more than 100%, there's nothing really different about the calculation. We know that 300% = 3, so 300% of 8 is $3 \cdot 8 = 24$. This is the amount of the increase, so the answer is $8 + 24 = 32$.

□

> **Important:** In problems of the sort "compute an n% increase or decrease of x," we first multiply n% by x to determine the amount of the increase or decrease. Then we add or subtract this amount from x to get our answer.
>
> Alternatively, we can first add or subtract n% from 100%, and then compute $(100 + n)$% of x (if we are increasing by n%) or compute $(100 - n)$% of x (if we are decreasing by n%).
>
> Use whichever method seems easier for the quantities that you are working with.

We can also go the other direction: given the change in the quantity, we can compute the percent by which the quantity increased or decreased.

> **Problem 8.16:** Describe the percent increase or decrease given by the following changing quantities:
>
> (a) an increase from 100 to 130
>
> (b) a change from 60 to 210
>
> (c) a change from 8129 to 16258
>
> (d) a decrease from 80 to 20
>
> (e) a change from $\frac{2}{3}$ to $\frac{1}{6}$
>
> (f) a change from 3.8 to 9.5
>
> (g) a change from 271 to 0

Solution for Problem 8.16:

(a) First, we compute the amount of the increase or decrease. In this case, the quantity changed from 100 to 130, so it increased by 30.

   Next, we write this increase as a percentage of the *original* quantity. We know that 30 is 30% of 100, so the change from 100 to 130 is a 30% increase.

(b) The amount of the increase is $210 - 60 = 150$, so we need to express 150 as a percentage of 60. We compute:
$$\frac{150}{60} = \frac{5}{2} = \frac{250}{100} = 250\%.$$
Thus an increase from 60 to 210 is an increase of 250% from 60.

(c) The amount of the increase is $16258 - 8129 = 8129$. This is 100% of the original quantity 8129, so the increase is 100%.

   Note that $16258 = 2(8129)$, and thus a 100% increase in 8129 gives us $2(8129)$. This is true for any number:

> **Important:** A 100% increase in a quantity means that the quantity doubles.

(d) The amount of the decrease is 60. As a percent of the original number, this is

$$\frac{60}{80} = \frac{3}{4} = 75\%.$$

So the decrease from 80 to 20 is a 75% decrease from 80.

(e) The calculation works the same way even if the quantities are fractions. The amount of the decrease from $\frac{2}{3}$ to $\frac{1}{6}$ is

$$\frac{2}{3} - \frac{1}{6} = \frac{4}{6} - \frac{1}{6} = \frac{3}{6} = \frac{1}{2}.$$

As a percent of the original quantity $\frac{2}{3}$, this is

$$\frac{\frac{1}{2}}{\frac{2}{3}} = \frac{1}{2} \div \frac{2}{3} = \frac{1}{2} \cdot \frac{3}{2} = \frac{3}{4} = 75\%.$$

So the decrease from $\frac{2}{3}$ to $\frac{1}{6}$ is a decrease of 75%.

(f) The amount of the increase is $9.5 - 3.8 = 5.7$. The percent of this increase is

$$\frac{5.7}{3.8} = \frac{57}{38} = \frac{3}{2} = 150\%.$$

(g) We can first solve this the "long" way: the amount of the decrease is $271 - 0 = 271$. As a percent of the original quantity, this is

$$\frac{271}{271} = 1 = 100\%.$$

Thus, a decrease from 271 to 0 is a 100% decrease of 271.

But we can also observe that for any positive number x, decreasing from x to 0 is a decrease of x from x. But x is 100% of x, so this is a 100% decrease of x. In essence, we are removing "all of x from x," which is 100%.

> **Important:** A 100% decrease in a positive quantity means that the quantity becomes 0.

□

Let's look at a few word problems that might come up in everyday life.

Problem 8.17: In 2009, Heart & Sole Shoe Company sold 15 million pairs of shoes. In 2010, they increased advertising, and they sold 20% more shoes than in 2009. How many pairs of shoes did they sell in 2010?

Solution for Problem 8.17: As usual with word problems, the first task is to convert the English words into a mathematical statement. In this problem it's pretty straightforward: we are looking for the quantity that is 20% more than 15 million. The amount of the increase is

$$20\% \cdot (15 \text{ million}) = \frac{1}{5} \cdot 15 \text{ million} = 3 \text{ million}.$$

Therefore, the total sales for 2010 are equal to the sales for 2009 plus the amount of the increase, which gives us

$$15 \text{ million} + 3 \text{ million} = 18 \text{ million}$$

pairs of shoes sold in 2010. □

Problem 8.18: An iZest computer (made by Lemon Computer Co.) has a retail price of $600. Jim's House of Electronics is having a "20%-off sale," in which all items are discounted to 20% less than retail. Abigail also has a coupon for 30% off the sale price of any Lemon computer. How much does Abigail have to pay for a new iZest?

Solution for Problem 8.18: Here's a wrong solution—see if you can figure out the mistake:

Bogus Solution: The store has decreased the price by 20%, and the coupon decreases the price by another 30%. So the total decrease is $20\% + 30\% = 50\%$ of the price, which is $50\% \cdot \$600 = \frac{1}{2} \cdot \$600 = \$300$. Therefore, Abigail's price is $\$600 - \$300 = \$300$.

The problem is that percentage decreases don't add as in the Bogus Solution above. That's because the second decrease is taken from the new decreased price (after applying the first decrease), not the original price. This may not be clear, so let's see how it works in this problem. We will apply the decreases one at a time.

First, the store decreases the price by 20%. The amount of the decrease is $20\% \cdot \$600 = \$120$, so the sale price offered by the store is $\$600 - \$120 = \$480$.

Next, Abigail applies her coupon that decreases the *new price* by 30%. The amount of the decrease is $30\% \cdot \$480 = \$144$, and thus the final price that Abigail pays is $\$480 - \$144 = \$336$. □

Let's take another look at Problem 8.18 and see another explanation for what's going on, and why we can't just add percentages. When the store has its 20%-off sale, it is decreasing the price of the computer by 20%. This means that the new sale price is $100\% - 20\% = 80\%$ of the original price.

> **Important:** When a quantity is decreased by x%, then $(100-x)$% of the quantity remains.

Thus, the price of the computer is now $80\% \cdot \$600 = \$480$.

Then, when Abigail uses her coupon, the *new price* is decreased by 30%, so $100\% - 30\% = 70\%$ of the new price remains. Thus, the final purchase price is $70\% \cdot \$480 = \$336$.

When we write both decreases together, we see that we end up *multiplying* percents:

$$\begin{aligned}
\text{Final price} &= 70\% \cdot (\text{Sale price}) \\
&= 70\% \cdot (80\% \cdot (\text{Retail price})) \\
&= (70\% \cdot 80\%) \cdot (\text{Retail price}) \\
&= 56\% \cdot (\text{Retail Price}) \\
&= 56\% \cdot \$600 = \frac{56}{100} \cdot \$600 = 56 \cdot \$6 = \$336.
\end{aligned}$$

Also notice that we finished up with 56% of the original retail price, so that total discount from the retail price to the final price was $100\% - 56\% = 44\%$. Thus, a 20% decrease followed by a 30% decrease produces a total 44% decrease. A bit strange! We'll ask you to explore this somewhat bizarre arithmetic further in a Challenge Problem.

The next problem illustrates another important principle:

> **Problem 8.19:**
>
> (a) In 2005 the population of Cedar Falls was 16,000. In 2010, the population was 20,000. By what percent did the population increase from 2005 to 2010?
>
> (b) In 2015 the population is projected to decrease by 25% from its 2010 level. What is the projected population in 2015?

Solution for Problem 8.19:

(a) The amount of the increase was $20{,}000 - 16{,}000 = 4{,}000$, so as a percent of the original population, the increase was

$$\frac{4{,}000}{16{,}000} = \frac{4}{16} = \frac{1}{4} = 25\%.$$

Thus the population increased by 25% from 2005 to 2010.

(b) You might try the following "shortcut":

> **Bogus Solution:** In part (a), the population increased by 25%. So in part (b), when we decrease by 25%, we get back to where we started. Therefore the population in 2015 is the same as the population in 2005, which is 16,000.

Much like in Problem 8.18, this is not what actually happens. We will see what really happens when we do the computation.

We compute that 25% of the 2010 population is

$$(25\%) \cdot 20{,}000 = \frac{1}{4} \cdot 20{,}000 = 5{,}000.$$

So the population from 2010 to 2015 is projected to decrease by 5,000, and the 2015 population is projected to be
$$20{,}000 - 5{,}000 = 15{,}000.$$

$\square$

Again, perhaps this is a bit of a surprise! When the population increases by 25% from 2005 to 2010, and then decreases by 25% from 2010 to 2015, we don't end up back where we started—instead, we end up with a *smaller* population. In fact, an increase by a percentage between 0% and 100%, followed by a decrease by the same percentage, will always result in a smaller amount!

> **WARNING!!** Percent increases and decreases don't "cancel each other out."
> ☢ You need to compute each percent change separately.

You can explore this phenomenon more in Exercise 8.3.11.

> **Problem 8.20:** Wendy's stock in GloboSuperOmni Corp is worth $500 at the start of January. In each month, the stock goes up 10% in value. What is the stock worth at the end of March?

Solution for Problem 8.20: First, we'll do this the long way, and then we'll present a shortcut.

Method 1: Compute all the increases separately. We have three 10% increases back-to-back-to-back.

The first is an increase of 10% · $500 = $50, so the value is $500 + $50 = $550 at the end of January.

The second is an increase of 10% · $550 = $55, so the value is $550 + $55 = $605 at the end of February.

The third is an increase of 10% · $605 = $60.50, so the value is $605 + $60.50 = $665.50 at the end of March.

Method 2: Compute all the increases at once. Each 10% increase results in 100% + 10% = 110% of the quantity; thus, a 10% increase in a quantity is the same as multiplying the quantity by 110%. Therefore, three successive increases of 10% is the same as multiplying the quantity three times by 110%. This gives us

$$\text{Final amount} = 110\% \cdot 110\% \cdot 110\% \cdot \$500 = (110\%)^3 \cdot \$500.$$

We can cube a percent just like we cube any other number:

$$(110\%)^3 = \left(\frac{11}{10}\right)^3 = \frac{11^3}{10^3} = \frac{1331}{1000}.$$

So the final amount is

$$\text{Final amount} = (110\%)^3 \cdot \$500 = \frac{1331}{1000} \cdot \$500 = 1331 \cdot \$0.50 = \$665.50.$$

□

Problem 8.20 shows a little bit of the magic of **compound interest**. Specifically, we determined in Problem 8.20 that after three consecutive 10% increases, an initial amount of $500 increases to $665.50. This is greater than if, instead of three separate 10% increases, we had done just a single 30% increase. A single increase of 30% would have been an increase of 30% · $500 = $150, giving a final amount of $650. So by taking three consecutive 10% increases instead of a single 30% increase, Wendy ends up with an extra $15.50 in her pocket.

Exercises

8.3.1

(a) What number is 20% more than 15?

(b) What number is 30% less than 40?

(c) What number is 150% more than $\frac{2}{3}$?

(d) What number is 50% more than $\frac{1}{7}$?

(e) What number is 80% less than $\frac{3}{10}$?

(f) What number is 60% more than 4.8?

8.3.2 In the original 1999 U.S. version of the game show *Who Wants to Be a Millionaire*, the dollar values of each question were as shown in the following table:

Number	Value	Number	Value
1	$100	8	$8,000
2	$200	9	$16,000
3	$300	10	$32,000
4	$500	11	$64,000
5	$1,000	12	$125,000
6	$2,000	13	$250,000
7	$4,000	14	$500,000
		15	$1,000,000

Between which two consecutive questions is the percent increase of the value the smallest? *(Source: AMC 8)*

8.3.3 At the grocery store last week, SuperSugarSweet candy bars were priced at 4 bars for $5. This week, they are on sale at 5 bars for $4. What is the percent change in the price per candy bar this week as compared to last week?

8.3.4 Karl bought five folders from Pay-A-Lot at a cost of $2.50 each. Pay-A-Lot had a 20%-off sale the following day. How much could Karl have saved on the purchase by waiting a day? *(Source: AMC 8)*

8.3.5 Ana's monthly salary was $2000 in May. In June, she received a 20% raise. In July, she received a 20% pay cut. After the two changes in June and July, what was Ana's monthly salary? *(Source: AMC 8)*

8.3.6 A dress originally priced at $80 is put on sale at 25% off. If 10% tax is added to the sale price, then what is the total cost of the dress?

8.3.7 Penni Precisely buys $100 worth of stock in each of three companies: Alabama Almonds, Boston Beans, and California Cauliflower. After one year, AA was up 20%, BB was down 25%, and CC was unchanged. For the second year, AA was down 20% from the previous year, BB was up 25% from the previous year, and CC was unchanged. Order the final values of the stocks from low to high. *(Source: AMC 8)*

8.3.8 A pet shop offers an iguana for $80 and a parakeet for $40. During a sale, Chris bought the iguana at a 40% discount and the parakeet at a 55% discount. The total amount saved on Chris's new pets was what percent of the total of their original prices?

8.3.9 On December 1, Tom's House of Dollhouses increased the prices on all of its dolls by 25%. In January, Tom is having a sale where all dolls are priced 20% off the December prices. For any doll, is the January price higher than, lower than, or the same as the November price for that same doll? Does your answer depend on the doll's original price?

8.3.10★ Dave is playing blackjack at his local casino. He starts with $1,000 and on each hand he bets 50% of his money. If he wins a hand, then he wins whatever he bet, but if he loses a hand, then he loses whatever he bet. After playing 5 hands, he has won 3 hands and has lost 2 hands. How much money does Dave have after the 5 hands? Does it matter which 3 of the 5 hands he won? **Hints:** 108, 89

8.3.11★

(a) Suppose $0 < p < 100$. If we increase 100 by $p\%$ and then decrease the new quantity by $p\%$, then what is the final quantity (in terms of p)? Is it larger or smaller than 100?

(b) Suppose $0 < q < 100$. If we decrease 100 by $q\%$ and then increase the new quantity by $q\%$, then what is the final quantity (in terms of q)? Is it larger or smaller than 100?

8.4 Summary

A **percent** is another way of writing a fraction. We can write

$$x\% = \frac{x}{100}$$

where x is any number. So percents are nothing really new:

> **Concept:** A percent is just a number. It's a fraction with a hidden denominator of 100.

Sometimes the word "percentage" is used instead of "percent."

> **Concept:** Remember, a percent is just a fraction, so all of the things that we can do with fractions, we can do with percents too.

> **Important:** Many percents come up so often that you'll probably memorize them. The "quarter" percents are very common:
>
> $$25\% = \frac{25}{100} = \frac{1}{4}, \qquad 50\% = \frac{50}{100} = \frac{1}{2}, \qquad 75\% = \frac{75}{100} = \frac{3}{4}.$$
>
> You should also immediately recognize that $10\% = \frac{10}{100} = \frac{1}{10}$, so any percent that is a multiple of 10% is easy to compute:
>
> $$20\% = 2 \cdot 10\% = \frac{2}{10} = \frac{1}{5}, \qquad 30\% = 3 \cdot 10\% = \frac{3}{10},$$
>
> and so on.

One reason that percents are so commonly used is that they are easy to represent using decimals. As we've already seen, decimals are nice because they let us use our familiar base-10 number system to write fractions as well as integers. Since percents are based on 100, we see that 1 percent is equal to 1 one-hundredth, which we write as

$$1\% = \frac{1}{100} = 0.01.$$

Because percents are used frequently in the real world, they show up a lot in word problems. The key ideas for percent word problems are the same as for any type of word problem:

> **Concept:**
> - Read the problem carefully!
>
> - Convert the words to mathematics.
>
> - Solve the mathematical problem.
>
> - Write your answer in terms of the word problem, and make sure that it makes sense.

Percents are commonly used to represent an increase or decrease to some quantity. In these situations, we take a percent times the *original* quantity and add or subtract it to get a new quantity.

For example, the quantity that is "a 30% increase from 400" is computed by first computing 30% of 400:

$$30\% \text{ of } 400 = 30\% \cdot 400 = \frac{3}{10} \cdot 400 = 120,$$

and then adding this increase to our original 400 to get $400 + 120 = 520$. We could also compute this quantity by realizing that

a 30% increase from 400

is the same quantity as

130% of 400,

and then

$$130\% \text{ of } 400 = 130\% \cdot 400 = \frac{13}{10} \cdot 400 = 13 \cdot 40 = 520.$$

REVIEW PROBLEMS

8.21 Compute 40% of 20% of 10% of 80,000. *(Source: MATHCOUNTS)*

8.22 18% of 50 is what percent of 24?

8.23 If there are 240 boys in a school with a total of 960 students, then what percent of the students are girls?

8.24 The grading scale shown to the right is used at Jones Junior High. The fifteen scores in Mr. Freeman's class were:

$$89, 72, 54, 97, 77, 92, 85, 74, 75, 63, 84, 78, 71, 80, 90.$$

In Mr. Freeman's class, what percent of the students received a grade of C?

Score	Grade
90-100	A
80-89	B
70-79	C
60-69	D
0-59	F

8.25 The glass gauge on a cylindrical coffee maker shows there are 45 cups left when the coffee maker is 36% full. How many cups of coffee does it hold when it is full? *(Source: AMC 8)*

8.26 During the softball season, Judy had 35 hits. Among her hits were 1 home run, 1 triple, and 5 doubles. The rest of her hits were singles. What percent of her hits were singles? *(Source: AMC 8)*

8.27 Any quarter has a face value of $0.25. An eccentric collector offers to buy state quarters for 600% of their face value. At that rate, how much will Larry receive for his collection of all 50 state quarters?

8.28   Katie wants a fancy new music player that costs $300. Katie can buy it in her home state and pay 8% sales tax, or she can drive to a neighboring state and pay only 5% sales tax. How much does Katie save on the player if she drives to the neighboring state?

8.29   Sally is playing basketball. After she takes 20 shots, she has made 55% of her shots. After she takes 5 more shots, she raises her percentage of shots made to 56%. How many of the last 5 shots did she make? *(Source: AMC 8)*

8.30   200 students enrolled in the *Percentages 101* class in 2010. A 20% increase in enrollment is expected each year. How many students are expected to enroll in the class in 2012?

8.31   The January price of a television was $2200. This price was raised by 10% to produce the February price of the television. The February price was decreased by 15% to produce the March price of the television. What was the March price?

8.32   Antoinette gets 70% on a 10-problem test, 80% on a 20-problem test, and 90% on a 30-problem test. If the three tests are combined into one 60-problem test, then what is her overall percent, rounded to the nearest whole percent? *(Source: AMC 8)*

8.33   Suppose Paul receives a 6% raise every year. After four such raises, what is the total percentage increase to the nearest whole percent?

8.34   Jack had a bag of 128 apples. He sold 25% of them to Jill. Next he sold 25% of those remaining to June. Of those apples still in his bag, he gave the most shiny one to his teacher. How many apples did Jack have then? *(Source: AMC 8)*

8.35   A shopper buys a $100 coat on sale for 20% off. An additional $5 is taken off the sale price by using a discount coupon. A sales tax of 8% is paid on the final selling price. What is the total amount the shopper pays for the coat? *(Source: AMC 8)*

8.36   Polly the Penguin invested $250 in the Antarctic stock market. During the first year her investment suffered a 15% loss, but during the second year the remaining investment showed a 20% gain. Over the two-year period, what was the percent loss or gain in Polly's investment?

8.37   Sale prices at the Ajax Outlet Store are 50% below original prices. On Saturdays, an additional discount of 20% off the sale price is given. What is the Saturday price of a coat whose original price is $180? *(Source: AMC 8)*

8.38   Jack and Jill both work at the King's Ice Cream Shoppe. The King levies a 20% sales tax on all purchases. A customer comes in and orders an ice cream cone that costs 5 borks (the bork is a currency equal to 100 borklets). The customer also has a coupon for 10% off.

Jack says: "The total price will be highest if we first apply the 10% coupon to the price of the cone, and then compute the sales tax on the discounted price."

Jill says: "No—the total price will be highest if we first add the sales tax to the original price of the cone, and then apply the coupon."

Who's right?

Challenge Problems

8.39 If 25% of n is 18, then what is 125% of n? *(Source: MATHCOUNTS)*

8.40 If 20% of a number is 12, then what is 30% of the same number? *(Source: AMC 8)*

8.41 Find x if 20% of x equals 12% of $(x + 20)$. *(Source: MATHCOUNTS)*

8.42 Three bags of jelly beans contain 26, 28, and 30 beans. In each bag, the percent of the beans that are yellow is 50%, 25%, and 20%, respectively. All three bags of candy are dumped into one bowl. What percent of the beans in the bowl are yellow? Round your answer to the nearest integer. *(Source: AMC 8)*

8.43 Cody and Tyler were once the same height. Since then, Tyler has grown 20%, while Cody has grown half as much as Tyler. Cody's height is now 5 feet, 6 inches. How tall is Tyler now?

8.44 Miki has a dozen oranges of the same size and a dozen pears of the same size. Miki can use her juicer to extract 8 ounces of pear juice from 3 pears and 8 ounces of orange juice from 2 oranges. She makes a pear-orange juice blend from an equal number of pears and oranges. What percent of the blend is pear juice? *(Source: AMC 8)*

8.45 At some point in the season, the Unicorns had won 60% of their basketball games. After that point, they won 8 more games and lost 2, to finish the season having won 65% of their games. How many games did the Unicorns play during the season? **Hints:** 58

8.46 If 100 is decreased by a% and the result is decreased by b%, then what is the total percent decrease (in terms of a and b)? (You can assume that both a and b are between 0 and 100.)

8.47★ Grapes are 80% water (by weight), and raisins are 20% water (by weight). If we start with 500 grams of grapes and remove enough water to turn them into raisins, then what is the weight of the raisins that result? **Hints:** 156, 112

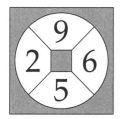 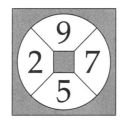 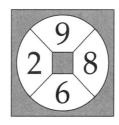 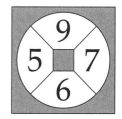

The intelligence of a crowd is the square root of the number of people in it. – Terry Pratchett

CHAPTER 9 _____

_____Square Roots

Back in Chapter 2, we learned about finding the square of a number. In this chapter, we investigate going in the other direction—we start with the square, and figure out what number was squared to produce the square.

Throughout this chapter, you should only use a calculator if you are told to do so.

9.1 From Squares to Square Roots

The square of 4 is 16. Going the other direction, we say that the **square root** of 16 is 4. We write this with symbols as

$$\sqrt{16} = 4.$$

You might wonder why can't we say that $\sqrt{16}$ is -4, since the square of -4 is also 16. The answer is that we simply don't allow $\sqrt{16}$ to be negative. We *define* the square root of a number n to be the *nonnegative* number whose square is n. So, the only choice for $\sqrt{16}$ is 4.

> **Definition:** The **square root** of a nonnegative number n is the nonnegative number whose square is n. We express the square root as $\sqrt{n}$, where the $\sqrt{\ }$ symbol is called a **radical**.

Both of the appearances of "nonnegative" in this definition are very important! It makes sense that n must be nonnegative in order to define $\sqrt{n}$. Whether a number is negative, 0, or positive, when we multiply that number by itself, the resulting product cannot be negative. So, we can't find the square root of a negative number.

The second "nonnegative" in our definition tells us that $\sqrt{n}$ cannot be negative. We define $\sqrt{n}$ this way in part because it would be a pain to have to say that we want the nonnegative result every time we use a square root. For example, which is easier:

"The length of the side of the square is $\sqrt{16}$ inches,"

or

"The length of the side of the square is $\sqrt{16}$ inches, where we mean the positive value of $\sqrt{16}$."

The first one is much simpler. In most basic applications, we only care about the nonnegative number whose square is n, so we define $\sqrt{n}$ to be this nonnegative number.

Obviously, simply saying "4" is even easier than saying "$\sqrt{16}$." When we "evaluate," "calculate," or "simplify" a square root expression, we try to write it in a form that doesn't include a radical.

> **Important:** In this chapter, we often will use the exponent laws from Chapter 2. Two laws in particular that we use a lot in this chapter are
>
> $$a^b \cdot a^c = a^{b+c} \qquad \text{and} \qquad \left(a^b\right)^c = a^{bc}.$$

Problems

Problem 9.1: Why do the following two problems have different answers?

(i) Find all values of x for which $x^2 = 36$.

(ii) Find all values of x for which $x = \sqrt{36}$.

Problem 9.2: Evaluate each of the following square roots:

(a) $\sqrt{25}$ (b) $\sqrt{144}$ (c) $\sqrt{529}$ (d) $\sqrt{1600}$

Problem 9.3: Evaluate each of the following:

(a) $\sqrt{11^2}$ (c) $\sqrt{(-23)^2}$ (e) $\sqrt{4^5}$ **Hints:** 70

(b) $\sqrt{465916594 3^2}$ (d) $\sqrt{7^4}$ **Hints:** 137

Problem 9.4: Simplify each of the following:

(a) $\sqrt{(5 \cdot 10 \cdot 7)^2}$ (c) $\sqrt{490000}$ (e) $\sqrt{1764}$

(b) $\sqrt{64 \cdot 25}$ (d) $\sqrt{2^6 \cdot 3^2 \cdot 5^4}$ (f) $\sqrt{69696}$

Problem 9.5: Simplify $\sqrt{6^5 + 6^5 + 6^5 + 6^5 + 6^5 + 6^5}$.

Problem 9.6: Evaluate each of the following:

(a) $\left(\sqrt{81}\right)^2$ (b) $\left(\sqrt{5621641}\right)^2$

Problem 9.7:
(a) Find x if $\sqrt{x+6} = 12$.
(b) Find x if $\sqrt{4x-5} = -5$.

Problem 9.1: Why do the following two problems have different answers?

  (i) Find all values of x for which $x^2 = 36$.

  (ii) Find all values of x for which $x = \sqrt{36}$.

Solution for Problem 9.1: For the equation $x^2 = 36$, both $x = -6$ and $x = 6$ are solutions. But for the equation $x = \sqrt{36}$, only $x = 6$ is a solution. The equation $x^2 = 36$ means we have to find *all* numbers whose squares equal 36, while the equation $x = \sqrt{36}$ asks us only to find the *nonnegative* number whose square equals 36. □

Problem 9.2: Evaluate each of the following square roots:

(a) $\sqrt{25}$ (b) $\sqrt{144}$ (c) $\sqrt{529}$ (d) $\sqrt{1600}$

Solution for Problem 9.2:

(a) Since $5^2 = 25$, we have $\sqrt{25} = 5$.

(b) Since $12^2 = 144$, we have $\sqrt{144} = 12$.

(c) Since $23^2 = 529$, we have $\sqrt{529} = 23$. But what if we don't remember what number 529 is the square of? Then we can try squaring different numbers, hoping to find a number whose square is 529. We notice that $20^2 = 400$, which is less than 529, so we need to square a number larger than 20 to get 529. The square of an even number is even, but 529 is odd, so we only need to try odd numbers. 21^2 ends in 1, so that doesn't work. We then compute 23^2 and find that it equals 529, which means $\sqrt{529} = 23$.

  Notice that we saved ourselves a lot of effort by thinking a bit about squares before trying to square any numbers at all.

(d) Since $40^2 = 1600$, we have $\sqrt{1600} = 40$.

□

Problem 9.3: Evaluate each of the following:

(a) $\sqrt{11^2}$

(b) $\sqrt{4659165943^2}$

(c) $\sqrt{(-23)^2}$

(d) $\sqrt{7^4}$

(e) $\sqrt{4^5}$

Solution for Problem 9.3:

(a) We have $11^2 = 121$, so $\sqrt{11^2} = \sqrt{121}$. Since $\sqrt{121}$ equals the number whose square is 121, and 121 is the square of 11, we have

$$\sqrt{11^2} = \sqrt{121} = 11.$$

Now we see that we didn't even need to compute 11^2 in the first place. By definition, $\sqrt{11^2}$ equals the nonnegative number whose square is 11^2. Since 11 is obviously the nonnegative number whose square is 11^2, we have $\sqrt{11^2} = 11$.

> **Important:** If $n \geq 0$, then $\sqrt{n^2} = n$.

(b) Squaring 4659165943 would be a pain, but our work in part (a) shows us that we don't have to. Since 4659165943 is the nonnegative number whose square is 4659165943^2, we have $\sqrt{4659165943^2} = 4659165943$.

(c) What's wrong with this solution:

> **Bogus Solution:** Since we square -23 to get $(-23)^2$, we know that $\sqrt{(-23)^2}$ is -23.

We define square roots to be nonnegative! So, the result cannot be -23.

> **WARNING!!** The relationship $\sqrt{n^2} = n$ is only true if $n \geq 0$. It is *not* true if n is negative.

We could square -23, and then take the square root of the result in order to compute $\sqrt{(-23)^2}$, but we can find the answer a little more quickly. A number and its negative have the same square:

$$(-23)^2 = ((-1) \cdot 23)^2 = (-1)^2 \cdot 23^2 = 1 \cdot 23^2 = 23^2.$$

So, we have

$$\sqrt{(-23)^2} = \sqrt{23^2} = 23.$$

As an Exercise, you'll use this insight to find a way to express $\sqrt{n^2}$ when n is negative.

(d) We could multiply 7^4 out, but that would be quite a pain. We do know how to take the square root of a perfect square, so let's try to write 7^4 as a perfect square. Fortunately, because the exponent in 7^4 is even, we can write 7^4 as a square using exponent laws:

$$7^4 = 7^{2 \cdot 2} = (7^2)^2.$$

So, we have

$$\sqrt{7^4} = \sqrt{(7^2)^2} = \sqrt{49^2} = 49.$$

(e) Again, we could just multiply 4^5 out, but we'd like to find a faster way to find its square root. In part (d) above, we were able to write 7^4 as the square of a number because the exponent in 7^4 is even. But the exponent of 4^5 is odd, so it looks like we can't use the same process here. However, 4 is a perfect square. We have

$$4^5 = (2^2)^5 = 2^{2 \cdot 5} = 2^{5 \cdot 2} = (2^5)^2.$$

We have now written 4^5 as the square of an integer, so we can take its square root:

$$\sqrt{4^5} = \sqrt{(2^5)^2} = \sqrt{(32)^2} = 32.$$

□

In our final part, we used a very useful strategy:

> **Concept:** When working with powers of integers, it's often helpful to use the smallest base possible.

We used this strategy above when we wrote 4^5 as 2^{10}.

Problem 9.4: Simplify each of the following:

(a) $\sqrt{(5 \cdot 10 \cdot 7)^2}$ (c) $\sqrt{490000}$ (e) $\sqrt{1764}$

(b) $\sqrt{64 \cdot 25}$ (d) $\sqrt{2^6 \cdot 3^2 \cdot 5^4}$ (f) $\sqrt{69696}$

Solution for Problem 9.4:

(a) We know that if n is nonnegative, then $\sqrt{n^2}$ equals n, so

$$\sqrt{(5 \cdot 10 \cdot 7)^2} = 5 \cdot 10 \cdot 7 = 350.$$

(b) We recognize 64 and 25 as perfect squares, so we can write $64 \cdot 25$ as the square of an integer:

$$64 \cdot 25 = 8^2 \cdot 5^2 = (8 \cdot 5)^2.$$

So, we have $\sqrt{64 \cdot 25} = \sqrt{8^2 \cdot 5^2} = \sqrt{(8 \cdot 5)^2} = 8 \cdot 5 = 40.$

(c) We notice that 49 and 10000 are perfect squares, so we have

$$\sqrt{490000} = \sqrt{49 \cdot 10000} = \sqrt{7^2 \cdot 100^2} = \sqrt{(7 \cdot 100)^2} = 7 \cdot 100 = 700.$$

Of course, you might have noticed right away that $700^2 = 490000$ because $7^2 = 49$, and squaring a number with 2 zeros at the end gives a number with 4 zeros at the end.

(d) We know how to take the square root of a perfect square, so let's try to write $2^6 \cdot 3^2 \cdot 5^4$ as a perfect square. Fortunately, all of the exponents in $2^6 \cdot 3^2 \cdot 5^4$ are even, so each of $2^6, 3^2$, and 5^4 is a perfect square:

$$2^6 \cdot 3^2 \cdot 5^4 = (2^{3 \cdot 2}) \cdot (3^{1 \cdot 2}) \cdot (5^{2 \cdot 2}) = (2^3)^2 \cdot (3^1)^2 \cdot (5^2)^2 = (2^3 \cdot 3^1 \cdot 5^2)^2.$$

Now, we can find our square root:

$$\sqrt{2^6 \cdot 3^2 \cdot 5^4} = \sqrt{(2^3 \cdot 3^1 \cdot 5^2)^2} = 2^3 \cdot 3^1 \cdot 5^2 = 8 \cdot 3 \cdot 25 = 600.$$

(e) We know how to take the square root of a product of squares, so we try to write 1764 as the product of perfect squares. We start by noticing that 1764 is divisible by 4, which is a perfect square. Since $1764/4 = 441$, we have $1764 = 4 \cdot 441$. Now, we might recognize 441 as a perfect square. But if we don't, all is not lost. While 441 is obviously not divisible by 4, it is divisible by 9. We have $441 = 9 \cdot 49$. Both 9 and 49 are perfect squares! We can take the square root now:

$$\sqrt{1764} = \sqrt{4 \cdot 441} = \sqrt{4 \cdot 9 \cdot 49} = \sqrt{2^2 \cdot 3^2 \cdot 7^2} = \sqrt{(2 \cdot 3 \cdot 7)^2} = 2 \cdot 3 \cdot 7 = 42.$$

We can check our work by squaring 42. We find that $42^2 = 1764$, so we do indeed have $\sqrt{1764} = 42$.

(f) As in the previous part, we repeatedly find perfect square factors and we write 69696 as a product of perfect squares. We start with factors of 4:

$$69696 = 4 \cdot 17424 = 4 \cdot 4 \cdot 4356 = 4 \cdot 4 \cdot 4 \cdot 1089.$$

Next, we try 9, and we find

$$69696 = 4 \cdot 4 \cdot 4 \cdot 1089 = 4 \cdot 4 \cdot 4 \cdot 9 \cdot 121.$$

We've written 69696 as a product of squares, so we can quickly find its square root:

$$\sqrt{69696} = \sqrt{4 \cdot 4 \cdot 4 \cdot 9 \cdot 121} = \sqrt{(2 \cdot 2 \cdot 2 \cdot 3 \cdot 11)^2} = \sqrt{264^2} = 264.$$

Rather than hunting for perfect square divisors of 69696, we could have first found the prime factorization of 69696, and then used our approach from part (d). With plenty of pencil pushing, we find that $69696 = 2^6 \cdot 3^2 \cdot 11^2$, so

$$\sqrt{69696} = \sqrt{2^6 \cdot 3^2 \cdot 11^2} = \sqrt{(2^3 \cdot 3 \cdot 11)^2} = 2^3 \cdot 3 \cdot 11 = 264.$$

□

Problem 9.5: Simplify $\sqrt{6^5 + 6^5 + 6^5 + 6^5 + 6^5 + 6^5}$.

Solution for Problem 9.5: Once again, we can avoid a lot of computation with a little bit of thinking. There are 6 copies of 6^5 added in the sum, so we have

$$6^5 + 6^5 + 6^5 + 6^5 + 6^5 + 6^5 = 6 \cdot 6^5.$$

Next, we apply an exponent law to find

$$6 \cdot 6^5 = 6^1 \cdot 6^5 = 6^{1+5} = 6^6.$$

Therefore, we have $\sqrt{6^5 + 6^5 + 6^5 + 6^5 + 6^5 + 6^5} = \sqrt{6^6} = \sqrt{(6^3)^2} = 6^3 = 216.$ □

Problem 9.6: Evaluate each of the following:

(a) $\left(\sqrt{81}\right)^2$

(b) $\left(\sqrt{5621641}\right)^2$

Solution for Problem 9.6:

(a) Since $9^2 = 81$, we have $\sqrt{81} = 9$, so $\left(\sqrt{81}\right)^2 = (9)^2 = 81$. In other words, when we square the square root of 81, we get 81. Is that a coincidence?

(b) Finding the square root of 5621641 sure would be a pain, but part (a) suggests there might be a shortcut. The square root of 5621641 is the number we must square to get 5621641. So, when we square the square root of 5621641, we get 5621641. In other words, there was nothing special about 81 in the previous part.

> **Important:** For any nonnegative number n, we have
>
> $$\left(\sqrt{n}\right)^2 = n.$$

So, we have $\left(\sqrt{5621641}\right)^2 = 5621641$.

□

We finish this section by solving equations involving square roots.

Problem 9.7:
(a) Find x if $\sqrt{x+6} = 12$.
(b) Find x if $\sqrt{4x-5} = -5$.

Solution for Problem 9.7:

(a) We haven't seen an equation like this before, but we do know how to solve linear equations. So, if we can figure out what number $x + 6$ must equal, then we can solve the problem.

> **Concept:** When you must solve a new type of equation, try to find a way to turn the equation into a type of equation you know how to solve.

By our definition of square root, $\sqrt{x+6}$ is the nonnegative number whose square is $x+6$. Since $\sqrt{x+6} = 12$, we know that 12 is the number whose square is $x + 6$. Therefore, we must have $x + 6 = 12^2$, so $x + 6 = 144$. Subtracting 6 from both sides of the equation gives $x = 138$.

(b) By our definition of square root, $\sqrt{4x - 5}$ is the nonnegative number whose square is $4x - 5$. Since $\sqrt{4x - 5}$ must be nonnegative, it cannot ever equal -5. This means that the equation $\sqrt{4x - 5} = -5$ has no solution.

$\square$

Exercises

9.1.1 Evaluate the following square roots. As an extra challenge, try computing them without writing anything.

(a) $\sqrt{196}$

(b) $\sqrt{441}$

(c) $\sqrt{37^2}$

(d) $\sqrt{2^{12}}$

(e) $\sqrt{3600 \cdot 25}$

(f) $\sqrt{8 \cdot 6 \cdot 147}$

9.1.2 Compute $\sqrt{1368900}$.

9.1.3 Evaluate $\sqrt{(-7)^4}$.

9.1.4 How can we simplify $\sqrt{n^2}$ if n is negative?

9.1.5 Simplify $\sqrt{3^2 + 4^2}$. *(Source: MATHCOUNTS)*

9.1.6 Tammy was computing $\sqrt{110889}$ and came up with 331 as her answer. She immediately knew that she was wrong; how?

9.1.7 If x is negative and $x^2 = 81$, what is the value of x? *(Source: MATHCOUNTS)*

9.1.8 If $\sqrt{n} = 4$, what is the value of n^2? *(Source: MATHCOUNTS)*

9.1.9 Find x if $\sqrt{2x + 1} = 13$.

9.1.10★ What values of t satisfy $\sqrt{t^2 - 15} = 7$? **Hints:** 155

9.2 Square Roots of Non-square Integers

In the previous section, we only worked with square roots of perfect squares. In this section, we investigate square roots of integers that are not perfect squares.

We'll start with $\sqrt{2}$. Does $\sqrt{2}$ even exist? Is there a number whose square is 2? We know that there isn't an integer that equals $\sqrt{2}$, since there is no integer whose square is 2. Is there a quotient of two integers (a fraction) whose square is 2? The ancient Greeks believed so for quite some time, and legend has it that the man who finally proved that no such quotient exists was drowned at sea for upsetting this belief. (You will have a chance to prove for yourself that no such quotient exists as a Challenge Problem. Don't worry, no one will drown you at sea if you succeed!)

So, there isn't an integer whose square is 2, and there isn't a fraction whose square is 2. But the number $\sqrt{2}$ does exist! It's a new kind of number that we call an **irrational number**.

> **Definition:** An **irrational number** is a number that cannot be expressed as the quotient of two integers.

We can't express $\sqrt{2}$ as an integer or a fraction, so we can't express it exactly as a decimal, either. However, we can *approximate* it using one important rule:

> **Important:** If a and b are nonnegative numbers such that $a > b$, then we have $\sqrt{a} > \sqrt{b}$. In other words, when comparing the square roots of two nonnegative numbers, the larger number has the larger square root. Similarly, if $\sqrt{a} > \sqrt{b}$, then $a > b$.

Since $1^2 = 1$ and $2^2 = 4$, we expect that the number whose square is 2 must be between 1 and 2. Our rule above tells us that this intuition is correct. In this section, we'll learn how to use this rule repeatedly to approximate $\sqrt{2}$ to as many decimal places as we like, but we will never be able to write a decimal expression that exactly equals $\sqrt{2}$. Moreover, a decimal approximation of $\sqrt{2}$ does not ever regularly repeat the way the repeating decimals we studied in Section 6.4 do.

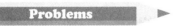
Problems

> **Problem 9.8:**
> (a) Evaluate $\left(\sqrt{5}\right)^2$.
> (b) Evaluate $\left(\sqrt{8}\right)^6$.

> **Problem 9.9:**
> (a) Explain why $\sqrt{2}$ must be less than 1.5.
> (b) Estimate $\sqrt{2}$ to the nearest tenth.

> **Problem 9.10:** Which integers have a square root that is greater than 7 and less than 8?

Problem 9.11: How many integers are between $\sqrt{13}$ and $\sqrt{131}$?

Problem 9.12: Find the largest integer less than $\sqrt{80,999,599}$.

Problem 9.13: Which is larger, $7 \cdot \sqrt{11}$ or $6 \cdot \sqrt{15}$?

Problem 9.8:

(a) Evaluate $\left(\sqrt{5}\right)^2$.

(b) Evaluate $\left(\sqrt{8}\right)^6$.

Solution for Problem 9.8:

(a) By definition, $\sqrt{5}$ is the number whose square is 5. So, while we can't write a decimal or fraction that exactly equals $\sqrt{5}$, we do know that the square of $\sqrt{5}$ is simply 5.

(b) We know how to square $\sqrt{8}$, but here we want the sixth power. Once again, our exponent laws help us. Taking the sixth power of a number is the same as first squaring the number and then cubing the result:

$$\left(\sqrt{8}\right)^6 = \left(\sqrt{8}\right)^{2\cdot 3} = \left[\left(\sqrt{8}\right)^2\right]^3 = (8)^3 = 512.$$

$\square$

Problem 9.9:

(a) Explain why $\sqrt{2}$ must be less than 1.5.

(b) Estimate $\sqrt{2}$ to the nearest tenth.

Solution for Problem 9.9:

(a) Since $1.5^2 = 2.25$, any number that is at least 1.5 has a square that is at least 2.25. This means that no number that is at least 1.5 can be the square root of 2. So, the square root of 2 must be less than 1.5.

(b) So far, we know that $\sqrt{2}$ is between 1 and 1.5. Since 1.5^2 is closer to 2 than 1^2 is, we think that $\sqrt{2}$ is probably closer to 1.5 than to 1. Therefore, we try squaring 1.4 next. We have $1.4^2 = 1.96$, so we need to square a slightly larger number than 1.4 to get 2. We find that $1.41^2 = 1.9881$ and $1.42^2 = 2.0164$, so $\sqrt{2}$ is between 1.41 and 1.42. Therefore, $\sqrt{2}$ rounded to the nearest tenth is 1.4.

$\square$

In a similar method as we used to estimate $\sqrt{2}$, we can estimate the square root of any non-square number. We square numbers that we think are close to the desired square root. We then compare the resulting squares to the number whose square root we are trying to find. For example, in Problem 9.9, we found $1.4^2 = 1.96$ and $1.5^2 = 2.25$. Since 2 is between 1.96 and 2.25, we know that $\sqrt{2}$ is between 1.4 and 1.5.

Problem 9.10: Which integers have a square root that is greater than 7 and less than 8?

Solution for Problem 9.10: Since 7 is the square root of 49 and 8 is the square root of 64, the square root of any integer between 49 and 64 is between 7 and 8. We can visualize this on the number line:

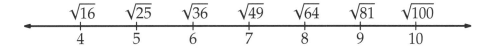

So, the following integers have square roots greater than 7 and less than 8:

$$50, 51, 52, 53, 54, 55, 56, 57, 58, 59, 60, 61, 62, 63.$$

$\square$

Just as we can find square roots that fall between integers, we can find integers that fall between square roots.

Problem 9.11: How many integers are between $\sqrt{13}$ and $\sqrt{131}$?

Solution for Problem 9.11: First, we figure out which two consecutive integers $\sqrt{13}$ is between. To do so, we find the two consecutive perfect squares that 13 falls between. Since 13 is between 9 and 16, we know that $\sqrt{13}$ is between 3 and 4. Similarly, since 131 is between 121 (which is 11^2) and 144 (which is 12^2), we know that $\sqrt{131}$ is between 11 and 12. Again, we can visualize these relationships with a number line:

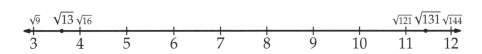

So, the integers between $\sqrt{13}$ and $\sqrt{131}$ are the integers from 4 up to 11. There are 8 such integers. $\square$

Problem 9.12: Find the largest integer less than $\sqrt{80{,}999{,}599}$.

Solution for Problem 9.12: We start by trying to find an integer near $\sqrt{80{,}999{,}599}$. Since $81 = 9^2$, we start by considering $\sqrt{81{,}000{,}000}$. We're in luck, since this is an integer:

$$\sqrt{81{,}000{,}000} = \sqrt{81 \cdot 1{,}000{,}000} = \sqrt{9^2 \cdot 1000^2} = \sqrt{(9 \cdot 1000)^2} = 9000.$$

So, $\sqrt{80{,}999{,}599}$ is less than 9000. The next perfect square smaller than 9000^2 is 8999^2. Rather than computing 8999^2 to compare it to $80{,}999{,}599$, we remember what we learned about consecutive squares on page 62. Since $9000^2 = 81{,}000{,}000$, we have

$$8999^2 = 9000^2 - 9000 - 8999 = 81{,}000{,}000 - 9000 - 8999 = 80{,}991{,}000 - 8999,$$

which is definitely less than $80{,}999{,}599$. So, the largest integer less than $\sqrt{80{,}999{,}599}$ is 8999. $\square$

Problem 9.13: Which is larger, $7 \cdot \sqrt{11}$ or $6 \cdot \sqrt{15}$?

Solution for Problem 9.13: We typically write the product of a number and a square root without using a multiplication symbol. So, we write $2\sqrt{3}$ to refer to the product of 2 and $\sqrt{3}$, and in this problem we are asked to compare $7\sqrt{11}$ and $6\sqrt{15}$.

We know how to compare two square roots. The order of two square roots is the same as the order of the squares of the two square roots. For example, we know $\sqrt{11} > \sqrt{10}$ because $11 > 10$. Similarly, the order of any two nonnegative numbers is the same as the order of their squares. Maybe comparing squares will work on this problem, too.

> **Concept:** When faced with a new problem, try strategies that you have used to solve similar problems.

Applying the exponent law $(ab)^2 = a^2b^2$, we have

$$\left(7\sqrt{11}\right)^2 = (7)^2\left(\sqrt{11}\right)^2 = (49)(11) = 539,$$
$$\left(6\sqrt{15}\right)^2 = (6)^2\left(\sqrt{15}\right)^2 = (36)(15) = 540.$$

These two results are easy to compare. Since $6\sqrt{15}$ has a larger square than $7\sqrt{11}$ (and both numbers are nonnegative), we know that $6\sqrt{15}$ is larger than $7\sqrt{11}$. $\square$

> **Concept:** We can often compare expressions involving square roots by comparing the squares of the expressions.

Exercises

9.2.1 Round each of the following square roots to the nearest integer.

(a) $\sqrt{78}$ (b) $\sqrt{200}$ (c) $\sqrt{4004}$

9.2.2 How many integers are between $\sqrt{7}$ and $\sqrt{220}$?

9.2.3 What is the largest integer that is less than $\sqrt{83} - \sqrt{35}$?

9.2.4 Compute $\left(\sqrt{14}\right)^4$.

9.2.5 What integer is closest to $4\sqrt{5}$?

9.2.6 How many digits are in the square root of the perfect square 108,868,356?

9.2.7 Between what two consecutive integers on the number line is the sum $\sqrt{30} + \sqrt{50}$ located? *(Source: MATHCOUNTS)*

9.2.8 Which of the following numbers is largest: $\sqrt{75}$, $\frac{75}{9}$, or 50% of $\frac{68}{4}$? *(Source: MATHCOUNTS)*

9.3 Arithmetic with Square Roots

In this section we explore how to multiply, divide, add, and subtract square roots.

 **Problems**

Problem 9.14:

(a) For what integer n is $\sqrt{4} \cdot \sqrt{25} = \sqrt{n}$?

(b) Compute $\left(\sqrt{2} \cdot \sqrt{3}\right)^2$.

(c) For what integer n is $\sqrt{2} \cdot \sqrt{3} = \sqrt{n}$?

(d) If a and b are nonnegative, then must we have $\sqrt{a} \cdot \sqrt{b} = \sqrt{ab}$? Why or why not?

Problem 9.15: Compute each of the following:

(a) $\sqrt{2} \cdot \sqrt{8}$

(b) $\sqrt{18} \cdot \sqrt{50}$

(c) $\sqrt{24} \cdot \sqrt{10} \cdot \sqrt{15}$

(d) $(5\sqrt{3}) \cdot (3\sqrt{27})$

Problem 9.16: Compute each of the following:

(a) $\sqrt{\frac{49}{4}}$

(b) $\sqrt{\frac{54}{384}}$

(c) $\sqrt{11\frac{1}{9}}$

(d) $\frac{\sqrt{54}}{\sqrt{6}}$

(e) $\frac{\sqrt{63}}{\sqrt{28}}$

Problem 9.17:

(a) Compute $\sqrt{0.64}$.

(b) Compute $\sqrt{2.25}$.

(c) Evaluate $\sqrt{0.000169}$.

(d) What integer is closest to $\sqrt{14.4}$?

Problem 9.18: Is $\sqrt{4} + \sqrt{9}$ equal to $\sqrt{13}$?

Problem 9.19: Is $\sqrt{5^2 + 12^2}$ equal to $5 + 12$?

Problem 9.20: In Section 9.1, we "simplified" square roots of perfect squares by writing them as integers. In Section 9.2, we discovered that some square roots cannot be expressed as integers. We say that we "simplify" such a square root when we write it in the form $a\sqrt{b}$ where a and b are integers and b has no perfect square factors besides 1. For example, we can simplify $\sqrt{12}$ as $2\sqrt{3}$.

(a) Confirm that $\sqrt{12}$ and $2\sqrt{3}$ are equal by squaring both.

(b) Simplify $\sqrt{18}$.

(c) Simplify $\sqrt{432}$.

(d) Simplify $\sqrt{1176}$.

Problem 9.21: Simplify $\sqrt{25x^8}$.

Problem 9.22: What integer does $\sqrt{50} - \sqrt{18} - \sqrt{8}$ equal?

Problem 9.14:

(a) For what integer n is $\sqrt{4} \cdot \sqrt{25} = \sqrt{n}$?

(b) Compute $\left(\sqrt{2} \cdot \sqrt{3}\right)^2$.

(c) For what integer n is $\sqrt{2} \cdot \sqrt{3} = \sqrt{n}$?

(d) If a and b are nonnegative, then must we have $\sqrt{a} \cdot \sqrt{b} = \sqrt{ab}$? Why or why not?

Extra! Imagining what results if there were numbers whose squares are negative leads
➤➤➤➤ to a very rich area of mathematics. We call such numbers **imaginary numbers**. (No, we're not joking!) You'll learn a lot more about imaginary numbers as you study more math and science.

Solution for Problem 9.14:

(a) We have $\sqrt{4} = 2$ and $\sqrt{25} = 5$, so $\sqrt{4} \cdot \sqrt{25} = 2 \cdot 5 = 10$. Since $10 = \sqrt{100}$, we have

$$\sqrt{4} \cdot \sqrt{25} = \sqrt{100},$$

so $n = 100$. Notice that $\sqrt{4} \cdot \sqrt{25} = \sqrt{4 \cdot 25}$. Is that a coincidence? Let's see.

(b) We have

$$\left(\sqrt{2} \cdot \sqrt{3}\right)^2 = \left(\sqrt{2}\right)^2 \cdot \left(\sqrt{3}\right)^2 = 2 \cdot 3 = 6.$$

(c) Since the square of $\sqrt{2} \cdot \sqrt{3}$ is 6, we know that $\sqrt{2} \cdot \sqrt{3}$ must equal the square root of 6. So, we have $n = 6$:

$$\sqrt{2} \cdot \sqrt{3} = \sqrt{6} = \sqrt{2 \cdot 3}.$$

(d) Yes, if a and b are nonnegative, then $\sqrt{a} \cdot \sqrt{b} = \sqrt{ab}$. We can use parts (b) and (c) as a guide to see why. To see that $\sqrt{a} \cdot \sqrt{b}$ is the square root of ab, we must show that the square of $\sqrt{a} \cdot \sqrt{b}$ is ab:

$$\left(\sqrt{a} \cdot \sqrt{b}\right)^2 = \left(\sqrt{a}\right)^2 \cdot \left(\sqrt{b}\right)^2 = ab.$$

Since the square of $\sqrt{a} \cdot \sqrt{b}$ is ab, we have $\sqrt{a} \cdot \sqrt{b} = \sqrt{ab}$.

$\square$

> **Important:** If a and b are nonnegative, then
>
> $$\sqrt{a} \cdot \sqrt{b} = \sqrt{ab}.$$

Problem 9.15: Compute each of the following:

(a) $\sqrt{2} \cdot \sqrt{8}$

(b) $\sqrt{18} \cdot \sqrt{50}$

(c) $\sqrt{24} \cdot \sqrt{10} \cdot \sqrt{15}$

(d) $(5\sqrt{3}) \cdot (3\sqrt{27})$

Solution for Problem 9.15:

(a) Applying the principle we just learned, we have

$$\sqrt{2} \cdot \sqrt{8} = \sqrt{2 \cdot 8} = \sqrt{16} = 4.$$

(b) We have

$$\sqrt{18} \cdot \sqrt{50} = \sqrt{18 \cdot 50} = \sqrt{900} = 30.$$

(c) Here, we apply $\sqrt{a} \cdot \sqrt{b} = \sqrt{ab}$ twice:

$$\sqrt{24} \cdot \sqrt{10} \cdot \sqrt{15} = \sqrt{24 \cdot 10} \cdot \sqrt{15}$$
$$= \sqrt{240} \cdot \sqrt{15}$$
$$= \sqrt{240 \cdot 15}$$
$$= \sqrt{3600}$$
$$= 60.$$

Notice that we can use $\sqrt{a} \cdot \sqrt{b} = \sqrt{ab}$ "in reverse" to see that $\sqrt{3600} = 60$:

$$\sqrt{3600} = \sqrt{36 \cdot 100} = \sqrt{36} \cdot \sqrt{100} = 6 \cdot 10 = 60.$$

(d) Here, we rearrange the product so that we can combine the square roots:

$$(5\sqrt{3}) \cdot (3\sqrt{27}) = 5 \cdot \sqrt{3} \cdot 3 \cdot \sqrt{27}$$
$$= (5 \cdot 3) \cdot (\sqrt{3} \cdot \sqrt{27})$$
$$= 15 \cdot \sqrt{3 \cdot 27}$$
$$= 15 \cdot \sqrt{81}.$$

Typically, we don't write out (or even think about) all those intermediate steps. We would usually think

$$(5\sqrt{3}) \cdot (3\sqrt{27}) = 15\sqrt{81} = 15 \cdot 9 = 135.$$

The $15\sqrt{81}$ comes from multiplying the numbers outside the radicals in $(5\sqrt{3}) \cdot (3\sqrt{27})$ to get 15 and multiplying the numbers inside the radicals to get $\sqrt{81}$.

$\square$

Now that we have explored multiplication, let's look at division.

Problem 9.16: Compute each of the following:

(a) $\sqrt{\dfrac{49}{4}}$

(b) $\sqrt{\dfrac{54}{384}}$

(c) $\sqrt{11\tfrac{1}{9}}$

(d) $\dfrac{\sqrt{54}}{\sqrt{6}}$

(e) $\dfrac{\sqrt{63}}{\sqrt{28}}$

Solution for Problem 9.16:

(a) We recognize that the numerator and denominator of $\frac{49}{4}$ are perfect squares, and we have

$$\sqrt{\frac{49}{4}} = \sqrt{\frac{7^2}{2^2}} = \sqrt{\left(\frac{7}{2}\right)^2} = \frac{7}{2}.$$

(b) First, we simplify the fraction:

$$\frac{54}{384} = \frac{9 \cdot 6}{64 \cdot 6} = \frac{9}{64}.$$

The numerator and denominator of $\frac{9}{64}$ are perfect squares, and we have

$$\sqrt{\frac{54}{384}} = \sqrt{\frac{9}{64}} = \sqrt{\frac{3^2}{8^2}} = \sqrt{\left(\frac{3}{8}\right)^2} = \frac{3}{8}.$$

(c) In the first two parts, we were able to find the square roots of fractions, so we write the mixed number $11\frac{1}{9}$ as a fraction:

$$11\frac{1}{9} = 11 \cdot \frac{9}{9} + \frac{1}{9} = \frac{100}{9}.$$

Once again, the numerator and denominator are perfect squares, and we have

$$\sqrt{11\frac{1}{9}} = \sqrt{\frac{100}{9}} = \sqrt{\frac{10^2}{3^2}} = \sqrt{\left(\frac{10}{3}\right)^2} = \frac{10}{3} = 3\frac{1}{3}.$$

(d) We notice that $54/6$ equals 9, so we expect that $\frac{\sqrt{54}}{\sqrt{6}} = \sqrt{9}$. We can test this by squaring $\frac{\sqrt{54}}{\sqrt{6}}$:

$$\left(\frac{\sqrt{54}}{\sqrt{6}}\right)^2 = \frac{\left(\sqrt{54}\right)^2}{\left(\sqrt{6}\right)^2} = \frac{54}{6} = 9.$$

Since the square of $\frac{\sqrt{54}}{\sqrt{6}}$ is 9, we know that $\frac{\sqrt{54}}{\sqrt{6}} = \sqrt{9} = 3$.

Looking back at our first three parts, we see three examples in which

$$\sqrt{\frac{x^2}{y^2}} = \frac{\sqrt{x^2}}{\sqrt{y^2}}.$$

So, we expect that if a is nonnegative and b is positive, then

$$\frac{\sqrt{a}}{\sqrt{b}} = \sqrt{\frac{a}{b}}.$$

To see why this is true, we square $\frac{\sqrt{a}}{\sqrt{b}}$:

$$\left(\frac{\sqrt{a}}{\sqrt{b}}\right)^2 = \frac{\left(\sqrt{a}\right)^2}{\left(\sqrt{b}\right)^2} = \frac{a}{b}.$$

Since the square of $\frac{\sqrt{a}}{\sqrt{b}}$ is $\frac{a}{b}$, we have $\frac{\sqrt{a}}{\sqrt{b}} = \sqrt{\frac{a}{b}}$. (This probably isn't a surprise; it is just like our rule for multiplying square roots!)

> **Important:** If a is nonnegative and b is positive, then
>
> $$\frac{\sqrt{a}}{\sqrt{b}} = \sqrt{\frac{a}{b}}.$$

Applying this to our problem, we have

$$\frac{\sqrt{54}}{\sqrt{6}} = \sqrt{\frac{54}{6}} = \sqrt{9} = 3.$$

(e) We apply the principle we learned in the previous part, and then simplify the resulting fraction:

$$\frac{\sqrt{63}}{\sqrt{28}} = \sqrt{\frac{63}{28}} = \sqrt{\frac{9 \cdot 7}{4 \cdot 7}} = \sqrt{\frac{9}{4}} = \frac{3}{2}.$$

□

Problem 9.17:

(a) Compute $\sqrt{0.64}$.

(b) Compute $\sqrt{2.25}$.

(c) Evaluate $\sqrt{0.000169}$.

(d) What integer is closest to $\sqrt{14.4}$?

Solution for Problem 9.17:

(a) We know that $8^2 = 64$, but we want $\sqrt{0.64}$, not $\sqrt{64}$. We want the square root of a decimal, so we guess that the square root is also a decimal. A natural guess is that 0.8 is the square root of 0.64. We compute $0.8^2 = 0.64$, which tells us that $\sqrt{0.64} = 0.8$.

But what if we weren't able to guess the answer like this? We know how to deal with square roots of fractions, so we write the decimal as a fraction:

$$\sqrt{0.64} = \sqrt{\frac{64}{100}} = \frac{\sqrt{64}}{\sqrt{100}} = \frac{8}{10} = 0.8.$$

(b) We may recognize that $225 = 15^2$. We then note that $1.5^2 = 2.25$, so $\sqrt{2.25} = 1.5$.

As in part (a), we also could have converted the decimal into a fraction. We have $2.25 = 2 + 0.25 = 2 + \frac{1}{4} = \frac{9}{4}$, so

$$\sqrt{2.25} = \sqrt{\frac{9}{4}} = \frac{3}{2} = 1.5.$$

(c) First, we notice that $169 = 13^2$. Inspired by the first two parts, we might try 1.3, but

$$1.3^2 = 1.69,$$

not 0.000169. Squaring any number with only one digit past the decimal point results in a number with two digits after the decimal point. Let's see what happens when we square a number with two digits after the decimal point:

$$0.13^2 = 0.0169.$$

Squaring a number with two digits after the decimal point gives a number with four digits after the decimal point. Next, we try squaring a number with three digits after the decimal point:

$$0.013^2 = 0.000169.$$

As expected, squaring a number with three digits after the decimal point gives a number with six digits after the decimal point, and we see that $\sqrt{0.000169} = 0.013$.

We can use fractions to see why squaring a number with three digits after the decimal point gives a number with six digits after the decimal point. If a number has three digits after the decimal point, then it equals an integer divided by 10^3. When we square this quotient, we get an integer divided by 10^6, which is a decimal with six digits past the decimal point. For example, we have $0.013 = \frac{13}{1000} = \frac{13}{10^3}$, and

$$0.013^2 = \left(\frac{13}{10^3}\right)^2 = \frac{13^2}{(10^3)^2} = \frac{169}{10^{3\cdot2}} = \frac{169}{10^6} = 0.000169.$$

(d) We notice that 144 is 12^2, but this observation doesn't help us at all with this problem! We have $12^2 = 144$, which is too large, and $1.2^2 = 1.44$, which is too small, so knowing that $144 = 12^2$ doesn't give us a quick way to compute $\sqrt{14.4}$.

Fortunately, we aren't asked to compute $\sqrt{14.4}$. We are only asked to approximate it to the nearest integer. Since 14.4 is between 9 and 16, we know that $\sqrt{14.4}$ is between 3 and 4. Moreover, 14.4 is much closer to 16 than to 9, so we expect that $\sqrt{14.4}$ is closer to 4 than 3. We check by computing $3.5^2 = 12.25$. Since $3.5^2 < 14.4$, we know that $\sqrt{14.4} > 3.5$, which means the closest integer to $\sqrt{14.4}$ is 4.

$\square$

Problem 9.18: Is $\sqrt{4} + \sqrt{9}$ equal to $\sqrt{13}$?

Solution for Problem 9.18: Since $\sqrt{4} = 2$ and $\sqrt{9} = 3$, we have $\sqrt{4} + \sqrt{9} = 2 + 3 = 5$. Since $5 = \sqrt{25}$, not $\sqrt{13}$, we know that $\sqrt{4} + \sqrt{9}$ is *not* equal to $\sqrt{13}$. $\square$

WARNING!! If a and b are positive, then $\sqrt{a} + \sqrt{b}$ is **NEVER** equal to $\sqrt{a+b}$.

Let's take a look at another common mistake people make when working with square roots.

Problem 9.19: Is $\sqrt{5^2 + 12^2}$ equal to $5 + 12$?

Solution for Problem 9.19:   We have

$$\sqrt{5^2 + 12^2} = \sqrt{25 + 144} = \sqrt{169} = \sqrt{13^2} = 13,$$

and

$$5 + 12 = 17.$$

So, $\sqrt{5^2 + 12^2}$ is not equal to $5 + 12$. $\square$

> **WARNING!!**   If a and b are positive, then the value of $\sqrt{a^2 + b^2}$ is **NEVER** equal to $a + b$.

Problem 9.20:   In Section 9.1, we "simplified" square roots of perfect squares by writing them as integers. In Section 9.2, we discovered that some square roots cannot be expressed as integers. We say that we "simplify" such a square root when we write it in the form $a\sqrt{b}$ where a and b are integers and b has no perfect square factors besides 1. For example, we can simplify $\sqrt{12}$ as $2\sqrt{3}$.

(a) Confirm that $\sqrt{12}$ and $2\sqrt{3}$ are equal by squaring both.

(b) Simplify $\sqrt{18}$.

(c) Simplify $\sqrt{432}$.

(d) Simplify $\sqrt{1176}$.

Solution for Problem 9.20:

(a) We have $\left(\sqrt{12}\right)^2 = 12$ by the definition of square root. We also have

$$\left(2\sqrt{3}\right)^2 = 2^2\left(\sqrt{3}\right)^2 = 4(3) = 12.$$

If two nonnegative numbers have the same square, then the two numbers must be the same. So, because $\left(\sqrt{12}\right)^2 = \left(2\sqrt{3}\right)^2$, we know that $\sqrt{12} = 2\sqrt{3}$.

(b) We can use the fact that $\sqrt{ab} = \sqrt{a} \cdot \sqrt{b}$ to simplify:

$$\sqrt{18} = \sqrt{9 \cdot 2} = \sqrt{9} \cdot \sqrt{2} = 3\sqrt{2}.$$

Since 2 has no perfect square factors besides 1, we cannot simplify $\sqrt{2}$.

(c) We might notice right away that $432 = 144 \cdot 3$, so

$$\sqrt{432} = \sqrt{144 \cdot 3} = 12\sqrt{3}.$$

However, if we don't see this right away (and most people won't), we can simplify the square root in smaller steps. First, we take out two factors of 4:

$$\sqrt{432} = \sqrt{4 \cdot 108} = 2\sqrt{108} = 2\sqrt{4 \cdot 27} = 2 \cdot \sqrt{4} \cdot \sqrt{27} = 2 \cdot 2\sqrt{27} = 4\sqrt{27}.$$

Next, we note that 27 is divisible by the perfect square 9:

$$\sqrt{432} = 4\sqrt{27} = 4\sqrt{9 \cdot 3} = 4 \cdot \sqrt{9} \cdot \sqrt{3} = 4 \cdot 3\sqrt{3} = 12\sqrt{3}.$$

Since 3 has no perfect square factors besides 1, we cannot simplify further.

(d) Since the last two digits of 1176 form a number that is divisible by 4, we know that 1176 is divisible by 4. Therefore, we can start simplifying $\sqrt{1176}$ by writing

$$\sqrt{1176} = \sqrt{4 \cdot 294} = 2\sqrt{294}.$$

294 is not divisible by 4 or by 9. Rather than hunting for higher and higher square factors, we find the prime factorization of 294. This allows us to work with simpler numbers right away, since 294 is divisible by 2 and by 3 (but not by 4 or 9). We find that $294 = 2 \cdot 3 \cdot 7^2$. Aha! We've found another square factor:

$$\sqrt{1176} = 2\sqrt{294} = 2\sqrt{7^2 \cdot 2 \cdot 3} = 2 \cdot 7\sqrt{2 \cdot 3} = 14\sqrt{6}.$$

6 has no square factors besides 1, so we cannot simplify any further.

$\square$

Problem 9.21: Simplify $\sqrt{25x^8}$.

Solution for Problem 9.21:   We have $\sqrt{25x^8} = \sqrt{25} \cdot \sqrt{x^8} = 5\sqrt{x^8}$. Since $x^8 = x^{4 \cdot 2} = (x^4)^2$, we can simplify $\sqrt{x^8}$. We have

$$5\sqrt{x^8} = 5\sqrt{(x^4)^2} = 5x^4.$$

We can write $\sqrt{(x^4)^2} = x^4$ because x^4 is always nonnegative. $\square$

One reason we simplify radicals is so that it is clear when two numbers are the same. For example, if I get $\sqrt{12}$ as the answer to a problem, and someone else gets $2\sqrt{3}$, then only by simplifying my answer do we see that we have found the same answer. Our next problem gives us an even more convincing reason to simplify radicals.

Problem 9.22: What integer does $\sqrt{50} - \sqrt{18} - \sqrt{8}$ equal?

Solution for Problem 9.22: We start by simplifying the square roots. We find

$$\sqrt{50} = \sqrt{25 \cdot 2} = 5\sqrt{2},$$
$$\sqrt{18} = \sqrt{9 \cdot 2} = 3\sqrt{2},$$
$$\sqrt{8} = \sqrt{4 \cdot 2} = 2\sqrt{2},$$

so

$$\sqrt{50} - \sqrt{18} - \sqrt{8} = 5\sqrt{2} - 3\sqrt{2} - 2\sqrt{2}.$$

Since $\sqrt{2}$ is common to all three terms on the right side, we can simplify our result as follows:

$$\sqrt{50} - \sqrt{18} - \sqrt{8} = 5\sqrt{2} - 3\sqrt{2} - 2\sqrt{2}$$
$$= (5 - 3 - 2) \cdot \sqrt{2}$$
$$= 0 \cdot \sqrt{2}$$
$$= 0.$$

0 is *much* simpler than $\sqrt{50} - \sqrt{18} - \sqrt{8}$. $\square$

> **Concept:** Simplifying square roots sometimes allows us to simplify expressions.

Exercises

9.3.1 Evaluate the following expressions. As an extra challenge, try evaluating them without writing anything down. *(Source: MATHCOUNTS)*

(a) $\sqrt{2} \cdot \sqrt{18}$

(b) $\sqrt{8} \cdot \sqrt{50}$

(c) $\sqrt{120} \cdot \sqrt{30}$

(d) $\sqrt{6} \cdot \sqrt{15} \cdot \sqrt{10}$

(e) $\sqrt{50} \cdot \sqrt{6} \cdot \sqrt{27}$

(f) $2^3 + \sqrt{32} \cdot 2\sqrt{2} \div 8$

(g) $\sqrt{\frac{1}{9} + \frac{1}{16}}$

(h) $\sqrt{2\frac{1}{4}} + \sqrt{1\frac{7}{9}}$

(i) $\sqrt{0.000081}$

9.3.2 Let t be any number. Simplify $\sqrt{64t^{64}}$.

9.3.3 Find $\sqrt{250}$ to the nearest tenth, given that $\sqrt{10}$ to the nearest hundredth is 3.16.

9.3.4 Evaluate $\sqrt{x} \cdot \sqrt{z}$ if $x = \frac{5}{27}$ and $z = \frac{5}{3}$.

9.3.5 Let $A = \sqrt{1.44}$, $B = \frac{13}{11}$, $C = \sqrt{8} - 2\sqrt{2}$, and $D = \frac{3}{5} + \frac{3}{4}$. List the letters in order from least to greatest value. *(Source: MATHCOUNTS)*

9.3.6 Simplify each of the following:

(a) $\sqrt{363}$ (b) $\sqrt{525}$ (c) $\sqrt{3168}$

9.3.7 Simplify $3\sqrt{75} + 2\sqrt{27}$.

9.3.8★ Let x be a nonnegative number. Simplify $\sqrt{75x} \cdot \sqrt{2x} \cdot \sqrt{14x}$. *(Source: MATHCOUNTS)*

9.3.9★ Simplify $\frac{\sqrt{375}+\sqrt{60}}{\sqrt{5}}$.

9.4 Summary

Definition: The **square root** of a nonnegative number n is the nonnegative number whose square is n. We express the square root as $\sqrt{n}$, where the $\sqrt{}$ symbol is called a **radical**.

WARNING!! The square root of a nonnegative number is a nonnegative number by definition. For example, we have $\sqrt{16} = 4$. We *never* say that $\sqrt{16}$ is -4.

Square roots satisfy the following properties for all nonnegative numbers a and b:

- $\left(\sqrt{a}\right)^2 = a$

- $\sqrt{a^2} = a$

- $\sqrt{a} \cdot \sqrt{b} = \sqrt{ab}$

- If $b \neq 0$, then $\sqrt{\dfrac{a}{b}} = \dfrac{\sqrt{a}}{\sqrt{b}}$.

- If $a < b$, then $\sqrt{a} < \sqrt{b}$.

- If $\sqrt{a} > \sqrt{b}$, then $a > b$.

WARNING!! If a and b are positive, then $\sqrt{a} + \sqrt{b}$ is **NEVER** equal to $\sqrt{a + b}$.

WARNING!! If a and b are positive, then the value of $\sqrt{a^2 + b^2}$ is **NEVER** equal to $a + b$.

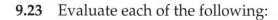

REVIEW PROBLEMS

9.23   Evaluate each of the following:

(a) $\sqrt{(27)(12)}$

(b) $\sqrt{2 \cdot 18 \cdot 40 \cdot 10}$

(c) $\sqrt{7 \cdot 2} \cdot \sqrt{2^3 \cdot 7^3}$

(d) $\sqrt{24} \cdot 2\sqrt{54}$

(e) $\sqrt{3} \cdot \sqrt{5} \cdot \sqrt{15}$

(f) $\sqrt{24} \cdot \sqrt{18} \cdot \sqrt{12}$

(g) $\sqrt{5\frac{4}{9}}$

(h) $\sqrt{12\frac{1}{4}}$

(i) $\sqrt{2.89}$

(j) $\dfrac{\sqrt{24}}{\sqrt{30}} \div \dfrac{\sqrt{20}}{3\sqrt{25}}$

(k) $\sqrt{3^5 + 3^5 + 3^5}$

(l) $\sqrt{5^5 + 5^5 + 5^5 + 5^5 + 5^5}$

9.24   What is the value of the expression $\sqrt{x^3 - 2^y}$ when $x = 5$ and $y = 2$? *(Source: MATHCOUNTS)*

9.25   Simplify $\sqrt{28 + \sqrt{1296}}$.

9.26   Which perfect cubes less than 100 have square roots that are integers?

9.27   If $x^2 = 16$, what is the sum of all possible values of x? *(Source: MATHCOUNTS)*

9.28   Find n if $\sqrt{n} = \sqrt{81} - \sqrt{16}$.

9.29

(a)   Solve the equation $\sqrt{9 + 4y} = 11$.

(b)   Solve the equation $6 - \sqrt{z + 1} = 9$.

9.30   What integer is closest to $-\sqrt{23}$?

9.31   For each of the following, state whether the expression is positive or negative:

(a) $10 - \sqrt{101}$

(b) $10 - 3\sqrt{11}$

(c) $4\sqrt{33} - 5\sqrt{21}$

9.32   How many integers are between $\sqrt{37}$ and $5\sqrt{11}$?

9.33   The formula $d = \sqrt{1.5h}$ gives the distance (d) in miles you can see to the horizon from a height of h feet above the earth. To the nearest mile, how many miles can you see to the horizon from the top of the Empire State Building at 1250 feet? *(Source: MATHCOUNTS)*

9.34   What is the greatest integer that is less than $\sqrt{80} + \sqrt{120}$?

9.35   Arrange the following numbers from least to greatest: $15, 4\sqrt{14}, 3\sqrt{26},$ and $6\sqrt{6}$.

9.36   Find the integer closest to $\sqrt{42.3}$.

9.37 What percent of $12\sqrt{12}$ is $3\sqrt{3}$? *(Source: MATHCOUNTS)*

9.38 Simplify each of the following:

(a) $\sqrt{360}$ (b) $\sqrt{936}$ (c) $\sqrt{10164}$

9.39 Find the integer nearest to $\sqrt{98} - \sqrt{50}$.

9.40 For how many positive integers k is $k\sqrt{5}$ less than 10?

9.41 Simplify $4\sqrt{60} - 2\sqrt{135}$.

9.42 Evaluate $\left(\sqrt{3} - \sqrt{27} + \sqrt{75}\right)^2$.

Challenge Problems ▶

9.43

(a) For what positive number t is $t^2 = 9^6$?

(b) For what positive number t is $t^2 = 9^5$?

9.44 Find z if $\frac{1}{\sqrt{z}} = 5$.

9.45 For how many different *negative* values of r is $\sqrt{r + 200}$ a positive integer?

9.46 The **geometric mean** of two nonnegative numbers is the square root of their product.

(a) What is the geometric mean of 24 and 150?

(b) Is it possible for the geometric mean of two non-integers to be an integer?

9.47 For what value of x does the square root of x^3 equal 27?

9.48 If the expression below equals an integer, what is the smallest possible value of n?

$$\sqrt{\frac{3}{1} \times \frac{4}{2} \times \frac{5}{3} \times \cdots \times \frac{n+2}{n}}$$

(Source: MATHCOUNTS)

9.49 Express $\dfrac{9}{2\sqrt{3}}$ so that there is no square root in the denominator. **Hints:** 157
(Source: MATHCOUNTS)

9.50 The square root of 5 is 2.236 to the nearest thousandth. Find $\sqrt{\frac{1}{5}}$ to the nearest hundredth.
(Source: MATHCOUNTS)

9.51 In this problem, we discover the number x such that $4^x = 2$.

(a) According to the laws of exponents, how can we write the product $4^x \cdot 4^x$ as a single power of 4?

(b) If $4^x = 2$, then what integer does $4^x \cdot 4^x$ equal?

(c) Use the first two parts to find x.

9.52 Just as the square root of a number m is the nonnegative number whose square equals m, the **cube root** of a number n is the number whose *cube* is n. We write the cube root of n as $\sqrt[3]{n}$. Similarly, $\sqrt[4]{n}$ is the nonnegative number whose fourth power is n.

(a) What is $\sqrt[3]{8}$?

(b) What is $\sqrt[3]{216}$?

(c) Is $\sqrt[3]{-1000}$ defined? If so, what is it?

(d) Find every integer that equals its own cube root.

(e) What is $\sqrt[4]{81}$?

(f) What is $\sqrt[4]{256}$?

9.53

(a) Compute $\left(\sqrt{11} - \sqrt{7} \right)\left(\sqrt{11} + \sqrt{7} \right)$.

(b) Express $\dfrac{1}{\sqrt{5} - \sqrt{2}}$ without square roots in the denominator.

9.54 What is the smallest positive integer k such that $\sqrt{84k}$ is an integer?

9.55 For what values of x does $7^2 + \frac{1}{x^2} = 25^2$?

9.56 Let x and y be two positive numbers such that

$$\frac{\left(\frac{1}{2}\right)^2 + \left(\frac{1}{3}\right)^2}{\left(\frac{1}{4}\right)^2 + \left(\frac{1}{5}\right)^2} = \frac{13x}{41y}.$$

Express $\sqrt{x} \div \sqrt{y}$ as a fraction. *(Source: MATHCOUNTS)*

9.57 Determine the values of x for which the expression $\sqrt{\frac{x+1}{x-1}}$ is not defined. *(Source: MATH-COUNTS)*

9.58 Find the sum of all values of r for which $\sqrt{(r-3)^2} = 9$.

9.59 Find all values of h such that $\dfrac{3\sqrt{27}}{h} = \dfrac{h}{27\sqrt{3}}$. **Hints:** 125

9.60 Solve for x: $\sqrt{5-2x} = \dfrac{10}{\sqrt{5-2x}}$. **Hints:** 68

9.61★ In Section 9.2, we used the following fact many times:

If a and b are nonnegative and $a > b$, then $\sqrt{a} > \sqrt{b}$.

In this problem, we explain why this is true. In the following parts, suppose that a and b are nonnegative.

(a) Show that if $\sqrt{a} > \sqrt{b}$, then $a > b$.

(b) Show that if $\sqrt{a} = \sqrt{b}$, then $a = b$.

(c) Show that if $\sqrt{a} < \sqrt{b}$, then $a < b$.

(d) Combine the first three parts to show that if $a > b$, then $\sqrt{a} > \sqrt{b}$.

9.62★ Let x be a number between 0 and 1. Show that $\sqrt{x}$ is greater than x. **Hints:** 92, 162

9.63★ For how many 2-digit integers n is $\sqrt{6n}$ an integer? **Hints:** 151, 5, 4

9.64★ In this problem, we show that $\sqrt{2}$ is an **irrational number**, which means that it cannot be expressed as a quotient of two integers. We will use a powerful technique called **proof by contradiction**. We start by imagining that we can write $\sqrt{2}$ as the quotient of two integers, and then show that this leads to something impossible.

(a) Suppose that we can express $\sqrt{2}$ as the quotient of two integers. We can express any quotient of two integers in simplest form, which means that the numerator and denominator have no common factors greater than 1. So, we suppose that there are some integers p and q for which $\sqrt{2} = \frac{p}{q}$, and $\frac{p}{q}$ is in simplest form. What must $\frac{p^2}{q^2}$ equal?

(b) Explain why p must be even.

(c) Since p must be even, there must be some integer r such that $p = 2r$. Use this to show that q must be even also.

(d) In the previous two parts, we showed that p and q are both even. Why does this contradict our setup in the first part? Why does this tell us that $\sqrt{2}$ is irrational?

 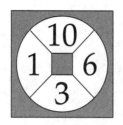 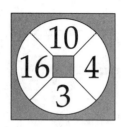 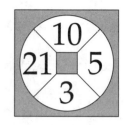

Our brain has two halves: one is responsible for the multiplication of polynomials and languages, and the other half is responsible for orientation of figures in space and all the things important in real life. Mathematics is geometry when you have to use both halves. – Vladimir Arnold

CHAPTER 10

Angles

For the next three chapters, we will cover a variety of topics in geometry. We will restrict our study to **planar** figures, which essentially are figures that can be drawn on a piece of paper.

In this chapter, we explore ways to describe and measure geometric figures called **angles**. We'll introduce many new terms throughout this chapter. Don't worry about memorizing all of them. As you use them, you'll learn them without having to memorize them.

10.1 Measuring Angles

A dot. A speck. In geometry, it's a **point**. If you lived on a point, you'd be awfully bored. There would be no up and down, no right and left. You couldn't move any amount in any direction.

$$\overset{\bullet}{P}$$

Figure 10.1: A Point

In order to tell one point from another, we usually label them with capital letters, such as point P in Figure 10.1 above.

$$A \bullet\!\!\-\!\!-\!\!-\!\!-\!\!-\!\!-\!\!-\!\!-\!\!-\!\!-\!\!\bullet B$$

Figure 10.2: A Segment

Now, say you got so bored on one point that you just had to go to another point. A straight path from one point to another is called a **line segment**, or just a **segment**. The two points at the ends of a segment are called the **endpoints** of the segment. We use these endpoints to label the segment. For example, $\overline{AB}$ in Figure 10.2 is the segment connecting A and B.

If we continue a segment forever past its endpoints in both directions, we form a **line**.

Figure 10.3: A Line

Line $\overleftrightarrow{AB}$ is shown in Figure 10.3. We sometimes use a lowercase letter to identify a line, such as line k in the figure. The arrows at the ends indicate that the line continues forever in both directions. We often leave off these arrows in diagrams.

If we instead continue the segment forever past only one endpoint, we'll trace out a path called a **ray**. The starting point of a ray is called the ray's **origin**, so point A is the origin of the ray below.

Figure 10.4: A Ray

We refer to the ray in Figure 10.4 as $\overrightarrow{AB}$. Note that we write the origin first in the name $\overrightarrow{AB}$; the ray above cannot be called $\overrightarrow{BA}$.

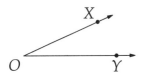

When two rays share an origin, they form an **angle**. In the diagram at the left, rays $\overrightarrow{OX}$ and $\overrightarrow{OY}$ share origin O. The common origin is called the **vertex** of the angle, and the rays $\overrightarrow{OX}$ and $\overrightarrow{OY}$ are called the **sides** of the angle. We use the symbol $\angle$ to indicate an angle, and we use a point on each side and the vertex to identify the angle. So, we can refer to the angle on the left as $\angle XOY$.

Notice that when we write the angle as $\angle XOY$, we put the vertex in the middle. We could also refer to the angle as $\angle YOX$, but not as $\angle XYO$. Sometimes we don't have to use three letters to refer to an angle. When it's very clear what angle we're talking about, we can just name it with the vertex: $\angle O$.

Two intersecting lines also make angles. Lines $\overleftrightarrow{AB}$ and $\overleftrightarrow{CD}$ at the right intersect at P. Here, we can't just write $\angle P$, since there are many different possible angles this could mean, such as $\angle APC$, $\angle APD$, $\angle DPB$, or $\angle BPC$. We might even be referring to $\angle APB$. Intersecting segments (including those that share an endpoint, such as $\overline{PD}$ and $\overline{PB}$ in the diagram) also form angles.

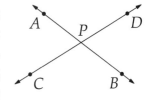

Now that we know what angles are, we need a way to measure them so that we can compare one angle to another.

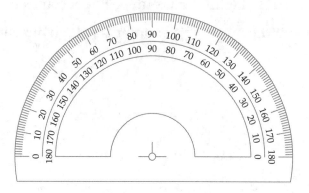

Figure 10.5: A Protractor

Just as we use a ruler to measure the lengths of segments, we use a **protractor** to measure angles. Roughly speaking, an angle's measure is how "open" the angle is. Our protractor above shows half a circle (which we call a **semicircle**) divided into 180 equal pieces. Each of these little pieces is one **degree** of the semicircle, so that an entire semicircle consists of 180 degrees. A full circle can be split into two semicircles, and each of these semicircles consists of 180 degrees. So, a full circle has 360 degrees. We use the symbol ° for degrees, so that a whole circle is 360°.

> **Sidenote:** Using 360 for the number of degrees in a circle comes from the ancient Babylonians. The Babylonians used a number system with 60 digits, instead of our decimal system, which only has 10 digits. When choosing a number of degrees for a whole circle, they were likely influenced by their number system and possibly by astronomy (a year has around 360 days).
>
> 360 is also a convenient choice for the number of degrees in a circle because it is divisible by lots of different numbers. We often work with angles whose measures are $\frac{1}{12}$, $\frac{1}{6}$, $\frac{1}{4}$, or $\frac{1}{3}$ of a circle. Using 360 as the number of degrees in a circle makes all of these angles have integer degree measures. Had we used 100 degrees for a circle instead, we'd have to deal with measures such as $12\frac{1}{2}$ degrees, $8\frac{1}{3}$ degrees, and so on.

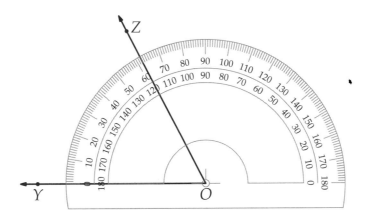

Figure 10.6: Measuring an Angle

Figure 10.6 shows how we use a protractor to measure an angle. We place the protractor on the angle so that the vertex of the angle is at the center point of the protractor, and one side of the angle is along the "zero line" along the bottom of the protractor. We then read that there are 62 degrees between sides $\overrightarrow{OZ}$ and $\overrightarrow{OY}$ of $\angle YOZ$, so we say that $\angle YOZ = 62°$. Sometimes angle measures are written with an m before $\angle$ to indicate measure: $m\angle YOZ = 62°$.

Problems

Problem 10.1: Find the measures of $\angle AOB$, $\angle CXD$, $\angle DXE$, and $\angle CXE$. (You should use a protractor for this problem.)

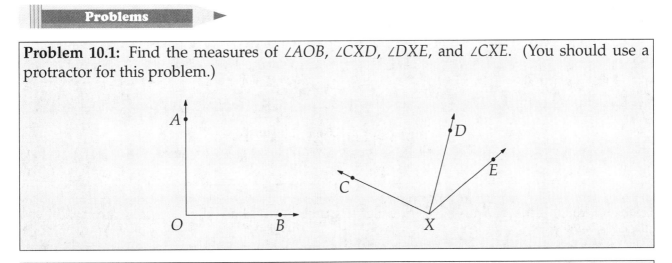

Problem 10.2: The clock at the right shows a time of 3:30.

(a) What is the measure of the smaller angle between the hour and minute hands of a clock at 5 p.m.?

(b) What is the measure of the smaller angle between the hour and minute hands of a clock at 5:24 p.m.?

Problem 10.3: Find the value of x in the diagram below without using a protractor.

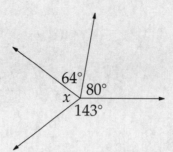

Problem 10.4: In the figure below, AOB is a straight line. What is the measure of $\angle AOB$?

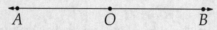

Problem 10.5: In the figure, lines $\overleftrightarrow{PQ}$ and $\overleftrightarrow{RS}$ meet at point O and $\angle SOP = 37°$. What is the measure of $\angle POR$?

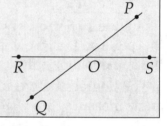

Problem 10.6: Lines $\overleftrightarrow{WX}$ and $\overleftrightarrow{YZ}$ intersect at point P such that $\angle YPX = 61°$. Find $\angle WPZ$.

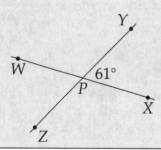

Problem 10.7: Lines $\overleftrightarrow{WX}$ and $\overleftrightarrow{YZ}$ intersect at point P. Explain why we must always have $\angle WPZ = \angle YPX$.

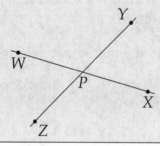

Problem 10.8: The measure of one angle formed by two intersecting lines is three times the measure of another angle formed by the lines. In this problem, we find the measures of the angles formed by the lines.

(a) Draw a diagram for the problem.

(b) Let x be the measure of the smaller angle mentioned in the problem. Find the measure of each angle in the diagram in terms of x. Write these measures in your diagram.

(c) Find the measures of all angles formed by the lines.

Problem 10.1: Find the measures of $\angle AOB$, $\angle CXD$, $\angle DXE$, and $\angle CXE$. (You should use a protractor for this problem.)

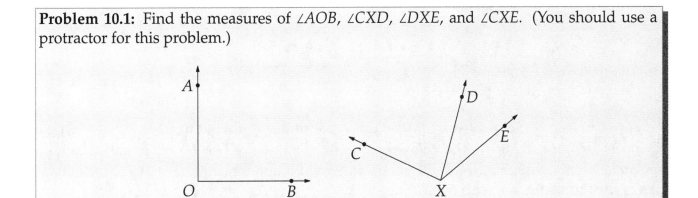

Solution for Problem 10.1: Here are the steps we follow to use our protractor to measure angles:

1. Place the protractor on the angle so that the vertex of the angle is exactly where the center of the circle would be if the protractor were a whole circle. Your protractor should clearly show this center point: it's near the middle of the straight side.

2. Turn the protractor so that one side of the angle is along the "zero line," which is the line through the center point along the straight edge of the protractor.

3. Find where the other side of the angle meets the curved side of the protractor. (We may need to extend this side of the angle to reach the curved side of the protractor.) There should be two numbers where this side meets the curved edge. If less than half the protractor's semicircle is inside the angle, then the measure of the angle is the smaller number of degrees. Otherwise, the measure is the larger number of degrees. If the numbers are equal, then both equal the measure of the angle.

Extra! *[The universe] cannot be read until we have learned the language and become familiar*
▪▪▶ ▪▪▶ ▪▪▶ ▪▪▶ *with the characters in which it is written. It is written in mathematical language, and the letters are triangles, circles and other geometrical figures, without which means it is humanly impossible to comprehend a single word.*

–Galileo Galilei

For ∠AOB, we put our protractor on the page as shown below. We line up side $\overrightarrow{OB}$ of the angle with the zero line of the protractor, placing the center point of the protractor over O. We find that side $\overrightarrow{OA}$ hits the curved edge at 90°.

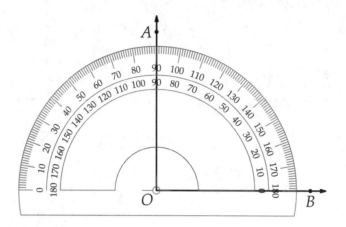

When we follow this procedure with ∠CXD, we find that there are two numbers where $\overrightarrow{XD}$ meets the curved edge in the following diagram. Since ∠CXD is less than half the entire semicircle, its measure must be the smaller of the two numbers where $\overrightarrow{XD}$ meets the curved edge of the protractor. So, we have ∠CXD = 80°.

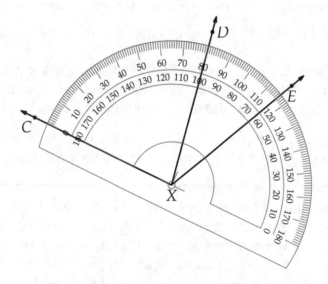

We can also use the diagram above to find the measure of ∠CXE. Once again, our angle hits a point on the curved edge with two numbers, but this time we know the angle is greater than 90° (since the angle is more than half the semicircle). Thus, we know that ∠CXE = 116°. We can also use this placement of the protractor to measure ∠DXE. Since $\overrightarrow{XE}$ meets the curved edge of the protractor at 116 and $\overrightarrow{XD}$ hits it at 80, we see that ∠DXE cuts off 116 − 80 = 36 degrees. So, we have ∠DXE = 36°.

We could also have placed the protractor as in the diagram below to find that ∠DXE = 36°.

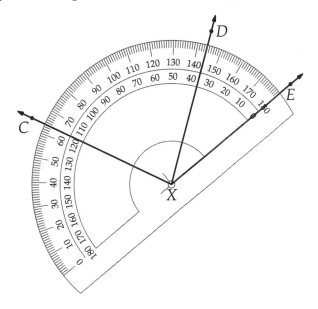

Notice that ∠CXD + ∠DXE = ∠CXE. This isn't a coincidence! Since ∠CXD and ∠DXE share a side and a vertex, putting them together gives ∠CXE. If two angles share a vertex and a side, we call the angles **adjacent**. □

We saw in Problem 10.1 that knowing whether an angle is greater than or less than 90° is necessary for finding its measure using a protractor. This 90° is such an important measure that 90° angles have a special name, **right angles**. We usually mark right angles with a little box as shown in ∠JKL at the right. Two lines, rays, or line segments that form a right angle are said to be **perpendicular**. $\overline{JK}$ and $\overline{KL}$ are perpendicular in the diagram; we can use the symbol ⊥ to write this as $\overline{JK} \perp \overline{KL}$.

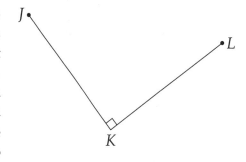

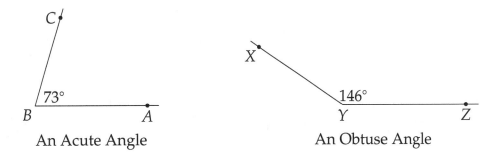

An Acute Angle   An Obtuse Angle

Angles that are less than 90° are called **acute**, and those that are greater than 90° but less than 180° are called **obtuse**. Sometimes we write the measure of an angle inside the angle as shown above.

Problem 10.2: The clock at the right shows a time of 3:30.

(a) What is the measure of the smaller angle between the hour and minute hands of a clock at 5 p.m.?

(b) What is the measure of the smaller angle between the hour and minute hands of a clock at 5:24 p.m.?

Solution for Problem 10.2:

(a) The twelve hour marks are evenly spaced around the clock, so each two consecutive marks are 360/12 = 30 degrees apart. For example, the mark for 1 o'clock is 30 degrees from the mark for 2 o'clock. At 5 p.m., the minute hand is pointing at the mark for 12 o'clock and the hour hand is pointing directly at the mark for 5 o'clock. These two marks are $5 \cdot 30 = 150$ degrees apart, so the angle between the hour and minute hands is 150°.

Notice that we ask for the smaller angle because there's another angle between the two hands—the angle formed by going the "long way" around from the minute hand to hour hand. Such an angle is called a **reflex angle**, which you'll investigate in the exercises.

(b) What's wrong with this solution:

> **Bogus Solution:** There are 60 minutes in an hour, so each minute corresponds to 360/60 = 6 degrees. At 5:24, the minute hand points at minute 24. Each pair of consecutive hour marks is 60/12 = 5 minutes apart, so at 5:24 the hour hand points at minute $5 \cdot 5 = 25$. Therefore, the minute and hour hands are only 1 minute apart, which means the angle between them is 6°.

The Bogus Solution is incorrect because the hour hand moves between 5:00 and 5:24, too! During a full hour, the hour hand moves 30 degrees, since it moves from one hour mark to the next mark. So, in 24 minutes, the hour hand moves $\frac{24}{60}$ of 30 degrees, which is

$$\frac{24}{60} \cdot 30 = \frac{2}{5} \cdot 30 = 12$$

degrees. The minute hand moves 360/60 = 6 degrees each minute. At 5:25, the minute hand will point at the 5 o'clock mark on the clock. So, at 5:24, the minute hand is 6 degrees shy of the 5 o'clock mark. Since the hour hand is 12 degrees past the 5 o'clock mark on the clock, the angle between the hands measures 6 + 12 = 18 degrees.

Another way we can think about the location of the hour hand is to think about how much the hour hand moves each minute. Since the hour hand moves 30 degrees in an hour, it moves 0.5 degrees each minute. So, in 24 minutes, it moves 12 degrees past minute 25. The minute hand is 6 degrees before minute 25 at 5:24, so the two hands are 18 degrees apart.

$\square$

Problem 10.3: Find the value of x in the diagram at the right without using a protractor.

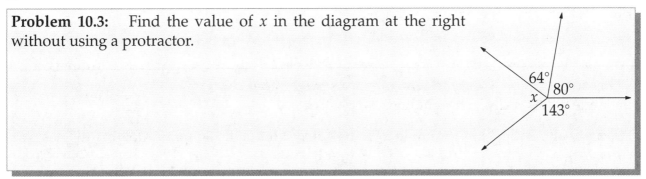

Solution for Problem 10.3: Imagine we had a protractor that had a full circle instead of just a semicircle. Since a semicircular protractor has 180 degrees, the full circular one has 360 degrees, as shown below.

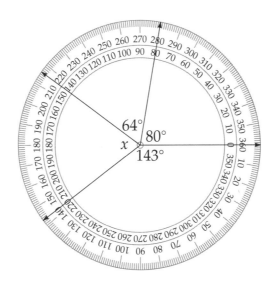

Of course, the problem says we can't use a protractor to measure the angle! However, thinking about this circular protractor lets us see that the measures of the four angles around the central point must add up to 360 degrees. So, $x + 80° + 64° + 143° = 360°$, which means $x = 73°$. $\square$

Problem 10.4: In the figure below, AOB is a straight line. What is the measure of $\angle AOB$?

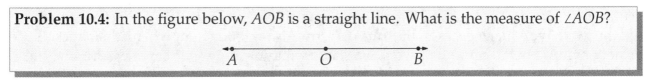

Solution for Problem 10.4: If we don't see the answer right away, we can try to figure out what portion of a circle the angle cuts off. We draw a circle with center O as in the diagram to the right. Now we can see that the angle cuts off half a circle (whichever side of the line we pick). So,

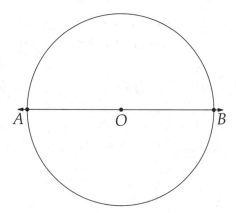

$$\angle AOB = \frac{1}{2}(360°) = 180°.$$

This angle's name is easy to remember: a **straight angle** is an angle that is really a straight line. □

Straight angles appear too simple to be useful, but often the simplest tools are the best.

Problem 10.5: In the figure, lines $\overleftrightarrow{PQ}$ and $\overleftrightarrow{RS}$ meet at O and we have $\angle SOP = 37°$. What is the measure of $\angle POR$?

Solution for Problem 10.5: Since $\angle SOP$ and $\angle POR$ together make $\angle ROS$, which is a straight angle, we know that $\angle SOP + \angle POR = 180°$. So, we have $\angle POR = 180° - \angle SOP = 180° - 37° = 143°$. □

Two angles that add to $180°$ are called **supplementary angles**, and each angle is called a **supplement** of the other. As we have seen, when two lines intersect like $\overleftrightarrow{PQ}$ and $\overleftrightarrow{RS}$ in Problem 10.5, any two adjacent angles thus formed are supplementary because together they make a straight angle.

Similarly, angles that add to $90°$ are called **complementary angles**, and each angle is called a **complement** of the other.

Problem 10.6: Lines $\overleftrightarrow{WX}$ and $\overleftrightarrow{YZ}$ intersect at point P such that $\angle YPX = 61°$. Find $\angle WPZ$.

Solution for Problem 10.6: Angle YPX sure looks equal in measure to $\angle WPZ$, and it "makes sense" that the two have equal measures, but "makes sense" isn't good enough in mathematics. Since it's not obvious how to compute $\angle WPZ$, we start by finding angles we can measure.

> **Concept:** When you can't find the answer right away, try finding whatever you can—you might discover something that leads to the answer. Better yet, you might learn something even more interesting than the answer. The best problem solvers are explorers.

Since $\angle YPX$ and $\angle WPY$ together make a straight angle, we have $\angle YPX + \angle WPY = 180°$. Thus, $\angle WPY = 180° - \angle YPX = 180° - 61° = 119°$.

Similarly, since $\angle WPY$ and $\angle WPZ$ together make a straight angle, we have

$$\angle WPZ = 180° - \angle WPY = 180° - 119° = 61°.$$

☐

As we thought, we do indeed have $\angle WPZ = \angle YPX$ in Problem 10.6. Let's see if that's just a coincidence.

Problem 10.7: Lines $\overleftrightarrow{WX}$ and $\overleftrightarrow{YZ}$ intersect at point P. Explain why we must always have $\angle WPZ = \angle YPX$.

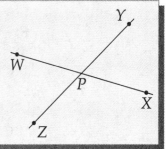

Solution for Problem 10.7: What's wrong with this explanation:

> **Bogus Solution:** Suppose $\angle YPX = 72°$. Since $\angle WPX$ is a straight angle, we know that $\angle WPY = 180° - 72° = 108°$. Similarly, we have $\angle WPZ = 180° - \angle WPY = 72°$. Therefore, $\angle WPZ = \angle YPX$.

Every statement in the Bogus Solution is true. However, it doesn't tell us that we *always* have $\angle WPZ = \angle YPX$ no matter what measure $\angle YPX$ has. It only tell us what happens when $\angle YPX = 72°$. What if $\angle YPX$ has a different measure?

Fortunately, we can use our example as a guide to show that we always have $\angle WPZ = \angle YPX$. Since $\overleftrightarrow{WPX}$ is a line, we have

$$\angle YPX = 180° - \angle WPY.$$

Since $\overleftrightarrow{YPZ}$ is a line, we have

$$\angle WPZ = 180° - \angle WPY.$$

Combining these two equations gives $\angle YPX = 180° - \angle WPY = \angle WPZ$.

This explanation is a long way of saying, "Since $\angle YPX$ and $\angle WPZ$ are supplementary to the same angle, we must have $\angle YPX = \angle WPZ$." ☐

Notice that our explanation does not depend at all on the measure of ∠YPX. The explanation works no matter how the lines intersect.

When two lines intersect, angles that are opposite each other are called **vertical angles**. So, ∠WPZ and ∠YPX in the diagram below are vertical angles. (Yes, this is a bit of a weird name—they don't look "vertical"!) As we showed in Problem 10.7, vertical angles always have the same measure.

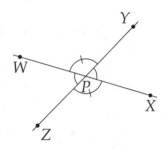

Congruent angles are angles that have the same measure. We often use little arcs to mark congruent angles. In the diagram to the right, ∠WPZ and ∠YPX each have a single little arc in them to show that they are equal. Angles ∠WPY and ∠XPZ also are vertical angles, so they are equal. We put a little tick mark on the arcs at these angles to show that these two angles are equal to each other, but not necessarily equal to our first pair of equal angles (which have arcs without tick marks).

> **Important:** Supplementary, right, obtuse, vertical, acute... by now the number of new names must be driving you nuts. Don't memorize what all these names mean now. The names are not that important. Besides, as you continue your study of geometry, you'll eventually see them so much you'll just know them anyway.
>
> The concepts are more important than the words for solving problems. "Angles like ∠WPZ and ∠YPX in Problem 10.7 are congruent" means something without any more information. "Vertical angles are congruent" doesn't tell you anything until you reach for your math dictionary to look up vertical angles.
>
> The words will be important for communicating the concepts. For now, though, focus on the ideas. The words will come naturally.

Problem 10.8: The measure of one angle formed by two intersecting lines is three times the measure of another angle formed by the lines. Find the measures of all angles formed by the lines.

Solution for Problem 10.8: We start with the diagram at the right. Intersecting lines form two pairs of congruent angles, as shown. We let x be the measure of each of the smaller angles. The problem tells us that each of the other two angles has measure $3x$. We label all four angles with their measures. We now have angles with measures x and $3x$ that together form a line. This gives us $x + 3x = 180°$, so $4x = 180°$ and $x = 45°$. Therefore, two of the angles formed by the lines have measure 45° and the other two have measure $3x = 135°$. □

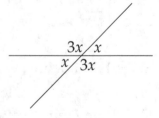

Drawing the initial diagram in Problem 10.8 and adding the expressions for the angle measures to the diagram made seeing the solution much easier.

> **Concept:** If a geometry problem doesn't have a diagram, draw one yourself. As you find information about the diagram, such as expressions for angle measures, include that information in the diagram.

Exercises

10.1.1 In the diagram at the left below, $\angle ABC$ is a right angle and $\angle XBC = 28°$. What is the measure of $\angle ABX$?

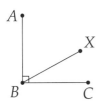

Figure 10.7: Diagram for Problem 10.1.1   Figure 10.8: Diagram for Problem 10.1.2

10.1.2 In the diagram on the right above, the five rays are equally spaced around the central point. What is the measure of each of the acute angles thus formed?

10.1.3 Unless you have an itty-bitty protractor, the sides of the angle shown at the right probably don't reach the curved edge of your protractor. How can you still use your protractor to measure the angle? What is the measure of the angle?

10.1.4 Line k in the diagram on the right is a straight line. What is the value of x?

$$x° + 10° \quad x°$$

k

10.1.5 Ray $\overrightarrow{BX}$ divides right angle $\angle ABC$ into $\angle ABX$ and $\angle CBX$. If the ratio of their measures is $1 : 5$, what is the measure of the smaller angle?

10.1.6 The measure of an angle is $15°$ more than twice its supplement. Find the measure of the angle.

10.1.7 In our solution to Problem 10.2, we found that the hands of a clock make an angle of $18°$ at 5:24. But the $18°$ angle is not the only angle between the hands that we might measure. We might instead go the "long way around" to get from one hand to other. The "long way around" angle is called a **reflex angle**. Such an angle is marked with the arc in the diagram to the right. What is the measure of the reflex angle between the hands of a clock at 5:24? (Note: we are always referring to the non-reflex angle between two rays if we don't specifically say "reflex angle" when referring to the angle.)

10.1.8 Martians measure angles in clerts. There are 500 clerts in a full circle. How many clerts are in a right angle? *(Source: AMC 8)*

10.1.9★ In the diagram at the left below, three segments intersect at O, and $\overline{OD}$ divides $\angle COE$ into two equal angles. The ratio of $\angle COB$ to $\angle BOF$ is $7:2$. What is the number of degrees in $\angle COD$? *(Source: MATHCOUNTS)*

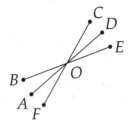

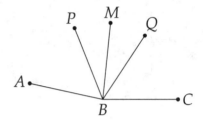

Figure 10.9: Diagram for Problem 10.1.9   Figure 10.10: Diagram for Problem 10.1.10

10.1.10★ In the diagram on the right above, $\overline{BM}$ divides $\angle ABC$ into two angles with the same measure. $\overline{BP}$ and $\overline{BQ}$ divide $\angle ABC$ into three angles with the same measure. If $\angle MBQ = 28°$, then what is $\angle CBP$?

10.2   Parallel Lines

Having learned about what happens when two lines meet, we should wonder about what happens if they don't. If two lines in a plane do not meet, we say that they are **parallel**. We can indicate that lines $\overleftrightarrow{AB}$ and $\overleftrightarrow{CD}$ are parallel by writing $\overleftrightarrow{AB} \parallel \overleftrightarrow{CD}$.

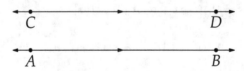

As shown above, we can use little arrows to mark lines that are parallel. Those little arrows can really clutter up a diagram, so we won't always include them.

Problems

Problem 10.9: Draw a pair of parallel lines like those shown below. Then draw a line that crosses both of the parallel lines. With a protractor, measure all the angles formed between your line and both of the parallel lines. Write the angle measures in the angles you form. Try it again with a different pair of parallel lines. Do you notice anything interesting?

Problem 10.10: Lines m and n are parallel, and we are given the measure of one angle in the diagram as shown. Find the values of $a, b, c, w, x, y,$ and z.

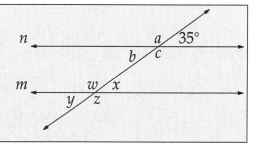

Problem 10.11: A chicken starts at point X on one side of a road. It starts walking across the road along a path that makes a 22° angle with the side of the road, as shown. Before making it to the other side, the chicken makes a sharp turn (at point Y) and starts along a new path, which makes a 71° angle with the old path, as shown. If the opposite sides of the road are parallel, what is the measure of the acute angle that the path of the chicken makes with the far side of the road at point Z?

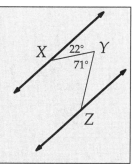

We start studying parallel lines by taking a look at the angles formed when a line intersects a pair of parallel lines.

Problem 10.9: Draw a pair of parallel lines like those shown below. Then draw a line that crosses both of the parallel lines. With a protractor, measure all the angles formed between your line and both of the parallel lines. Write the angle measures in the angles you form. Try it again with a different pair of parallel lines. Do you notice anything interesting?

Solution for Problem 10.9: In the diagram to the right, we have parallel lines $\overleftrightarrow{CG}$ and $\overleftrightarrow{DF}$, and we have added line $\overleftrightarrow{EH}$, which meets $\overleftrightarrow{CG}$ and $\overleftrightarrow{DF}$ at A and B, respectively. We call a line that cuts across parallel lines a **transversal**. Measuring all 8 angles in the diagram, we find the measures shown. There are two groups of 4 equal angles!

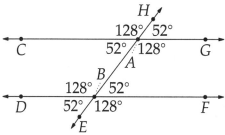

We could have seen that some of these angles are equal without using a protractor. We must have $\angle HAG = \angle BAC$ and $\angle ABF = \angle DBE$ because these are pairs of vertical angles. But why are the acute angles at A equal to the acute angles at B?

One way to see why is to imagine sliding line $\overleftrightarrow{DF}$ on top of $\overleftrightarrow{CG}$ so that point B is on top of point A. Then, $\angle ABF$ would be right on top of $\angle HAG$. This isn't a proof, but it does give us some idea why these angles have the same measure.

Each obtuse angle in the diagram can be combined with one of the acute angles to form a straight line. So, each obtuse angle is supplementary to each acute angle. □

Important: ⚠️ The angles formed when a transversal intersects two parallel lines come in two groups of four equal angles as shown:

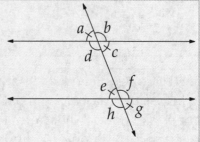

$$a = c = e = g$$
$$b = d = f = h$$

Each of the first set of angles is supplementary to each of the second set of angles. That is, the sum of any angle in the first group and any angle in the second group is 180°. So, either all 8 angles are right angles, or 4 of them are acute while the other 4 are obtuse.

Problem 10.10: Lines m and n are parallel, and we are given the measure of one angle in the diagram as shown. Find the values of $a, b, c, w, x, y,$ and z.

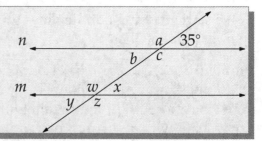

Solution for Problem 10.10: When a transversal intersects parallel lines, equal angles come in groups of four as we saw in Problem 10.9. Therefore, we know that $b = x = y = 35°$. We also know that each angle in the other "group of four" has a measure that is supplementary to 35°:

$$a = c = w = z = 180° - 35° = 145°.$$

□

We have seen that a transversal forms two sets of four equal angles when it intersects two parallel lines. We can use these relationships in reverse! That is, we can use the angle relationships we just learned to figure out when lines are parallel.

For example, in the diagram at the right, line j intersects lines k and ℓ. If we can determine that $x = t$ or $x = u$, then we know that $k \parallel \ell$. Similarly if we determine that $x + v = 180°$ or $x + s = 180°$, then we know that $k \parallel \ell$.

Now that we understand the relationships between angles when a transversal intersects parallel lines, let's try a more challenging problem.

Problem 10.11: A chicken starts at point X on one side of a road. It starts walking across the road along a path that makes a 22° angle with the side of the road, as shown. Before making it to the other side, the chicken makes a sharp turn (at point Y) and starts along a new path, which makes a 71° angle with the old path, as shown. If the opposite sides of the road are parallel, what is the measure of the acute angle that the path of the chicken makes with the far side of the road at point Z?

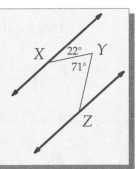

Solution for Problem 10.11: We'd like to use what we know about parallel lines and angles, but neither $\overline{XY}$ nor $\overline{YZ}$ intersects both sides of the road. So, we add a third line, through point Y and parallel to both sides of the road, as shown in the diagram below. We'll label this line ℓ, and let the sides of the road be j and k. Both $\overline{XY}$ and $\overline{YZ}$ are transversals that intersect a pair of parallel lines. Now we can use what we know about angles and parallel lines.

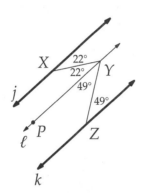

Since $j \parallel \ell$, we know that the acute angle that $\overline{XY}$ makes with ℓ equals the acute angle $\overline{XY}$ makes with j. We include this information in the diagram by writing 22° inside $\angle PYX$ in our diagram. We then find $\angle PYZ$ by subtracting $\angle PYX$ from the value of $\angle XYZ$ that we are given in the problem. We find that

$$\angle PYZ = \angle XYZ - \angle XYP = 71° - 22° = 49°.$$

Finally, because $\ell \parallel k$, the acute angle that $\overline{YZ}$ makes with k is congruent to the acute angle $\overline{YZ}$ makes with ℓ. So the path of the chicken makes a 49° angle with the far side of the road. □

As seen in Problem 10.11, parallel lines are so helpful that sometimes we add an extra parallel line to a problem in order to find a solution.

Concept: There's more than meets the eye in many geometry problems! Sometimes we have to add more to an initial diagram in order to solve a problem.

Exercises

10.2.1 In the diagram on the right, we have $\overline{AB} \parallel \overline{CD}$ and $\overline{AD} \parallel \overline{BC}$. If $\angle A = 73°$, then what is the measure of $\angle C$?

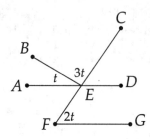

10.2.2 In the diagram on the left below, we have $j \parallel k$. Find x.

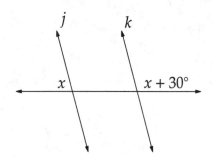

Figure 10.11: Diagram for Problem 10.2.2   Figure 10.12: Diagram for Problem 10.2.3

10.2.3 In the diagram on the right above, $\overline{AD}$ and $\overline{CF}$ intersect at point E, and $\overline{AD} \parallel \overline{FG}$. We also have $\angle CEB = 3\angle AEB$ and $\angle EFG = 2\angle AEB$, as shown. Find the measure of $\angle CED$ in degrees.

10.2.4 Lines j and k are parallel. If line ℓ is perpendicular to line j, then must line ℓ be perpendicular to line k?

10.2.5 If I draw 8 parallel lines on a piece of paper, into how many different non-overlapping regions will the lines divide the paper?

10.2.6 In the diagram, line d is perpendicular to line a, and line d is parallel to line c. Line b passes through the intersection of lines a and c. If the acute angle between lines a and b measures $47°$, then what is the measure of the acute angle between lines b and d?

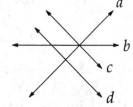

10.2.7 Line m intersects lines j and k forming angles with the measures shown at the right. Are lines j and k parallel?

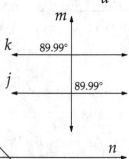

10.2.8★ Lines m and n are parallel. Two rays are drawn from point A, forming angles with m and n with the measures shown. What is the measure of the acute angle formed by these two rays?
Hints: 56

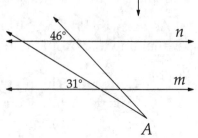

10.3 Angles in Polygons

A **polygon** is a simple closed figure consisting entirely of line segments. By "closed figure," we mean that if we trace the entire figure, our start point and end point are the same. By "simple," we mean that the figure does not intersect itself. Three polygons are shown on the left below. Three figures that are not polygons are shown on the right below.

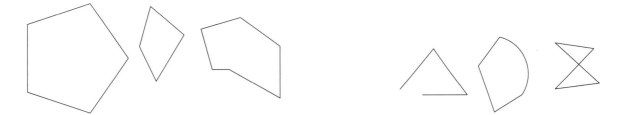

The line segments that form the boundaries of a polygon are the **sides** of the polygon. If we connect two vertices that are not adjacent on the polygon, we form a **diagonal**, such as diagonal $\overline{AE}$ in the diagram.

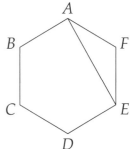

Each pair of consecutive sides of a polygon meet at a **vertex** of the polygon. An **interior angle** is an angle inside a polygon that is formed by a pair of consecutive sides of the polygon.

We often refer to polygons by their vertices, such as hexagon $ABCDEF$ above. When referring to a polygon by its vertices, we list the vertices in order going around the polygon. We can start with any vertex and go in either order around the polygon. So, we could refer to the polygon above as $DCBAFE$, but we wouldn't refer to it as $ACFEDB$.

You're already familiar with many polygons—triangles, squares, and rectangles are all polygons. We sometimes include the triangle symbol, $\triangle$, to make clear that we are referring to a triangle, not an angle. So, $\triangle ABC$ refers to triangle ABC while $\angle ABC$ refers to angle ABC.

We have special names for some polygons based on the number of sides they have:

Number of sides	Polygon name
3	triangle
4	quadrilateral
5	pentagon
6	hexagon
7	heptagon
8	octagon
9	nonagon
10	decagon
12	dodecagon

Problem 10.12:

(a) Use a protractor to find the measures of the three angles in each of the triangles below.

(b) Can you guess a statement that is always true about the sum of the interior angles in a triangle?

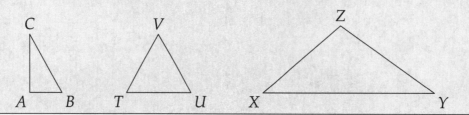

Problem 10.13: In the diagram below, we have drawn $\overleftrightarrow{DE}$ through A parallel to $\overline{BC}$. Our goal in this problem is to explain why our guess from the previous problem is correct.

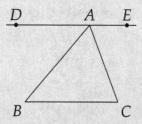

(a) Find an angle in the diagram that must be equal to $\angle ABC$.

(b) Find an angle in the diagram that must be equal to $\angle ACB$.

(c) Explain why the sum of the interior angles in any triangle must be 180°.

Problem 10.14: The measure of one angle of a triangle is double the measure of another angle of the triangle, and 15 degrees greater than the measure of the third angle of the triangle. What are the measures of the angles of the triangle?

Problem 10.15: A triangle is a **right triangle** if one of its angles is right. A triangle is an **obtuse triangle** if one of its angles is obtuse, and a triangle is an **acute triangle** if all three of its angles are acute.

(a) Is it possible for a triangle to have more than one angle that is right or obtuse?

(b) Explain why the acute angles in a right triangle must sum to 90°.

(c) If the measures of two angles of a triangle have a sum equal to the measure of the third angle, must the triangle be a right triangle?

Problem 10.16:

(a) What is the sum of the measures of the interior angles of a square?

(b) Draw 2 quadrilaterals that are not squares and measure their interior angles with a protractor. Sum the resulting measures for each quadrilateral. Notice anything interesting?

(c) Make a conjecture (guess) about the sum of the interior angles of a quadrilateral based on your observations in the first two parts. Use what you know about triangles to explain why your guess is correct.

Problem 10.17: Our goal in this problem is to find the value of x in the diagram below.

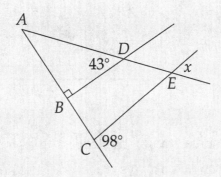

(a) Find the measures of the interior angles of $\triangle ABD$.

(b) Find the measures of the interior angles of $BCED$.

(c) Find x.

Problem 10.18:

(a) What is the sum of the interior angles of a pentagon? Of a hexagon?

(b) Find a formula for the sum of the interior angles of a polygon with n sides.

(c) A **regular polygon** is a polygon in which all of the sides have the same length and all of the angles have the same measure. What is the measure of each interior angle of a regular pentagon? Of a regular octagon?

Problem 10.19: The pentagon in the diagram below is regular. Find angle measure x.

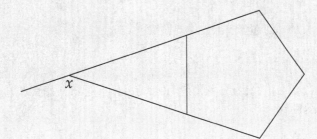

Problem 10.20: When we extend the sides of a triangle past the vertices, we form **exterior angles** of the triangle. For example, the angles with measures x, y, and z on the right are exterior angles of $\triangle ABC$, while the angles with measures a, b, and c are interior angles of the triangle.

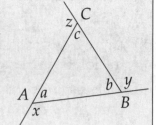

(a) What is $a + b + c$?

(b) What is $a + x$?

(c) What is $x + y + z$?

(d) Suppose you start at A facing B, walk along $\overline{AB}$ to vertex B, then turn towards C and walk along $\overline{BC}$ to C, then turn towards A and walk along $\overline{CA}$ back to your starting point, then turn towards B. How does this "trip" give us a quick explanation for the answer to part (c)?

Problem 10.12:

(a) Use a protractor to find the measures of the three angles in each of the triangles below.

(b) Can you guess a statement that is always true about the sum of the interior angles in a triangle?

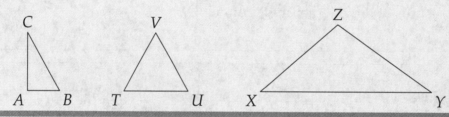

Solution for Problem 10.12:

(a) Using a protractor to measure the angles, we find the following measures:

$$\begin{array}{cccc}
\triangle ABC & \angle A = 90° & \angle B = 60° & \angle C = 30° \\
\triangle TUV & \angle T = 60° & \angle U = 60° & \angle V = 60° \\
\triangle XYZ & \angle X = 40° & \angle Y = 35° & \angle Z = 105°
\end{array}$$

(b) In each triangle, the sum of the angles is $180°$.

$\square$

Is it just a coincidence that the sum of the angles is the same for all three triangles in Problem 10.12? Let's investigate.

Problem 10.13: Show that the sum of the measures of the interior angles of any triangle is $180°$.

Solution for Problem 10.13: We start by drawing a triangle and by writing what we want to show is true:

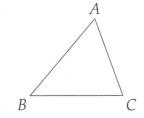

$$\angle ABC + \angle CAB + \angle BCA = 180°.$$

We don't know much about angles yet, but we do have one clue for the next step. We might wonder, "*Where have we seen* 180° *before?*" Answer: A straight angle.

In the diagram at the right, we combine this clue and our success in Problem 10.11 with adding an extra parallel line to a diagram. We draw $\overleftrightarrow{DE}$ through A parallel to $\overline{BC}$. As shown, we then have $\angle DAB = \angle ABC$ and $\angle EAC = \angle BCA$. Since $\angle DAE$ is a straight angle, we have

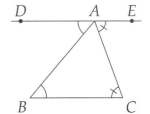

$$\angle DAB + \angle CAB + \angle EAC = 180°.$$

Substituting $\angle DAB = \angle ABC$ and $\angle EAC = \angle BCA$ into this equation gives

$$\angle ABC + \angle CAB + \angle BCA = 180°.$$

> **Important:** The sum of the interior angles in any triangle is 180°.

Problem 10.14: The measure of one angle of a triangle is double the measure of another angle of the triangle, and 15 degrees greater than the measure of the third angle of the triangle. What are the measures of the angles of the triangle?

Solution for Problem 10.14: We start where we do with many word problems. We assign variables and try to make an equation using the information in the problem. Let x be the measure of the initial angle. We know that the measure of this angle is twice the measure of another angle. So, this second angle must be half the first angle, which means the second angle has measure $x/2$.

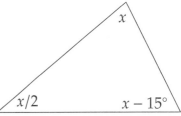

Finally, the initial angle is 15° more than the third angle, which means the third angle has measure $x - 15°$. Now, we can write an equation. The sum of the angles in any triangle is 180°, so we must have

$$x + \frac{x}{2} + (x - 15°) = 180°.$$

Combining the terms with x on the left side gives

$$\frac{5x}{2} - 15° = 180°.$$

Adding 15° to both sides gives

$$\frac{5x}{2} = 195°.$$

Multiplying both sides by $\frac{2}{5}$ isolates x and gives

$$x = (195°) \cdot \frac{2}{5} = \frac{390°}{5} = 78°.$$

Therefore, the other two angles have measures $\frac{x}{2} = 39°$ and $x - 15° = 63°$.

We can check our answer by making sure that the angles add up to 180°. We find that $78° + 39° + 63° = 180°$, so our answer is indeed correct. □

Notice that we didn't end our solution to Problem 10.14 when we found x. The problem asks for the measures of all three angles of the triangle, not just one of them.

> **WARNING!!** Your last step in solving a problem should be making sure you've answered the question that is asked in the problem.

Problem 10.15: A triangle is a **right triangle** if one of its angles is right. A triangle is an **obtuse triangle** if one of its angles is an obtuse angle, and a triangle is an **acute triangle** if all three of its angles are acute.

(a) Is it possible for a triangle to have more than one angle that is right or obtuse?

(b) Explain why the acute angles in a right triangle must sum to 90°.

(c) If the measures of two angles of a triangle have a sum equal to the measure of the third angle, must the triangle be a right triangle?

Solution for Problem 10.15:

(a) No. The sum of the angles in a triangle is 180°. If two of the angles equal 90°, then the third angle must be 0° in order for the three angles to add to 180°. But we can't have a 0° angle in a triangle! Similarly, if two angles were greater than 90°, then the sum of these would be greater than 180°, so the three angles couldn't possibly add to 180°. This means that a triangle can't have more than one angle that is right or obtuse.

(b) The angles of a triangle sum to 180°. If one angle is 90°, then the sum of the other two must be $180° - 90° = 90°$. So, the acute angles of a right triangle must sum to 90°.

(c) Suppose the third angle has measure x. Since the sum of the measures of the first two angles is also x, the sum of all three angles is $2x$. So, we must have $2x = 180°$, which means $x = 90°$ and the triangle must indeed be a right triangle.

□

Problem 10.16:

(a) What is the sum of the interior angles of a square?

(b) Draw 2 quadrilaterals that are not squares and measure their interior angles with a pro-tractor. Sum the resulting measures for each quadrilateral. Notice anything interesting?

(c) Make a conjecture (guess) about the sum of the interior angles of a quadrilateral based on your observations in the first two parts. Use what you know about triangles to explain why your guess is correct.

Solution for Problem 10.16:

(a) Each of the interior angles of a square is a right angle, so the sum of the angles of a square is $4(90°) = 360°$.

(b) Below are two examples. In each case, the sum of the angles is $360°$.

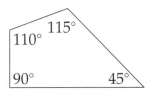
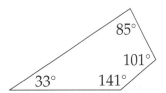

(c) We don't yet know how to find the sum of the interior angles in a polygon with 4 angles, but we do know how to find the sum of the interior angles of a polygon with 3 angles. The sum of the interior angles of a triangle is $180°$. The first two parts of this problem make us suspect that the sum of the angles of any quadrilateral is $360°$, and $360°$ is 2 times $180°$. So, we look for a way to break a quadrilateral into two triangles. Fortunately, as shown at the right, it's easy to split a quadrilateral into two triangles—we draw a diagonal!

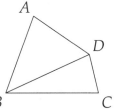

After splitting quadrilateral $ABCD$ into triangles ABD and BCD, we see that the sum of the interior angles of $ABCD$ equals the sum of the angles of $\triangle ABD$ and the sum of the angles of $\triangle BCD$. So, the sum of the angles of $ABCD$ equals the sum of the angles of two triangles, which is $360°$, as expected.

□

> **Important:** The interior angles of any quadrilateral add to $360°$.
>
>

Our key step in finding the sum of the angles of a quadrilateral was breaking the quadrilateral into triangles with a diagonal of the quadrilateral.

> **Concept:** We can tackle many geometry problems involving complicated shapes by breaking the shapes into triangles.

You might be wondering what happens if one of the diagonals of a quadrilateral is *outside* the quadrilateral, as we see for quadrilateral $WXYZ$ at the right. We say that $WXYZ$ is a **concave** quadrilateral because one of its diagonals is outside the quadrilateral. A quadrilateral in which both diagonals are inside the quadrilateral is called a **convex** quadrilateral. Fortunately, diagonal $\overline{XZ}$ is inside $WXYZ$, so we can still see that the interior angles of $WXYZ$ sum to $360°$. (Even though one of those angles is greater than $180°$!)

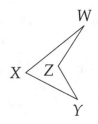

Problem 10.17: Find the value of x in the diagram at the right.

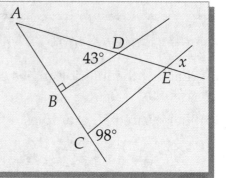

Solution for Problem 10.17: We can't immediately find x, but we can find the measures of several other angles. As we find measures of other angles, we include them in our diagram. First, the little box in the diagram at B tells us that $\overline{BD} \perp \overline{AC}$, so $\angle ABD = \angle DBC = 90°$.

Next, we know the measures of two angles of $\triangle ABD$, so we can find the third. From $\triangle ABD$, we have $\angle A + 90° + 43° = 180°$, so $\angle A = 47°$.

Since $\angle ACE$ together with the $98°$ angle in the diagram make a straight angle, we have $\angle ACE = 180° - 98° = 82°$. Similarly, $\angle BDE = 180° - 43° = 137°$.

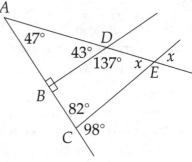

Using vertical angles at E, we see that $\angle AEC = x$. We include this expression and all of the measures we found above in the diagram on the right. We use little boxes at B to indicate right angles.

Now, we see that we have enough information to find x. We can either use $\triangle ACE$ or quadrilateral $BCED$. From $\triangle ACE$, we have

$$47° + 82° + x = 180°,$$

so $x = 51°$.

Had we used quadrilateral $BCED$, we would have found

$$90° + 82° + x + 137° = 360°,$$

so $x = 51°$, as before. $\square$

> **Concept:** The process we used to solve Problem 10.17 is often called **angle**
> **chasing**. When angle chasing, we repeatedly find measures of an-
> gles, add those measures to our diagram, and then look for more
> angles whose measures we can determine.

We've found the sum of the angles of any triangle, and of any quadrilateral. You know what comes next: polygons with even more angles!

> **Problem 10.18:**
>
> (a) What is the sum of the interior angles of a pentagon? Of a hexagon?
>
> (b) Find a formula for the sum of the interior angles of a polygon with n sides.
>
> (c) A **regular polygon** is a polygon in which all of the sides have the same length and all of the angles have the same measure. What is the measure of each interior angle of a regular pentagon? Of a regular octagon?

Solution for Problem 10.18:

(a) As shown on the left below, we can break a pentagon up into three triangles. So, the sum of the interior angles of a pentagon is $3(180°) = 540°$.

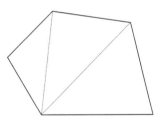 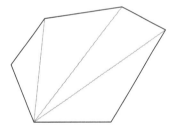

Similarly, we can break a hexagon up into four triangles, as shown on the right above. So, the sum of the interior angles of a hexagon is $4(180°) = 720°$.

(b) We can split a 4-sided polygon into 2 triangles, a 5-sided polygon into 3 triangles, and a 6-sided polygon into 4 triangles. Similarly, we can split a polygon with n sides into $n - 2$ triangles. So, the interior angles of a polygon with n sides must sum to $180(n - 2)$ degrees.

> **Important:** The sum of the interior angles in an n-sided polygon is $180(n - 2)$
> degrees.

(c) The five angles of a pentagon sum to $540°$. In a regular polygon, all five angles have the same measure, so each must be $540°/5 = 108°$.

An octagon has 8 sides and 8 interior angles. Using our formula from the previous part, the sum of these 8 angles is $180(8 - 2) = 180(6) = 1080$ degrees. In a regular octagon, each of these angles has the same measure, so each must be $1080/8 = 135$ degrees.

□

Just as some quadrilaterals are concave, so are some polygons with more than 4 sides. A **concave** polygon is a polygon in which at least one of the diagonals is *outside* the polygon. For example, diagonal $\overline{AC}$ is outside hexagon *ABCDEF* at the right, so *ABCDEF* is a concave polygon. A polygon in which all the diagonals are inside the polygon is called a **convex** polygon. It's a bit harder to prove, but the interior angles of a concave polygon with n sides add to $180(n-2)$ degrees, just like the interior angles of a convex polygon.

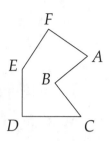

Problem 10.19: The pentagon in the diagram below is regular. Find angle measure x.

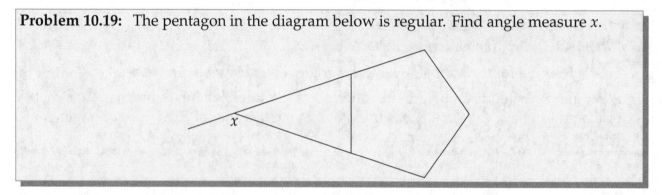

Solution for Problem 10.19: It isn't immediately clear how to find the measure of the angle we seek, so we start by finding what we can. As we saw in the previous problem, each angle of a regular pentagon is 108°. We place these measures in our diagram:

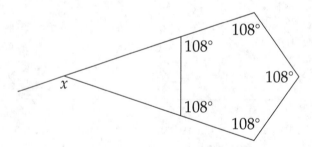

Now, we can see that two of the angles of the triangle measure $180° - 108° = 72°$. We place these measures in our diagram:

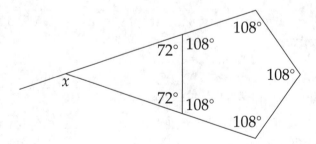

The angles in the triangle must add to 180°, so the missing angle in the triangle has measure $180° - 72° - 72° = 36°$. We place this measure in our diagram:

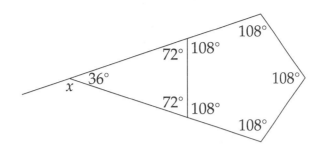

Finally, the angle marked x together with the $36°$ angle make a straight angle, so we have $x + 36° = 180°$. This gives us $x = 180° - 36° = 144°$. □

Now that we have a good handle on the interior angles of a polygon, let's take a look at the angles we form when we extend sides of a polygon past the vertices of the polygon.

Problem 10.20: When we extend the sides of a triangle past the vertices, we form **exterior angles** of the triangle. For example, the angles with measures x, y, and z on the right are exterior angles of $\triangle ABC$, while the angles with measures a, b, and c are interior angles of the triangle.

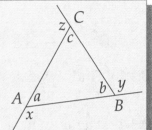

(a) What is $a + b + c$?

(b) What is $a + x$?

(c) What is $x + y + z$?

(d) Suppose you start at A facing B, walk along $\overline{AB}$ to vertex B, then turn towards C and walk along $\overline{BC}$ to C, then turn towards A and walk along $\overline{CA}$ back to your starting point, then turn towards B. How does this "trip" give us a quick explanation for the answer to part (c)?

Solution for Problem 10.20:

(a) The sum of the interior angles of a triangle is $180°$, so $a + b + c = 180°$.

(b) The angles with measures a and x together make a straight angle, so $a + x = 180°$.

(c) We start by finding whatever information we can about x, y, and z. From part (b), we have $x = 180° - a$. Similarly, we have $b + y = 180°$ and $c + z = 180°$. So, we have $y = 180° - b$ and $z = 180° - c$. Adding our expressions for x, y, and z gives

$$x + y + z = (180° - a) + (180° - b) + (180° - c)$$
$$= 540° - a - b - c$$
$$= 540° - (a + b + c).$$

In part (a), we found that $a + b + c = 180°$, so

$$x + y + z = 540° - (a + b + c) = 540° - 180° = 360°.$$

(d) Imagine taking a walk all the way around the triangle along the sides of the triangle. Suppose we start at A, facing point B. When we walk from A to B and then turn to face C, we turn counterclockwise at B by an angle with measure y. Similarly, when we walk from B to C and turn to face A, we turn counterclockwise by an angle with measure z. Finally, when we walk from C to A and turn to face B, we turn counterclockwise by an angle with measure x. At this point, we're back facing in the same direction we were facing when we started our journey around the triangle. So, the three turns have turned us a full $360°$. The three turns together are by a total angle measure of $x + y + z$, so $x + y + z = 360°$.

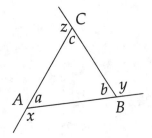

What happens if we take a similar walk around a polygon with more sides?

□

Exercises

10.3.1 Find the measure of $\angle ABD$ in the diagram at the right if $\angle A = 47°$ and $\angle C = 72°$.

10.3.2 The measures of the angles of a triangle are in the ratio $1 : 4 : 5$. What is the measure of the smallest angle?

10.3.3 What is the measure of each angle of a regular polygon with 20 sides?

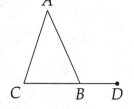

10.3.4 The two polygons in the diagram on the left below are regular. Find $\angle RQS$.

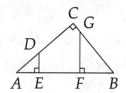

Figure 10.13: Diagram for Problem 10.3.4   Figure 10.14: Diagram for Problem 10.3.5

10.3.5 In the diagram on the right above, we have $\angle DAE = 41°$. What is the measure of $\angle CGF$?

10.3.6 Find the value of x in the diagram on the right.

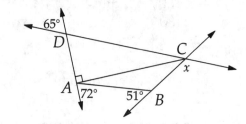

10.3.7 Find angle measures x and y in the diagram on the right.

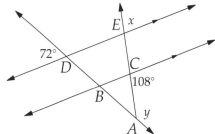

10.3.8 Is it possible for a pentagon to have three interior angles that are reflex angles? (Reminder: A reflex angle is an angle whose measure is between 180° and 360°.)

10.3.9★ In Problem 10.20, we showed that the sum of the exterior angles of a triangle is 360°. Explain why the sum of the exterior angles of any convex polygon must be 360°. **Hints:** 153, 83

10.4 Summary

Definitions:

- A **point** is, well, a point. The great Greek mathematician Euclid called a point "that which has no part." We can't do much better than that vague description. We typically label points with capital letters.

- A straight path connecting two points is called a **segment**, and the original two points are the **endpoints** of the segment. We refer to a segment by its endpoints, such as $\overline{AB}$. We remove the bar to refer to the length of the segment: AB.

- If we start at a point, then head in one direction forever, we form a **ray**. Our starting point is the **vertex** of the ray, and we identify a ray as $\overrightarrow{AB}$, where A is the vertex of the ray and B is some other point on the ray.

- If we continue a line segment past its endpoints forever in both directions, we form a **line**, which we write as $\overleftrightarrow{AB}$.

Definitions: Two rays that share an origin form an **angle**. The common origin of the rays is the **vertex** of the angle. We use the symbol $\angle$ to refer to an angle, and we use a point on each side and the vertex to identify the angle, such as $\angle XOY$ at the right. We sometimes use just the vertex to identify the angle when it is clear what angle we mean. For example, we can write $\angle O$ to refer to the angle at the right.

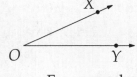

We can use a **protractor** to measure angles (see page 380). The **semicircular** arc of the protractor is divided into 180 degrees, so that a whole circle is 360 degrees.

Definitions:

- An angle smaller than 90° is an **acute angle**.

- A 90° angle is a **right angle**. Lines, segments, or rays that form a right angle are said to be **perpendicular**.

- An angle between 90° and 180° is an **obtuse angle**.

- An angle that measures 180° is a **straight angle**.

- An angle that measures between 180° and 360° is a **reflex angle**.

Definitions:

- Two angles whose measures add to 180° are **supplementary angles**. Angles that together make up a straight angle form a particularly useful example of supplementary angles.

- Two angles whose measures add to 90° are **complementary angles**.

- Two angles that have the same measure are called **congruent angles**.

- When two lines intersect, they form two pairs of **vertical angles**, such as ∠WPZ and ∠YPX on the right. Vertical angles are congruent.

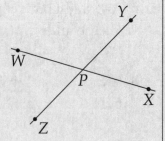

Definitions: Two lines that do not intersect are **parallel**. A line that intersects multiple parallel lines is called a **transversal line**.

Important: The angles formed when a transversal intersects two parallel lines come in two groups of four equal angles as shown:

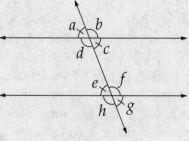

$$a = c = e = g$$
$$b = d = f = h$$

Each of the first set of angles is supplementary to each of the second set of angles.

> **Important:** The relationships described above when a transversal intersects two lines can also be used to show that two lines are parallel.

A **polygon** is a simple closed figure with line segments as boundaries. For example, all triangles are polygons. Several polygons are shown on the right. The line segments that form the boundaries of a polygon are the **sides** of the polygon. Each pair of consecutive sides of a polygon meet at a **vertex** of the polygon.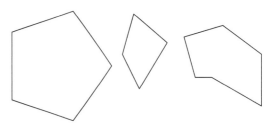
Each angle inside a polygon formed by a pair of consecutive sides is called an **interior angle** of the polygon. If we connect two vertices that are not adjacent on the polygon, we form a **diagonal** of the polygon.

> **Important:** The sum of the interior angles in a triangle is 180°, and the sum of the interior angles of a polygon with n sides is $180(n-2)$ degrees.

> **Definitions:** Triangles can be classified by their angles.
>
> - A triangle with a right angle as an interior angle is a **right triangle**.
>
> - A triangle with an obtuse angle as an interior angle is a **obtuse triangle**.
>
> - A triangle in which all three angles are acute is an **acute triangle**.

> **Important:** When we extend the sides of a triangle past the vertices, we form **exterior angles** of the triangle. For example, the angles with measures x, y, and z on the right are exterior angles of $\triangle ABC$, while the angles with measures a, b, and c are interior angles of the triangle. The sum of the exterior angles of any triangle is 360°.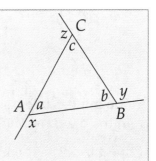

 REVIEW PROBLEMS ▶

10.21 Two lines intersect such that the measure of one of the angles formed by the lines is five times the measure of another of the angles formed by the lines. What are the measures of the angles formed by the lines?

10.22 Find ∠BAE in the diagram at the left below.

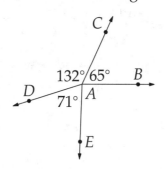

Figure 10.15: Diagram for Problem 10.22

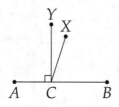

Figure 10.16: Diagram for Problem 10.23

10.23 In the diagram at the right above, we have $\overrightarrow{OW} \perp \overrightarrow{OY}$ and $\overrightarrow{OX} \perp \overrightarrow{OZ}$. If ∠WOZ is five times ∠XOY, then what is the measure of ∠XOY?

10.24 What is the number of degrees in the smaller angle between the hour hand and the minute hand on a clock at 8:30?

10.25 A revolving restaurant rotates one complete revolution every 56 minutes. In the 21 minutes it takes to eat the peaches jubilee dessert, through how many degrees does the restaurant revolve? *(Source: MATHCOUNTS)*

10.26 In the diagram on the left below, the measure of ∠ACX is 50% greater than the measure of ∠BCX. Angle ACY is a right angle. What is the measure of ∠XCY?

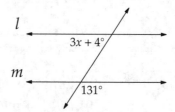

Figure 10.17: Diagram for Problem 10.26

Figure 10.18: Diagram for Problem 10.27

10.27 A line intersects parallel lines l and m forming angles with measures $3x + 4°$ and $131°$, as shown in the diagram on the right above. Find the value of x.

10.28 If line a is perpendicular to two different lines b and c, then must we have $b \parallel c$?

10.29

(a) Find x in the diagram at the right.

(b) Find ∠R in the diagram at the right.

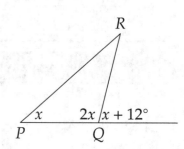

10.30 In the diagram on the right, we have $\overline{EG} \parallel \overline{DH}$.

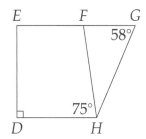

(a) Find $\angle DEF$.

(b) Find $\angle EFH$.

(c) Find $\angle FHG$.

10.31 One angle of a triangle has measure $20°$ greater than another angle of the triangle and half the measure of the third angle of the triangle. Find the measures of all three angles.

10.32 In the diagram at the right, side $\overline{BC}$ of $\triangle ABC$ is extended past B to a point D. Explain why $\angle ABD$ must equal $\angle A + \angle C$.

10.33 The four angles of a quadrilateral are in the ratio of $1 : 2 : 3 : 4$. What is the measure of the smallest angle? *(Source: MATHCOUNTS)*

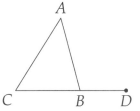

10.34 Find angle measures x and y in the figure on the left below. Note that the double arrows on $\overleftrightarrow{HE}$ and $\overrightarrow{DI}$ mean that $\overleftrightarrow{HE} \parallel \overrightarrow{DI}$.

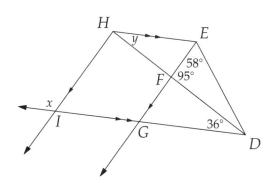

Figure 10.19: Diagram for Problem 10.34

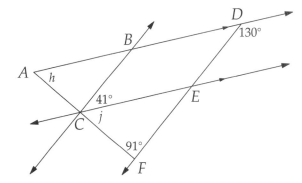

Figure 10.20: Diagram for Problem 10.35

10.35 Find angle measures h and j in the diagram on the right above.

10.36 What is the measure of each interior angle of a regular nonagon?

Challenge Problems

10.37 Find the degree measure of an angle whose complement is 25% of its supplement. *(Source: AMC 12)*

10.38 If ∠A = 20° and ∠AFG = ∠AGF in the diagram at the right, then how many degrees is ∠B + ∠D? *(Source: AMC 8)*

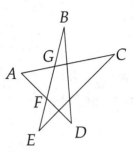

10.39 Point A is on the edge of a circular disk. Every day at noon, the disk is rotated 150° in a counter-clockwise direction. What day of the week will it be the next time point A is at the same position that it was at 10 a.m. on Saturday? *(Source: MATHCOUNTS)*

10.40 Find angle measures q and r in the diagram on the left below.

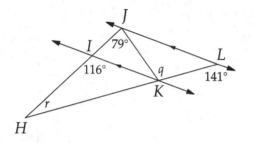

Figure 10.21: Diagram for Problem 10.40   Figure 10.22: Diagram for Problem 10.41

10.41 Find the value of x in the diagram at the right above. **Hints:** 60

10.42★ In quadrilateral ABCD angle BAD and angle CDA are divided into three equal angles as shown. What is the measure of ∠AFD in degrees? *(Source: MATHCOUNTS)* **Hints:** 50

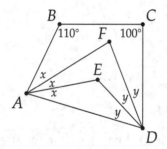

Figure 10.23: Diagram for Problem 10.42   Figure 10.24: Diagram for Problem 10.43

10.43★ Draw a five-pointed star like the one shown at the right above. Find the sum of the measures of the angles at the five points of the star. Notice anything interesting? Test your observation for a few more stars, and then see if you can explain why it must be true. **Hints:** 142, 63

10.44★ What is the greatest number of acute interior angles that a decagon can have? (Note: the decagon may be concave!) **Hints:** 10, 18

 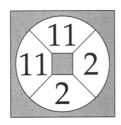 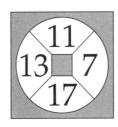 

Probably no symbol in mathematics has evoked as much mystery, romanticism, misconception, and human interest as the number pi. – William L. Schaaf

CHAPTER **11**

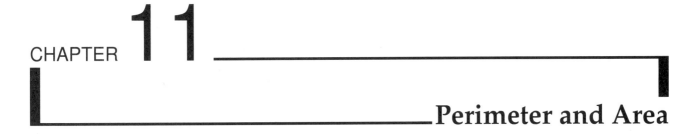

Perimeter and Area

In this chapter, we discuss methods to measure the size of geometric objects. You're probably familiar with many of the formulas and concepts we will discuss in this chapter. The goals of this chapter are to give you better intuition for why these formulas work and to apply them to challenging problems.

11.1 Measuring Segments

Back in Section 10.1, we introduced the line segment.

$$A \bullet \!\!\!\!-\!\!\!\!-\!\!\!\!-\!\!\!\!-\!\!\!\!-\!\!\!\!-\!\!\!\!-\!\!\!\!- \bullet B$$

Figure 11.1: A Segment

Recall that we use the endpoints to label the segment. For example, $\overline{AB}$ is the segment from A to B. To refer to the length of the segment, we omit the bar. For example, if you measure $\overline{AB}$ in Figure 11.1 with a ruler, you'll find that AB equals 2 inches. We often leave out the units in geometry problems. So, for example, we might write $AB = 2$.

One special point on a segment is the segment's **midpoint**, which is the point halfway between the endpoints.

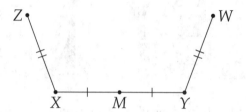

Figure 11.2: A Midpoint and Marking Segments of Equal Length

In Figure 11.2, M is the midpoint of $\overline{XY}$. In the diagram, we indicate that $XM = MY$ with the little tick marks along $\overline{XM}$ and $\overline{MY}$. We say that two segments are **congruent** if they have the same length. If we have more than one group of congruent segments, we use a different number of tick marks for each. For example, the pairs of tick marks on $\overline{ZX}$ and $\overline{WY}$ above indicate that $ZX = WY$, and that these lengths need not be the same as XM and MY.

One way to measure a closed figure is by the total length of its boundary. We call this the **perimeter** of the figure. For example, the perimeter of a polygon is the sum of the lengths of its sides.

 **Problems**

Problem 11.1: Farmer Fred wants to fence the oddly-shaped region shown in bold at the right. If each of the squares shown has sides that are 10 feet long, and fence costs $7 per foot, then how much will Fred's fence cost?

Problem 11.2: A triangle is called **equilateral** if all of its sides have the same length. In the diagram at the right, all three triangles are equilateral. Point D is the midpoint of $\overline{AC}$ and G is the midpoint of $\overline{AE}$. If $AB = 4$, then what is the perimeter of $ABCDEFG$?
(Source: AMC 8)

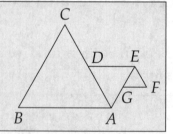

Problem 11.3: Points B and C are on segment $\overline{AD}$ such that $AC : CD = 3 : 1$ and B is the midpoint of $\overline{AC}$. If $BC = 6$, then what is AD?

Problem 11.4: A triangle is called **isosceles** if two of its sides are congruent. The two congruent sides are called the **legs** of the triangle and the other side is called the **base** of the triangle. Suppose an isosceles triangle has perimeter 45 and the length of each leg is twice the length of the base. What is the length of the base?

Problem 11.5:

(a) Mary leaves home and walks 7 miles in one direction before stopping for lunch. Jeff leaves from the same home and walks 4 miles before stopping for lunch. Is it possible for Mary and Jeff to have lunch 12 miles apart?

(b) Is it possible for a triangle to have side lengths 4, 7, and 12? Why or why not?

(c) Suppose a triangle has side lengths a, b, and c. Is it possible for $a + b$ to be less than c? Is it possible for $a + b$ to equal c?

Problem 11.1: Farmer Fred wants to fence the oddly-shaped region shown in bold at the right. If each of the squares shown has sides that are 10 feet long, and fence costs $7 per foot, then how much will Fred's fence cost?

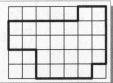

Solution for Problem 11.1: We could figure out the length of each bit of fence, and then add up all these lengths. But there's a more clever solution. Suppose the farmer started at the upper right corner, point P in the diagram on the right, and walked clockwise all the way around the region along the fence. His path will always take him directly down, left, up, or right on our

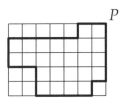

diagram. He'll walk downward along 5 squares and back up along 5 squares. Similarly, he'll walk 7 squares to the left and 7 squares to the right. So, in total, he walks along

$$5 + 5 + 7 + 7 = 24$$

sides of the squares. Each of the 24 side lengths is 10 feet, so he walks 240 feet. The fence costs $7 per foot, so Fred's fence costs $(240)(\$7) = \$1680$. $\square$

Another quick way to find the length of the fence is to rearrange the fence into a simpler shape. We do so by moving the parts of the fence that are inside the grid out to the boundary of the grid, as shown on the right. The old path of the fence inside the grid is shown in gray. The new path is clearly a rectangle, whose perimeter we can quickly find. The top and the bottom of the rectangle are congruent, and the left and the right sides are congruent. As before, we find that the perimeter is a total of $2(5 + 7) = 24$ side lengths of the squares in the original diagram.

> **Important:** Opposite sides of a rectangle are congruent. We often call the lengths of adjacent sides of a rectangle the **length** and the **width** of the rectangle. So, if the length of a rectangle is l and the width is w, then the perimeter of the rectangle is $2(l + w)$.

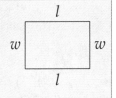

Problem 11.2: A triangle is called **equilateral** if all of its sides have the same length. In the diagram at the right, all three triangles are equilateral. Point D is the midpoint of $\overline{AC}$ and G is the midpoint of $\overline{AE}$. If $AB = 4$, then what is the perimeter of $ABCDEFG$? (Source: AMC 8)

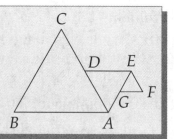

Solution for Problem 11.2: The desired perimeter is

$$AB + BC + CD + DE + EF + FG + GA.$$

Since $\triangle ABC$ is equilateral and $AB = 4$, we know that $BC = AC = 4$ as well. Because D is the midpoint of $\overline{AC}$, we have $AD = CD = AC/2 = 4/2 = 2$. Since $\triangle ADE$ is equilateral and $AD = 2$, we have $AE = DE = AD = 2$. Then, because G is the midpoint of $\overline{AE}$, we have $AG = GE = AE/2 = 2/2 = 1$. And since $\triangle GEF$ is equilateral, we have $GF = EF = GE = 1$.

That whole paragraph is just a long way of saying "Long segments have length 4, medium segments have length 2, and short segments have length 1." The sides of $ABCDEFG$ consist of two long segments ($\overline{AB}$ and $\overline{BC}$), two medium segments ($\overline{CD}$ and $\overline{DE}$), and three short segments ($\overline{EF}$, $\overline{FG}$, and $\overline{GA}$), so the perimeter is $2(4) + 2(2) + 3(1) = 15$.

Notice that our final answer equals the sum of the perimeters of $\triangle ABC$ and $\triangle EFG$. We can see why with a clever rearrangement:

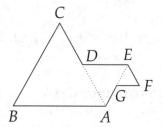 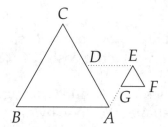

In the diagram on the left above, we draw segments $\overline{AD}$ and $\overline{EG}$ dotted. The desired perimeter is the sum of the lengths of the solid segments. Since $\triangle ADE$ is equilateral, we have $AD = DE$. Since G is the midpoint of $\overline{AE}$, we have $EG = AG$. In the diagram on the right, we draw $\overline{DE}$ dotted instead of $\overline{AD}$, and draw $\overline{AG}$ dotted instead of $\overline{EG}$. Since $DE = AD$ and $AG = EG$, the total length of all the solid segments in the resulting diagram on the right is the same as the desired perimeter. $\square$

Problem 11.3: Points B and C are on segment $\overline{AD}$ such that $AC : CD = 3 : 1$ and B is the midpoint of $\overline{AC}$. If $BC = 6$, then what is AD?

Solution for Problem 11.3: We start with a quick sketch to help guide us. We must make sure to get the points in the right order. Since B and C are on $\overline{AD}$, we know that A and D are at the ends of the segment. Since B is the midpoint of $\overline{AC}$, we know that B is between A and C. The equation $AC : CD = 3 : 1$ tells us that $\overline{AC}$ is longer than $\overline{CD}$, so C is closer to D than to A. We also write the given length $BC = 6$ in our diagram, as shown.

> **Concept:** Diagrams help organize information in geometry problems. Quick sketches can help you avoid errors, and give you hints to find solutions.

Since B is the midpoint of $\overline{AC}$, we have $AB = BC$, so $AB = 6$, as well. We add this information to our diagram.

> **Concept:** Update your diagram as you find more information.

All we have left to find is CD. We now have $AC = AB + BC = 12$, so the given ratio $AC : CD = 3 : 1$ tells us that $12 : CD = 3 : 1$. Multiplying the ratio on the right by 4 gives us $12 : CD = 12 : 4$, so $CD = 4$. Finally, we have $AD = AC + CD = 16$. $\square$

> **Problem 11.4:** A triangle is called **isosceles** if two of its sides are congruent. The two congruent sides are called the **legs** of the triangle and the other side is called the **base** of the triangle. Suppose an isosceles triangle has perimeter 45 and each leg is twice the length of the base. What is the length of the base of the triangle?

Solution for Problem 11.4: We assign a variable to the quantity we seek. Let b be the length of the base of the triangle. Since the length of each leg is twice the length of the base, each leg has length $2b$. We can display all this information in a diagram, as shown at the right. Since the perimeter of the triangle is 45, we have

$$b + 2b + 2b = 45.$$

Simplifying the left side gives $5b = 45$, and dividing by 5 gives $b = 9$. Therefore, the length of the base is 9. $\square$

> **Concept:** Assigning variables can be just as useful in geometry problems as in other types of problems.

We combined this strategy with our "organize geometric information with a diagram" strategy to solve the problem.

In Problems 11.2 and 11.4, we introduced equilateral triangles and isosceles triangles. An equilateral triangle is also an isosceles triangle. That is, "isosceles" does not mean that the base must have a different length than the legs. A triangle with no two sides congruent is called **scalene**. "Scalene" is just a fancy way to say "not isosceles."

Problem 11.5:

(a) Mary leaves home and walks 7 miles in one direction before stopping at noon for lunch. The same day, Jeff leaves from the same home and walks 4 miles before also stopping at noon for lunch. Is it possible for Mary and Jeff to have lunch 12 miles apart?

(b) Is it possible for a triangle to have side lengths 4, 7, and 12? Why or why not?

(c) Suppose a triangle has side lengths a, b, and c. Is it possible for $a + b$ to be less than c? Is it possible for $a + b$ to equal c?

Solution for Problem 11.5:

(a) Mary and Jeff will be farthest apart at lunchtime if they walk in opposite directions. If they walk in opposite directions, they will be $7 + 4 = 11$ miles apart. Therefore, they cannot have lunch 12 miles apart.

(b) We can view this as essentially the same as the previous part. The side of length 7 represents Mary's hike and the side of length 4 represents Jeff's hike. If we let the distance between Mary and Jeff at lunchtime be the length of the third side, then part (a) tells us that the third side length cannot be more than 11. Therefore, if the lengths of two sides of a triangle are 4 and 7, then the third side length cannot possibly be 12. Similarly, no triangle can have side lengths 4, 7 and 11.

(c) We can think about this the same way as we did the previous two parts. Suppose Mary starts from home and hikes a miles while Jeff starts from the same home and hikes b miles. The farthest apart they can be at the end of their hikes is $a + b$ miles. So, if $c > a + b$, they can't possibly be c miles apart.

As in part (b), we can consider Mary's hike to be one side of a triangle, Jeff's hike to be another side of the triangle, and the segment connecting the endpoints of their hikes to be the third side of the triangle. So, the vertices of this triangle are the endpoints of the two hikes and the home where they both began. Mary and Jeff can't be more than $a + b$ apart at lunchtime, so the third side length of this triangle can't possibly be longer than the sum of the lengths of the other two sides. Similarly, it is impossible for any triangle to have side lengths a, b, and c if $c > a + b$.

Next, we consider whether or not we can have $a + b = c$. The only way Mary's and Jeff's hikes can end $a + b$ miles apart is if they walk in opposite directions. This means that their home is on the segment connecting the endpoints of their hikes. In other words, the "triangle" is just a line segment, as shown in the diagram. So, we cannot make a triangle with side lengths a, b, c if $a + b = c$.

$\square$

In Problem 11.5, we discovered that if a, b, and c are the side lengths of a triangle, then $a + b > c$. This powerful relationship is called the **Triangle Inequality**. We also often write the Triangle Inequality as:

> **Important:** For any three points A, B, and C, we have
>
> $$AB + BC \geq AC.$$
>
> We have $AB + BC = AC$ if and only if B is on $\overline{AC}$.

In other words, to get from point A to point C, it's shorter to go straight from A to C than to go first to some other point B not on $\overline{AC}$. The Triangle Inequality is just a fancy way of saying, "The shortest path between two points is a straight line."

Exercises

11.1.1 If each square in the diagram at the right has side length 1, then what is the perimeter of the figure traced in bold?

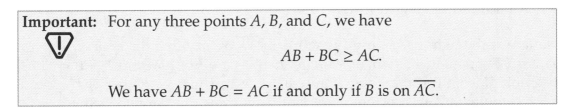

11.1.2 I am drawing a picture on a 12 inch by 16 inch rectangular piece of paper for my art class. My teacher tells me that I must leave a 1 inch margin on all sides of the paper, since that region will be covered by the frame. What is the perimeter of the region in which I can still draw?

11.1.3 Segment $\overline{AB}$ is 12 inches long. Points X and Y are selected on $\overline{AB}$ such that $\overline{AX}$ and $\overline{BY}$ are congruent, and the ratio of AX to AY is $1 : 4$. What is the length of $\overline{BX}$?

11.1.4 The sides of a triangle have lengths 6.5, 10, and s, where s is a positive integer. What is the smallest possible value of s? *(Source: AMC 8)*

11.1.5 One side of an isosceles triangle is three times as long as another side of the triangle. If the perimeter of the triangle is 140, then what is the length of the base of the triangle?

11.1.6 Squares are constructed on each of the sides of a triangle as shown to the right. If the perimeter of the triangle is 17, then what is the perimeter of the nine-sided figure that is composed of the remaining three sides of each of the squares?

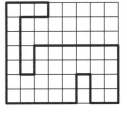

11.1.7★ Suzanne has determined that swimming the length of a rectangular pool 60 times is the same distance as swimming its perimeter 18 times. What is the ratio of the width to the length of this swimming pool? *(Source: MATHCOUNTS)*

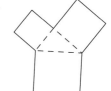

11.1.8★ An isosceles triangle has integer side lengths and perimeter 25. What are the possible values of the length of each leg? **Hints:** 149

11.2 Area

While perimeter gives us a way of measuring the boundary of a closed figure, we use **area** to measure the space contained inside the figure.

The square at the right has sides of length 1 inch. We say that the area of this square is "1 square inch," where "square inch" is a unit of area just like "inch" is a unit of length. If the sides of the square were 1 foot long, then the square's area would be "1 square foot." Rather than writing out "square inch" or "square foot," we sometimes abbreviate the units using an exponent: "1 square inch" can be written "1 in^2," and "1 square foot" can be written "1 ft^2."

If we leave the units out and have a square with side length 1, then its area is "1 square unit," but we usually leave the "square units" out and just say that the area is 1. We call a square with side length 1 a **unit square**.

Of course, we'd like to find the area of more than just squares with side length 1! We can think of the area of a figure as the number of unit squares that are needed to cover the figure. As you probably know, the area of a rectangle is the product of its length and width.

> **Definition:** The area of a rectangle with length l and width w is $l \cdot w$.

For example, in rectangle $WXYZ$ at the right, the length is 5 and the width is 3. So, the area of $WXYZ$ is $3 \cdot 5 = 15$ square units. The diagram at the right gives us a good idea why this formula for the area of a rectangle works when the rectangle's length and width are integers. The formula works for any rectangle, even if the length and the width of the rectangle are not integers.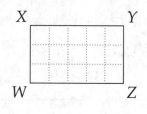

Finally, we sometimes use brackets to refer to area, so we write $[WXYZ] = 15$ to mean that the area of $WXYZ$ is 15 square units.

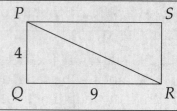

Problem 11.6: In rectangle $PQRS$, we have $PQ = 4$ and $QR = 9$. What is the area of $\triangle PQR$?

Problem 11.7: The **legs** of a right triangle are the sides of the triangle that form a right angle. Suppose the legs of a right triangle have lengths a and b. Find a formula for the area of the triangle in terms of a and b.

Problem 11.8: Ravi and Ranu are trying to decide how to paint a rectangular wall that is 18 feet long and 8 feet high. Ravi wants to paint a right triangle, as shown on the left below. Ranu wants to paint a more interesting triangle, like the one shown on the right.

Ravi's Triangle

Ranu's Triangle

(a) What is the area of the region that Ravi wants to paint?

(b) Divide the wall with Ranu's triangle into two rectangles such that the painted portion of each rectangle is a right triangle. What is the area of the region that Ranu wants to paint?

Problem 11.9: Use your observations in the previous problem to describe how to find the area of any acute triangle.

Problem 11.10: Ravi and Ranu are expanding their house so that the wall that was 18 feet by 8 feet before will become 25 feet by 8 feet. Ravi still wants a triangle that reaches from one corner to the opposite corner, but he doesn't want to use any more paint than he used for his triangle on the old wall. Ranu says they'll just keep the bottom of the triangle the same, and extend the top to the new corner, as shown below:

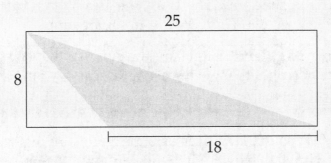

Is Ranu correct? Does Ravi need the same amount of paint for this triangle as he needed for his triangle in Problem 11.8?

Problem 11.11: A **median** of a triangle is a segment that connects a vertex of the triangle to the midpoint of the opposite side. For example, in the diagram on the right, $\overline{AM}$ is a median of $\triangle ABC$. Show that a median of a triangle divides the triangle into two pieces with equal area.
Hints: 136

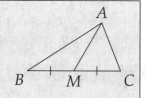

Problem 11.12: Tina wants to carpet a room that has the unusual shape shown on the right with solid lines. Each dotted square in the diagram has side length 5 feet. What is the area of Tina's carpet?

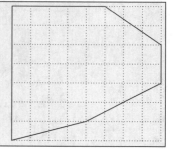

We can use our formula for the area of a rectangle to find the area of a right triangle.

Problem 11.6: In rectangle $PQRS$, we have $PQ = 4$ and $QR = 9$. What is the area of $\triangle PQR$?

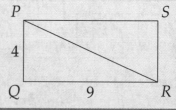

Solution for Problem 11.6: The area of the rectangle is $4 \cdot 9 = 36$ square units. Drawing diagonal $\overline{PR}$ divides the rectangle into two right triangles. These triangles have the same side lengths and angles, so they have the same area. Therefore, the area of each triangle is half the area the rectangle. Specifically, the area of $\triangle PQR$ is $36/2 = 18$ square units. □

Problem 11.7: The **legs** of a right triangle are the sides of the triangle that form a right angle. Suppose the legs of a right triangle have lengths a and b. Find a formula for the area of the triangle in terms of a and b.

Solution for Problem 11.7: Problem 11.6 gives us a guide for finding the formula. We start with a rectangle with sides of length a and b. This rectangle has area ab. Drawing a diagonal of the rectangle produces two right triangles, each with legs of length a and b. As in the previous problem, these right triangles have the same area, so the area of each is half the area of the rectangle. Therefore, the area of a right triangle with legs of length a and b is $ab/2$. □

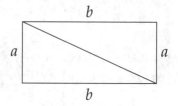

> **Important:** The area of a right triangle is half the product of the lengths of its
> legs.

We'll often use the term "legs" to refer to the lengths of the legs rather than the segments themselves. So, for example, we can write that the area of a right triangle is half the product of its legs.

Problem 11.8: Ravi and Ranu are trying to decide how to paint a rectangular wall that is 18 feet long and 8 feet high. Ravi wants to paint a right triangle, as shown on the left below. Ranu wants to paint a more interesting triangle, like the one shown on the right.

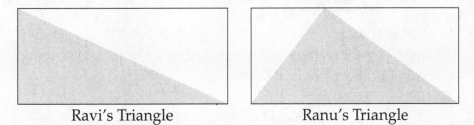

Ravi's Triangle   Ranu's Triangle

(a) What is the area of the region that Ravi wants to paint?

(b) Divide the wall with Ranu's triangle into two rectangles such that the painted portion of each rectangle is a right triangle. What is the area of the region that Ranu wants to paint?

Solution for Problem 11.8:

(a) Ravi's triangle is a right triangle, so its area is half the product of its legs. This means Ravi's triangle has area $(8)(18)/2 = 72$ square feet.

(b) We only know how to find the areas of rectangles and right triangles, but Ranu's triangle is neither of these. So, we split Ranu's triangle into pieces we can handle. We draw a segment from the top vertex of Ranu's triangle to the floor such that this segment is perpendicular to the floor. This segment has length 8 feet because the top of the room is 8 feet from the floor. Ranu's original triangle is now divided into two right triangles, and we know how to find the area of right triangles.

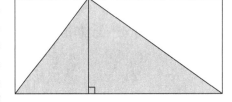

Ranu's Triangle

Unfortunately, we don't know the lengths of both legs of the right triangles. However, we don't need to know them! Our extra segment divides the original rectangle into two smaller rectangles. Ranu's triangle covers half of each of these rectangles, so her triangle covers half of the original rectangle, just like Ravi's does. Therefore, the area of Ranu's triangle is the same as the area of Ravi's triangle, $(8)(18)/2 = 72$ square feet.

We also could have used a little algebra to see that the area of Ranu's triangle is half the area of the rectangle. We label the vertices as shown at right. We then have

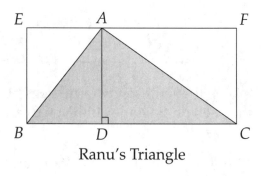

$$[ABC] = [ABD] + [ADC] = \frac{(BD)(AD)}{2} + \frac{(DC)(AD)}{2}$$
$$= \frac{(BD)(AD) + (DC)(AD)}{2}$$
$$= \frac{(BD + DC)(AD)}{2}$$
$$= \frac{(BC)(AD)}{2}.$$

Ranu's Triangle

Since BC equals the length of rectangle $EBCF$ and AD equals the width, we see that the area of $\triangle ABC$ is indeed half the area of $EBCF$.

□

It's quite a coincidence that Ravi's triangle and Ranu's triangle turned out to have the same area. Or is it? Let's investigate. To do so, we'll use the same key strategy we used to find the area of Ranu's triangle:

> **Concept:** If you don't know how to find the area of a figure, try breaking the figure into pieces you can handle.

Problem 11.9: Describe how to find the area of any acute triangle.

Solution for Problem 11.9: Let ABC be an acute triangle. We'll approach finding the area of $\triangle ABC$ in the same way that we found the area of Ranu's triangle in Problem 11.8. We draw a line segment from A to $\overline{BC}$ such that the new segment is perpendicular to $\overline{BC}$. We call this new segment an **altitude** of the triangle. The altitude $\overline{AD}$ divides $\triangle ABC$ into two right triangles, $\triangle ABD$ and $\triangle ACD$.

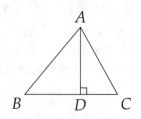

Next, we'll build a rectangle around $\triangle ABC$, to play the role that the wall played in Problem 11.8. The length of the rectangle is BC and its width equals AD, so the area of the rectangle is $(AD)(BC)$.

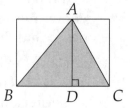

$\overline{AD}$ divides the larger rectangle into two smaller rectangles, and $\triangle ABC$ covers exactly half of each of these rectangles. Therefore, $\triangle ABC$ covers half of the larger rectangle, which means that the area of $\triangle ABC$ is $(AD)(BC)/2$. □

> **Important:** To find the area of an acute triangle, we select one side to be the base of the triangle. The perpendicular segment from the vertex opposite the base to the base is the **altitude** to that base. The area then is
> $$\frac{\text{base length} \times \text{altitude length}}{2}.$$
>
> For example, in triangle ABC shown, $\overline{AD}$ is the altitude to base $\overline{BC}$, and we have
> $$[ABC] = \frac{AD \cdot BC}{2}.$$

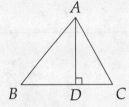

The length of an altitude of a triangle is sometimes also called a **height** of the triangle. We can think of the area of a triangle as "Half the base length times the height."

Each side of a triangle can be considered a base of the triangle. Therefore, each triangle has three altitudes, one for each base. For example, $\triangle ABC$ at the right has altitudes $\overline{AD}$, $\overline{BE}$, and $\overline{CF}$, and we can write the area of the triangle using any of these:

$$[ABC] = \frac{AD \cdot BC}{2} = \frac{BE \cdot AC}{2} = \frac{CF \cdot AB}{2}.$$

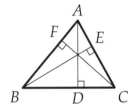

> **Sidenote:** We say that three lines are **concurrent** if they share a common point. As suggested by the altitudes of $\triangle ABC$ above, the three altitudes of any triangle are concurrent. The point at which the three altitudes meet is called the **orthocenter** of the triangle.

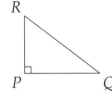

Our area rule works for right triangles, too! In a right triangle, each leg is an altitude to the other leg of the triangle. For example, in right triangle PQR on the left, the leg $\overline{PQ}$ is also the altitude from Q to leg $\overline{PR}$. So, our formula from Problem 11.9 suggests that the area is $(PQ)(PR)/2$, which does indeed match the formula we already know for the area of a right triangle.

Extra! Back on page 421, we learned that if the side lengths of a triangle are a, b, and c, then $a + b > c$. There's a very similar inequality for the three heights of a triangle. If x, y, and z are the heights from the three vertices of a triangle, then
$$\frac{1}{x} + \frac{1}{y} > \frac{1}{z}.$$

Why must this inequality be true?

Problem 11.10: Ravi and Ranu are expanding their house so that the wall that was 18 feet by 8 feet before will become 25 feet by 8 feet. Ravi still wants a triangle that reaches from one corner to the opposite corner, but he doesn't want to use any more paint than he used for his triangle on the old wall. Ranu says they'll just keep the bottom of the triangle the same, and extend the top to the new corner, as shown below:

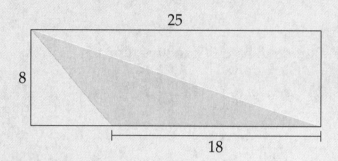

Is Ranu correct? Does Ravi need the same amount of paint for this triangle as he needed for his triangle in Problem 11.8?

Solution for Problem 11.10: If we try the same strategy as in Problem 11.9, we run into a problem. We can't split Ranu's triangle into two right triangles with an altitude from the top vertex of her triangle. We'll have to come up with a different strategy to find the area.

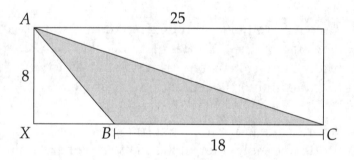

Fortunately, we have some shapes in the diagram whose areas we can find easily. Right triangle AXC has area $(25)(8)/2 = 100$ ft^2. That's not enough information to find the area of $\triangle ABC$. But there's another right triangle in the diagram: $\triangle AXB$. The lengths of the legs of $\triangle AXB$ are $AX = 8$ feet and $BX = XC - BC = 25 - 18 = 7$ feet, so the area of $\triangle AXB$ is $(7)(8)/2 = 28$ ft^2. Now, we can find the area of $\triangle ABC$ by subtracting the area of $\triangle AXB$ from the area of $\triangle AXC$:

$$[ABC] = [AXC] - [AXB] = 100 - 28 = 72 \text{ ft}^2.$$

Ranu is correct! The area is the same as before, even though the new triangle extends all the way out to the new corner. $\square$

We can extend our earlier triangle area rule, to make a rule that works for any triangle.

> **Important:** To find the area of a triangle, we select one side to be the "base" of
> the triangle. The perpendicular segment from the vertex opposite
> the base to the line containing the base is the **altitude** to that base.
> The area is
> $$\frac{\text{base length} \times \text{altitude length}}{2}.$$

The only new part of this rule is that we included "the line containing"
in the definition of "altitude." In other words, we sometimes have to
extend the base of a triangle in order to draw the altitude to that base. For
example, in obtuse triangle ABC on the right, to draw the altitude from
C, we first extend side $\overline{AB}$ past A. The altitude is the dashed segment
from C perpendicular to the extended side.

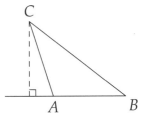

Problem 11.11: A **median** of a triangle is a segment that connects a
vertex of the triangle to the midpoint of the opposite side. For example,
in the diagram on the right, $\overline{AM}$ is a median of $\triangle ABC$. Show that a
median of a triangle divides the triangle into two pieces with equal
area.

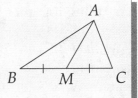

Solution for Problem 11.11: In the diagram, median $\overline{AM}$ divides $\triangle ABC$ into
triangles ABM and ACM. $\overline{AX}$ is the altitude from vertex A in both triangles.
So, we have

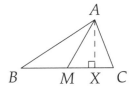

$$[ABM] = \frac{(BM)(AX)}{2} \quad \text{and} \quad [ACM] = \frac{(CM)(AX)}{2}.$$

We have $BM = CM$ because M is the midpoint of $\overline{BC}$. Therefore, triangles ABM and ACM have
the same area. $\square$

Problem 11.12: Tina wants to carpet a room that has the unusual
shape shown on the right with solid lines. Each dotted square in the
diagram has side length 5 feet. What is the area of Tina's carpet?

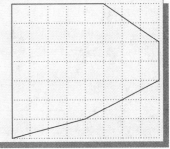

Solution for Problem 11.12: We don't have a nice formula for such an oddly shaped region.
Fortunately, we can break the region up into pieces we can handle. We'll show two different
approaches.

Method 1: Break up the region into rectangles and triangles. There are lots and lots of ways we can do this. On the right below, we've shown one way that produces rectangles and triangles that we can handle easily. Remembering that each of the dotted squares has side length 5 feet, we can find the areas of the pieces as shown, in square feet.

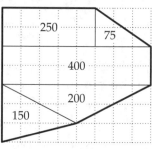

For example, the rectangle in the upper left has length $5 \cdot 5 = 25$ feet and width $2 \cdot 5 = 10$ feet, so its area is $(25)(10) = 250$ square feet. The right triangle in the upper right has legs with lengths $2 \cdot 5 = 10$ feet and $3 \cdot 5 = 15$ feet, so its area is $(10)(15)/2 = 75$ square feet.

Next, consider the triangle in the lower left. Its vertical side has length $3 \cdot 5 = 15$ feet. The altitude to this side consists of four dotted square side lengths, so the altitude has length $4 \cdot 5 = 20$ feet. The area of this triangle then is $(15)(20)/2 = 150$ square feet. In a similar way, we can find the areas of the other two pieces.

Adding together the areas of the five regions gives a total of 1075 square feet.

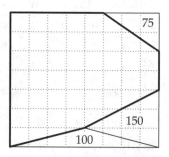

Method 2: View the desired region as what's left when rectangles and triangles are cut away from a larger rectangle. Here, we think of Tina's room as what's left when we start with a big rectangle and cut away pieces. One way to do so in a way that allows us to compute the area is shown at the right. The large rectangle has length $8 \cdot 5 = 40$ feet and width $7 \cdot 5 = 35$ feet, so it has area $(40)(35) = 1400$ ft^2. We then find the areas of the three triangle pieces outside Tina's room as shown in the diagram. To get the area of Tina's room, we subtract the areas of these triangular pieces from the area of the large rectangle. Again, we find that Tina's room has area $1400 - 75 - 150 - 100 = 1075$ square feet. □

> **Concept:** Solving problems using two different methods is an excellent way to check your answer.

> **Concept:** We can sometimes find the areas of complicated regions by splitting them into pieces we can handle, or by viewing them as the result of cutting pieces away from a larger region with a simpler shape.

Exercises

11.2.1 If the length of a certain rectangle is increased by 1, then the area of the rectangle is increased by 12. If instead, the width is increased by 2, then the area of the rectangle is increased by 42. What is the area of the original rectangle?

11.2.2 In the diagram at the right, rectangle $ABCD$ and right triangle BCE have the same area. Find the ratio AB/AE.

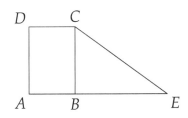

11.2.3 A rectangular tile is 2 inches by 3 inches. What is the least number of tiles that are needed to completely cover a square region 2 feet on each side? *(Source: MOEMS)*

11.2.4 A triangular corner region is sliced off of a rectangular region as shown on the right. What is the area of the pentagonal region $ABEFD$ that remains? *(Source: MATHCOUNTS)*

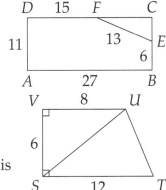

11.2.5 Find the area of $\triangle STU$ in the diagram at the right.

11.2.6 If the length of a rectangle is increased by 20% and its width is decreased by 10%, then the area is increased by what percent?

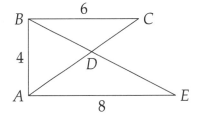

11.2.7 Triangle ABC in the diagram on the left below has an area of 26 cm². Point Y is the midpoint of median $\overline{BX}$. What is the area of triangle AYB?

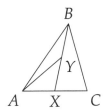

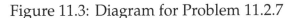

Figure 11.3: Diagram for Problem 11.2.7   Figure 11.4: Diagram for Problem 11.2.8

11.2.8★ In the figure on the right above, $\angle EAB$ and $\angle ABC$ are right angles, $AB = 4$, $BC = 6$, $AE = 8$, and $\overline{AC}$ and $\overline{BE}$ intersect at D. What is the difference between the areas of $\triangle ADE$ and $\triangle BDC$? *(Source: AMC 10)* **Hints:** 27

Extra! We noted back on page 427 that the altitudes of a triangle are
➠➠➠➠ concurrent at a point we call the orthocenter. How does this happen in an obtuse triangle? In an obtuse triangle, two of the altitudes don't even go inside the triangle! But if we draw the lines containing the altitudes, then these lines are concurrent at a point outside the triangle. An example is shown at the right. An obtuse triangle is shown in bold, and the three lines containing the triangle's altitudes meet at the orthocenter, which is outside the triangle.

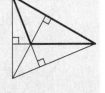

Extra Challenge: Where is the orthocenter of a right triangle?

11.3   Circles

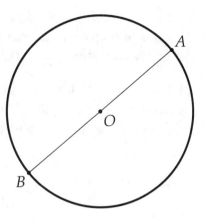

You probably recognize the bold curve at the right as a **circle**. This circle consists of all points that are 1 inch from point O. Point O is called the **center** of the circle. Any line segment from the center of a circle to the circle itself is called a **radius** of the circle. So, for example, $\overline{OA}$ is a radius of the circle. We also use the term "radius" to refer to the length of such a segment. So, the radius of the circle at the right is 1 inch. A **diameter** of the circle is a line segment that connects two points on the circle and passes through the center of the circle. As with "radius," we can also use the word "diameter" to refer to the length of a diameter. The diameter of a circle is twice its radius, since each diameter consists of two radii ("radii" is the plural of radius).

> **Definition:**   A **circle** consists of all points that are a fixed distance, called the **radius** of the circle, from a given point, called the **center** of the circle.

The perimeter of a circle is called the circle's **circumference**. Before reading the rest of this section, try a little experiment. Get a string, and find numerous circular objects. Measure the distance around each object by wrapping the string around it. Then measure the diameter of the object. Finally, for each object find the quotient

$$\frac{\text{Distance Around the Object}}{\text{Diameter of Object}}.$$

You should find that in each case the quotient is a little more than 3. (If you get anything much different, try measuring and dividing again!)

In every circle, the circumference divided by the diameter equals the same number. This special number is called **pi** and is almost always written as the Greek letter π, pronounced "pie." Just as with $\sqrt{2}$, we can't write a decimal number that equals π, but we can approximate π. To the nearest hundredth, π rounds to 3.14.

> **Sidenote:** For some reason, memorizing huge portions of π is a bit of a sport among math-lovers. This should help you get started:
>
> 3.14159265358979323846264338327950288419716939937510582
> 09749445923078164062862089986280348253421170679821480866
> 51328230664709384460955058223172535940812848111745028416
> 02701938521105559644622948954930381964428810975 6...
>
> (Please don't tell your parents you got this π-memorizing idea from us.)

Like $\sqrt{2}$, pi is an **irrational number**. Its decimal expansion does not terminate and does not ever get to the point where the same set of numbers is repeated over and over. So, there are no shortcuts to memorizing digits of pi! (To be clear, there's no good reason to be memorizing tons of digits of π—some people just find it fun.)

In addition to the circumference of a circle, the area of a circle is also related to π:

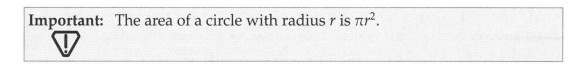

Important: The area of a circle with radius r is πr^2.

We can get a sense for why this formula is true by slicing up a circle and rearranging the pieces. On the left below, we have a circle with radius r that is divided into 16 equal pieces by 16 equally spaced radii. These pieces are called **sectors**.

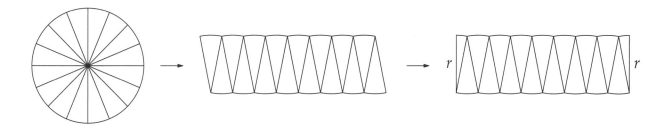

Next, we rearrange the sectors as shown in the second figure above. Then, we take half of one of the end sectors and slide it to the other end as shown in the final figure on the right above. This final figure resembles a rectangle.

The circumference of the original circle is equally divided among the top and bottom of our "rectangle." So, the "length" of the "rectangle" is half the circumference of the circle, which is $(2\pi r)/2 = \pi r$. The "width" of the "rectangle" is simply the radius of the circle, which is r.

Since the area of a rectangle is its length times its width, the area of our "rectangle" is $(\pi r)(r) = \pi r^2$. The "rectangle" is composed of the exact same pieces as our original circle, so the area of the circle is the same as the area of the "rectangle." This isn't a completely accurate explanation for why the area of the original circle is πr^2, since the "rectangle" isn't exactly a rectangle. But, hopefully it gives you some intuition for why the formula is true.

Problem 11.13: What is the radius of a circle that has circumference 54π centimeters?

Problem 11.14: If 1 gallon of paint is enough to paint the interior of a circle with diameter 10 meters, then what is the diameter of the largest circle whose interior I can paint with 4 gallons of paint?

Problem 11.15: My rectangular house is 30 feet by 40 feet.

(a) My goat Cassidy is outside on a 20-foot long leash that is connected to a corner of my house. What is the area of the region in which Cassidy can roam?

(b) If I lengthen Cassidy's leash to 50 feet, then what is the area of the region in which Cassidy can roam?

Problem 11.16: Two quarter-circles are drawn with their centers at opposite vertices of a square, as shown at the right. If the side length of the square is 6, then what is the area of the shaded region between the quarter-circles?

Problem 11.13: What is the radius of a circle that has circumference 54π centimeters?

Solution for Problem 11.13: Since the circumference of a circle divided by the circle's diameter is π, the circumference of a circle is always π times the diameter of the circle. So, a circle with circumference 54π centimeters has diameter 54 centimeters. Therefore, the radius of the circle is $54/2 = 27$ centimeters. $\square$

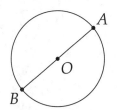

> **Important:** If a circle has radius r, diameter d, and circumference C, then we have $d = 2r$ and $C = \pi d = 2\pi r$.

Problem 11.14: If 1 gallon of paint is enough to paint the interior of a circle with diameter 10 meters, then what is the diameter of the largest circle whose interior I can paint with 4 gallons of paint?

Solution for Problem 11.14: First, we find the area of the region we can paint with 1 gallon. A circle with diameter 10 meters has radius 5 meters, so its area is $\pi(5^2) = 25\pi$ square meters. Since 1 gallon can cover 25π square meters, we know that 4 gallons can cover $4(25\pi) = 100\pi$ square meters. Let r be the radius in meters of the largest circle we can paint with 4 gallons. Then, we must have $\pi r^2 = 100\pi$, so $r^2 = 100$, which means $r = 10$. The radius of the new circle is 10 meters, so the new circle's diameter is $2 \cdot 10 = 20$ meters. $\square$

In Problem 11.14, we saw that doubling the radius (or diameter) of a circle multiplies its area by 4. Similarly, suppose we start with a circle that has radius r and then multiply the radius by k to make a new circle. The area of the original circle is πr^2. The area of the new circle is $\pi(kr)^2 = \pi k^2 r^2 = k^2(\pi r^2)$, which is k^2 times the area of the original circle.

> **Important:** Multiplying the radius of a circle by k multiplies the area of the circle by k^2.

Problem 11.15: My rectangular house is 30 feet by 40 feet.

(a) My goat Cassidy is outside on a 20-foot long leash that is connected to a corner of my house. What is the area of the region in which Cassidy can roam?

(b) If I lengthen Cassidy's leash to 50 feet, then what is the area of the region in which Cassidy can roam?

Solution for Problem 11.15:

(a) We start with a diagram. The rectangle at the right is my house, and Cassidy's leash is connected at corner A. Since the leash is 20 feet long, Cassidy can reach any point outside the house that is within 20 feet of point A. So, Cassidy can reach any outside point that is inside the circle centered at A with radius 20 feet. This region is shaded in the diagram; Cassidy can't reach the quarter of the circle that is inside the house. She can roam throughout the $\frac{3}{4}$ of the circle that is outside the house. The area of this region is

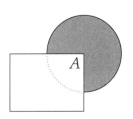

$$\frac{3}{4}\left(20^2\pi\right) = \frac{3}{4}(400\pi) = 300\pi \text{ square feet.}$$

(b) As in the previous part, Cassidy can roam throughout $\frac{3}{4}$ of a circular region with radius 50 feet, which is the large darkly-shaded region in the diagram below. This region is $\frac{3}{4}$ of a circle with radius 50 feet. The area of this region is

$$\frac{3}{4}\left(50^2\pi\right) = \frac{3}{4}(2500\pi) = 1875\pi \text{ square feet.}$$

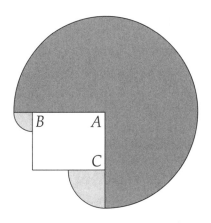

However, because Cassidy's leash is longer than each side of my house, she can go around two other corners of my house. Since the length of my house is 40 feet, when Cassidy reaches point B, she has another 10 feet of leash. So, she can reach any outside point that is within 10 feet of B. This means she can reach any point in an additional quarter-circular region at point B with radius 10 feet. This region is shaded lightly in the diagram. The area of this region is $\frac{1}{4}$ the area of a full circle with radius 10, or

$$\frac{1}{4}\left(10^2\pi\right) = \frac{1}{4}(100\pi) = 25\pi \text{ square feet.}$$

Similarly, the width of my house is 30 feet, so when Cassidy gets to point C, she has another 20 feet of leash. Therefore, she can reach any point in a quarter-circular region at point C with radius 20 feet. This region is also shaded lightly in the diagram. The area of this quarter-circular region is

$$\frac{1}{4}\left(20^2\pi\right) = \frac{1}{4}(400\pi) = 100\pi \text{ square feet.}$$

Adding together the areas of all three regions, the total area that Cassidy can reach is

$$25\pi + 100\pi + 1875\pi = 2000\pi \text{ square feet.}$$

□

Sometimes we have to be quite creative to find the area of an oddly-shaped region.

Problem 11.16: Two quarter-circles are drawn with their centers at opposite vertices of a square, as shown at the right. If the side length of the square is 6, then what is the area of the shaded region between the quarter-circles?

Solution for Problem 11.16: Here are a couple different ways to tackle this problem:

Method 1: Break the shaded region into pieces. We label our square $ABCD$, and draw diagonal $\overline{BD}$ to split the shaded region into two identical pieces. Now, we just have to find the area of one shaded piece, and then we can double that area to get our answer.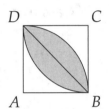

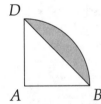 Each shaded piece is what remains after we remove an isosceles right triangle from a quarter-circle. The radius of the quarter-circle is 6, so its area is $\frac{1}{4}(6^2\pi) = \frac{1}{4}(36\pi) = 9\pi$. Both legs of the right triangle have length 6, so the area of the right triangle is $\frac{(6)(6)}{2} = \frac{36}{2} = 18$. So, we have

$$\text{Shaded piece} = (\text{Quarter-circle}) - (\text{Triangle}).$$

Therefore, the area of the shaded piece is $9\pi - 18$.

We have to be careful! The original shaded region consists of two pieces like the one whose area we just found. So, the area of the original shaded region is

$$2(9\pi - 18) = 18\pi - 36.$$

Method 2: Creative overcounting! Imagine we paint each quarter-circular region gray. When we do so, we will paint the overlap region twice, so it will end up darker than the once-painted regions, as shown in the diagram at the right. That is, while painting the two semi-circles, we paint the entire square once and give the darkly-shaded region a second coat of paint. So, we have:

$$\text{Two Quarter-circles} = (\text{Square}) + (\text{Darkly-Shaded Region}).$$

Rearranging this gives us

$$\text{Darkly-Shaded Region} = (\text{Two Quarter-circles}) - (\text{Square}).$$

As we saw above, each quarter-circle has area 9π, so the two together have an area of 18π. The area of the square is $6^2 = 36$, so the area of the darkly-shaded region is $18\pi - 36$. □

Exercises

11.3.1   Jane is running on a circular track with a radius of 50 yards. A mile is 1760 yards. What is the least number of complete laps she must run to cover a distance at least 4 miles?

11.3.2   I have a circular garden that is 40 feet in diameter. I need 3000 seeds to plant the whole garden. How many seeds would I need if the diameter of the garden were tripled?

11.3.3   A circle and three different lines are drawn on a sheet of paper. What is the largest possible number of points of intersection of these figures? *(Source: AMC 8)*

11.3.4   The ratio of the circumferences of two circles is $3 : 5$. What is the ratio of their areas? *(Source: MATHCOUNTS)*

11.3.5   In the diagram on the right, triangle ABC is a right triangle and a semicircle with diameter $\overline{AB}$ is drawn. If $AB = 20$, $AC = 16$, and $BC = 12$, then what is total shaded area in the diagram?

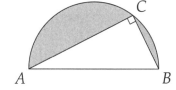

11.3.6   What is the total shaded area in the figure below? *(Source: MATHCOUNTS)*

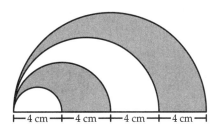

11.4   Summary

The **perimeter** of a closed figure is the total length of its boundary. For example, the perimeter of a rectangle with length l and width w is $2(l + w)$.

> **Important:** For any three points A, B, and C, we have
> $$AB + BC \geq AC.$$
> We have $AB + BC = AC$ if and only if B is on $\overline{AC}$. This relationship is called the **Triangle Inequality**.

The **area** of a closed figure is the number of unit squares (or pieces of squares) needed to exactly cover the figure. We sometimes use brackets to refer to area, so that [*ABC*] means the area of △*ABC*. The area of a rectangle equals the product of its length and width.

> **Important:** To find the area of a triangle, we select one side to be the "base" of the triangle. The perpendicular segment from the vertex opposite the base to the line containing the base is the **altitude** to that base. The area then is
>
> $$\frac{\text{base length} \times \text{altitude length}}{2}.$$

A **circle** consists of all points that are a fixed distance, called the **radius** of the circle, from a given point, called the **center** of the circle. We also use the word "radius" to describe a segment from the center of the circle to a point on the circle. A **diameter** is a line segment that connects two points on the circle and passes through the circle's center. We also use the word "diameter" to mean the length of a diameter. The perimeter of a circle is called the circle's **circumference**.

> **Important:** If a circle has diameter d and radius r, then:
>
> - $d = 2r$.
>
> - The circumference of the circle is πd, or $2\pi r$, where π is a number that is approximately 3.14. (The symbol π is called "pi.")
>
> - The area of the circle is πr^2.

 REVIEW PROBLEMS

11.17 Segment $\overline{LN}$ has midpoint M, and point N is the midpoint of segment $\overline{LP}$. What is the ratio of MN to LP?

11.18 The length and width of a rectangle are each increased by 10%.

(a) By what percent is the perimeter of the rectangle increased?

(b) By what percent is the area of the rectangle increased?

11.19 The perimeter of a hexagon is 300 units. One side of the hexagon is 45 units long and the lengths of the other sides are in the ratio $1 : 2 : 3 : 4 : 5$. Find the positive difference between the lengths of the longest and shortest sides. *(Source: MATHCOUNTS)*

11.20 An architect draws a rectangular room to scale. The drawing is 12 cm long and 8 cm wide. The shorter dimension of the actual room is 20 feet. What is the perimeter of the actual room?

11.21 Square tiles 9 inches on a side exactly cover the floor of a rectangular room. The border tiles are white and all other tiles are blue. The room measures 18 feet by 15 feet. How many tiles are white? *(Source: MOEMS)*

11.22 If adjacent sides meet at right angles in the figure at the right, what is the number of centimeters in the perimeter of the figure? *(Source: MATHCOUNTS)*

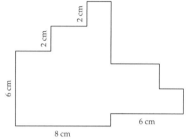

11.23 I start with a piece of paper that is an equilateral triangle with side length 9 inches. From each corner of this triangle, I cut away an equilateral triangle with side length 3 inches. What is the perimeter of the figure that remains after I have removed these three pieces?

11.24 *ABC* is an equilateral triangle. *ABUVWXYZ* is a regular octagon and *BCMNO* is a regular pentagon. The triangle is outside both the octagon and the pentagon, but shares a side with each. If the perimeter of *BUVWXYZACMNO* is 160, then what is the perimeter of *ABC*?

11.25 A pentagon train is made by attaching regular pentagons with one-inch sides so that each pentagon, except the two on the ends, is attached to exactly two other pentagons along sides as shown. How many inches are in the perimeter of a pentagon train made from 85 pentagons? *(Source: MATHCOUNTS)*

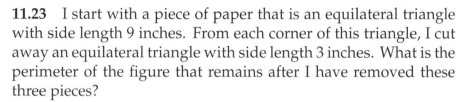

11.26 How many different integers can possibly be the third side length of a triangle in which the other two sides have lengths 7 and 19?

11.27 The perimeters of two squares are in the ratio 2 : 7. What is the ratio of the area of the smaller square to the area of the larger square? *(Source: MATHCOUNTS)*

11.28 The area of a square is 36 square centimeters. A rectangle has the same perimeter as the square. The length of the rectangle is twice its width. What is the area of the rectangle? *(Source: MOEMS)*

11.29 In the figure, $AB = 12$ cm and $BC = AD = 8$ cm. We also have $\overline{BC} \perp \overline{AB}$ and $\overline{DA} \perp \overline{AB}$. How many square centimeters are shaded?

11.30 A rectangular floor, 9 ft by 11 ft, is covered completely by tiles. Each tile is either a 2 ft by 3 ft rectangle or a square 1 ft on a side. No tiles overlap. What is the least total number of tiles that could have been used to cover the floor? *(Source: MOEMS)*

11.31 Find the length of the altitude from B to $\overline{AC}$ in triangle ABC at the left below.

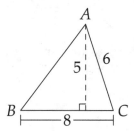

Figure 11.5: Diagram for Problem 11.31   Figure 11.6: Diagram for Problem 11.32

11.32 Find the area of $MNOP$ on the right above.

11.33 The ratio of the radii of two circles is 5 : 2. What is the ratio of their areas?

11.34 What is the greatest number of points at which a circle and a hexagon can intersect?

11.35 Circle X has a radius of π. Circle Y has a circumference of 8π. Circle Z has an area of 9π. List the circles in order from smallest to largest radius. *(Source: AMC 8)*

11.36 A farmer has a square lot that is 200 feet on each side. She has a very powerful sprinkler that sprays water in a circle. She doesn't want to waste any water, so she'll set her sprinkler so that it doesn't spray any water outside her lot. What is the largest percentage of her lot that she can water? (Answer to the nearest whole percent.)

11.37 Two quarter-circles are drawn inside a rectangle as shown. The two quarter-circles meet at a point on a side of the rectangle. If the radius of each quarter-circle is 6 inches, then what is the area of the shaded region?

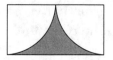

11.38 Semicircles of diameter 2 inches are lined up as shown at the right. What is the area, in square inches, of the shaded region in a 1-foot length of this pattern? *(Source: MATHCOUNTS)*

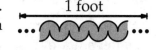

Challenge Problems

11.39 Points A, B, C, and D lie on a line in alphabetical order. If $AB : BD = 5 : 7$ and $AC : CD = 13 : 11$, determine the ratio $AB : BC : CD$. *(Source: MATHCOUNTS)*

11.40 In rectangle $ABCD$, point X is the midpoint of $\overline{AD}$ and Y is the midpoint of $\overline{CD}$. What fraction of the area of the rectangle is enclosed by $\triangle AXY$?

11.41 Point T is on side $\overline{QR}$ of $\triangle PQR$. Find the ratio QT/QR if the area of $\triangle PQT$ is 75 and the area of $\triangle PTR$ is 40. **Hints:** 53

11.42 In the diagram on the right, $WXYZ$ is a rectangle. The area of triangle ZXA is 36, and $ZA = 3AY$.

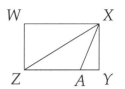

(a) If $XY = 12$, then what is the area of rectangle $WXYZ$?

(b) If $XY = 9$, then what is the area of rectangle $WXYZ$?

(c) If $XY = 6$, then what is the area of rectangle $WXYZ$?

(d) Do you notice a pattern in your answers to the first three parts? Will this pattern hold for other values of XY?

11.43 What is the side length of a regular polygon whose interior angles each measure 168 degrees and whose perimeter is 120 cm?

11.44 In quadrilateral $ABCD$, each of the side lengths is an integer, and $AD = BC$. If we have $AB : AD = 2 : 5$ and $AD : CD = 3 : 4$, then what is the smallest possible perimeter of the quadrilateral? **Hints:** 128, 150

11.45 $ABCDEF$ is a regular hexagon in which diagonal $\overline{AD}$ has length 16. Find the perimeter of $ABCDEF$. **Hints:** 67

11.46 Rebecca walks 100 feet in a straight line. She then turns 20 degrees to the left and walks another 100 feet, and then turns 20 degrees to the left again. She continues this pattern until she reaches the point where she started. How far did she walk? **Hints:** 25

11.47 In the figure shown, points D, E, and F are the midpoints of semicircles ADB, BEC, and DFE, respectively. If the radius of each semicircle is 1, then what is the area of the shaded region? *(Source: MATHCOUNTS)* **Hints:** 20

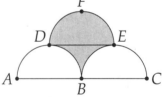

11.48 Teri has sticks of length 9 inches, 12 inches, and 14 inches. She cuts the same amount off of each stick. After cutting this amount off each stick, she is no longer able to make a triangle by attaching the sticks end to end. What is the smallest amount Teri could have cut off of each stick?

11.49★ Suppose we have $AB = 8$, $BC = 10$, $CD = 16$, and $DA = 12$ in quadrilateral $ABCD$. How many different possible integer values are there for AC? *(Source: MATHCOUNTS)*

11.50★ Points $E, F, G,$ and H are midpoints of sides of square $ABCD$ as shown. If $\overline{AB}$ is 20 units long, then what is the area of the shaded region? **Hints:** 76

  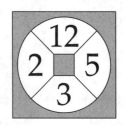 

Choose always the way that seems the best, however rough it may be; custom will soon render it easy and agreeable. – Pythagoras

CHAPTER **12**

Right Triangles and Quadrilaterals

12.1 The Pythagorean Theorem

In a right triangle, the side of the triangle opposite the right angle is called the **hypotenuse** and the other two sides are called the **legs** of the triangle. We also often use the terms "legs" and "hypotenuse" to refer the lengths of the legs and hypotenuse of a right triangle.

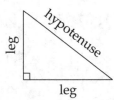

In this section, we explore one of the most famous math theorems, the **Pythagorean Theorem**, which is a powerful relationship among the sides of a right triangle. We'll start by walking through one of the many proofs of the Pythagorean Theorem. ("Pythagorean" is pronounced "puh-thag-uh-ree-uhn.")

 **Problems**

Problem 12.1: Four identical right triangles with legs of lengths 3 and 4 are attached to the sides of square $WXYZ$ as shown, such that $PW = QX = RY = SZ = 3$ and $PX = QY = RZ = SW = 4$.

(a) Explain why $\angle PWS = 180°$, and why $PQRS$ is a square.

(b) What is the area of $PQRS$?

(c) Find the area of $WXYZ$.

(d) Find WX.

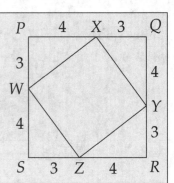

Problem 12.2: In this problem, we follow in the steps of the previous problem to prove the Pythagorean Theorem. We start again with four copies of a right triangle, attached to the sides of square $WXYZ$ as shown at the right. Let the lengths of the legs of each triangle be a and b, as shown, and let the hypotenuse of each right triangle have length c.

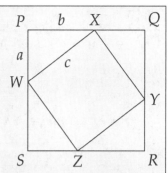

(a) Find the area of $WXYZ$ in terms of c.

(b) Find the area of $PQRS$ in terms of a and b.

(c) Find the area of $WXYZ$ in terms of a and b.

(d) Show that $a^2 + b^2 = c^2$.

Problem 12.3: Find the missing side lengths in each of the three triangles shown below.

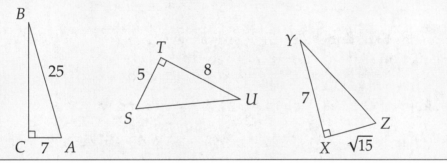

Problem 12.4: Must the hypotenuse of a right triangle be the longest side of the triangle? Why or why not?

Problem 12.5: In Problems 12.1 and 12.3, we have seen two right triangles in which all three side lengths are integers. Can you find any more right triangles in which all three side lengths are integers? **Hints:** 47

Problem 12.6:

(a) Find the hypotenuse of a right triangle whose legs are $3 \cdot 4$ and $4 \cdot 4$.

(b) Find the hypotenuse of a right triangle whose legs are $3 \cdot 5$ and $4 \cdot 5$.

(c) Find the hypotenuse of a right triangle whose legs are $3 \cdot 2011$ and $4 \cdot 2011$.

(d) Find the hypotenuse of a right triangle whose legs are $\frac{3}{100101}$ and $\frac{4}{100101}$.

Problem 12.7: The length of one leg of a right triangle is 210 and the triangle's hypotenuse has length 750. What is the length of the other leg?

Problem 12.1: Four identical right triangles with legs of lengths 3 and 4 are attached to the sides of square $WXYZ$ as shown, such that $PW = QX = RY = SZ = 3$ and $PX = QY = RZ = SW = 4$.

(a) Explain why $\angle PWS = 180°$, and why $PQRS$ is a square.

(b) What is the area of $PQRS$?

(c) Find the area of $WXYZ$.

(d) Find WX.

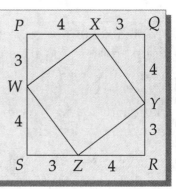

Solution for Problem 12.1:

(a) Back on page 402, we learned that the acute angles of a right triangle add to 90°. Therefore, in right triangle PWX we have

$$\angle PWX + \angle PXW = 90°.$$

Since triangles SWZ and PXW are identical, we have $\angle SWZ = \angle PXW$. Substituting this into the equation above gives

$$\angle PWX + \angle SWZ = 90°.$$

We are told that $WXYZ$ is a square, so $\angle XWZ = 90°$, and we have

$$
\begin{aligned}
\angle PWS &= \angle PWX + \angle XWZ + \angle SWZ \\
&= \angle PWX + 90° + \angle SWZ \\
&= 90° + (\angle PWX + \angle SWZ) \\
&= 90° + 90° \\
&= 180°.
\end{aligned}
$$

Therefore, $\angle PWS$ is a straight angle. This means that W is on $\overline{PS}$. Similarly, each vertex of $WXYZ$ is on one of the sides of quadrilateral $PQRS$. Each side of $PQRS$ has length $3 + 4 = 7$, and each angle of $PQRS$ is the right angle of one of the triangles. So, all the sides of $PQRS$ are congruent, and all the angles of $PQRS$ are congruent, which means $PQRS$ is a square.

(b) Since $PQRS$ is a square with side length 7, its area is $7^2 = 49$.

(c) Each right triangle has area $(3)(4)/2 = 6$ square units. Removing the four right triangles from $PQRS$ leaves $WXYZ$, so we have

$$[WXYZ] = [PQRS] - 4(6) = 49 - 24 = 25.$$

(d) The area of $WXYZ$ is the square of its side length. Because the area of $WXYZ$ is 25, its side length must be $\sqrt{25}$, which equals 5.

$\square$

Problem 12.2: In this problem, we follow in the steps of the previous problem to prove the Pythagorean Theorem. We start again with four copies of a right triangle, attached to the sides of square $WXYZ$ as shown at the right. Let the lengths of the legs of each triangle be a and b, as shown, and let the hypotenuse of each right triangle have length c.

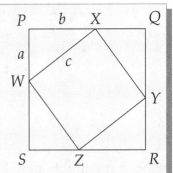

(a) Find the area of $WXYZ$ in terms of c.

(b) Find the area of $PQRS$ in terms of a and b.

(c) Find the area of $WXYZ$ in terms of a and b.

(d) Show that $a^2 + b^2 = c^2$.

Solution for Problem 12.2:

(a) Since $WXYZ$ is a square with side length c, its area is c^2.

(b) As in the previous problem, $PQRS$ is a square, and the vertices of $WXYZ$ are on the sides of $PQRS$. Each side of $PQRS$ has length $a + b$, so the area of $PQRS$ is $(a+b)^2$. We can expand $(a + b)^2$ with the distributive property:

$$\begin{aligned}
[PQRS] = (a + b)^2 &= (a + b)(a + b) \\
&= a(a + b) + b(a + b) \\
&= a^2 + ab + ba + b^2 \\
&= a^2 + ab + ab + b^2 \\
&= a^2 + 2ab + b^2.
\end{aligned}$$

(c) The area of each of the right triangles is $ab/2$, so the four right triangles together have area $4(ab/2) = 2ab$. We can find the area of $WXYZ$ in terms of a and b by subtracting the areas of the triangles from the area of $PQRS$:

$$\begin{aligned}
[WXYZ] = [PQRS] - 4(ab/2) \\
= a^2 + 2ab + b^2 - 2ab \\
= a^2 + b^2.
\end{aligned}$$

(d) In part (a), we found that $[WXYZ] = c^2$, and in part (c), we found that $[WXYZ] = a^2 + b^2$. Equating our expressions for $[WXYZ]$, we have

$$a^2 + b^2 = c^2.$$

□

> **Important:** The **Pythagorean Theorem** tells us that in any right triangle, the sum of the squares of the legs equals the square of the hypotenuse. So, in the diagram to the right, we have
>
>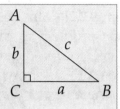
>
> $$a^2 + b^2 = c^2.$$

Our work in Problem 12.2 is the same as the work we did in Problem 12.1, except that we replaced the numbers in Problem 12.1 with variables a, b, and c in Problem 12.2.

> **Concept:** Specific examples can sometimes be used as guides to discover proofs.

The Pythagorean Theorem also works "in reverse." By this, we mean that if the side lengths of a triangle satisfy the Pythagorean Theorem, then the triangle must be a right triangle. So, for example, if we have a triangle with side lengths 3, 4, and 5, then we know that the triangle must be a right triangle because $3^2 + 4^2 = 5^2$.

Let's get a little practice using the Pythagorean Theorem.

> **Problem 12.3:** Find the missing side lengths in each of the three triangles shown below.
>
>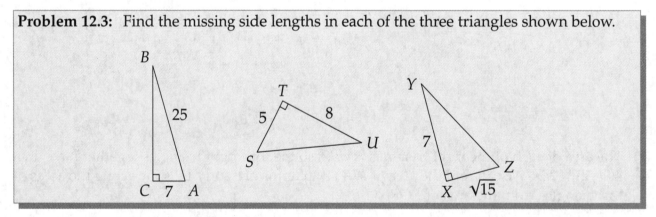

Solution for Problem 12.3: What's wrong with this solution:

> **Bogus Solution:** Applying the Pythagorean Theorem to $\triangle ABC$ gives
>
> $$7^2 + 25^2 = BC^2.$$
>
> Therefore, we find $BC^2 = 49 + 625 = 674$. Taking the square root gives us $BC = \sqrt{674}$.

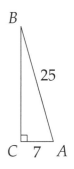

This solution is incorrect because it applies the Pythagorean Theorem incorrectly. Side $\overline{BC}$ is a leg, not the hypotenuse. Applying the Pythagorean Theorem to $\triangle ABC$ correctly gives

$$AC^2 + BC^2 = AB^2.$$

Substituting $AC = 7$ and $AB = 25$ gives us $7^2 + BC^2 = 25^2$, so $49 + BC^2 = 625$. Subtracting 49 from both sides gives $BC^2 = 576$. Taking the square root of 576 gives $BC = 24$. (Note that $(-24)^2 = 576$ too, but we can't have a negative length, so BC cannot be -24.)

> **WARNING!!** Be careful when applying the Pythagorean Theorem. Make sure you correctly identify which sides are the legs and which is the hypotenuse.

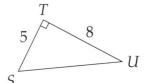

Applying the Pythagorean Theorem to $\triangle STU$ gives

$$ST^2 + TU^2 = SU^2,$$

so we have $5^2 + 8^2 = SU^2$ from the side lengths given in the problem. Therefore, we have $SU^2 = 25 + 64 = 89$. Taking the square root gives us $SU = \sqrt{89}$.

In $\triangle XYZ$, the Pythagorean Theorem gives us

$$XY^2 + XZ^2 = YZ^2,$$

so $7^2 + (\sqrt{15})^2 = YZ^2$. This gives us $49 + 15 = YZ^2$, so $YZ^2 = 64$ and $YZ = 8$. $\square$

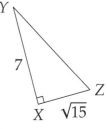

> **WARNING!!** A common mistake when using the Pythagorean Theorem to find the hypotenuse length of a right triangle is forgetting that the hypotenuse is squared in the equation, too. One quick way to avoid this error is to consider the three side lengths after finding the hypotenuse.
>
> For example, suppose a right triangle has legs of lengths 3 and 4. The hypotenuse clearly can't be $3^2 + 4^2 = 25$, because the lengths 3, 4, and 25 don't satisfy the Triangle Inequality. Taking the square root of 25, we see that the hypotenuse should be 5, not 25.

Problem 12.4: Must the hypotenuse of a right triangle be the longest side of the triangle? Why or why not?

Solution for Problem 12.4: Yes. The square of the hypotenuse equals the sum of the squares of the legs. The sum of any two positive numbers is greater than both of the numbers being added. So, the square of the hypotenuse must be greater than the square of each leg. Therefore, the hypotenuse must be longer than each leg. □

Problem 12.5: In Problems 12.1 and 12.3, we have seen two right triangles in which all three side lengths are integers. Can you find any more right triangles in which all three side lengths are integers?

Solution for Problem 12.5: There are lots and lots of right triangles in which all three side lengths are integers! To search for some, we can list the first 20 positive perfect squares:

$$1, 4, 9, 16, 25, 36, 49, 64, 81, 100, 121, 144, 169, 196, 225, 256, 289, 324, 361, 400.$$

Then, we look for pairs of squares that add up to another square. We immediately see $9+16 = 25$, which is $3^2 + 4^2 = 5^2$. We already saw this example in Problem 12.1. We also see $25 + 144 = 169$, which is $5^2 + 12^2 = 13^2$. So, a right triangle with legs of lengths 5 and 12 has a hypotenuse with length 13. We also find $64 + 225 = 289$, which is $8^2 + 15^2 = 17^2$. This gives us a right triangle with 8 and 15 as the legs and 17 as the hypotenuse. □

A **Pythagorean triple** is a group of three positive integers that satisfy the equation $a^2 + b^2 = c^2$. So, for example, $\{3, 4, 5\}$ is a Pythagorean triple, as are $\{5, 12, 13\}$ and $\{8, 15, 17\}$. There are lots of interesting patterns in Pythagorean triples. See if you can find more Pythagorean triples, and look for patterns that you can use to find more Pythagorean triples.

We can find one such important pattern by looking back at our list of squares:

$$1, 4, 9, 16, 25, 36, 49, 64, 81, 100, 121, 144, 169, 196, 225, 256, 289, 324, 361, 400.$$

We find that $36 + 64 = 100$, which is $6^2 + 8^2 = 10^2$. Here, the side lengths are double those of the first triangle we saw with sides of lengths 3, 4, and 5. We might wonder if tripling these three side lengths also gives us another right triangle. Indeed, we see that $9^2 + 12^2 = 15^2$, since $81 + 144 = 225$. Let's investigate further.

Problem 12.6:
(a) Find the hypotenuse of a right triangle whose legs are $3 \cdot 4$ and $4 \cdot 4$.
(b) Find the hypotenuse of a right triangle whose legs are $3 \cdot 5$ and $4 \cdot 5$.
(c) Find the hypotenuse of a right triangle whose legs are $3 \cdot 2011$ and $4 \cdot 2011$.
(d) Find the hypotenuse of a right triangle whose legs are $\frac{3}{100101}$ and $\frac{4}{100101}$.

Solution for Problem 12.6:

(a) The legs have lengths 12 and 16. Letting the hypotenuse be c, the Pythagorean Theorem gives us
$$c^2 = 12^2 + 16^2 = 144 + 256 = 400.$$

Taking the square root gives us $c = 20$. Notice that $20 = 5 \cdot 4$.

(b) The legs have lengths 15 and 20. Letting the hypotenuse be c, the Pythagorean Theorem gives us

$$c^2 = 15^2 + 20^2 = 225 + 400 = 625.$$

Taking the square root gives us $c = 25$. Notice that $25 = 5 \cdot 5$.

(c) The legs have lengths 6033 and 8044. Um, squaring those doesn't look like much fun. Let's see if we can find a more clever way to solve this problem. We know that a right triangle with legs 3 and 4 has hypotenuse 5. In part (a), we saw that if the legs of a right triangle are $3 \cdot 4$ and $4 \cdot 4$, then the hypotenuse is $5 \cdot 4$. In part (b), we saw that if the legs of a right triangle are $3 \cdot 5$ and $4 \cdot 5$, then the hypotenuse is $5 \cdot 5$. It looks like there's a pattern!

> **Concept:** Searching for patterns is a powerful problem-solving strategy.

It appears that if the legs of a right triangle are $3x$ and $4x$, then the hypotenuse is $5x$. We can test this guess with the Pythagorean Theorem. Suppose the legs of a right triangle are $3x$ and $4x$. Then, the sum of the squares of the legs is

$$(3x)^2 + (4x)^2 = 3^2x^2 + 4^2x^2 = 9x^2 + 16x^2 = 25x^2.$$

Since

$$(5x)^2 = 5^2x^2 = 25x^2,$$

we have $(3x)^2 + (4x)^2 = (5x)^2$, which means that the length of the hypotenuse is indeed $5x$.

This means that we don't have to square 6033 and 8044! A right triangle with legs of lengths $3 \cdot 2011$ and $4 \cdot 2011$ has a hypotenuse with length $5 \cdot 2011 = 10055$.

(d) There's nothing in our explanation in part (c) that requires x to be a whole number; it can be a fraction, too! So, in a right triangle with legs of length $3 \cdot \frac{1}{100101}$ and $4 \cdot \frac{1}{100101}$, the hypotenuse has length $5 \cdot \frac{1}{100101} = \frac{5}{100101}$.

$\square$

Our work in Problem 12.6 is an example of why knowing common Pythagorean triples is useful. Any time we have a right triangle in which the legs have ratio $3 : 4$, then we know that all three sides of the triangle are in the ratio $3 : 4 : 5$. As we saw in the final two parts of Problem 12.6, this can allow us to find the hypotenuse quickly without using the Pythagorean Theorem directly.

We can also sometimes use this approach to quickly find the length of a leg when we know the lengths of the other leg and the hypotenuse.

> **Problem 12.7:** The length of one leg of a right triangle is 210 and the triangle's hypotenuse has length 750. What is the length of the other leg?

Solution for Problem 12.7: We find the ratio of the given leg length to the hypotenuse length, hoping it will match the corresponding ratio in one of the Pythagorean triples we know. We have $210 : 750 = \frac{210}{30} : \frac{750}{30} = 7 : 25$, so the ratio of the given leg to the hypotenuse is $7 : 25$. This reminds us of the $\{7, 24, 25\}$ Pythagorean triple that we saw in Problem 12.3. Since the ratio of the known leg to the hypotenuse is $7 : 25$, we know that all three sides are in the ratio $7 : 24 : 25$. The first leg is $7 \cdot 30$ and the hypotenuse is $25 \cdot 30$, so the other leg of the right triangle is $24 \cdot 30 = 720$. $\square$

> **Important:** If we multiply all three side lengths of a right triangle by the same positive number, then the three new side lengths also satisfy the Pythagorean Theorem. In other words, if side lengths a, b, and c satisfy $a^2 + b^2 = c^2$, then $(na)^2 + (nb)^2 = (nc)^2$, for any positive number n.

Exercises

12.1.1 Find the missing side lengths below:

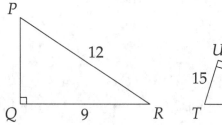 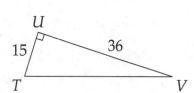 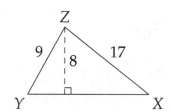

12.1.2 Bill walks $\frac{1}{2}$ mile south, then $\frac{3}{4}$ mile east, and finally $\frac{1}{2}$ mile south. How many miles is he, in a direct line, from his starting point? *(Source: AMC 8)*

12.1.3 Find a formula for the length of a diagonal of a rectangle with length l and width w.

12.1.4 The bases of a 39-foot pole and a 15-foot pole are 45 feet apart, and both poles are perpendicular to the ground. The ground is flat between the two poles. What is the length of the shortest rope that can be used to connect the tops of the two poles?

12.1.5 A square, a rectangle, a right triangle, and a semicircle are combined to form the figure at the right. Find the area of the whole figure in square units.

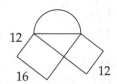

12.1.6★ Find the hypotenuse of a right triangle whose legs have lengths 4900049 and 6300063.

12.2 Some Special Triangles

In this section, we use the Pythagorean Theorem to investigate a few common special types of triangles.

 **Problems**

Problem 12.8: *DEF* is an isosceles triangle with *DE* = *EF* = 26 and *DF* = 20.

(a) Suppose *M* is on base $\overline{DF}$ such that $\overline{EM}$ is an altitude of the isosceles triangle. Why must *M* be the midpoint of $\overline{DF}$?

(b) Find the area of △*DEF*.

Problem 12.9:

(a) Suppose △*ABC* is equilateral with side length 6. Find the length of an altitude of △*ABC*.

(b) Find the area of △*ABC*.

Problem 12.10:

(a) If one leg of an isosceles right triangle has length 5, then what are the lengths of the other leg and the hypotenuse of the triangle?

(b) If one leg of an isosceles right triangle has length 8, then what are the lengths of the other leg and the hypotenuse of the triangle?

(c) If we know the length of one leg of an isosceles right triangle, then what's a fast way to find the length of the hypotenuse?

Problem 12.11: A **30-60-90 triangle** is a triangle whose angles measure 30°, 60°, and 90°.

(a) Describe how to divide an equilateral triangle into two identical 30-60-90 triangles.

(b) Suppose the leg opposite the 30° angle in a 30-60-90 triangle has length 2. Use your answer to part (a) to find the hypotenuse of the triangle. What is the length of the other leg?

(c) Suppose the leg opposite the 30° angle in a 30-60-90 triangle has length *s*. In terms of *s*, what are the lengths of the hypotenuse and the other leg of the triangle?

Problem 12.8: *DEF* is an isosceles triangle with *DE* = *EF* = 26 and *DF* = 20.

(a) Suppose *M* is on base $\overline{DF}$ such that $\overline{EM}$ is an altitude of the isosceles triangle. Why must *M* be the midpoint of $\overline{DF}$?

(b) Find the area of △*DEF*.

Solution for Problem 12.8:

(a) Triangles *DEM* and *FEM* are right triangles. Applying the Pythagorean Theorem to both gives

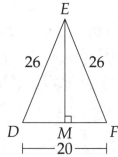

$$DM^2 + EM^2 = DE^2 = 26^2 = 676,$$
$$FM^2 + EM^2 = EF^2 = 26^2 = 676.$$

Since the right-hand sides of these equations are equal, the left-hand sides must be equal, too. So, we have $DM^2 + EM^2 = FM^2 + EM^2$, which means that $DM^2 = FM^2$. Therefore, we have $DM = FM$, which means that M is the midpoint of $\overline{DF}$.

> **Important:** The altitude to the base of an isosceles triangle divides the base into two congruent segments.

(b) Since M is the midpoint of $\overline{DF}$, we have $DM = DF/2 = 10$. Applying the Pythagorean Theorem to $\triangle DEM$ gives $DM^2 + EM^2 = DE^2$, so

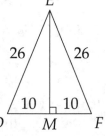

$$10^2 + EM^2 = 26^2.$$

This gives us $EM^2 = 26^2 - 10^2 = 676 - 100 = 576$. We take the square root to find that $EM = 24$. (Notice that we also could have found EM by noticing that leg $\overline{DM}$ has length $5 \cdot 2$ and hypotenuse $\overline{DE}$ has length $13 \cdot 2$. So, using the $\{5, 12, 13\}$ Pythagorean triple, we know that the other leg has length $12 \cdot 2$.) The area of $\triangle DEF$ then is $(DF)(EM)/2 = 240$ square units.

$\square$

> **Concept:** Building right triangles and applying the Pythagorean Theorem is one of the most common methods for finding lengths in geometry problems.

In Problem 12.8, we discovered that we can think of an isosceles triangle as a pair of identical right triangles glued together along a common leg. This way of viewing an isosceles triangle reveals another important fact about isosceles triangles:

> **Important:** In an isosceles triangle, the angles opposite the equal sides have the same measure. If two sides of a triangle are equal, then the angles opposite those sides are equal. Similarly, if two angles of a triangle are equal, then the sides opposite those angles are equal.

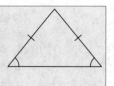

The equal angles of an isosceles triangle are called the **base angles** of the triangle, and the other angle is called the **vertex angle** of the triangle.

Problem 12.9:

(a) Suppose $\triangle ABC$ is equilateral with side length 6. Find the length of an altitude of $\triangle ABC$.

(b) Find the area of $\triangle ABC$.

Solution for Problem 12.9:

(a) We start by drawing altitude $\overline{CD}$ of the triangle. Because $CA = CB$, we know that this altitude divides base $\overline{AB}$ into two equal pieces. So, we have $AD = DB = 3$. Applying the Pythagorean Theorem to $\triangle ADC$ gives

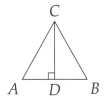

$$AD^2 + DC^2 = AC^2.$$

Since $AD = 3$ and $AC = 6$, we have $3^2 + DC^2 = 6^2$, which means $DC^2 = 6^2 - 3^2 = 36 - 9 = 27$. Taking the square root gives $DC = \sqrt{27} = \sqrt{9 \cdot 3} = 3\sqrt{3}$.

(b) Now that we have the length of an altitude, we can find the area:

$$[ABC] = \frac{(AB)(CD)}{2} = \frac{(6)(3\sqrt{3})}{2} = \frac{6}{2} \cdot 3\sqrt{3} = 3 \cdot 3\sqrt{3} = 9\sqrt{3} \text{ square units.}$$

□

Problem 12.10:

(a) If one leg of an isosceles right triangle has length 5, then what are the lengths of the other leg and the hypotenuse of the triangle?

(b) If one leg of an isosceles right triangle has length 8, then what are the lengths of the other leg and the hypotenuse of the triangle?

(c) If we know the length of one leg of an isosceles right triangle, then what's a fast way to find the length of the hypotenuse?

Solution for Problem 12.10:

(a) Since the triangle is isosceles, two of the sides must have the same length. We know that the hypotenuse of a right triangle is the longest side of the triangle. So, it must be the legs that have the same length in an isosceles right triangle. This means the other leg of the triangle in the problem has length 5, too. We then use the Pythagorean Theorem to find the hypotenuse. If we let c be the hypotenuse, then the Pythagorean Theorem tells us that

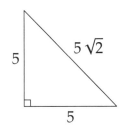

$$c^2 = 5^2 + 5^2 = 25 + 25 = 50.$$

Taking the square root gives us

$$c = \sqrt{50} = \sqrt{25 \cdot 2} = 5\sqrt{2}.$$

We conclude that each leg of the right triangle has length 5 and the hypotenuse has length $5\sqrt{2}$.

(b) We follow essentially the same steps as in the previous part. Since the triangle is isosceles, the legs have the same length, so the second leg has length 8. If we let c be the hypotenuse, then the Pythagorean Theorem tells us that

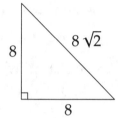

$$c^2 = 8^2 + 8^2 = 64 + 64 = 128.$$

Taking the square root gives us

$$c = \sqrt{128} = \sqrt{64 \cdot 2} = 8\sqrt{2}.$$

We conclude that each leg of the right triangle has length 8 and the hypotenuse has length $8\sqrt{2}$.

(c) So far, we have seen an isosceles right triangle with side lengths $5, 5, 5\sqrt{2}$ and one with side lengths $8, 8, 8\sqrt{2}$. It sure looks like there's a pattern. We know that the legs of an isosceles right triangle must always have the same length, but is it always true that the hypotenuse is $\sqrt{2}$ times each leg?

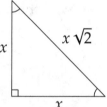

We investigate by assigning a variable to the leg length. Suppose each leg has length x. Then, the sum of the squares of the legs is $x^2 + x^2$, which equals $2x^2$. So, the Pythagorean Theorem tells us that the square of the hypotenuse equals $2x^2$, which means the length of the hypotenuse is $\sqrt{2x^2}$. We can simplify $\sqrt{2x^2}$ as follows:

$$\sqrt{2x^2} = \sqrt{x^2} \cdot \sqrt{2} = x\sqrt{2}.$$

We therefore see that the hypotenuse is $\sqrt{2}$ times as long as each leg. (As a side note, we usually write $x\sqrt{2}$ instead of $\sqrt{2}x$ to make it clear that the x is not inside the radical.)

$\square$

> **Important:** In an isosceles right triangle, the legs are congruent and the hypotenuse is $\sqrt{2}$ times as long as each leg.
>
>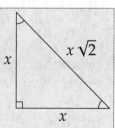

Note that the two acute angles of an isosceles right triangle must be congruent, since they are opposite the congruent sides of the triangle. Because the acute angles of a right triangle must sum to 90°, each of these two angles has measure 90°/2 = 45°. For this reason, isosceles right triangles are often referred to as **45-45-90 triangles**.

Problem 12.11: A **30-60-90 triangle** is a triangle whose angles measure 30°, 60°, and 90°.

(a) Describe how to divide an equilateral triangle into two identical 30-60-90 triangles.

(b) Suppose the leg opposite the 30° angle in a 30-60-90 triangle has length 2. Use your answer to part (a) to find the hypotenuse of the triangle. What is the length of the other leg?

(c) Suppose the leg opposite the 30° angle in a 30-60-90 triangle has length s. In terms of s, what are the lengths of the hypotenuse and the other leg of the triangle?

Solution for Problem 12.11:

(a) First, we note that all three angles of an equilateral triangle must be equal, because any two of the angles are opposite equal sides of a triangle. So, all three angles of an equilateral triangle have measure 180°/3 = 60°. Therefore, when we drew an altitude in the equilateral triangle in Problem 12.9, we formed a right triangle in which one of the acute angles is 60°. The acute angles of a right triangle sum to 90°, so the other acute angle has measure 90° − 60° = 30°.

(b) Inspired by our observation in part (a), we see that we can make an equilateral triangle by attaching two identical 30-60-90 triangles along the longer legs of the triangles. This is shown at the right, where we have combined right triangles ABD and ACD to form equilateral triangle ABC.

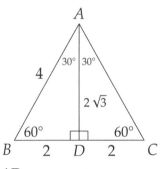

The legs opposite the 30° angles in each triangle have length 2, so $BD = CD = 2$. Therefore, each side of the equilateral triangle has length $BD + CD = 2 + 2 = 4$, so the hypotenuse of each 30-60-90 triangle is 4. Finally, we can use the Pythagorean Theorem to find AD.

From right triangle ABD, we have

$$BD^2 + AD^2 = AB^2.$$

Since $BD = 2$ and $AB = 4$, we have $2^2 + AD^2 = 4^2$, so $AD^2 = 4^2 - 2^2 = 16 - 4 = 12$. Taking the square root gives $AD = \sqrt{12} = \sqrt{4 \cdot 3} = 2\sqrt{3}$. We conclude that if the shorter leg of a 30-60-90 triangle has length 2, then the other leg has length $2\sqrt{3}$ and the hypotenuse has length 4.

(c) In the previous part, we found a 30-60-90 triangle with side lengths $2, 2\sqrt{3}, 4$. Look closely at Problem 12.9, and you'll see a 30-60-90 triangle with side lengths $3, 3\sqrt{3}, 6$. It looks like

---

there's a pattern! Let's see if this pattern always holds, so we don't have to go through all this work for every 30-60-90 triangle.

We again start with two identical 30-60-90 triangles attached to form an equilateral triangle. Instead of starting with a value for the length of the short leg, we'll use a variable. Suppose the shorter leg of each triangle has length s, so the equilateral triangle has side length $2s$. Then, we apply the Pythagorean Theorem to ABD to find that

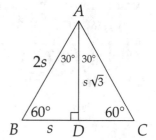

$$BD^2 + AD^2 = AB^2.$$

Since $BD = s$ and $AB = 2s$, we have $s^2 + AD^2 = (2s)^2$. Since $(2s)^2 = 2^2s^2 = 4s^2$, we have $s^2 + AD^2 = 4s^2$. Subtracting s^2 from both sides gives $AD^2 = 3s^2$. Finally, taking the square root gives

$$AD = \sqrt{3s^2} = \sqrt{s^2}\sqrt{3} = s\sqrt{3}.$$

This confirms the pattern we saw! For any 30-60-90 triangle with short leg of length s, the longer leg has length $s\sqrt{3}$ and the hypotenuse has length $2s$. In other words, the side lengths of a 30-60-90 triangle always come in the ratio

Leg opposite 30° angle : Leg opposite 60° angle : Leg opposite 90° angle = $1 : \sqrt{3} : 2$.

□

Important: In a right triangle with acute angles of 30° and 60°, the side lengths are in the ratio $1 : \sqrt{3} : 2$ as shown to the right. Such a triangle is often called a **30-60-90 triangle**.

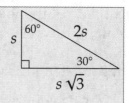

Exercises

12.2.1 Find the missing side lengths below:

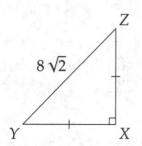

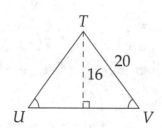

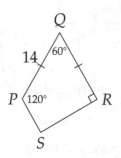

12.2.2   In △*ABC*, we have *AB* = *BC* and ∠*B* = 68°. Find ∠*A*.

12.2.3   In △*JKL*, we have ∠*J* = 3∠*K* = 90° and *JL* = 4. Find *KL* and *JK*.

12.2.4   The base of an isosceles triangle is 24 and its area is 60. What is the length of one of the equal sides? *(Source: AMC 8)*

12.2.5   The circle in the diagram at the right has radius 12 and center *O*. Points *A* and *B* are on the circumference of the circle such that ∠*AOB* = 60°.

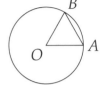

(a) We call $\overline{AB}$ a **chord** of the circle because its endpoints are on the circle. Find *AB*.

(b) An **arc** of a circle is a portion of the circle's circumference. There are two arcs from *A* to *B* in the diagram. Find the length of the shorter of these two arcs.

(c) A **sector** of a circle is a portion of the circle's interior that is bounded by two radii and an arc of the circle. Just as there are two arcs from *A* to *B*, a short arc and a long arc, there are two sectors of the circle formed by ∠*AOB*. One is "inside" the acute angle ∠*AOB*, and the other is the portion of the circle outside this angle. Find the area of the smaller of these sectors.

12.2.6★

(a) Let △*XYZ* be an equilateral triangle with side length *s*. Find a formula for the area of △*XYZ* in terms of *s*. **Hints:** 3, 107

(b) The circle in the diagram at the right has radius 12 and center *O*. Points *A* and *B* are on the circumference of the circle such that ∠*AOB* = 60°. Find the area of the region between $\overline{AB}$ and the shorter arc from *A* to *B*. **Hints:** 6, 39

12.3   Types of Quadrilaterals

We have already seen two common types of quadrilaterals. A **rectangle** is a quadrilateral in which all four angles are right angles. The opposite sides of a rectangle are parallel and have the same length. A **square** is a rectangle in which all four sides are congruent.

Figure 12.1: A Rectangle   Figure 12.2: A Square

In this section, we explore a few more special types of quadrilaterals.

Problems

Problem 12.12: A **rhombus** is a quadrilateral in which all four sides have the same length.

(a) Is every square also a rhombus?

(b) Is every rhombus also a square?

Problem 12.13: Explain how to arrange four 3-4-5 right triangles so that together they form a rhombus with side length 5.

Problem 12.14: $ABCD$ is a rhombus in which the diagonals have lengths $AC = 8$ and $BD = 12$. In this problem, we'll find the area of $ABCD$.

(a) What is the area of $\triangle ABC$? **Hints:** 126

(b) What is the area of $ABCD$?

Problem 12.15: Find a formula for the area of a rhombus with diagonals of lengths x and y.

Problem 12.16: Find the area of a square that has diagonal length $8\sqrt{2}$.

Problem 12.17: A **parallelogram** is a quadrilateral in which both pairs of opposite sides are parallel.

(a) Is every rectangle also a parallelogram?

(b) Is every parallelogram also a rectangle?

Problem 12.18: In this problem, we find a method to calculate the area of the parallelogram shown at the right.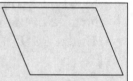

(a) Find a way to cut the parallelogram into two pieces and reassemble those two pieces to form a rectangle.

(b) Explain a method for finding the area of a parallelogram.

Extra! The dazzling tiling "proof without words" shown at the
➡➡➡➡ right of the Pythagorean Theorem comes from **Annairizi of Arabia** (circa 900 AD). See if you can figure out how it works! *Source: Proofs Without Words II by Roger Nelsen*

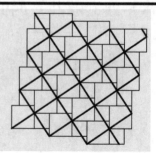

Problem 12.19: A **trapezoid** is a quadrilateral in which two sides are parallel. The two parallel sides of a trapezoid are called the **bases** of the trapezoid and the other sides are called the **legs** of the trapezoid. On the left below, $\overline{AB}$ and $\overline{CD}$ are the bases of trapezoid $ABCD$, and $\overline{AD}$ and $\overline{BC}$ are the legs. The distance between the two bases of a trapezoid is called the **height** of the trapezoid.

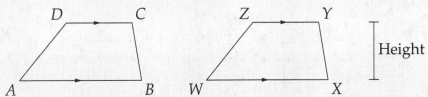

In this problem we discover a method for finding the area of a trapezoid.

(a) Find a way to arrange the two identical trapezoids above so that together they form a parallelogram.

(b) Find the area of the parallelogram from part (a) in terms of the base lengths and the height of the trapezoid.

(c) Explain why the following method for finding the area of a trapezoid works:

$$\text{Area} = \frac{1}{2} \times \text{Height} \times \text{Sum of Base Lengths.}$$

Problem 12.20: Find the area of each quadrilateral below.

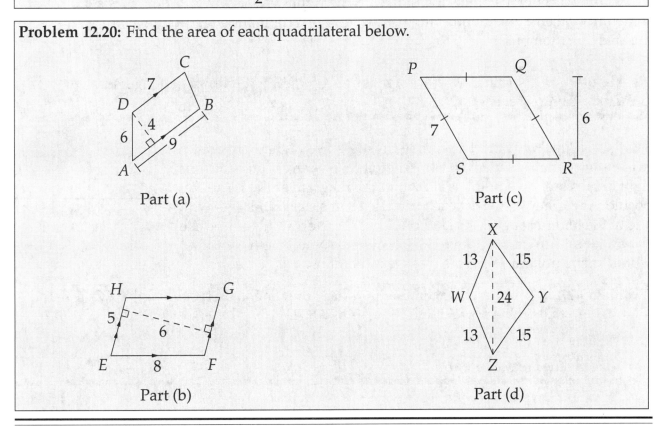

Part (a)

Part (c)

Part (b)

Part (d)

> **Problem 12.12:** A **rhombus** is a quadrilateral in which all four sides have the same length.
>
> (a) Is every square also a rhombus?
>
> (b) Is every rhombus also a square?

Solution for Problem 12.12:

(a) Yes. All four sides of a square have the same length, so a square is a rhombus.

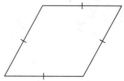

A Square is a Rhombus   This Rhombus is Not a Square

(b) No. A square must have all four angles equal, but a rhombus doesn't have to have all four angles equal. For example, the rhombus on the right above is clearly not a square.

☐

The word rhombus comes from an ancient Greek word that means "spinning top." By drawing a rhombus point-down, like on the right, we see why a rhombus is also sometimes called a "diamond." Taking this view of a rhombus suggests a way to find the area of a rhombus.

> **Problem 12.13:** Explain how to arrange four 3-4-5 right triangles so that together they form a rhombus with side length 5.

Solution for Problem 12.13: The sum of the measures of the right angles of the four triangles is $4 \cdot 90° = 360°$. Therefore, we can arrange the four right angles around a point as shown in the diagram at the right. We position the triangles so that each triangle shares each of its legs with one of the other triangles. The hypotenuses then form a diamond-like quadrilateral in which all four sides have the same length. In other words, the hypotenuses are the sides of a rhombus. ☐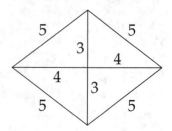

> **Problem 12.14:** *ABCD* is a rhombus in which the diagonals have lengths $AC = 8$ and $BD = 12$. In this problem, we'll find the area of *ABCD*.
>
> (a) What is the area of $\triangle ABC$?
>
> (b) What is the area of *ABCD*?

Solution for Problem 12.14:

(a) We can view rhombus *ABCD* as two isosceles triangles, *ABC* and *ADC*, glued together at their bases. Because these triangles are isosceles, the altitudes from *B* and *D* to $\overline{AC}$ meet at the midpoint of $\overline{AC}$, which we'll call *O*. Since ∠*COD* and ∠*BOC* are right angles, together they form straight angle *BOD*. This means that diagonal $\overline{BD}$ passes through *O*, as shown in the diagram. We see then that diagonals $\overline{DB}$ and $\overline{AC}$ are perpendicular, and $\overline{DB}$ divides

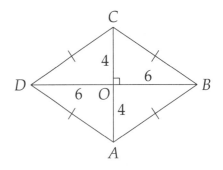

$\overline{AC}$ into two equal pieces. Similarly, $\overline{AC}$ also divides $\overline{DB}$ into two equal pieces. We therefore say that the diagonals of a rhombus **bisect** each other.

> **Important:** The diagonals of a rhombus are perpendicular and bisect each other.

Now we can find the area of △*ABC*. Base $\overline{AC}$ has length 8 and altitude $\overline{BO}$ is half $\overline{BD}$, so it has length 6. Therefore, the area of △*ABC* is $(AC)(BO)/2 = (8)(6)/2 = 24$.

(b) Just as $[ABC] = 24$, we also have $[ADC] = 24$, so $[ABCD] = [ABC] + [ADC] = 48$.

□

> **Problem 12.15:** Find a formula for the area of a rhombus with diagonals of lengths *x* and *y*.

Solution for Problem 12.15: We can follow the steps of Problem 12.14 to show that the area of any rhombus is half the product of its diagonals. To see this even more quickly, we can use the fact that the diagonals of a rhombus are perpendicular.

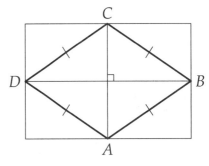

As shown at the right, we draw a rectangle around the rhombus such that each side of the rectangle is parallel to one of the diagonals of the rhombus. The lengths of the diagonals of the rhombus equal the length and width of the rectangle, so the area of the rectangle is the product of the lengths of the diagonals of the rhombus.

These diagonals also split the rectangle into four smaller rectangles. Half of each of these rectangles is inside the rhombus, so the area of the rhombus is half the area of the rectangle. Therefore, the area of the rhombus is half the product of the lengths of its diagonals, so the area of a rhombus with diagonals of lengths *x* and *y* is $xy/2$. □

> **Important:** The area of a rhombus equals half the product of its diagonals.

Viewing a rhombus as a combination of four identical right triangles lets us make another discovery. In rhombus $ABCD$ at the right, because $\angle BDA = \angle DBC$, we know that $\overline{AD} \parallel \overline{BC}$. Similarly, we have $\overline{CD} \parallel \overline{AB}$.

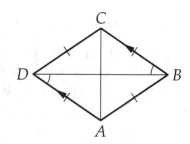

 Important: The opposite sides of a rhombus are parallel.

Problem 12.16: Find the area of a square that has diagonal length $8\sqrt{2}$.

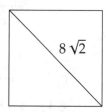

Solution for Problem 12.16: Solution 1: Find the length of each side of the square. Each diagonal of a square divides the square into two isosceles right triangles. The hypotenuse of an isosceles right triangle is $\sqrt{2}$ times the length of a leg of the triangle. So, because the square's diagonal has length $8\sqrt{2}$, each side of the square has length 8. Therefore, the area of the square is $8^2 = 64$ square units.

Solution 2: A square is a rhombus! Because a square is a rhombus, its area is half the product of its diagonals. A square's diagonals are congruent, so the area of the square is

$$\frac{(8\sqrt{2})(8\sqrt{2})}{2} = \frac{(8 \cdot 8)(\sqrt{2} \cdot \sqrt{2})}{2} = \frac{64 \cdot 2}{2} = 64 \text{ square units.}$$

$\square$

Problem 12.17: A **parallelogram** is a quadrilateral in which both pairs of opposite sides are parallel.

(a) Is every rectangle also a parallelogram?

(b) Is every parallelogram also a rectangle?

Solution for Problem 12.17:

(a) Yes. Because consecutive angles of a rectangle add to 180°, the opposite sides any rectangle are parallel. Therefore, every rectangle is also a parallelogram.

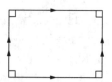

(b) No. The parallelogram on the right is clearly not a rectangle.

$\square$

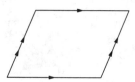

Since all squares are rectangles, squares are parallelograms, too. Moreover, we noticed back on page 462 that the opposite sides of a rhombus are parallel. So, every rhombus is also a parallelogram. But a quick glance at either parallelogram above shows that not every parallelogram is a rhombus.

Problem 12.18: In this problem, we find a method to calculate the area of the parallelogram shown at the right.

(a) Find a way to cut a parallelogram into two pieces, and reassemble those two pieces to form a rectangle.

(b) Explain a method for finding the area of a parallelogram.

Solution for Problem 12.18:

(a) We can turn the parallelogram into a rectangle by cutting off a right triangle from one side and sliding it to the other side, as shown below:

(b) One side of the resulting rectangle in part (a) is a side of the original parallelogram. We'll call this the "base" of the parallelogram. The other side length of the rectangle equals the distance between the base and the opposite side. We'll call this distance a "height" of the parallelogram. The area of a rectangle equals its length times its width, so the area of the rectangle on the right above equals the product of the base and the height of the parallelogram.

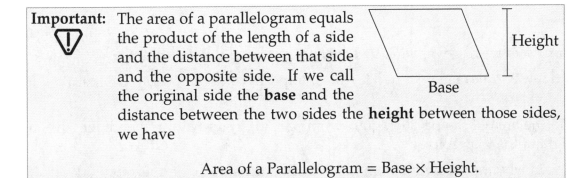

Important: The area of a parallelogram equals the product of the length of a side and the distance between that side and the opposite side. If we call the original side the **base** and the distance between the two sides the **height** between those sides, we have

$$\text{Area of a Parallelogram} = \text{Base} \times \text{Height}.$$

Extra! In 1897, the Indiana state legislature almost passed a bill that set the value of π to exactly 3.2. The House voted unanimously for it and it passed a first reading in the Senate. Fortunately, a math professor was visiting the legislature at the same time and advised that the bill be postponed indefinitely, effectively killing it.

There is a height associated with each pair of parallel sides of a parallelogram. So there are two heights of a parallelogram, just as there are three different distances we might use for the height of a triangle. In the diagram on the right, we have labeled the two heights of $ABCD$ as h_1 and h_2. We can use either one with the appropriate base to find the area:

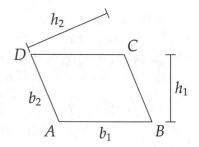

$$[ABCD] = b_1 h_1 = b_2 h_2.$$

Our rearrangement in Problem 12.18 gives us some intuition for why the opposite sides of any parallelogram are congruent. As an exercise, you'll explain why the opposite angles of a parallelogram are congruent. ("Opposite angles" of a parallelogram are a pair of angles of the parallelogram that do not share a side.)

> **Important:** The opposite sides of a parallelogram are congruent, and the opposite angles of a parallelogram are congruent.

Problem 12.19: A **trapezoid** is a quadrilateral in which two sides are parallel. The two parallel sides of a trapezoid are called the **bases** of the trapezoid and the other sides are called the **legs** of the trapezoid. On the left below, $\overline{AB}$ and $\overline{CD}$ are the bases of trapezoid $ABCD$, and $\overline{AD}$ and $\overline{BC}$ are the legs. The distance between the two bases of a trapezoid is called the **height** of the trapezoid.

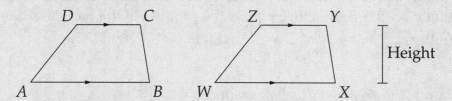

In this problem we discover a method for finding the area of a trapezoid.

(a) Find a way to arrange the two identical trapezoids above so that together they form a parallelogram.

(b) Find the area of the parallelogram from part (a) in terms of the base lengths and the height of the trapezoid.

(c) Explain why the following method for finding the area of a trapezoid works:

$$\text{Area} = \frac{1}{2} \times \text{Height} \times \text{Sum of Base Lengths}.$$

Solution for Problem 12.19:

(a) We first spin $WXYZ$ around as shown below:

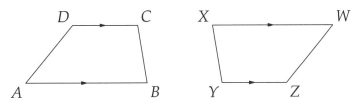

We have $BC = XY$ because the trapezoids are identical. This means we can push these two trapezoids together so that $\overline{BC}$ and $\overline{XY}$ overlap, thereby forming a parallelogram:

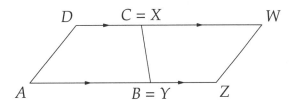

(b) The area of parallelogram $ADWZ$ in the previous part equals the product of base length AZ and the height between $\overline{AZ}$ and $\overline{DW}$. The length AZ equals the sum of the bases of one of the trapezoids, and the height of the parallelogram is the same as the height of the trapezoids. So, the area of $ADWZ$ equals the product of the height of each trapezoid times the sum of one trapezoid's bases.

(c) The area of each trapezoid is half the area of the parallelogram, so

$$\text{Area of Trapezoid} = \frac{(\text{Height}) \times (\text{Sum of Bases})}{2}.$$

$\square$

Important: The area of a trapezoid is half the product of its height and the sum of its bases. For the trapezoid at the right, we have

$$\text{Area} = \frac{a+b}{2} \cdot h.$$

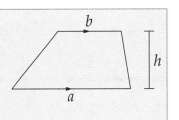

The line segment that connects the midpoints of the legs of a trapezoid is called the **median** of the trapezoid. In the diagram at the right, the median is shown dashed. The median of a trapezoid is parallel to the trapezoid's bases, and has length equal to half the sum of the trapezoid's base lengths. We can visualize these relationships by including the medians in the manipulations we used in Problem 12.19:

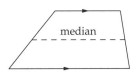

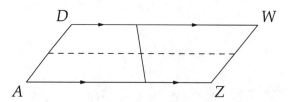

Since the length of the median is half the sum of the bases, the area of a trapezoid equals the product of the trapezoid's height and median.

You might be wondering if a parallelogram is a trapezoid. Unfortunately, there isn't a good answer. Some people define a trapezoid as having *exactly* one pair of opposite sides parallel, so a parallelogram would not be a trapezoid. Other people define a trapezoid as having *at least* one pair of opposite sides parallel; by this definition, a parallelogram would be a trapezoid.

Problem 12.20: Find the area of each quadrilateral below.

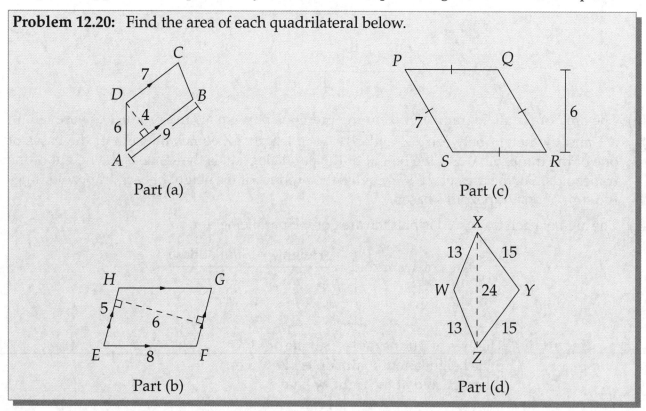

Solution for Problem 12.20:

(a) *ABCD* is a trapezoid with height 4 and bases with lengths 7 and 9. So, we have

$$[ABCD] = \frac{7+9}{2} \cdot 4 = \frac{16}{2} \cdot 4 = 8 \cdot 4 = 32$$

square units.

(b) *EFGH* is a parallelogram. The dashed segment with length 6 is a height between the opposite sides with length 5. So, *EFGH* has area $5 \cdot 6 = 30$ square units.

(c) Since all four sides of *PQRS* have the same length, *PQRS* is a rhombus. But we don't know the lengths of its diagonals. What will we do?

A rhombus is also a parallelogram, so its area can be computed as base times height. We have $SR = PS = 7$, and the area of *PQRS* is $7 \cdot 6 = 42$ square units.

(d) Unfortunately, *WXYZ* isn't one of the special quadrilaterals we have studied so far. But it does consist of two isosceles triangles with the same base, just like a rhombus does. Maybe we can use a strategy similar to the one we used on a rhombus. In the two isosceles triangles, we draw the altitudes to $\overline{XZ}$. Since *WXZ* and *YXZ* are isosceles, we know that altitudes $\overline{WM}$ and $\overline{YM}$ meet at the midpoint of $\overline{XZ}$, as shown. Now we have a problem we can handle.

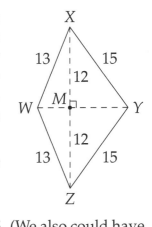

We apply the Pythagorean Theorem to $\triangle WXM$ to find *WM*. We have

$$WM^2 + XM^2 = WX^2,$$

so $WM^2 + 144 = 169$. This gives us $WM^2 = 169 - 144 = 25$, so $WM = 5$. (We also could have recalled the Pythagorean triple $\{5, 12, 13\}$.) Therefore, we have

$$[WXZ] = \frac{(WM)(XZ)}{2} = \frac{(5)(24)}{2} = (5)(12) = 60 \text{ square units.}$$

Similarly, we apply the Pythagorean Theorem to $\triangle YMX$ to find

$$YM^2 + XM^2 = XY^2,$$

so $YM^2 + 144 = 225$. This gives us $YM^2 = 225 - 144 = 81$, so $YM = 9$. (We also could have recalled the Pythagorean triple $\{9, 12, 15\}$.) We then have

$$[YXZ] = \frac{(YM)(XZ)}{2} = \frac{(9)(24)}{2} = (9)(12) = 108 \text{ square units.}$$

Combining the areas of isosceles triangles *WXZ* and *YXZ* gives us

$$[WXYZ] = [WXZ] + [YXZ] = 60 + 108 = 168 \text{ square units.}$$

□

The quadrilateral in part (d) of Problem 12.20 is called a **kite**. A kite is a quadrilateral in which the sides can be split into two pairs of equal adjacent sides. As we just discovered in Problem 12.20, the diagonals of a kite are perpendicular.

Exercises

12.3.1 A square and a triangle have equal perimeters. The lengths of the three sides of the triangle are 6.2 cm, 8.3 cm, and 9.5 cm. What is the area of the square? *(Source: AMC 8)*

12.3.2 Label each statement as true or false, and explain why your answer is correct.

(a) If a quadrilateral has four equal sides, then it is a square.

(b) If a quadrilateral has at least one pair of equal sides, then it is a rectangle.

(c) A quadrilateral can have exactly two right angles among its interior angles.

(d) The diagonals of a rectangle have the same length.

12.3.3

(a) If *EFGH* is a parallelogram and $\angle E = 41°$, then find the other angles of the parallelogram.

(b) Explain why the opposite angles of a parallelogram are congruent.

12.3.4 Mrs. Jones has a backyard in the shape of a square that is 27 feet on each side. After dividing each side into thirds, she wants to plant grass in the shaded areas shown in the diagram. How many square feet of the backyard will remain without grass? *(Source: MATHCOUNTS)*

12.3.5 Find the area of *PQRS* on the left below.

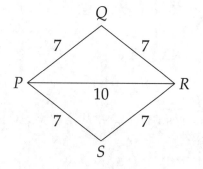

Figure 12.3: Diagram for Problem 12.3.5

$$D \quad\longrightarrow\quad C$$
$$9 \quad 6$$
$$A \quad 12 \quad B$$

Figure 12.4: Diagram for Problem 12.3.6

12.3.6 In the diagram on the right above, *ABCD* is a parallelogram. What is the height between opposite sides $\overline{AD}$ and $\overline{BC}$?

12.3.7 One base of a trapezoid has length 8 inches and the height of the trapezoid is 4 inches. If the trapezoid's area is 80 square inches, then what is the length of the other base of the trapezoid?

12.3.8 In trapezoid *WXYZ*, we have $\overline{WX} \parallel \overline{YZ}$ and $\angle W = 39°$. Which other angle measures of the trapezoid can we determine, and what are their values?

12.3.9 In Problem 12.19, we found a method for arranging the two identical trapezoids such that together they form a parallelogram. Explain why the figure formed in our solution to part (a) on page 465 is indeed a parallelogram.

12.3.10★ In the text, we learned that the area of a trapezoid equals the product of the length of its median and its height. In other words, it has the same area as a rectangle whose dimensions equal the median length and the height of the trapezoid. So, we should be able to cut up a trapezoid and rearrange the pieces to form a rectangle with dimensions equal to the median length and the height of the trapezoid. Explain how to do so for the trapezoid at the right. **Hints:** 121

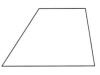

12.4 Summary

In a right triangle, the side of the triangle opposite the right angle is called the **hypotenuse** and the other two sides are called the **legs** of the triangle. We also often use the terms "legs" and "hypotenuse" to refer the lengths of the legs and hypotenuse of a right triangle.

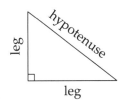

Important: The **Pythagorean Theorem** tells us that in any right triangle, the sum of the squares of the legs equals the square of the hypotenuse. So, in the diagram to the right, we have

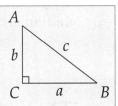

$$a^2 + b^2 = c^2.$$

The Pythagorean Theorem also works in reverse: if the sum of the squares of two sides of a triangle equals the square of the third side, then the triangle is a right triangle.

A **Pythagorean triple** is a group of three positive integers that satisfy the Pythagorean Theorem equation. So, for example, $\{3, 4, 5\}$ is a Pythagorean triple, as are $\{5, 12, 13\}$ and $\{8, 15, 17\}$. There are infinitely many Pythagorean triples.

Important: If we multiply all three side lengths of a right triangle by the same positive number, then the three new side lengths also satisfy the Pythagorean Theorem. In other words, if side lengths a, b, and c satisfy $a^2 + b^2 = c^2$, then $(na)^2 + (nb)^2 = (nc)^2$ for any number n.

Important: In an isosceles triangle, the angles opposite the equal sides have the same measure. If two sides of a triangle are equal, then the angles opposite those sides are equal. Similarly, if two angles of a triangle are equal, then the sides opposite those angles are equal.

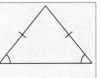

Important: In an isosceles right triangle, the legs are congruent and the hypotenuse is $\sqrt{2}$ times as long as each leg. An isosceles triangle is often called a **45-45-90 triangle**.

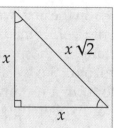

Important: In a right triangle with acute angles of 30° and 60°, the side lengths are in the ratio $1 : \sqrt{3} : 2$ as shown to the right. Such a triangle is often called a **30-60-90 triangle**.

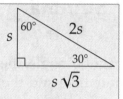

Definitions: A **trapezoid** is a quadrilateral with two parallel sides. The segment connecting the midpoints of the other two sides is the **median** of the trapezoid, and the distance between the two parallel sides is the **height** of the trapezoid.

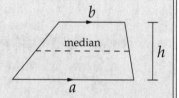

Important:

- The median of a trapezoid is parallel to the bases of the trapezoid, and equal in length to the average of the lengths of the bases.

- The area of a trapezoid equals the height of the trapezoid times the length of the median of the trapezoid. So, the area of the trapezoid above is $h(a + b)/2$.

Definition: A **parallelogram** is a quadrilateral in which both pairs of opposite sides are parallel.

Important:

- The area of a parallelogram is the product of a side length (the base) and the distance between that side and the opposite side of the parallelogram. This distance between opposite sides is called a **height** of the parallelogram.

- In any parallelogram, the opposite sides are equal, and the opposite angles are equal.

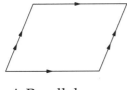

A Parallelogram

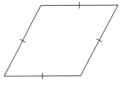

A Rhombus

Definition: A quadrilateral is a **rhombus** if all of its sides are equal.

> **Important:**
> ⚠
>
> - Every rhombus is a parallelogram. Therefore, everything that is true about parallelograms is true about every rhombus.
>
> - The diagonals of a rhombus are perpendicular. The area of a rhombus is half the product of its diagonals (and also equals its base times its height).

Definition: A quadrilateral in which all angles are equal is a **rectangle**.

> **Important:**
> ⚠
>
> - All rectangles are parallelograms, so all that is true of parallelograms is true of rectangles.
>
> - Let two consecutive sides of a rectangle have lengths ℓ and w. The area of the rectangle is ℓw, and the diagonals of the rectangle both have length $\sqrt{\ell^2 + w^2}$.

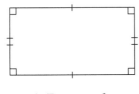

A Rectangle

A Square

Definition: A quadrilateral in which all sides are equal and all angles are equal is a **square**.

> **Important:**
> ⚠
>
> - Each square is a parallelogram, a rectangle, and a rhombus, so all that is true of parallelograms, rectangles, or rhombuses is true of squares.
>
> - If the side length of a square is s and its diagonal is d, then $d = s\sqrt{2}$ and the area of the square is s^2, or $d^2/2$.

> **WARNING!!** Although every rhombus is a parallelogram, not every parallelogram is a rhombus. Therefore, if we prove a property that is true for every rhombus, this property is not necessarily true for every parallelogram. (The same warning holds for rectangles—rectangles are parallelograms, but not all parallelograms are rectangles, etc.)

REVIEW PROBLEMS

12.21 Two bicyclists start at the intersection of two perpendicular roads. One rides east at a rate of 9 miles per hour, while the other rides south at a rate of 12 miles per hour. How many miles are in the shortest distance between them at the end of 3 hours? *(Source: MATHCOUNTS)*

12.22 A right triangle has one leg of length 48 and hypotenuse with length 52. What is the length of the other leg? (Challenge: Try to do this problem in your head.)

12.23 Pat knows that one leg of a certain right triangle is 300 cm and the hypotenuse is 400 cm. Pat notes that $300 = 3 \cdot 100$ and $400 = 4 \cdot 100$, and then uses the $\{3, 4, 5\}$ Pythagorean triple to determine that the other leg must be $5 \cdot 100 = 500$ cm. Explain why Pat's method doesn't work, and determine the correct length of the other leg of the triangle.

12.24

(a) What is the area of a right triangle that has legs with lengths 7 inches and 24 inches?

(b) What is the length of the altitude to the hypotenuse of the triangle in part (a)?

12.25 Find the area of the quadrilateral on the left below.

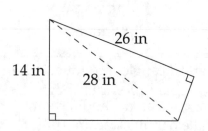
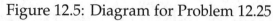

Figure 12.5: Diagram for Problem 12.25

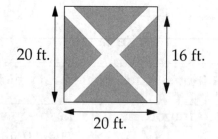

Figure 12.6: Diagram for Problem 12.26

12.26 A garden is laid out in the fashion shown in the diagram at the right above. If only the shaded isosceles right triangles are used for planting, what is the total area, in square feet, that is to be used for planting? *(Source: MATHCOUNTS)*

12.27 In $\triangle ABC$, we have $\angle A = 30°$, $\angle B = 60°$, and $AB = 8$. Find BC, AC, and the area of $\triangle ABC$.

12.28

(a) What is the greatest possible angle measure in an isosceles triangle that has an angle measuring 54 degrees?

(b) What is the least possible angle measure in an isosceles triangle that has an angle measuring 54 degrees?

12.29 Find the perimeter and the area of the quadrilateral shown at the right.

12.30 The lengths of the diagonals of a rhombus are 10 inches and 24 inches. What are the perimeter and the area of the rhombus?

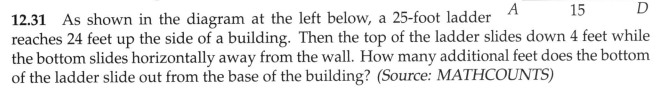

12.31 As shown in the diagram at the left below, a 25-foot ladder reaches 24 feet up the side of a building. Then the top of the ladder slides down 4 feet while the bottom slides horizontally away from the wall. How many additional feet does the bottom of the ladder slide out from the base of the building? *(Source: MATHCOUNTS)*

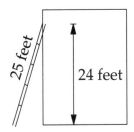

Figure 12.7: Diagram for Problem 12.31

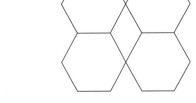

Figure 12.8: Diagram for Problem 12.32

12.32 A tessellation is composed of four regular hexagons and a rhombus as shown in the diagram on the right above. How many degrees are in an acute angle of the rhombus? *(Source: MATHCOUNTS)*

12.33 Label each statement as true or false, and explain why your answer is correct.

(a) A quadrilateral can have exactly three right angles among its interior angles.

(b) All squares are parallelograms.

(c) If both pairs of opposite angles of a quadrilateral are equal, then the quadrilateral is a parallelogram.

(d) The diagonals of a rhombus have the same length.

12.34 The measure of one interior angle of a rhombus is 79°. What are the measures of the other three interior angles?

12.35 The midpoints of the sides of square $WXYZ$ are connected to form another quadrilateral.

(a) Explain why the new quadrilateral must also be a square.

(b) If the area of $WXYZ$ is 900, then what is the area of the new quadrilateral?

12.36 The measures of two angles in a parallelogram add to 204°. Find the measure of each of the other two angles.

Challenge Problems

12.37 In the diagram at the left, O is the center of the circle, $MNOP$ is a rectangle, and the area of the circle is 100π. What is the length of diagonal $\overline{NP}$ of the rectangle?

12.38 In the diagram at the right, $\overline{AB} \parallel \overline{DC}$, and the area of $\triangle ABD$ is 2.5 times the area of $\triangle BDC$. If $AB + CD = 77$, then what is AB? **Hints:** 64, 79

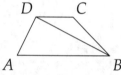

12.39 $ABCD$ is a square. M and N are midpoints of $\overline{AB}$ and $\overline{BC}$, respectively. What is the ratio of the area of $\triangle MBN$ to the area of $\triangle MDN$? Express your answer as a fraction in simplest form. *(Source: MATHCOUNTS)* **Hints:** 105

12.40 A 30-60-90 triangle is drawn on the exterior of equilateral triangle ABC as shown so that the hypotenuse of the right triangle is one side of the equilateral triangle. If the shorter leg of the right triangle is 6 units, what is AD? **Hints:** 115, 16

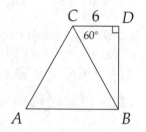

12.41 Quadrilateral $ABCD$ is a trapezoid with $\overline{AB}$ parallel to $\overline{CD}$. We know $AB = 20$ and $CD = 12$. What is the ratio of the area of triangle ACB to the area of trapezoid $ABCD$? *(Source: MATHCOUNTS)* **Hints:** 110, 74

12.42 As shown at the right, a circle with diameter 2 cm is centered at a vertex D of square $ABCD$ and intersects the square and equilateral triangle DCE at midpoints F and G, respectively. If an ant starts at point A and walks completely around the figure once along the bold path shown, then how far does the ant walk? *(Source: MATHCOUNTS)*

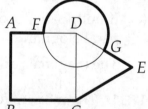

12.43 The diagonals of a rhombus are perpendicular and the area of a rhombus is half the product of the lengths of its diagonals. Similarly, the diagonals of a kite are perpendicular, and the area of a kite is half the product of its diagonals. Is it true that for any quadrilateral with perpendicular diagonals, the area of the quadrilateral equals half the product of its diagonals? Why or why not? **Hints:** 45

12.44

(a) In the text, we discovered the Pythagorean triples $\{3, 4, 5\}$; $\{5, 12, 13\}$; and $\{7, 24, 25\}$. Notice that in each of these triples, one leg is odd and the other two numbers differ by 1. Find the Pythagorean triple that has 9 and two other numbers that are 1 apart. **Hints:** 24

(b)★ For every odd number n greater than 1, is there a Pythagorean triple with n and two other numbers that are 1 apart?

(c) Do all Pythagorean triples have the form described in the first two parts?

12.45★ Kite $PQRS$ at the right is concave. If we have $PQ = QR = 20$, $PS = SR = 15$, and $QS = 7$, then what is the area of kite $PQRS$? **Hints:** 19, 8

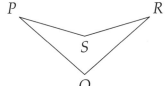

12.46★ A sheet of paper 12 inches by 18 inches is folded so that two opposite corners touch, as shown in the figures below. What is the area, in square inches, of the shaded triangle formed where the paper overlaps itself? **Hints:** 22, 152

12.47★ Find the area of a triangle whose sides have lengths 13, 14, and 15. **Hints:** 96, 86

12.48★ The shaded region at the right is called a **lune**. We form the lune by starting with a circle. We then draw an isosceles right triangle in which the vertex of the right angle is the center of the circle and the other two vertices of the triangle are on the circle. Finally, we draw a semicircle whose diameter is the hypotenuse of the isosceles right triangle. The portion of the semicircle that is outside the original circle is a lune. Show that the lune has the same area as the isosceles right triangle. **Hints:** 101

 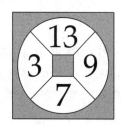 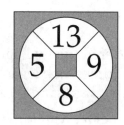 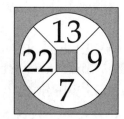

42.7 percent of all statistics are made up on the spot. – Steven Wright

CHAPTER **13**

Data and Statistics

In most of your classes, you probably have lots of graded assignments. At the end of the year, your teacher has a bunch of numbers from these assignments to tell how well you did. These numbers are **data**, or information, about how well you did in the course. So, at the end of the year, how does your teacher describe how you performed? Your teacher probably only reports a single number or letter rather than reporting the whole list. This single number is called a **statistic**.

In this chapter we consider ways to use statistics, and other visual depictions of data such as tables, graphs, and charts, to provide information about lists of numbers.

> **Sidenote:** The word "data" is used as both a singular and a plural noun. When referring to a specific group of numbers, we use "data" as a plural noun. For example, we could write, "The data we collected in the experiment are attached in an appendix." When referring to information as a general concept rather than to specific collections of numbers, we typically use "data" as a singular noun. For example, we might write, "Data is very important when trying to make good decisions."

13.1 Basic Statistics

One way to provide information about a list of numbers is to use a single number to describe some feature of the numbers in the list. Here are three basic ways to choose that representative value.

- **Average:** The average of a group of numbers is the sum of the numbers divided by the number of numbers in the group. For example, the average of 3, 5, 6, and 10 is $\frac{3+5+6+10}{4}$, which equals 6. The average is also called the **mean** or the **arithmetic mean**.

  We sometimes use the word "average" as a verb. For example, we may say that a basketball player averages 23 points per game. This means that the average of the player's point totals from all of her games is 23. An alternative way of saying this is that 23 is the player's average point total "over" all of her games.

- **Median:** If we list a group of numbers from least to greatest, the median of the group is the number in the middle. So, the median of the numbers in the list

$$4, 5, 7, 8, 11$$

  is 7. If there is an even number of numbers in the group, then the median is the average of the middle two numbers. For example, the median of the list

$$4, 5, 5, 7, 8, 11$$

  is the average of 5 and 7, which is $\frac{5+7}{2} = 6$.

- **Mode:** The mode of a group of numbers is the number that appears most frequently in the group. So, the mode of
$$3, 3, 3, 3, 4, 5, 6, 7$$

  is 3. A group can have multiple modes if there are multiple numbers that appear the same number of times. (We won't discuss mode very much because it's not as useful as average or median.)

> **Important:** When determining the average, median, or mode of a group of numbers, the order of the numbers in the group is not important. For example, the average of the list 2, 5, 9, 11, 13 and the average of the list 9, 13, 2, 11, 5 are the same (they're both 8), and the medians are the same too (they're both 9).

Average, median, and mode are examples of statistics. As you continue your study of math and science (and, indeed, any subject in which data is important), you'll learn about many more types of statistics.

> **Sidenote:** Another statistic that you'll sometimes see is **range**. The range of a group of numbers is the difference between the greatest number and the least number. For example, the range of the list 9, 13, 2, 11, 5 is $13 - 2 = 11$.

> **WARNING!!** Some textbooks and reference books refer to mean, median, and mode all as "averages." In day-to-day usage, the term "average" nearly always refers to the mean, so we have adopted this common usage of the term "average" in this text.

Problems

Problem 13.1: Suppose the following are your grades on tests this year:

$$73, 84, 100, 91, 92, 96, 84.$$

(a) What is the average of your test scores?

(b) What is the median of your test scores?

(c) What is the mode of your test scores?

Problem 13.2: In the first four of Homer's five bowling games, he gets scores of 212, 184, 165, and 173.

(a) What must Homer bowl in his fifth game to make his average score over the five games be 190?

(b) After Homer's fifth game, is it possible for the median score of the five games to be 190?

(c) All bowling scores are integers from 0 to 300. What are the possible values of the median of Homer's scores after his fifth game?

Problem 13.3: In this problem, we explore another way to think about average. The heights, in inches, of the people on my stilts team are

$$53, 54, 56, 53, 56, 57, 55, 53, 54, 54.$$

(a) What is the average height of the people on my team?

(b) For each person on the team who is taller than the average, find the positive difference between that person's height and the average height. Find the sum of these differences.

(c) For each person on the team who is shorter than the average, find the positive difference between the average height and that person's height. Find the sum of these differences.

(d) You should notice an interesting relationship between your answers in parts (b) and (c). (If you don't, then try the first three parts again.) Can you explain why this relationship occurs?

Problem 13.4: Suppose you average 82 on your first 7 tests in a class. What must you score on the eighth test to raise your average to 84?

Problem 13.5: In their first 6 games, the Sixers averaged 81 points. In their next 4 games, the Sixers averaged 73 points.

(a) What is the Sixers' average score for all 10 games?

(b) What must the Sixers average in their next 5 games so that 80 will be their average score over all 15 games?

Problem 13.6:

(a) Mary has five bags of candy. The numbers of pieces in the bags are 6, 8, 12, 14, and 15. What is the average number of pieces per bag?

(b) Mary adds 23 pieces to each bag. Now what is the average number of pieces per bag?

(c) Find the average of the following 6 numbers:

$$5647205, 5647203, 5647211, 5647212, 5647224, 5647217.$$

Problem 13.7: The mean of a set of five different positive integers is 15. The median is 18. What is the maximum possible value of the largest of these five integers? *(Source: AMC 8)*

Problem 13.1: Suppose the following are your grades on tests this year:

$$73, 84, 100, 91, 92, 96, 84.$$

(a) What is the average of your test scores?

(b) What is the median of your test scores?

(c) What is the mode of your test scores?

Solution for Problem 13.1:

(a) To find the average, we divide the sum of the scores by the number of scores:

$$\frac{73 + 84 + 100 + 91 + 92 + 96 + 84}{7} = \frac{620}{7} = 88\frac{4}{7}.$$

(b) First, we list the grades in order:

$$73, 84, 84, 91, 92, 96, 100.$$

The middle grade is 91, so the median is 91.

(c) The grade 84 occurs twice, and each other grade in the list only occurs once. Since 84 occurs more often than any other grade, 84 is the mode.

□

Problem 13.2: In the first four of Homer's five bowling games, he gets scores of 212, 184, 165, and 173.

(a) What must Homer bowl in his fifth game to make his average score over the five games be 190?

(b) After Homer's fifth game, is it possible for the median score of the five games to be 190?

(c) All bowling scores are integers from 0 to 300. What are the possible values of the median of Homer's scores after his fifth game?

Solution for Problem 13.2:

(a) Here are two solutions:

Solution 1: Assign a variable to the fifth score. We let x be Homer's score in the fifth game. Then, the average of the five scores is

$$\frac{212 + 184 + 165 + 173 + x}{5}.$$

Simplifying this gives $\frac{734 + x}{5}$. We'd like this to equal 190, so we have the equation

$$\frac{734 + x}{5} = 190.$$

We multiply both sides by 5 to get rid of the fraction, giving us $734 + x = 950$. Subtracting 734 from both sides gives $x = 950 - 734 = 216$.

Solution 2: Consider the sum of the 5 scores. We can skip all the algebra of our first solution and jump straight to the last step. If the average of the 5 scores is 190, then the sum of the 5 scores must be $5 \cdot 190$, which equals 950. So, to figure out what Homer needs in his fifth game, we simply subtract the first four scores from 950:

$$950 - 212 - 184 - 165 - 173 = 216.$$

Concept: The average of a list of numbers gives us information about the sum of the numbers in the list. Therefore, we can solve many problems about averages by thinking about sums.

(b) We start by listing the first four scores in order:

$$165, 173, 184, 212.$$

After we add a new score to the list, the median score will be the score in the middle of the ordered list. If the new score is greater than 184, then the new score will be after 184 in the ordered list, making 184 the middle number in the list. This would make 184 the median score. If the new score is not greater than 184, then 184 will be the fourth score in the ordered list. This would mean that the median is no greater than 184. Therefore, it's impossible for Homer to raise his median to 190.

(c) The previous part might make us wonder what values are possible for the median score. As noted, if the new score is greater than 184, then 184 is the median. Similarly, if the new score is less than 173, then 173 will be the middle score, and hence 173 will be the median. If the new score is between 173 and 184 (or equal to either), then that new score will be the median. Therefore, the median of the five scores can be any integer from 173 to 184, including 173 and 184.

□

Problem 13.3: In this problem, we explore another way to think about average. The heights, in inches, of the people on my stilts team are

$$53, 54, 56, 53, 56, 57, 55, 53, 54, 54.$$

(a) What is the average height of the people on my team?

(b) For each person on the team who is taller than the average, find the positive difference between that person's height and the average height. Find the sum of these differences.

(c) For each person on the team who is shorter than the average, find the positive difference between the average height and that person's height. Find the sum of these differences.

(d) You should notice an interesting relationship between your answers in parts (b) and (c). (If you don't, then try the first three parts again.) Can you explain why this relationship occurs?

Solution for Problem 13.3:

(a) The average height of the people on my team is

$$\frac{53 + 54 + 56 + 53 + 56 + 57 + 55 + 53 + 54 + 54}{10} = \frac{545}{10} = 54.5 \text{ inches.}$$

(b) There are four people whose heights are greater than the average, and their heights in inches are 56, 56, 57, 55. Subtracting 54.5 from each of these numbers gives 1.5, 1.5, 2.5, 0.5, and adding these differences gives $1.5 + 1.5 + 2.5 + 0.5 = 6$ inches.

(c) There are six people whose heights are less than the average, and their heights in inches are 53, 54, 53, 53, 54, 54. Subtracting each of these numbers from 54.5 gives 1.5, 0.5, 1.5, 1.5, 0.5, 0.5. Adding these differences gives $1.5 + 0.5 + 1.5 + 1.5 + 0.5 + 0.5 = 6$ inches.

(d) Our answers for parts (b) and (c) are the same! That is, the total difference between the 4 above-average heights and the average height equals the total difference between the average height and the 6 below-average heights. Let's see if this is just a coincidence.

   We take a look at how much we have to change each student's height to make that student's height equal to the average height:

											Sum
Old Height:	53	54	56	53	56	57	55	53	54	54	545
Change:	+1.5	+0.5	−1.5	+1.5	−1.5	−2.5	−0.5	+1.5	+0.5	+0.5	0
New Height:	54.5	54.5	54.5	54.5	54.5	54.5	54.5	54.5	54.5	54.5	545

The sum of the original heights divided by 10 equals the average, so the sum of the original heights is 10 times the average, or 545. Each new height equals the average height, so the sum of the new heights is also 10 times the average, or 545. Therefore, the sum of all of the heights doesn't change when we make everyone's height equal to the original average. This means the sum of all of our changes must be 0! So, the total amount that we decrease the above-average heights must equal the total amount that we increase the below-average heights.

$\square$

Parts (b)–(d) of Problem 13.3 gives us a new way to think about the average of a list of numbers:

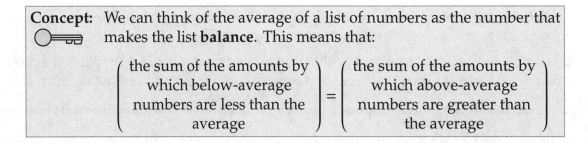

Concept: We can think of the average of a list of numbers as the number that makes the list **balance**. This means that:

$$\begin{pmatrix} \text{the sum of the amounts by} \\ \text{which below-average} \\ \text{numbers are less than the} \\ \text{average} \end{pmatrix} = \begin{pmatrix} \text{the sum of the amounts by} \\ \text{which above-average} \\ \text{numbers are greater than} \\ \text{the average} \end{pmatrix}$$

We saw this concept in Problem 13.3. In part (b), we computed the sum of the amounts by which the above-average heights in the list were greater than the average, and it was 6. In part (c), we computed the sum of the amounts by which the below-average heights in the list were less than the average, and again it was 6. The average of 54.5 was the number that "balanced" all of the heights in the list.

Let's put this new way of thinking about average to work in a problem.

Problem 13.4: Suppose you average 82 on your first 7 tests in a class. What must you score on the eighth test to raise your average to 84?

Solution for Problem 13.4: Solution 1: Consider the sum of all the tests. In order to have an average of 84 after 8 tests, the sum of the 8 test scores must be $8 \cdot 84 = 672$. The first 7 tests have an average of 82, so the sum of the first 7 scores is $7 \cdot 82 = 574$. Therefore, the eighth score must be $672 - 574 = 98$.

Solution 2: Compare each test to the average, and balance. If we replace each of the first 7 scores with the average score of 82, then we don't change the sum of the first 7 scores. (This is the same idea as what we did in part (d) of Problem 13.3.) We also don't change the sum of the first 8 scores, no matter what the eighth score is. Therefore, changing the first 7 scores to 82 doesn't change the average of the first 8 scores, either.

> **Concept:** The average of a list of numbers only depends on the number of items in the list and the sum of the items in the list. Therefore, if we change all of the items in the list to be equal to the list's average, then we don't change the average of the list.

We need an eighth score that makes the average of seven 82's and the eighth score equal to 84. To find that eighth score, we compare each score to the average score, keeping in mind that the new average of 84 must "balance" the eight scores. Each of the seven 82's is 2 fewer than the average 84, so their total amount less than the average is $7 \cdot 2 = 14$. Therefore, in order for the average to balance the scores, the new 8th score must be 14 greater than the average. Thus the eighth score must be $84 + 14 = 98$. $\square$

> **Problem 13.5:** In their first 6 games, the Sixers averaged 81 points. In their next 4 games, the Sixers averaged 73 points.
>
> (a) What is the Sixers' average score for all 10 games?
>
> (b) What must the Sixers average in their next 5 games so that 80 will be their average score over all 15 games?

Solution for Problem 13.5:

(a) To find the average score for all 10 games, we first find the sum of the scores for all 10 games. Since the Sixers average 81 points in the first 6 games, they score a total of $6 \cdot 81$ points in the first 6 games. Similarly, they score $4 \cdot 73$ points in the next 4 games. So, the total number of points they score in the 10 games is

$$6 \cdot 81 + 4 \cdot 73 = 486 + 292 = 778.$$

Therefore the average score over these 10 games is $\frac{778}{10} = 77.8$ points.

(b) To make their average after 15 games equal 80, they must score a total of $15 \cdot 80 = 1200$ points in the 15 games. In part (a), we saw that they scored 778 points in the first 10 games. So, in the final 5 games, they must score

$$1200 - 778 = 422$$

points. Therefore, their average score for the last 5 games must be $\frac{422}{5} = 84.4$ points.

We also could have used our balancing strategy from Problem 13.4. If the average after 15 games is 80 and the average for the first 10 games is 77.8, then the Sixers were 2.2 points per game below their 15-game average for the first 10 games. That's a total of $2.2 \cdot 10 = 22$ points below average for the first 10 games. So, they have to be a total of 22 points above average for the last 5 games. That's $\frac{22}{5} = 4.4$ points above average per game, so they have to average $80 + 4.4 = 84.4$ points in the final five games.

$\square$

Problem 13.6:

(a) Mary has five bags of candy. The numbers of pieces in the bags are 6, 8, 12, 14, and 15. What is the average number of pieces per bag?

(b) Mary adds 23 pieces to each bag. Now what is the average number of pieces per bag?

(c) Find the average of the following 6 numbers:

$$5647205, 5647203, 5647211, 5647212, 5647224, 5647217.$$

Solution for Problem 13.6:

(a) The average is $\frac{6+8+12+14+15}{5} = \frac{55}{5} = 11$.

(b) After increasing the number of pieces in each bag, the numbers of pieces in the bags are 29, 31, 35, 37, and 38. Now the average number of pieces per bag is $\frac{29+31+35+37+38}{5} = \frac{170}{5} = 34$. So, after Mary adds 23 pieces to each bag, the average is 23 higher. This isn't a coincidence. We can see why with some clever arithmetic. Rather than computing the number of candies in each bag after Mary adds 23 to each bag, we separate the additional candies in our computation of the average:

$$\frac{(6+23)+(8+23)+(12+23)+(14+23)+(15+23)}{5}$$

$$= \frac{6+8+12+14+15}{5} + \frac{23+23+23+23+23}{5}$$

$$= \frac{6+8+12+14+15}{5} + \frac{5 \cdot 23}{5}$$

$$= \frac{6+8+12+14+15}{5} + 23.$$

Since $\frac{6+8+12+14+15}{5}$ is the average before Mary adds candies, we see that the new average is simply 23 more than the old average.

We can follow the same steps to see that if Mary adds the same number of candies to each bag, then the average number of candies per bag increases by the amount she adds to each bag.

> **Important:** Suppose we have a list of numbers, and make a new list by adding
> ⚠ the same number, n, to each number in the original list. The
> average of the numbers in the new list is the sum of n and the
> average of the original list of numbers.

(c) We notice that the numbers only differ in their final two digits. Each number is 5647200 plus some two-digit number. Subtracting 5647200 from each number in the list gives

$$5, 3, 11, 12, 24, 17.$$

The average of these is $\frac{5+3+11+12+24+17}{6} = 12$. We now use the fact we discovered in the previous part. When we add 5647200 to each number in the list above, we recover the original list in the problem. Adding 5647200 to each number in a list increases the average of the list by 5647200. So, the desired average is $12 + 5647200 = 5647212$.

□

Problem 13.7: The mean of a set of five different positive integers is 15. The median is 18. What is the maximum possible value of the largest of these five integers? *(Source: AMC 8)*

Solution for Problem 13.7: Because there is an odd number of integers in the set, the middle number is the median. So, one number in the set is 18. Since the mean of the five integers is 15, the sum of the five numbers is $5 \cdot 15$, which equals 75. What's wrong with this solution:

Bogus Solution: We know that one of the numbers is 18, which means the other
 four sum to $75 - 18 = 57$. We want one of the numbers to be as large as possible, but they must all be positive, and they must all be different. So, we let the smallest three numbers be 1, 2, and 3. This leaves $57 - 1 - 2 - 3 = 51$ for the largest number.

We see that our solution is incorrect when we list the integers in order from least to greatest: $1, 2, 3, 18, 51$. The median of this list is 3, not 18.

We correct our mistake by remembering that the median must be in the middle. So, there are two integers in the set greater than 18 and two less than 18. We want the largest integer to be as large as possible, so we make the other three integers (besides the largest and 18) as small as possible. We do this by letting the two less than 18 be 1 and 2, and letting one of the integers greater than 18 be 19. This leaves

$$75 - 1 - 2 - 18 - 19 = 35$$

remaining for the largest possible integer. As a check, our list is $1, 2, 18, 19, 35$, and we see that this list has mean 15 and median 18, as required. □

The key to checking our answer was comparing our full solution, not just the final answer, to all parts of the original problem.

WARNING!! Be thorough when checking your answer; make sure your full
☢ solution fits with all parts of the problem.

Exercises ▶

13.1.1 Compute the average, median, and mode of the following list of numbers:

$$34, 13, 37, 24, 25, 13, 41, 23, 28, 31.$$

13.1.2   Jane averages 143 in her first six bowling games. Her scores in her next four games are all the same. If her bowling average over the ten games is also 143, then what did she bowl in each of the final four games?

13.1.3   In my science class, my teacher assigns each student a semester grade by finding the median of that student's test scores. There are seven tests each semester. I have scored 55, 78, 63, and 91 on the first four tests. What is the highest possible semester grade I can earn?

13.1.4   In a list of positive integers, all have different values. Their sum is 350. Their average is 50. One of the integers is 100. What is the greatest integer that can be in the list? *(Source: MOEMS)*

13.1.5   What number should be removed from the list

$$1, 2, 3, 4, 5, 6, 7, 8, 9, 10, 11$$

so that the average of the remaining numbers is 6.1? *(Source: AMC 8)*

13.1.6   In a group of five children, the average child's weight was 72 pounds. When a sixth child joined the group, the average child's weight became 73 pounds. What was the weight of the sixth child? *(Source: MOEMS)*

13.1.7   In Theresa's first 8 basketball games, she scored 7, 4, 3, 6, 8, 3, 1 and 5 points. In her ninth game, she scored fewer than 10 points and her points-per-game average for the nine games was an integer. In her tenth game, she scored fewer than 10 points and her points-per-game average for the ten games was an integer. What is the product of the number of points she scored in the ninth and tenth games? *(Source: AMC 8)*

13.1.8   There is a set of five positive integers whose average (mean) is 5, whose median is 5, and whose only mode is 8. What is the difference between the largest and smallest integers in the set? *(Source: AMC 8)*

13.1.9★

(a) What is the average of the smallest 7 positive integers?

(b) What is the average of the smallest n positive integers if n is odd?

(c) What is the average of the smallest n positive integers if n is even?

(d) What is the average of the integers from 21 to 31, including 21 and 31?

(e) Jenny makes a list of all the integers from a to b, including a and b. Find a formula in terms of a and b for the average of Jenny's numbers.

13.2   Limits of Basic Statistics

Now that we know how to compute average, median, and mode, we will think about what sort of information they tell us. And, perhaps more importantly, we will think about what sort of information they *don't* tell us.

 **Problems**

Problem 13.8: You have to choose one of four people in your math club to be your partner on a math assignment. You'd like to choose someone who is very good at math! Here are the four students' scores on their previous seven assignments:

Anna: 94, 93, 90, 93, 92, 91, 0

Bob: 98, 94, 33, 33, 96, 97, 23

Carol: 89, 88, 86, 88, 87, 84, 85

Doug: 100, 14, 3, 100, 11, 2, 21

(a) Which student has the highest average score?

(b) Which student has the highest median score?

(c) Which student has the highest mode score?

(d) Which student would you choose as your partner?

Problem 13.9: The average wealth of a person in Richville is $150,000 and the average wealth of a person in Poorville is $20,000.

(a) Suppose a person is called "filthy stinking rich" if the person has over one million dollars. Can we tell which town has more filthy stinking rich people?

(b) Can we tell which town has the higher median wealth?

(c) If both towns have the same number of people, can we tell which town has the higher total wealth?

(d) Suppose a person with $1,000,000 and 4 people who have $0 move into Richville. Will the average wealth of Richville go up or down?

Problem 13.10: The median wealth of a person in Goldtown is $150,000 and the median wealth of a person in Tintown is $20,000. Each town has 8000 people.

(a) Suppose a town qualifies for special government subsidies if each of at least half of its residents has less than $60,000. Does either town necessarily qualify for the subsidies?

(b) Can we tell which town has the higher average wealth?

(c) Suppose a person with $1,000,000,000 and 4 people who have $0 move into Goldtown. Will the median wealth of Goldtown go up or down?

Problem 13.8: You have to choose one of four people in your math club to be your partner on a math assignment. You'd like to choose someone who is very good at math! Here are the four students' scores on their previous seven assignments:

$$\text{Anna: } 94, 93, 90, 93, 92, 91, 0$$
$$\text{Bob: } 98, 94, 33, 33, 96, 97, 23$$
$$\text{Carol: } 89, 88, 86, 88, 87, 84, 85$$
$$\text{Doug: } 100, 14, 3, 100, 11, 2, 21$$

(a) Which student has the highest average score?

(b) Which student has the highest median score?

(c) Which student has the highest mode score?

(d) Which student would you choose as your partner?

Solution for Problem 13.8:

(a) Here are the averages:

$$\text{Anna's average} = \frac{94 + 93 + 90 + 93 + 92 + 91 + 0}{7} = \frac{553}{7} = 79,$$

$$\text{Bob's average} = \frac{98 + 94 + 33 + 33 + 96 + 97 + 23}{7} = \frac{474}{7} = 67\frac{5}{7},$$

$$\text{Carol's average} = \frac{89 + 88 + 86 + 88 + 87 + 84 + 85}{7} = \frac{607}{7} = 86\frac{5}{7},$$

$$\text{Doug's average} = \frac{100 + 14 + 3 + 100 + 11 + 2 + 21}{7} = \frac{251}{7} = 35\frac{6}{7}.$$

Carol has the highest average.

(b) We find the students' median scores by putting each student's scores in order from least to greatest:

$$\text{Anna: } 0, 90, 91, \underline{92}, 93, 93, 94$$
$$\text{Bob: } 23, 33, 33, \underline{94}, 96, 97, 98$$
$$\text{Carol: } 84, 85, 86, \underline{87}, 88, 88, 89$$
$$\text{Doug: } 2, 3, 11, \underline{14}, 21, 100, 100$$

For each student, the corresponding median is the middle number in the list. Each student's median is underlined. Bob has the highest median.

(c) The mode is the most frequent score. Each student has one repeated score, so we can quickly find each student's mode score:

Anna: 93   Bob: 33   Carol: 88   Doug: 100

Doug has the highest mode.

(d) There's no clearly correct answer to this question. Carol has the highest average, Bob has the highest median, and Doug has the highest mode. But you might be best off choosing Anna!

Looking at all of the scores, it's pretty clear that you probably don't want to choose Doug (the student with the highest mode). Most of the time he does very poorly. Mode is usually not a very helpful statistic.

Even though Bob has the highest median, Bob appears to be considerably more likely than Anna or Carol to do badly. So choosing Bob seems to bring a higher risk of a low score.

Carol, with the highest average, appears to be more reliable than Anna, but Anna's single bad score of 0 suggests that there may be some other explanation for her poor performance on that assignment. Maybe she simply didn't turn it in.

If you can be sure that Anna will show up, then it looks like she has a good chance to do better than Carol, because all of Anna's nonzero scores are higher than all of Carol's scores.

□

The key point of Problem 13.8 is that all of the basic statistics we have studied so far are usually poor substitutes for considering all of the data. Of course, sometimes we don't have all of the data available, or there is way too much data to consider all of it. As you study more statistics in the future, you'll learn methods for analyzing large batches of data.

For now, we'll take a closer look at the limitations of the basic tools we have studied so far. It's particularly important to understand the strengths and weaknesses of average and median, since these are the two statistics that people use (and misuse!) the most.

Problem 13.9: The average wealth of a person in Richville is $150,000 and the average wealth of a person in Poorville is $20,000.

(a) Suppose a person is called "filthy stinking rich" if the person has over one million dollars. Can we tell which town has more filthy stinking rich people?

(b) Can we tell which town has the higher median wealth?

(c) If both towns have the same number of people, can we tell which town has the higher total wealth?

(d) Suppose a person with $1,000,000 and 4 people who have $0 move into Richville. Will the average wealth of Richville go up or down?

Solution for Problem 13.9:

(a) First notice that we aren't given any information about how many people are in each town.

> **WARNING!!** Neither the average nor the median of a group of numbers tells us anything about how many numbers are in the group.

On the one hand, it's possible that everyone in Richville has exactly $150,000, so there is no one in Richville who is filthy stinking rich. At the same time, Poorville might consist of 100 people: one person with $2,000,000, who is definitely filthy stinking rich, and 99 people with no money at all. (Note that this does make the average wealth in Poorville equal to $20,000, as required.) In this case, Poorville has more filthy stinking rich people.

On the other hand, it's possible that everyone in Poorville has exactly $20,000 (so that no one is filthy stinking rich), while Richville consists of one filthy stinking rich person with $15,000,000 and 99 people who each have nothing. In this case, Richville has more filthy stinking rich people.

So without any additional information, we can't tell which town has more filthy stinking rich people.

(b) On the one hand, suppose the towns' populations are:

Richville	Poorville
50 people with $150,000 each	1 person with $1,000,000
	49 people with $0 each

The average and median wealth in Richville are each $150,000, whereas the average wealth in Poorville is ($1,000,000)/50 = $20,000 and the median wealth in Poorville is $0. In this case, Richville has a higher median wealth than Poorville.

On the other hand, suppose the towns' populations are:

Richville	Poorville
1 person with $1,500,000	10 people with $20,000 each
9 people with $0 each	

The average and median wealth in Poorville are each $20,000, whereas the average wealth in Richville is ($1,500,000)/10 = $150,000 and the median wealth in Richville is $0. In this case, Poorville has a higher median wealth than Richville.

So without any additional information, we can't tell which town has the higher median wealth.

> **Important:** We cannot determine anything about the median of a set of data just by knowing the average of the data.

(c) For each town, the average wealth equals the total wealth divided by the number of people. So, the total wealth equals the product of the average wealth and the number of people. If the two towns have the same number of people, then Richville must have the higher total wealth. Specifically, if both towns have n people, then Richville has a total wealth of $150,000n$, and Poorville has a total wealth of $20,000n$.

Note that this analysis only worked because we were told that the number of people in each town are the same. If we weren't given this additional bit of information, we couldn't tell which town had more total wealth. For example, if the population of Richville was just 1 and the population of Poorville was 10, then the total wealth of Richville would be $150,000\cdot1 = \$150,000$ whereas the total wealth of Poorville would be $20,000\cdot10 = \$200,000$. In this example, the total wealth of Poorville would be greater.

> **Important:** Without knowing the size of the data sets, we cannot compare the sums of the data just by comparing their averages.

(d) The average wealth equals the total wealth divided by the number of people. In other words, the average equals the amount each person would have if we divided the total wealth equally among the people. The five people who move into Richville have a total of $1,000,000. To keep the town average at $150,000 per person, these five new people only need a total of 5($150,000), which is $750,000. So, when these five new people come to town, there's an extra $250,000 above the total amount needed for $150,000 per person. This means that the average wealth in the town must go up when these five people arrive.

□

Problem 13.9 shows us some features and limitations of average. In particular, in our examples in parts (a), (b), and (d), we see that it is possible for a single number to have a huge effect on the average. For example, if an extremely rich person moves into your neighborhood, the average wealth of your neighborhood will rise a lot! But the other people in your neighborhood haven't gotten any richer, even though, judging by the average wealth of the neighborhood, it looks like the neighborhood has become much richer.

Problem 13.10: The median wealth of a person in Goldtown is $150,000 and the median wealth of a person in Tintown is $20,000. Each town has 8000 people.

(a) Suppose a town qualifies for special government subsidies if each of at least half of its residents has less than $60,000. Does either town necessarily qualify for the subsidies?

(b) Can we tell which town has the higher average wealth?

(c) Suppose a person with $1,000,000,000 and 4 people who have $0 move into Goldtown. Will the median wealth of Goldtown go up or down?

Solution for Problem 13.10:

(a) Suppose we line up everyone in Tintown based on how much wealth they have. The population of Tintown is even, so the median wealth, $20,000, is the average wealth of the two people in the middle. So, either the middle two people have $20,000 each, or the poorer of the two has less than $20,000. Either way, each person in the poorer half of the line has no greater than the median wealth, $20,000. Each of these people therefore has less than $60,000, so Tintown qualifies for the subsidies.

Over in Goldtown, the median wealth is $150,000. If we line up Goldtown from poorest to richest, then each person in the richer half of the line has at least $150,000. But all we know about the people in the poorer half of the line is that each person has no more than $150,000. It is possible for each person in the poorer half to have less than $60,000. For example, suppose each person in the poorer half of Goldtown has $50,000 and each person in the richer half of Goldtown has $250,000. Then, the median wealth of Goldtown is $150,000, but Goldtown still qualifies for the subsidy.

(b) The median value only tells us how much the "middle" person has in each town, and that half the people in town have at least this much. But the richest person in town could have any amount more than the median wealth. For example, it's possible that everyone in Goldtown has exactly $150,000, while everyone in Tintown has $20,000 except for one person who has tens of billions of dollars. In this case, Tintown could have much higher total wealth, and therefore higher average wealth, than Goldtown.

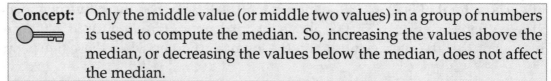

> **Concept:** Only the middle value (or middle two values) in a group of numbers is used to compute the median. So, increasing the values above the median, or decreasing the values below the median, does not affect the median.

(c) Suppose that, before the five new people arrive, we line up all the people in Goldtown based on their wealth, with the richest first and the poorest last. Since there are 8000 people, the median is the average wealth of the middle two people, who are the 4000th and 4001st people in the line.

When the five new people arrive and find their places in the line, the four with $0 will join the poorer end, and the person with $1,000,000,000 will be somewhere in the rich half of the line. So, in this new line there will be 8005 people. The person who joined the rich end causes the people who were previously 4000th and 4001st to be shifted back by 1, to 4001st and 4002nd in the line.

In this new line of 8005 people, the middle person is 4003rd in line. Most notably, this person is behind, and therefore not richer than, the two people whose average gave us the original median. That is, the new median cannot possibly be greater than the old median.

We can't actually say that the new median must be lower than the old median, since we might have many people in the middle with the same wealth. So, it's possible that the new median is the same as the old median, but the new median cannot be higher than the old median.

The interesting observation here is that the new people brought a total of one *billion* dollars to the town, but the median did not rise. That's because we added more poor people than rich people. Once again, we see that the actual values above and below the median value do not affect the median. The median only tells us what the middle is.

□

> **Concept:** Average and median only give us very limited information about a set of data. In particular, neither tells us anything about the size of the set, and median does not tell us anything about the total of the data in the set. Neither average nor median tells us anything about the other (that is, if we know the average, we don't know anything about the median; and if we know the median, we don't know anything about the average).
>
> We say that a number in a group of numbers is an **outlier** if it is very far from the other numbers in the group. Outliers can have a significant effect on average, but have little effect on the median.
>
> Sometimes, when analyzing data, people will remove outliers from a group of numbers before computing the average of the group. For example, a teacher might do this by throwing out a student's lowest exam grade before computing his or her average grade.

Exercises ▶

13.2.1 The median height of the players on my basketball team is 6 feet, 4 inches. What is the shortest that the tallest player on the team could possibly be?

13.2.2 The average wealth of a person in Richville is $150,000 and the average wealth of a person in Poorville is $20,000. Suppose Richville and Poorville combine to form Mediumville.

(a) Is it possible that the average wealth in Mediumville is exactly $20,000?

(b) Suppose one person from Richville refuses to join Mediumville. Then, is it possible that the average wealth of Mediumville is less than $20,000?

(c) If there were the same number of people in Poorville and Richville, then what is the average wealth of Mediumville?

(d) If the average wealth of Mediumville is $120,000, then which city was larger, Richville or Poorville?

13.2.3 Below are the average and median of test scores for Nick and Omar.

Nick: average 70, median 50

Omar: average 50, median 70

One of the students usually does OK, but when he does badly, he does very badly. The other one usually doesn't do very well, but when he does well, he does extremely well. Which is which?

13.3 Tables, Graphs, and Charts

In the first two sections of this chapter, we discussed methods for using single numbers to represent a collection of data. In this section, we explore a variety of ways to display data rather than just showing a list of numbers.

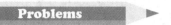 **Problems**

Problem 13.11: The **table** below tells us the number of students in sixth, seventh, and eighth grades at four middle schools. Each row corresponds to one of the middle schools. Three columns correspond to the number of students in each grade for each school, and the last column corresponds to the total number of students in each school.

Students in Middle School By Grade

	6th Grade	7th Grade	8th Grade	Total
East Middle School	213	241	217	671
West Middle School	135	142	120	
North Middle School	230	130		534
South Middle School	341		339	1023

(a) Complete the table by filling in the missing entries.

(b) How many more eighth graders are there in South Middle School than in East Middle School?

(c) Which grade has the most students total (across all schools)?

(d) Which school has the highest average number of students per grade?

(e) Which school is most likely to need more seventh grade teachers next year?

Problem 13.12: We asked a group of Art of Problem Solving students what they think about most during history class. The results are shown in the **bar chart** at the right. Describe each of the following statements as true, false, or not necessarily true or false:

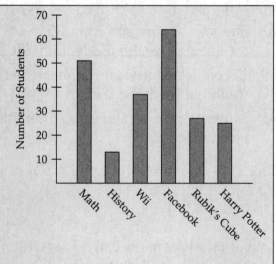

(a) More than three times as many students think most about math as think most about history.

(b) More students think most about math than Wii and Rubik's Cube put together.

(c) More than half the class thinks most about Facebook.

(d) Most students spend more time thinking about Wii than about Rubik's Cube.

Problem 13.13: There are two math teams at Beast Academy, The Little Monsters and The Bots. At the end of each day, each team graphs the total number of points it has earned. The teams use **line graphs** to graph their totals. Below are last week's graphs for The Little Monsters and The Bots:

The Little Monsters' points

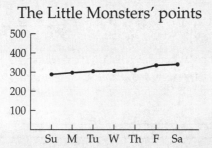

The Bots' points

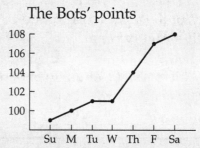

Describe each of the following as true, false, or not able to be determined from the graphs.

(a) The Bots had fewer points than The Little Monsters at the start of Monday, but more points than The Little Monsters at the end of Friday.

(b) The Bots earned more points than The Little Monsters between the start of Monday and the end of Friday.

(c) There was a day on which The Bots didn't earn any points.

(d) There was a weekday (not Saturday or Sunday) on which The Little Monsters didn't earn any points.

(e) The Little Monsters earned more than 24 points on Friday.

Problem 13.14: The scores on a history test are shown at the right in a **stem-and-leaf plot**. Each score in the plot has its tens digit to the left of the line and its units digit to the right of the line on the same row. So, the first row of the plot includes the scores 53, 57, and 59.

5	3 7 9
6	2 6 6 8 8
7	2 2 2 2 2 5 6 7 7 8 9
8	0 0 1 2 5 5 6
9	0 4 5 8

(a) What is the average score?

(b) What is the median score?

(c) What is the mode score?

(d) Represent the data with a bar chart in which there is one bar for each tens digit. That is, one bar is a count of all the scores from 50 to 59, another bar is a count of all the scores from 60 to 69, etc.

(e) Can you use your bar chart in part (d) to answer questions (a) through (c)? Which contains more information, your bar chart or the stem-and-leaf plot?

Problem 13.15: Members of the Gross Pie Association were asked for their favorite type of pie. The results of the poll are shown in the **pie chart** at the right. Pie charts are typically circular, and sliced into pieces that represent different categories. The sizes of the pieces correspond to the portion of the whole that each category represents. So, for example, the "Pickle" piece is nearly half the chart, because nearly half the people chose pickle pie. If 36 of the members chose cat-hair pie, then how many chose sawdust pie?

Favorite Gross Pie Flavor

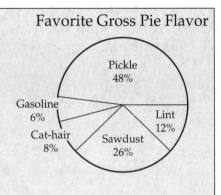

In a **table**, we organize data in columns and rows. Usually, the columns correspond to one type of information, and the rows correspond to another type of information. For example, in the table in our first problem below, each row corresponds to a school and each column corresponds to a grade level or levels. Each entry in the table then tells us how many students are in the corresponding grade(s) at the corresponding school.

Problem 13.11: The table below tells us the number of students in sixth, seventh, and eighth grades at four middle schools. Each row corresponds to one of the middle schools. Three columns correspond to the number of students in each grade for each school, and the last column corresponds to the total number of students in each school.

Students in Middle School By Grade

	6th Grade	7th Grade	8th Grade	Total
East Middle School	213	241	217	671
West Middle School	135	142	120	
North Middle School	230	130		534
South Middle School	341		339	1023

(a) Complete the table by filling in the missing entries.

(b) How many more eighth graders are there in South Middle School than in East Middle School?

(c) Which grade has the most students total (across all schools)?

(d) Which school has the highest average number of students per grade?

(e) Which school is most likely to need more seventh grade teachers next year?

Solution for Problem 13.11:

(a) The missing entry for West Middle School is the total, which is

$$135 + 142 + 120 = 397.$$

The missing entry for North Middle School is the number of 8th graders. Subtracting the numbers of 6th and 7th graders from the total gives us

$$534 - 230 - 130 = 174$$

eighth graders. Similarly, the number of 7th graders in South Middle School is

$$1023 - 341 - 339 = 343.$$

The completed table is shown below with the new numbers in bold:

Students in Middle School By Grade

	6th Grade	7th Grade	8th Grade	Total
East Middle School	213	241	217	671
West Middle School	135	142	120	**397**
North Middle School	230	130	**174**	534
South Middle School	341	**343**	339	1023

(b) South Middle School has 339 eighth graders, and East Middle School has 217 eighth graders, so South Middle School has $339 - 217 = 122$ more eighth graders.

(c) We sum each column to find the total number of students in each grade. We can include the results in our table by adding another row:

Students in Middle School By Grade

	6th Grade	7th Grade	8th Grade	Total
East Middle School	213	241	217	671
West Middle School	135	142	120	397
North Middle School	230	130	174	534
South Middle School	341	343	339	1023
Total	**919**	**856**	**850**	**2625**

The 6th grade has the most students.

(d) Since each school has the same number of grades, the school with the largest number of students has the highest average number of students per grade. So, South Middle School has the largest average number of students per grade. (South Middle School has 1023 students, so its average number of students per grade is $1023/3 = 341$.)

(e) This year's 6th grade students will be next year's 7th grade students. So, to see if a school needs more 7th grade teachers next year, we need to compare the number of 7th grade students this year to the number of 6th grade students this year. East, West, and South Middle Schools have fewer 6th graders than 7th graders, so they probably won't need more 7th grade teachers next year. North Middle School has 100 more 6th graders than 7th graders. Therefore, North Middle School is most likely to need more 7th grade teachers next year.

$\square$

Problem 13.12: We asked a group of Art of Problem Solving students what they think about most during history class. The results are shown in the **bar chart** at the right. Describe each of the following statements as true, false, or not necessarily true or false:

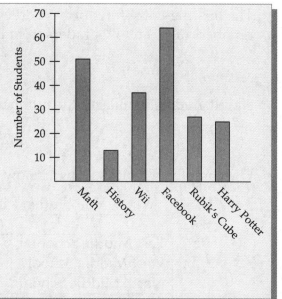

(a) More than three times as many students think most about math as think most about history.

(b) More students think most about math than Wii and Rubik's Cube put together.

(c) More than half the class thinks most about Facebook.

(d) Most students spend more time thinking about Wii than about Rubik's Cube.

Solution for Problem 13.12: The chart in this problem is called a **bar chart**, since it uses bars to represent the data. (Bar charts are also sometimes called **bar graphs**.)

(a) The number of students who think most about history is a little more than 10. The bar for history doesn't make it halfway between 10 and 20, so there are fewer than 15 students who think most about history. Three times 15 is 45, and the bar for math goes a little higher than 50. So, the number of students who think most about math is definitely more than three times the number who think most about history; hence, the statement in the problem is true.

(b) The number of students who think most about Wii is between 35 and 40, and the number who think most about Rubik's Cube is between 25 and 30. So, the sum of these is at least $25 + 35 = 60$. This total is definitely greater than the number of students who think most about math; hence, the statement in the problem is false.

(c) More students think most about Facebook than think most about any of the other options. However, the other options combined have a lot more students total than Facebook—in particular, the sum of the students thinking most about just Math or Wii looks to be about $50 + 40 = 90$, which is already definitely larger than the number of students thinking most about Facebook. Thus, less than half the students think most about Facebook, and the statement in the problem is false.

> **Sidenote:** When considering a set of people divided into groups, we use the word **plurality** to describe the group that consists of the most number of people. If the plurality consists of more than half the total number of people, then we say that it is a **majority** of the people. So, the students who think about Facebook the most in this problem are a plurality of the students, but not a majority.

(d) The bar for Wii is higher than that for the Rubik's Cube, but that only tells us that more students think about Wii *most of all* than think about Rubik's Cube *most of all*. We don't know anything about the other students. They might think about Rubik's Cube a lot without thinking about Wii at all. So, it's possible that most of the students spend more time thinking about Rubik's Cube than thinking about Wii. Thus, we cannot determine whether the statement in the problem is true or false.

□

> **Concept:** Bar charts are useful for comparing several quantities to each other with a quick glance.

Problem 13.13: There are two math teams at Beast Academy, The Little Monsters and The Bots. At the end of each day, each team graphs the total number of points it has earned. The teams use **line graphs** to graph their totals. Below are last week's graphs for The Little Monsters and The Bots:

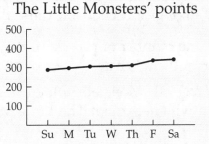

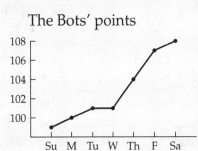

Describe each of the following as true, false, or not able to be determined from the graphs.

(a) The Bots had fewer points than The Little Monsters at the start of Monday, but more points than The Little Monsters at the end of Friday.

(b) The Bots earned more points than The Little Monsters between the start of Monday and the end of Friday.

(c) There was a day on which The Bots didn't earn any points.

(d) There was a weekday (not Saturday or Sunday) on which The Little Monsters didn't earn any points.

(e) The Little Monsters earned more than 24 points on Friday.

Solution for Problem 13.13:

(a) It sure looks like The Bots were behind The Little Monsters at the start of Monday, but way ahead of The Little Monsters at the end of Friday. But take a close look at the numbers on the graphs. The numbers on The Little Monsters' graph range from 100 to 500. The numbers on The Bots' graph also start at 100, but only go up 2 each time, to 108 at the largest. The Little Monsters' graph shows that their score was around 300 the whole week, while The Bots' score was always below 108. So, The Bots did start the week behind The Little Monsters, but The Bots were still far behind at the end of the week—the statement in the problem is false.

We sometimes use the term **scale** to refer to the numbers used along an axis of a graph or chart. The scales in the two graphs are very different.

(b) It looks like The Bots' score skyrocketed from Monday to Friday, while The Little Monsters' score only went up a tiny bit. But again, the scales of the two graphs are misleading. The Bots' score went from 99 points to 107 points, a gain of 8 points. It's hard to tell exactly how much The Little Monsters' score changed over the week, but it appears that they started close to 300 points and ended about a quarter of the way from 300 to 400. So, The Little Monsters probably earned around 25 points or so, total, which means The Little Monsters earned more points between Monday and Friday than The Bots. Thus, the statement in the problem is false. (The Bots probably chose the scale of their graph to make it look like they earned a ton of points!)

> **WARNING!!** Pay attention to the scales of graphs, particularly when two
> different quantities are being compared with graphs. Graphs
> can be made very misleading by strategically choosing the scale.

(c) The Bots ended Tuesday and Wednesday with the same number of points, so they didn't earn any points on Wednesday. The statement in the problem is true.

(d) It's very hard to tell from the graph whether or not The Little Monsters' total increased on Wednesday. So, we can't tell for sure from the graph whether or not The Little Monsters had a day on which they earned no points.

(e) The Little Monsters' graph goes upward from Thursday to Friday, but it's impossible to tell from the graph by exactly how much. So we can't tell if the statement in the problem is true or false. If The Little Monsters had chosen a different scale for their graph, then it might be easier to answer questions about their exact scores.

□

The graphs in Problem 13.13 are called **line graphs**. Line graphs are frequently used to show how a quantity changes over time.

While the first two parts of Problem 13.13 show us how the scale of a graph can be used to mislead or confuse, the last three parts show us that the choice of scale of a graph can determine how accurately we can read the graph.

> **Concept:** When creating a graph or chart, use a scale that makes clear the
> information you wish to convey.

For example, if The Little Monsters wanted to make more clear how many points they earned during the week, they might have chosen the scale in the graph at the right below.

The Little Monsters' points

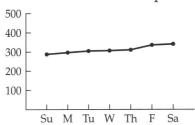

The Little Monsters' points

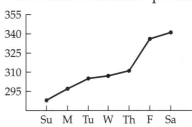

The same point totals were used to make these two graphs, but the graphs look very different! With the graph on the right, we can determine that there isn't a day on which The Little Monsters failed to score any points (so part (d) above is false). However, we still can't determine whether or not The Little Monsters earned more than 24 points on Friday, so we still can't decide whether statement (e) is true or false.

Problem 13.14: The scores on a history test are shown at the right in a **stem-and-leaf plot**. Each score in the plot has its tens digit to the left of the line and its units digit to the right of the line on the same row. So, the first row of the plot includes the scores 53, 57, and 59.

5	3 7 9
6	2 6 6 8 8
7	2 2 2 2 2 5 6 7 7 8 9
8	0 0 1 2 5 5 6
9	0 4 5 8

(a) What is the average score?

(b) What is the median score?

(c) What is the mode score?

(d) Represent the data with a bar chart in which there is one bar for each tens digit. That is, one bar is a count of all the scores from 50 to 59, another bar is a count of all the scores from 60 to 69, etc.

(e) Can you use your bar chart in part (d) to answer questions (a) through (c)? Which contains more information, your bar chart or the stem-and-leaf plot?

Solution for Problem 13.14:

(a) To find the average, we have to sum all of the scores and divide by the total number of scores. To count the scores, we simply count the digits that are to the right of the vertical line. There are 30 such numbers. To sum the numbers, we could write out all 30 numbers and add them, but that would take quite a bit of time. We can take a slight shortcut by adding each row. The first row has three numbers with 5 as the tens digit, and the digits to the right of the line are the units digits. So, the sum of the numbers in that row is $3(50) + 3 + 7 + 9 = 169$. Similarly, the sum of the numbers in the next row is $5(60) + 2 + 6 + 6 + 8 + 8 = 330$. The sum of the numbers in the 70s row is 822, the sum of the 80s row is 579, and the sum of the 90s row is 377. So, the sum of all of the numbers is

$$169 + 330 + 822 + 579 + 377 = 2277,$$

and the average of the numbers is $2277/30 = 75.9$.

(b) The numbers are essentially in order, with the numbers in each row going from least to greatest, and the numbers in each row all less than those in any lower row on the chart. So, we can easily scan through the list to find the middle number. There are thirty numbers total, so (since 30 is even) we must find the middle two numbers to compute the median, and the middle two are the 15th and 16th scores. There are 3 scores on the first row and 5 on the second, for a total of 8 scores less than 70. We therefore want the seventh and eighth scores in the 70s row, which are 76 and 77. The median is the average of these, which is 76.5.

(c) The mode is the score that occurs most. The string of 2s in the 70s row is easy to spot for the most common score, so 72 is the mode.

(d) The bar chart is shown at the right. The chart displays counts of how many times each of the options occurs. Such a chart is sometimes called a **histogram**. Notice that it is very similar to the stem-and-leaf plot. (We drew the bars horizontally rather than vertically in part to highlight this resemblance.) The lengths of the bars in the bar chart correspond to the lengths of the rows in the stem-and-leaf plot. This feature of stem-and-leaf plots allows them to be used in much the same manner as bar charts. For example, we can tell at a glance that many more students scored in the 70s than in the 90s.

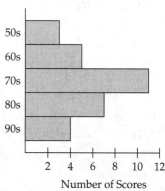

(e) We can't use the bar chart from part (d) to answer the questions in the first three parts. The stem-and-leaf plot allows us to keep all the values in the original data, while the grouping we did for the bar chart loses all the exact scores. The bar chart tells us what 10-point range each score is in, but doesn't tell us exactly what the scores are. This can give us a sense for the median and the average, but cannot tell us exactly what they are.

□

Problem 13.15: Members of the Gross Pie Association were asked for their favorite type of pie. The results of the poll are shown in the **pie chart** at the right. Pie charts are typically circular, and sliced into pieces that represent different categories. The sizes of the pieces correspond to the portion of the whole that each category represents. So, for example, the "Pickle" piece is nearly half the chart, because nearly half the people chose pickle pie. If 36 of the members chose cat-hair pie, then how many chose sawdust pie?

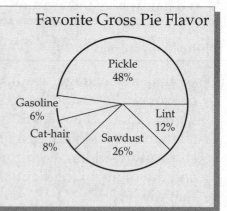

Solution for Problem 13.15: Solution 1: Figure out how many members total there are. Let x be the number of members in the club. The pie chart tells us that 8% of the people chose cat-hair pie.

Since 36 people chose cat-hair pie, and these people are 8% of the total, we must have

$$0.08x = 36.$$

Dividing both sides by 0.08 gives

$$x = \frac{36}{0.08} = \frac{3600}{8} = 450.$$

The pie chart tells us that 26% of the people chose sawdust pie. Since there are 450 people total, the number of people who chose sawdust pie is $0.26 \cdot 450 = 117$.

Solution 2: Compare cat-hair pie and sawdust pie directly. Since 26% of the people chose sawdust pie and 8% of the people chose cat-hair pie, we have the ratio

number who chose sawdust : number who chose cat-hair = 26 : 8.

Let s be the number of people who chose sawdust pie. Since 36 people chose cat-hair pie, the ratio above tells us

$$s : 36 = 26 : 8.$$

Writing the ratios as fractions gives

$$\frac{s}{36} = \frac{26}{8}.$$

Simplifying the fraction on the right side gives $\frac{s}{36} = \frac{13}{4}$. Multiplying by 36 gives

$$s = \frac{13}{4} \cdot 36 = 13 \cdot \frac{36}{4} = 13 \cdot 9 = 117.$$

Solution 3: Use number sense. We know that 36 people are 8% of the total. Dividing by 4, we see that 9 people are 2% of the total. Since $26\% = 13 \cdot 2\%$, we multiply these 9 people by 13 to see that 26% of the total equals $9 \cdot 13 = 117$ people. □

Pie charts are particularly good for displaying the portion of the total that each quantity is. Bar charts, on the other hand, are not as good at showing this information. To compare our pie chart to a bar chart, let's make a bar chart for the totals in Problem 13.15. We already know that 36 people chose cat-hair and 117 chose sawdust. We can use the first method in our solution above to compute the totals for the other favorite pie options. We find that $0.48(450) = 216$ people chose pickle, $0.06(450) = 27$ chose gasoline, and $0.12(450) = 54$ chose lint. These are shown in the bar chart on the right.

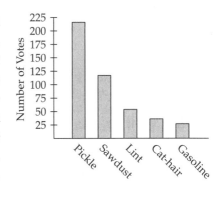

Both the bar chart and the original pie chart allow us to compare different options quickly. For example, we can quickly see that pickle is the winner, and about the same number of people chose gasoline as chose cat-hair. But the pie chart allows us to see more quickly what portion of the total chose each option. For example, it's very easy to see on the pie chart that around a quarter of the people chose sawdust pie. This isn't as clear in the bar chart.

The bar chart does have the advantage of allowing us to see the number of people who chose each option. The actual number of people is not reflected in the original pie chart. We could include this information on the pie chart if we like, as shown at the right. The sizes of the pieces in the pie chart still give us a sense of what portion of the whole each option is.

Favorite Gross Pie Flavor

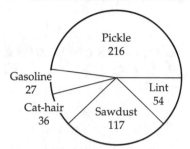

> **Concept:** A pie chart is often a good choice to represent data if the "portions of the whole" of various outcomes is the most important feature of the data.

Exercises

13.3.1 The histogram on the right shows the results when the students in my grade were asked how many pencils they have.

(a) What is the mode number of pencils?

(b) Compute the average number of pencils to the nearest hundredth.

(c) What is the median number of pencils?

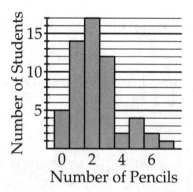

13.3.2 Each man in the Not Much Left club counts the number of hairs remaining on his head. They represent their results with the stem-and-leaf plot shown on the right.

0	1 1 3 5 6 8
1	0 2 2 2 4
2	3 9
4	0 5
5	6 8
7	5 6 9

(a) Find the average, median, and mode of the number of hairs each member has, based on the data in the table shown.

(b) If I, with my very full head of hair, join the club, which statistic will be affected the most: average, median, or mode?

(c)★ Upon checking the table a second time, the club finds that one digit in the stem-and-leaf table is incorrect. When the number is fixed, the average number of hairs on each head is correctly computed as 26.75. Which number in the table is incorrect, and what should it have been?

13.3.3 I have a pet griffin named Spot. Every year on Spot's birthday, I measure her height and graph it on my wall. Today is Spot's eighth birthday, and the graph on the right is a copy of the graph on my wall.

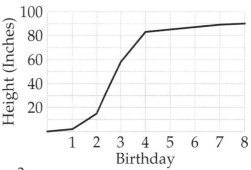

(a) During which year did Spot grow the most?

(b) After a griffin becomes an adult, she grows very slowly. At what age did Spot become an adult?

(c) On average, how many inches per year has Spot grown?

13.3.4 The 650 cartoon characters in Toontown voted for President, and the results are shown at the right.

Toontown Election Results

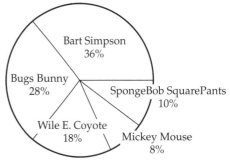

(a) By how many votes did Bart beat Bugs Bunny?

(b) Upon finding out that being President requires work, Bart quit, so they held a new election. Only the characters who originally voted for Bart voted for a different candidate in the new election. None of these characters voted for Mickey Mouse or for Bugs Bunny. Altogether, Wile E. Coyote received three times as many votes in the new election as SpongeBob did. Draw a pie chart for the new election.

13.4 Summary

We studied three **statistics**, which are numbers used to give information about groups of numbers:

- **Average**: The average of a group of numbers is the sum of the numbers divided by the number of numbers. So, the average of 3, 5, 6, and 10 is $\frac{3+5+6+10}{4}$, which equals 6. The average is also called the **mean** or the **arithmetic mean**.

- **Median**: If we list a group of numbers from least to greatest, the median of the group is the number in the middle. So, the median of the numbers in the list

$$4, 5, 7, 8, 11$$

is 7. If there is an even number of numbers, then the median is the average of the middle two numbers.

- **Mode**: The mode of a group of numbers is the number that appears most frequently in the group. So, the mode of

$$3, 3, 3, 3, 4, 5, 6, 7$$

is 3. A group can have multiple modes if there are multiple numbers that appear the same number of times.

Average and median are used much more often than mode. There are significant limitations on what these statistics can tell us about a group of data. The median only tells us what the middle number is (or the average of the middle two numbers). It doesn't tell us anything about how far the numbers in the group are from the middle. Numbers that are much greater or much less than most of the other numbers in a group are called **outliers**. Outliers tend to have a very large effect on the average of the group, but very little effect on the median.

There are many ways to display data, such as tables (page 496), bar charts (page 498), line graphs (page 499), stem-and-leaf plots (page 501), and pie charts (page 502).

REVIEW PROBLEMS

13.16 I have four dogs whose average weight is 63 pounds. I also have three cats. The average weight of all seven of my animals is 41 pounds. What is the average weight of my cats?

13.17 The average age of the ten people on my basketball team was 13.5, but then a 15-year-old joined our team and an 11-year-old quit the team. What is the average age of my team now?

13.18 The average of five numbers is 18. Let the first number be increased by 1, the second number by 2, the third number by 3, the fourth number by 4, and the fifth number by 5. What is the average of the list of increased numbers? *(Source: MOEMS)*

13.19 Suppose you took eight math tests this semester. If your average score on your first six tests was 84 and your average score on all eight tests was 86, then what was the average of your last two test scores?

13.20 Must the median of a group of consecutive integers equal the average of the group?

13.21 Larry writes a list of numbers that has average 14, median 21 and mode 11.

(a) Moe creates a list by adding 12 to each number in Larry's list. What are the average, median, and mode of Moe's list?

(b) Curly creates a list by multiplying each number in Larry's list by 2. What are the average, median, and mode of Curly's list?

13.22 Find the average of the following numbers:

$$940385988, 940385994, 940386003, 940385981, 940385991.$$

13.23 Each of 9 friends chooses her favorite positive integer.

(a) The median of the chosen numbers is 91. What is the smallest the average of the 9 chosen numbers could be?

(b) The median of the chosen numbers is 91. Is there a limit to how large the average of the chosen numbers can be? If so, what is the largest the average can be?

(c) The average of the chosen numbers is 91. What is the smallest the median of the 9 chosen numbers could be?

(d)★ The average of the chosen numbers is 91. What is the largest the median of the chosen numbers could be? **Hints:** 139

13.24 Consider the two lists of numbers below.

$$\text{List A: } 34, 54, 161, 443, 87, 43, 76, 339, 38, 654, 75, 164, 876$$
$$\text{List B: } 56747884, 54, 65, 12, 654, 765, 12, 34, 98, 56, 72, 34, 86$$

(a) Is it easy to tell quickly which list has the higher average?

(b) Is it easy to tell quickly which list has the higher median?

(c) What do the first two parts tell us about outliers?

13.25 The chart at the right shows where Meadow Lark Lane Middle School students do their homework. The options are their bedroom (BR), the kitchen (K), the dining room (D), and the family living room (FLR). Using these data, how many of the 880 students at the school do their homework in the dining room? *(Source: MATHCOUNTS)*

Where Do You Do Your Homework?

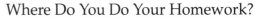
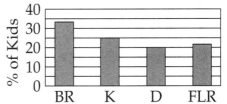

13.26 Five people live along a long, straight road. The table below gives the distance in miles between pairs of houses. For example, the distance between Adrian's house and Walter's house is 11 miles.

	Adrian	Dan	Laurie	Jon	Walter
Adrian	0		15		11
Dan	3	0	12	7	8
Laurie	15			5	
Jon	10	7	5	0	
Walter	11	8	4		

(a) Fill in the missing entries.

(b) Which two people live the farthest apart? Which two people live the closest?

(c) Draw an accurate map showing where the people live along the road.

| Challenge Problems ▶ |

13.27 There is a list of seven numbers. The average of the first four numbers is 5, and the average of the last four numbers is 8. If the average of all seven numbers is $6\frac{4}{7}$, then what number is common to both sets of four numbers? *(Source: AMC 8)* **Hints:** 139

13.28 The mean, median, and mode of the five numbers 5, 7, 8, A, B are equal. (The list has a single mode.) Find all possible values of $A + B$.

13.29 The Back In My Day club made the histogram at right to represent the ages of its members.

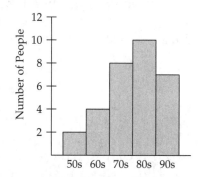

(a) What is the least possible median age of the members?

(b) What is the greatest possible median age?

(c) What is the least possible average age?

(d) What is the greatest possible average age?

13.30

(a) Two lists of numbers that have the same average are combined to form a longer list. Must the average of the new list be the same as the average of each of the original shorter lists?

(b) Two lists of numbers that have the same median are combined to form a longer list. Must the median of the new list be the same as the median of each of the original shorter lists?

(c) Two lists of numbers that have the same mode are combined to form a longer list. Is the mode of the new list necessarily the same as the mode of each of the original shorter lists?

(d) Two lists of numbers are combined to form a longer list. The mode of the new list is 3. Is it possible that neither of the original lists had 3 as its mode?

13.31 My four closest friends have weekly allowances of \$13, \$17, \$24, and \$30. What are the possible values of my weekly allowance if the median of our allowances equals the average of our allowances?

13.32 We asked 124 people to rank four card games from favorite (1ˢᵗ) to least favorite (4ᵗʰ). The results are shown in the table at the right. Two of the entries in the table are wrong. Fix the errors by changing two of the numbers in the table.

	1ˢᵗ	2ⁿᵈ	3ʳᵈ	4ᵗʰ
Magic	34	56	23	11
Pokemon	12	14	38	64
SET	57	41	23	3
Yu-Gi-Oh!	21	19	44	46

13.33★ For a set of ten numbers, removing the largest number decreases the average by 1. Removing the smallest number increases the average by 2. What is the positive difference between the largest and the smallest of these ten numbers? **Hints:** 54, 52

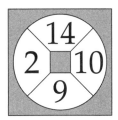 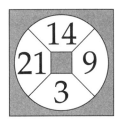  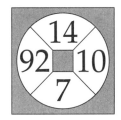

There are three types of people: those who can count and those who can't. – Unknown

CHAPTER **14**

Counting

You may be thinking: *"But I already know how to count: one, two, three, ..."*

True. But most counting problems do not involve simply counting a list or group of items. Usually we have to first figure out *what* we're counting, then we have to figure out *how* to count it.

One thing that we will repeat over and over in this chapter is

> **Important:** Don't memorize!

Don't think of this chapter as a series of problems in which you learn the "trick" for each problem type. Instead, you should learn and understand that counting problems call for a bit of thought, together with the appropriate use of addition, subtraction, multiplication, and/or division.

If you understand what you are adding, subtracting, multiplying, or dividing, and when to do what, then you won't need to memorize a bunch of different "tricks" for different problems. Instead, you'll know how to do lots of different problems because you will *understand* how to count.

We may have some new names for some of the techniques that we learn, but remember: at heart, it's just arithmetic. Nothing too fancy.

14.1 Counting with Addition and Subtraction

Problems

Problem 14.1: How many numbers are in the list

$$1, 2, 3, 4, 5, 6, 7, 8, 9, 10, 11, 12, 13, 14, 15, 16?$$

Problem 14.2: How many numbers are in the list

$$9, 10, 11, 12, 13, 14, 15, 16, 17, 18, 19, 20, 21, 22, 23, 24, 25, 26, 27?$$

We could also ask this problem as "How many numbers are there between 9 and 27 inclusive?" (**Inclusive** means that we include the 9 and the 27 in our count.)

Problem 14.3: Given two integers a and b, with $b > a$, find a formula for how many integers there are between a and b inclusive. (Remember, inclusive means that we include a and b in our count.)

Problem 14.4: How many multiples of 4 are between 25 and 101?

Problem 14.5:

(a) How many multiples of 10 are between 9 and 101?

(b) How many multiples of 10 are between 11 and 103?

(c) We know that $(101 - 9) = (103 - 11) = 92$, so shouldn't your answers to (a) and (b) be the same? Why aren't they?

Problem 14.6: At Brown High School, there are 12 players on the basketball team. All of the players are taking at least one foreign language class. The school offers only Spanish and French as its foreign language classes. 8 of the players are taking Spanish and 5 of the players are taking both languages. How many players are taking French?

Problem 14.7: Paul has 27 pet cats. 14 of them are short-haired. 11 of them are kittens. 5 of them are long-haired adult cats (not kittens). How many of them are short-haired kittens?

We'll start with the simplest counting task: counting lists of numbers. Some lists of numbers are really easy to count.

Problem 14.1: How many numbers are in the list

$$1, 2, 3, 4, 5, 6, 7, 8, 9, 10, 11, 12, 13, 14, 15, 16?$$

Solution for Problem 14.1: Obviously, there are 16 numbers. □

That was pretty easy. The counting was already done for us! Many other counting problems can be reduced to this type of counting.

Problem 14.2: How many numbers are in the list

$$9, 10, 11, 12, 13, 14, 15, 16, 17, 18, 19, 20, 21, 22, 23, 24, 25, 26, 27?$$

We could also ask this problem as "How many numbers are there between 9 and 27 inclusive?" (**Inclusive** means that we include the 9 and the 27 in our count.)

Solution for Problem 14.2: We could just count them from left to right and find that there are 19 numbers. However, a more clever way to approach this problem is to convert this problem into a problem like Problem 14.1, by subtracting 8 from every number in our list:

$$
\begin{array}{ccccc}
9 & 10 & 11 & \cdots & 27 \\
-8 & -8 & -8 & \cdots & -8 \\
\hline
1 & 2 & 3 & \cdots & 19
\end{array}
$$

We know how to count the new list! There are 19 items in the list. So, there are 19 items in our original list. □

Problem 14.2 illustrates a very important problem-solving idea.

> **Concept:** When presented with a complicated problem, try to turn it into a simpler problem that you know how to solve.

You may also notice that in Problem 14.2, if we subtract the ending and starting numbers of our list, then we get $27 - 9 = 18$. This is one fewer than the number of items (19) in the list. Perhaps such a formula holds for any two numbers. . . .

Problem 14.3: Given two integers a and b, with $b > a$, find a formula for how many integers there are between a and b inclusive.

Solution for Problem 14.3: We subtract $a - 1$ from each number from a to b, and we get a list of numbers starting at 1:

$$
\begin{array}{ccccc}
a & a+1 & a+2 & \cdots & b \\
-(a-1) & -(a-1) & -(a-1) & \cdots & -(a-1) \\
\hline
1 & 2 & 3 & \cdots & b-a+1
\end{array}
$$

Our new list then has $b - a + 1$ numbers in it, so our old list does too. So the answer is $b - a + 1$. □

Problem 14.4: How many multiples of 4 are between 25 and 101?

Solution for Problem 14.4: We see that $\frac{25}{4} = 6.25$, so the smallest multiple of 4 in our list is $4 \cdot 7 = 28$. Similarly, $\frac{101}{4} = 25.25$, so the largest multiple of 4 in our list is $4 \cdot 25 = 100$. Therefore our list is

$$28, 32, 36, \ldots, 100.$$

To convert it into a list that we know how to count, we can divide each number in our list by 4:

$$7, 8, 9, \ldots, 25.$$

We know how to count this list! Subtracting 6 from each number in the list gives

$$1, 2, 3, \ldots, 19.$$

So there are 19 numbers in the list. Therefore, there are 19 multiples of 4 between 25 and 101. □

You might have been tempted to use a little shortcut for Problem 14.4:

Bogus Solution: We can just compute

$$\frac{101 - 25}{4} = \frac{76}{4} = 19$$

to see there are 19 numbers in the list.

But that "shortcut" doesn't always work very well, as we can see in the next problem:

Problem 14.5:

(a) How many multiples of 10 are between 9 and 101?

(b) How many multiples of 10 are between 11 and 103?

(c) We know that $101 - 9 = 103 - 11 = 92$, so shouldn't your answers to (a) and (b) be the same? Why aren't they?

Solution for Problem 14.5: For this problem, it's easy enough to just list the multiples of 10.

(a) Our list is

$$10, 20, 30, \ldots, 100,$$

so there are 10 multiples.

(b) Our list is

$$20, 30, \ldots, 100,$$

so there are 9 multiples.

(c) The reason these answers are different is because 10 is in our list from part (a) but is not in our list from part (b). So the "shortcut" solution doesn't work! You can't count the number of multiples of 10 simply by calculating

$$\frac{101 - 9}{10} = \frac{103 - 11}{10} = \frac{92}{10} = 9.2.$$

How would you know whether the answer is 9 or 10?

□

> **WARNING!!** Beware of quick shortcuts! (Unless you can explain why your ☢ "shortcut" works.)

Counting is not always as simple as creating a list. Many counting problems require a little more thought. Let's look at an example:

> **Problem 14.6:** At Brown High School, there are 12 players on the basketball team. All of the players are taking at least one foreign language class. The school offers only Spanish and French as its foreign language classes. 8 of the players are taking Spanish and 5 of the players are taking both languages. How many players are taking French?

Before we work through the solution (for this problem or for any counting problem), always remember the following:

> **Important:** Don't just blindly add and subtract—think about what you're ⚠ doing!

Solution for Problem 14.6: The players that are taking French fall into two categories: those who are also taking Spanish, and those who aren't. If we can count the number of players in each category, then we can add those numbers together to get the total number of players taking French.

First, we note that the number of players taking French that are also taking Spanish is 5. (This is given in the problem statement.)

Next we count the number of players that are taking French but not Spanish. We're not provided this count directly, but we can figure it out from the given data. There are 12 players on the team, and 8 of them are taking Spanish. So, $12 - 8 = 4$ players are not taking Spanish. Since every player must be taking at least one language, these 4 players are taking French (and not Spanish).

So the number of players taking French is the sum:

(# of players taking French and Spanish) + (# of players taking French and not Spanish)

= 5 + 4

Therefore the answer is $5 + 4 = 9$. □

We can also use a picture to solve this problem:

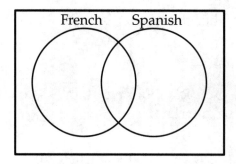

The picture above is called a **Venn diagram**. In the diagram we draw a circle for the players taking French and another circle for the players taking Spanish. The circles overlap because some players are taking both languages.

> **Concept:** We can use a Venn diagram whenever we wish to count things or
> people that occur in two or three overlapping groups.

We place dots in the circles to represent the players—one dot per player. A dot that is in the French circle but is not in the Spanish one represents a player taking French but not Spanish. A dot in the region that is in both circles represents a player taking both languages. A player taking Spanish but not French is represented by a dot inside the Spanish circle but not in the French one. Finally, a dot placed outside both circles represents a player who is in neither class.

Now we can use this diagram to solve the problem. We place 5 dots in the space inside of both circles, because there are 5 players in both classes. This gives the diagram below:

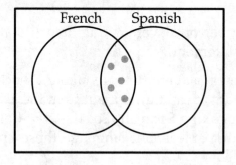

Next, since there are 8 players taking Spanish, and 5 dots are already inside the Spanish circle, there must be three more dots inside the Spanish circle that aren't in the French circle. We add these dots to the diagram:

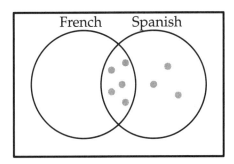

Since we have 12 total dots and we know there aren't any outside both circles (since there are no players who are not taking either language), there must be 4 left that are inside the French circle but not inside the Spanish circle. After adding these dots, our diagram looks like this:

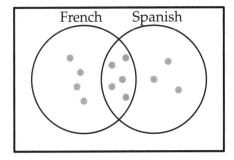

We've placed all of the students on the team into the diagram. Now we can use the completed diagram to answer the problem. There are a total of 9 dots inside the French circle on the left, so there are 9 players in the French class.

Obviously, if the numbers in the problem were bigger, it would be a chore to draw all those dots, so we usually use numbers to represent how many dots are in each region, as in the figure below.

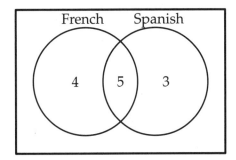

Notice that we started with the 5 players in both classes rather than with the "12 total players" or the "8 players in Spanish." This is because those 5 players are in a single region in our picture—if we instead had started with "8 players in Spanish," we wouldn't know how many to put in the intersection of the two circles and how many to put in the "just Spanish" section.

> **Important:** When using a Venn diagram, we try to start filling in the dia-
> gram using numbers that we know go into a single region of the
> diagram. Often, this means that we start in the middle of the
> diagram.

Let's look at another problem that can be solved using a Venn diagram:

Problem 14.7: Paul has 27 pet cats. 14 of them are short-haired. 11 of them are kittens. 5 of them are long-haired adult cats (not kittens). How many of them are short-haired kittens?

Solution for Problem 14.7: We draw a Venn diagram, with one circle for cats with short hair and one circle for cats which are kittens.

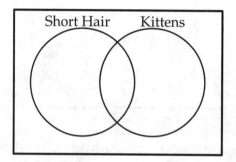

We can't immediately use the numbers 27, 14, or 11 from the problem, because there is no single region into which we can place any of these numbers. For example, although we know that there are 14 short-haired cats, we don't yet know how many of them are kittens (and would go in both circles) or how many of them are adults (and would go in the "short hair" circle but not in the "kittens" circle). However, we know there are 5 long-haired adult cats, and these 5 cats should be outside both circles. So we add that to our diagram by placing a "5" in the region outside both circles:

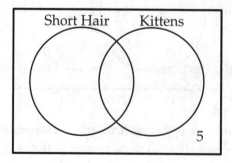

At this point, we still can't fill in any of the other numbers, so we'll introduce a variable. We can call the number of cats in one of the regions inside the circles x, and try to find other regions in terms of x. If we can, we usually want our variable to represent the answer to our problem. So we'll let the number of short-haired kittens (which are in the intersection of the circles) be x.

> **Concept:** When assigning a variable, it's usually best to let your variable represent the answer to the problem.

We place x into our Venn diagram below:

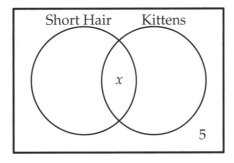

Since there are a total of 14 short-haired cats, and x of them are kittens, we know that $14 - x$ of them are not kittens. Therefore, we place $14 - x$ in the portion of the short-haired circle that does not overlap with the kittens. Similarly, we have $11 - x$ kittens which are not short-haired. Now our Venn diagram has an entry in every region:

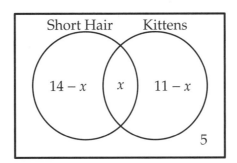

Our diagram is filled and we still don't know x, so at first it seems like we might be stuck. But there's one more piece of information that we haven't used yet, and that's the total number of cats, which is 27.

> **Concept:** If you get stuck on a problem, check if there's some more information from the problem that you haven't used yet.

This means that if we add all the quantities in our diagram, we must get 27:

$$(14 - x) + (11 - x) + x + 5 = 27.$$

This simplifies to $30 - x = 27$, so $x = 3$ is our answer. □

As a check, we can fill the numbers into our diagram:

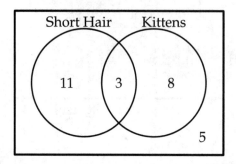

Now, not only can we read our answer directly from the diagram (there are 3 short-haired kittens), but we can also easily check that the data from our solution matches the data given in the problem description. This lets us do a quick check that we didn't make an obvious mistake. At a glance, we can confirm that there are 14 short-haired cats, 11 kittens, and 27 cats total.

Concept: It's always a good idea to check that your answer is consistent with the problem statement.

You will eventually (and may already) solve problems like Problem 14.7 without a diagram; however, you'll likely at least visualize a diagram or a table. Keeping a Venn diagram or a table in mind will help keep the problem clear and prevent you from making careless errors.

Exercises

14.1.1 How many numbers are in each of the following lists?

(a) $45, 46, 47, \ldots, 92, 93$

(b) $-27, -23, -19, \ldots, 33, 37$

(c) $162, 159, 156, \ldots, 69, 66$

14.1.2 I'm waiting in the lunch line. I'm 18th in line when counting from the front, and 24th when counting from the back. How many people are in the line?

14.1.3 There are 220 students in my school. 70 of them took French, 140 of them took Spanish, and 23 of them took both languages. How many of the students took neither French nor Spanish?

14.1.4 Of all the mathletes at Wantagh Middle School, 80% own computers and 40% are in band. However, 10% of all mathletes neither own computers nor are in band. What percent of all the mathletes both own computers and are in band? *(Source: MOEMS)*

14.1.5 For how many positive integer values of n are both $\frac{n}{3}$ and $3n$ three-digit integers? *(Source: AMC 8)*

14.1.6 At Annville Junior High School, 30% of the students in the Math Club are in the Science Club, and 80% of the students in the Science Club are in the Math Club. There are 15 students in the Science Club. How many students are in the Math Club? *(Source: AMC 8)*

14.1.7 There are 24 cars in my building's parking lot. All of the cars are red or white and have 2 or 4 doors. 15 of them are red, 8 of them are 4-door, and 4 of them are 2-door and white. How many of the cars are 4-door and red?

14.1.8★ How many two-digit positive numbers are divisible by 3 or 5? **Hints:** 36

14.2 The Multiplication Principle

Problems

Problem 14.8: You have three shirts and four pairs of pants. How many outfits consisting of one shirt and one pair of pants can you make?

Problem 14.9: In how many ways can we form an international commission if we must choose one European country from among 6 European countries, one Asian country from among 4, one North American country from among 3, and one African country from among 7?

Problem 14.10: In how many ways can we form a license plate using only digits (0–9) and capital letters (other than O and I), given that each plate has 6 characters, the first of which is a digit, and the second of which is a letter?

Problem 14.11: In how many ways can I arrange four different books from left to right on a shelf?

Problem 14.12: Your math club has 16 members. In how many ways can it select a president, a vice-president, and a treasurer if no member can hold more than one office?

Often we'll be counting the number of outcomes of a series of events. Here's an example of this type of problem.

Problem 14.8: You have three shirts and four pairs of pants. How many outfits consisting of one shirt and one pair of pants can you make?

Solution for Problem 14.8: In this problem, the number of possibilities is so small that we can just list them.

If our shirts are labeled S_1, S_2, S_3 and our pants are labeled P_1, P_2, P_3, P_4, then we can list all of the possible outfits:

$$S_1P_1,\ S_1P_2,\ S_1P_3,\ S_1P_4,\ S_2P_1,\ S_2P_2,\ S_2P_3,\ S_2P_4,\ S_3P_1,\ S_3P_2,\ S_3P_3,\ S_3P_4$$

So there are 12 outfits. □

Listing the outfits like this is somewhat annoying. We can better visualize the outfits by using a diagram. One sort of diagram is a **tree**, as shown below. We start at the dot at the top, and each arrow is a choice of one item: the first arrow (from the dot at the top) is the choice of pants, and the second arrow (from the choice of pants) is the choice of shirt. Each complete path of two arrows leads to a complete outfit.

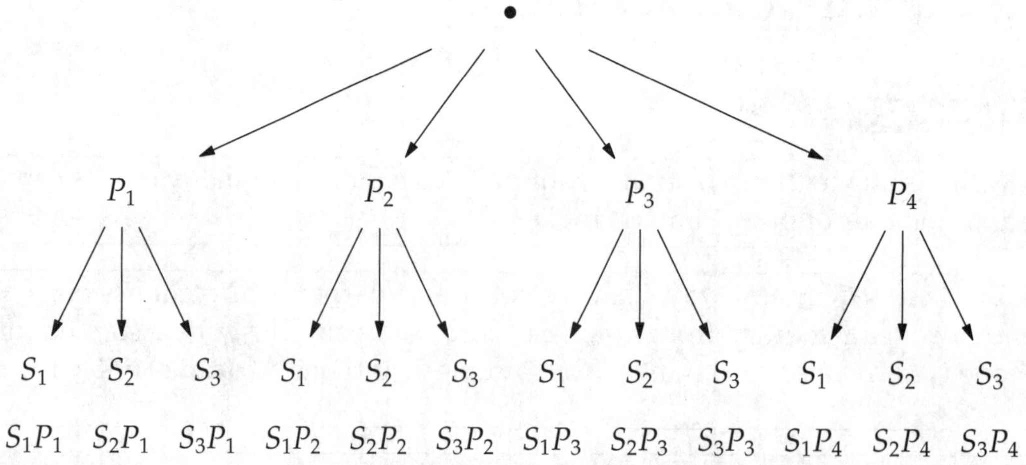

Another type of diagram we can use for Problem 14.8 is a **grid**. A grid looks a bit like a multiplication table: we put the choices of pants along the top and the choices of shirts along the side. Each box in the grid is a complete outfit, as shown below:

Shirts \ Pants	P_1	P_2	P_3	P_4
S_1	S_1P_1	S_1P_2	S_1P_3	S_1P_4
S_2	S_2P_1	S_2P_2	S_2P_3	S_2P_4
S_3	S_3P_1	S_3P_2	S_3P_3	S_3P_4

For both the tree and the grid, we can count outfits by using the following reasoning: we have four choices for the pants, and for each of these four choices of pants, we have three choices for the shirt. Therefore, there are $4 \cdot 3 = 12$ outfits.

> **Concept:** The point of drawing a tree or a grid is to keep our counting organized. Clear organization is very important for solving counting problems.

It's easy for us to draw a tree or a grid in Problem 14.8 because the numbers are small. Let's look at a more complicated version of the same type of problem.

Problem 14.9: In how many ways can we form an international commission if we must choose one European country from among 6 European countries, one Asian country from among 4, one North American country from among 3, and one African country from among 7?

Solution for Problem 14.9: Clearly drawing a grid or a tree is not going to be practical—there are too many choices! So we'll have to do this problem by reasoning out the answer.

We tackle a problem like this in steps.

Step 1: There are 6 ways to choose a European country.

Step 2: For each European country, we can choose an Asian country in 4 ways, for a total of $6 \cdot 4 = 24$ ways to choose both a European and an Asian country.

Step 3: For each pair of countries that we've chosen in Steps 1 and 2, we can choose a North American country in 3 ways. So there are $24 \cdot 3 = 72$ ways to choose 3 countries.

Step 4: For each triple of countries that we've chosen in Steps 1–3, we can choose an African country in 7 ways. So there are $72 \cdot 7 = 504$ ways to choose 4 countries.

So we see that there are $6 \cdot 4 \cdot 3 \cdot 7 = 504$ possibilities. $\square$

We say that the choices in Problem 14.9 are **independent**, meaning that each decision does not depend on the others and does not affect the others. Specifically, we choose a European country, then an Asian country, then a North American country, then an African country. Each choice doesn't depend on or affect the other choices.

> **Concept:** We use multiplication to count the number of outcomes from a sequence of independent events.

Problem 14.10: In how many ways can we form a license plate using only digits (0–9) and capital letters (other than O and I), given that each plate has 6 characters, the first of which is a digit, and the second of which is a letter?

Solution for Problem 14.10: Since each character does not depend on any of the other characters, our choices are independent. There are 10 choices for the first character (any digit from 0 through 9), there are 24 choices for the second character (any letter A–Z except for O or I), and there are 34 choices for each of the other four characters (any digit 0–9 or any letter A–Z, except O or I).

Therefore, since the choices are independent, we multiply the number of choices at each step, and we have

$$10 \cdot 24 \cdot 34 \cdot 34 \cdot 34 \cdot 34 = 10 \cdot 24 \cdot 34^4 = 320{,}720{,}640$$

ways to form our license plate. □

In some counting problems, we make a series of choices, but later choices will depend on some of the earlier choices. This is unlike the problems that we've done before. For example, in Problem 14.8, our choices of shirt didn't depend at all on our choice of pants. Things are a little bit different in the next problem.

Problem 14.11: In how many ways can I arrange four different books from left to right on a shelf?

Solution for Problem 14.11: We cannot just count $4 \cdot 4 \cdot 4 \cdot 4$, because once we place the first book on the left, we no longer have 4 choices for the second book. We can't reuse the first book, so we only have 3 choices remaining for the second book. Let's carefully count our choices step by step:

Step 1: We have 4 choices for which book to place on the left.

Step 2: Regardless of which book we chose in step 1, we have 3 books remaining, so we have 3 choices for the second book. Thus we have a total of $4 \cdot 3 = 12$ choices for the first two books on the left.

Step 3: We have 2 books remaining, so we have 2 choices for the third book. Thus we have a total of $12 \cdot 2 = 24$ choices for the first three books.

Step 4: We only have 1 book remaining, so we have 1 choice for the fourth book. Thus we have a total of $24 \cdot 1 = 24$ choices for all four books.

So the answer is 24. □

One important thing to note about Problem 14.11 is that although the choices themselves are not independent at each step, the *number* of choices at each step is independent of our previous choices. For example, no matter which book we choose in Step 1, we always have 3 remaining books to choose from in Step 2. Therefore, we can get our answer by multiplying the number of choices at each step, so that $4 \cdot 3 \cdot 2 \cdot 1 = 24$ is the answer.

If you're not yet convinced, we could represent our choices in this problem as a tree, where the books are labeled A, B, C, and D, as shown in the picture on the next page. We can see that there are 4 arrows from the starting dot for the first choice, then 3 arrows for the next choice, and so on, and indeed there are 24 possible arrangements.

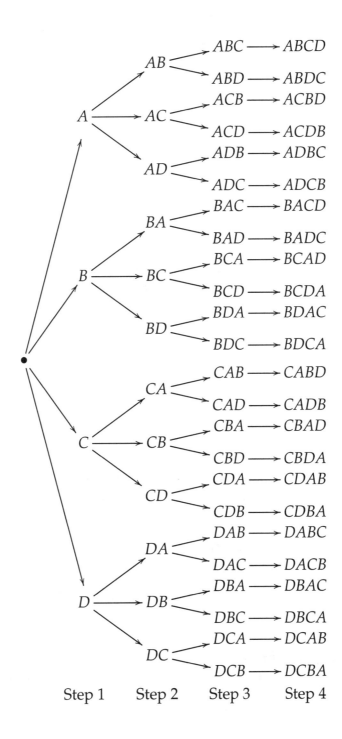

Step 1　　Step 2　　Step 3　　Step 4

Here's another example of a counting problem in which the choices are not independent.

Problem 14.12: Your math club has 16 members. In how many ways can it select a president, a vice-president, and a treasurer if no member can hold more than one office?

Solution for Problem 14.12: Once again, our choices are not independent. Once a student has been chosen president, she is not available to be chosen vice-president or treasurer. However, the number of choices we have for each position is the same no matter who is chosen.

We have 16 choices for president. Once we've chosen a president, then we have 15 people remaining to choose from for vice-president. Then, we have 14 people remaining to choose from for treasurer.

Therefore, there are

$$16 \cdot 15 \cdot 14 = 3360$$

ways to fill the three offices. $\square$

The last two problems contain examples of **permutations**. A permutation occurs whenever we have to choose several different items, one at a time, from a larger group of items.

Exercises

14.2.1 Suppose I have 7 shirts and 4 ties. How many shirt-and-tie outfits can I make?

14.2.2 For each of 9 colors, I have one shirt and one tie of that color. How many shirt-and-tie outfits can I make if I refuse to wear a shirt and a tie of the same color?

14.2.3 In how many ways can 5 people stand in a line?

14.2.4 A shopkeeper sells house numbers. She has a large supply of the digits 1, 2, 7, and 8, but no other digits. How many different three-digit house numbers could be made using only the digits in her supply?

14.2.5 How many four-digit positive integers are there such that the leftmost digit is odd, the second digit is even, and all four digits are different? *(Source: AMC 8)*

14.2.6 When the order of the digits of 2552 is reversed, the number remains the same. Such a number is called a **palindrome**. How many integers between 100 and 1000 are palindromes? *(Source: MOEMS)*

14.2.7★ Suppose that I have 5 different books, 2 of which are math books. In how many ways can I place my 5 books left-to-right on a shelf if I want a math book on both ends?

14.2.8★ How many integers between 99 and 999 contain exactly one 0? *(Source: AMC 8)*

14.3 Casework

Many counting problems can be solved by considering different cases—that is, by dividing what we're trying to count into two or more categories. This general approach is called **casework**. The key to solving problems using casework is to be organized, and to be careful that you don't skip any cases.

> Problems ▶

Problem 14.13: The figure to the right represents a road map between 4 villages, labeled A, B, C and D. The arcs indicate paths between the various villages. How many ways are there to go from A to D along the paths, if you can only move left to right? (For example, you can't go $ABABACD$; you can only go ACD or ABD.)

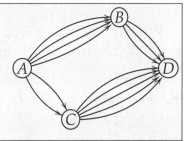

Problem 14.14: On the island of Abcdef, the alphabet has only 6 letters, and every word in their language has no more than 3 letters in it. How many words are possible? (A word can use a letter more than once, but 0 letters does not count as a word.)

Problem 14.15: How many pairs of positive integers (a, b) satisfy $a^2 + b < 24$?

Problem 14.16: A digital clock shows time in the form HH:MM. On a certain day, what is the number of minutes between 7:59 AM and 2:59 PM that HH is greater than MM? *(Source: MOEMS)*

Problem 14.13: The figure to the right represents a road map between 4 villages, labeled A, B, C and D. The arcs indicate paths between the various villages. How many ways are there to go from A to D along the paths, if you can only move left to right? (For example, you can't go $ABABACD$; you can only go ACD or ABD.)

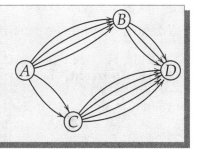

Solution for Problem 14.13: Broadly speaking, we have two ways to get from A to D: we can go through B or through C. We have to go through one of them, and we can't go through both. We say that these two choices are **exclusive**, because we must choose one or the other, but not both.

Our two exclusive choices will form our two cases.

Case 1: Go from A to D through B

There are 4 ways to get from A to B, and 3 ways to get from B to D, so there are $4 \cdot 3 = 12$ ways to get from A to D through B.

Case 2: Go from A to D through C

There are 2 ways to get from A to C, and 5 ways to get from C to D, so there are $2 \cdot 5 = 10$ ways to get from A to D through C.

To count the total number of ways to get from A to D, we now add the number of ways from each of our cases. There are 12 ways through B and another 10 ways through C, so there are a total of $12 + 10 = 22$ ways from A to D. □

Why did we multiply in some of the steps of Solution 14.13 (for example, counting the paths from A to D through B), but add in other steps (when we added the results from each case)?

To choose a path from A to D through B, we choose a path from A to B, **AND** independently choose a path from B to D, so we **multiply** the numbers of paths from A to B by the number of paths from B to D.

To choose a path from A to D through C, we choose a path from A to C, **AND** independently choose a path from C to D, so we **multiply** the numbers of paths from A to C by the number of paths from C to D.

To choose a path from A to D, we choose a path from A to D through B, **OR** choose a path from A to D through C, so we **add** the numbers of paths from A to D through B and the number of paths from A to D through C.

> **Concept:** When faced with a series of independent choices, one after the other, we **multiply** the number of options at each choice. When faced with exclusive cases (meaning we can't choose more than one), we **add** the number of options in each case.

Make sure you see the difference. Don't memorize it—understand it.

> **Important:** Don't memorize! Understand, and know.

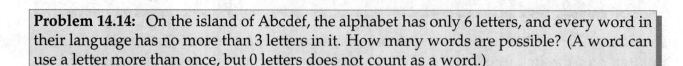

Problem 14.14: On the island of Abcdef, the alphabet has only 6 letters, and every word in their language has no more than 3 letters in it. How many words are possible? (A word can use a letter more than once, but 0 letters does not count as a word.)

Solution for Problem 14.14: Often, the tricky part of casework problems is deciding what the cases should be. For this problem, it makes sense to use as our cases the number of letters in each word.

Case 1: one-letter words

There are 6 one-letter words (each of the 6 letters is itself a 1-letter word).

Case 2: two-letter words

To form a two-letter word, we have 6 choices for our first letter, and 6 choices for our second letter. Thus there are $6 \cdot 6 = 36$ two-letter words possible.

Case 3: three-letter words

To form a three-letter word, we have 6 choices for our first letter, 6 choices for our second letter, and 6 choices for our third letter. Thus there are $6 \cdot 6 \cdot 6 = 216$ three-letter words possible.

So to get the total number of words in the language, we add the number of words from each of our cases. (We need to make sure that the cases are exclusive, meaning they don't overlap. But that's clear in this solution, since, for example, a word can't be both a 2-letter word and a 3-letter word at the same time.)

Therefore there are $6 + 36 + 216 = 258$ words possible on Abcdef. (I guess the Abcdefians don't have a lot to say.) □

Again, in this problem, you have to know when to multiply and when to add. When computing the number of 3-letter words, for example, we have to choose the first letter **AND** the second letter **AND** the third letter, so we **multiply** the number of choices for each letter to get the number of 3-letter words. However, when choosing a word from the language as a whole, we have to choose a 1-letter word **OR** a 2-letter word **OR** a 3-letter word, so we **add** the number of choices for each length of word to get the number of total words.

> **Problem 14.15:** How many pairs of positive integers (a, b) satisfy $a^2 + b < 24$?

Solution for Problem 14.15: It may not be obvious how to proceed with this problem, but a little experimentation might lead you to determine the possible values of a.

Since $0 < a^2 < 24$, we can see that a must be one of 1, 2, 3, or 4. So let's use these as our cases.

Case 1: $a = 1$

When $a = 1$, we must have $b < 24 - a^2 = 24 - 1 = 23$. Thus there are 22 possible choices for b when $a = 1$, since b can be any integer from 1 to 22.

Case 2: $a = 2$

When $a = 2$, we must have $b < 24 - 4 = 20$. Thus there are 19 possible choices for b when $a = 2$.

Case 3: $a = 3$

When $a = 3$, we must have $b < 24 - 9 = 15$. Thus there are 14 possible choices for b when $a = 3$.

Case 4: $a = 4$

When $a = 4$, we must have $b < 24 - 16 = 8$. Thus there are 7 possible choices for b when $a = 4$.

So to get the total number of pairs of positive integers satisfying the inequality, we add up all of our possible cases, and see that there are $22 + 19 + 14 + 7 = 62$ possible pairs. □

We can see from this problem that sometimes it's not immediately clear how we want to set up our different cases. Breaking up a problem into cases, and deciding what the different cases should be, is something that you'll get better at with practice. It is important to make sure that the cases are exclusive—that is, that they don't overlap—and also that every possible solution to the original problem is accounted for in one of the cases.

Problem 14.16: A digital clock shows time in the form HH:MM. On a certain day, what is the number of minutes between 7:59 AM and 2:59 PM that HH is greater than MM? *(Source: MOEMS)*

Solution for Problem 14.16: We first notice that the hours in the time period described in the problem are 8, 9, 10, 11, 12, 1, and 2. We can then do casework in two ways.

Method 1: Use the hours as the cases. In the 8-o'clock hour, the minutes from :00 to :07 (inclusive) satisfy the condition that the hour is greater than the minutes. Thus, there are 8 minutes in the 8-o'clock hour that we need to count.

The same logic shows that in the n-o'clock hour, there are n minutes that we need to count. So we just need to add up the hours: $8 + 9 + 10 + 11 + 12 + 1 + 2 = 53$, and our answer is that there are 53 minutes satisfying the condition of the problem.

Method 2: Use the minutes as the cases. We can list which hours each minute should be counted in. For example, the minute :00 should be counted in each hour, since it is less than all of the hours that we care about; on the other hand, the minute :10 should only be counted in the 11-o'clock and 12-o'clock hours. Here is the list:

Minute	Hour(s)	Number of hours
:00	8,9,10,11,12,1,2	7
:01	8,9,10,11,12,2	6
:02	8,9,10,11,12	5
:03	8,9,10,11,12	5
:04	8,9,10,11,12	5
:05	8,9,10,11,12	5
:06	8,9,10,11,12	5
:07	8,9,10,11,12	5
:08	9,10,11,12	4
:09	10,11,12	3
:10	11,12	2
:11	12	1

Minutes that are :12 or greater will never be counted. Therefore, the total number of minutes is

$$7 + 6 + 5 + 5 + 5 + 5 + 5 + 5 + 4 + 3 + 2 + 1 = 53.$$

□

14.3.1 We write the integers from 1 to 150 inclusive. What is the total number of digits that must be written?

14.3.2 I have two hats. In one hat are balls numbered 1 through 15. In the other hat are balls numbered 16 through 25. I first choose a hat, then from that hat, I choose 2 balls, without replacing the balls between selections. How many different ordered selections of 2 balls are possible? (By "ordered selections," we mean that "Ball 1 then ball 2" is considered different from "Ball 2 then ball 1.")

14.3.3

(a) How many paths are there from A to D in the diagram shown below, if we can only travel in the direction of the arrows?

(b) How many paths are there from D to H in the diagram shown below, if we can only travel in the direction of the arrows?

(c) How many paths are there from A to H in the diagram shown below, if we can only travel in the direction of the arrows?

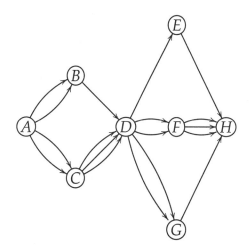

14.3.4 How many positive 3-digit numbers have the property that the first digit is at least three times the second digit?

14.3.5 How many positive 4-digit numbers have the last digit equal to the sum of the first two digits?

14.3.6 How many positive two-digit numbers have digits whose sum is a perfect square? *(Source: AMC 8)*

14.3.7★ How many squares of any size can be formed by connecting dots in the grid shown to the right? **Hints:** 33

14.4 Counting Pairs

> **Problems**

Problem 14.17: A round-robin tennis tournament consists of each player playing every other player exactly once. How many matches will be held during an 8-person round-robin tennis tournament?

Problem 14.18: A round-robin tennis tournament consists of each player playing every other player exactly once. Find a formula for the number of matches that will be held during a n-person round-robin tennis tournament, where $n \geq 2$.

Problem 14.19: Five women and four men are at a party.

(a) If each person shakes hands with each other person, then how many total handshakes are there?

(b) If no two men shake hands, but each woman shakes hands with each other person, then how many total handshakes are there?

Problem 14.20:

(a) How many diagonals does a triangle have?

(b) How many diagonals does a quadrilateral have?

(c) How many diagonals does a pentagon have?

(d) How many diagonals does a hexagon have?

(e) Find a formula for the number of diagonals in a polygon with n sides, where n is an integer greater than 2.

Problem 14.17: A round-robin tennis tournament consists of each player playing every other player exactly once. How many matches will be held during an 8-person round-robin tennis tournament?

Solution for Problem 14.17: Say you're one of the players. How many matches will you play?

Each player plays 7 matches, one against each of the other 7 players.

So what's wrong with the following reasoning?

> **Bogus Solution:** Each of the eight players plays 7 games, so there are $8 \cdot 7 = 56$ total games played.

Suppose two of the players are Alice and Bob. Among Alice's 7 matches is a match against Bob. Among Bob's 7 matches is a match against Alice. When we count the total number of matches as $8 \cdot 7$, the match between Alice and Bob is counted twice, once for Alice and once for Bob.

Therefore, since $8 \cdot 7 = 56$ counts each match twice, we must divide this total by 2 to get the total number of matches. Hence the number of matches in an 8-player round-robin tournament is $\frac{8 \cdot 7}{2} = 28$. $\square$

Here's another way to solve Problem 14.17. We'll go one player at a time, and keep a running count of the number of matches involving those players.

Let's start with Alice. We already know that Alice plays 7 matches.

Next, we move on to Bob. We also know that Bob plays 7 matches, but we've already counted the match that he plays with Alice. So Bob plays in 6 more matches that we haven't already counted. Therefore, our running total—the number of matches involving Alice or Bob—is $7 + 6 = 13$.

Then, we go to the next player, Carol. We know that Carol plays 7 matches, but we've already counted two of them: the one between Carol and Alice, and the one between Carol and Bob. So Carol plays in 5 more matches that we haven't already counted. Therefore, our running total—the number of matches involving Alice, Bob, or Carol—is $7 + 6 + 5 = 18$.

If we keep going in this manner, we'll eventually arrive at a grand total of

$$7 + 6 + 5 + 4 + 3 + 2 + 1 = 28$$

matches.

Problem 14.17 is an example of counting pairs of objects—in this case, pairs of players in a tennis tournament. Now that we know what happens with 8 players, let's take a look at what happens when there are n players. This is an example of **generalizing** a problem: we have solved the problem for a specific number, 8, and now we're going to find a formula that will work for any positive integer number of players.

> **Problem 14.18:** A round-robin tennis tournament consists of each player playing every other player exactly once. Find a formula for the number of matches that will be held during a n-person round-robin tennis tournament, where $n \geq 2$.

Solution for Problem 14.18: If we proceed as in the solution to Problem 14.17, we see that each of the n players must play every other player, so each player must play $n - 1$ matches. This leads to a preliminary count of $n(n - 1)$ matches.

But this method counts each match twice, once for each player. Thus we must divide by 2, to get the answer $\dfrac{n(n - 1)}{2}$. $\square$

Another way to approach the general tournament problem in Problem 14.18 is as follows:

Number the players from 1 through n.

Player 1 plays players $2, 3, \ldots, n$ for a total of $n - 1$ matches.

Player 2 plays players $1, 3, 4, \ldots, n$. But we've already counted the match between players 1 and 2. So we only need to add on the matches between player 2 and players $3, 4, \ldots, n$, for another $n - 2$ matches.

Similarly, for player 3, we've already counted the matches against players 1 and 2, so we need to add on the matches between player 3 and players $4, 5, \ldots, n$, for another $n - 3$ matches.

And so on.

So the total number of matches is the sum of our counts above, which is

$$(n - 1) + (n - 2) + (n - 3) + \cdots + 2 + 1.$$

Since this must match the count that we had before, we've just shown that

$$(n - 1) + (n - 2) + (n - 3) + \cdots + 2 + 1 = \frac{n(n - 1)}{2}.$$

Our work above gives us a formula for the sum of the first k positive integers! If we let $n = k + 1$ in the equation we just found (and reverse the order of the sum so our sum goes from 1 to k), then we get

$$1 + 2 + \cdots + (k - 2) + (k - 1) + k = \frac{(k + 1)(k)}{2}.$$

So, our counting explanations have given us an algebra formula!

> **Concept:** We can sometimes use counting explanations to find algebraic relationships.

We also could have used algebra to find a formula for the sum of the first k positive integers. We write

$$S = 1 + 2 + \cdots + (k - 1) + k.$$

We can, of course, just as easily write S in reverse order:

$$S = k + (k - 1) + \cdots + 2 + 1.$$

This may seems like a useless thing to do, but watch what happens when we add them together:

$$
\begin{array}{rcccccccc}
S & = & 1 & + & 2 & + \cdots + & k-1 & + & k \\
+ \quad S & = & k & + & k-1 & + \cdots + & 2 & + & 1 \\
\hline
2S & = & (k+1) & + & (k+1) & + \cdots + & (k+1) & + & (k+1)
\end{array}
$$

The last line has k copies of $k + 1$, and hence

$$2S = k(k + 1).$$

So, we divide by 2 to get $S = \frac{k(k+1)}{2}$.

> **Important:** For any positive integer k,
>
> $$1 + 2 + \cdots + (k - 1) + k = \frac{k(k + 1)}{2}.$$

Sidenote: Legend has it that the famous German mathematician Carl Friedrich Gauss (1777–1855) once used the above formula to very quickly compute the sum of the integers from 1 to 100. What is remarkable about this is that Gauss was only 7 years old at the time! His schoolteacher gave his class, as an exercise, the assignment to calculate

$$1 + 2 + 3 + \cdots + 99 + 100,$$

figuring that it would take the students many minutes. The teacher was quite surprised when young Gauss came up with the answer almost immediately! Gauss, even at age 7, recognized that there was a quick way to add consecutive integers, and used the same process that we used to prove our formula.

In some problems, we don't necessarily want to count *all* pairs, but just some of them.

Problem 14.19: Five women and four men are at a party.

(a) If each person shakes hands with each other person, then how many total handshakes are there?

(b) If no two men shake hands, but each woman shakes hands with each other person, then how many total handshakes are there?

Solution for Problem 14.19:

(a) There are 9 people total, and each must shake hands with each other person. So, each person shakes hands 8 times. This gives us a preliminary count of $9 \cdot 8$ handshakes. But this counts each handshake twice, once for each person in the handshake. So, we must divide by 2 to get a total of $9 \cdot 8/2 = 36$ handshakes. (Notice that this problem is essentially the same as the round-robin tournament problem, where we've replaced "matches" with "handshakes.")

(b) What's wrong with this solution:

> **Bogus Solution:** Each woman shakes hands with 8 other people, and there are 5 women, for a preliminary total of $8 \cdot 5 = 40$ handshakes. But this counts each handshake twice, once for each person in the handshake. So, we must divide by 2 to get a total of $40/2 = 20$ handshakes.

The problem here is that the count $8 \cdot 5$ does not count each handshake twice! A handshake between two women is counted twice, but a handshake between a man and a woman is counted only once, just for the woman.

> **WARNING!!** When dividing by 2 in a counting problem to correct for counting each item twice, make sure you really were counting each item twice!

We have to handle the handshakes between two women separately from handshakes between a man and a woman. Each of the 5 women shakes hands with 4 other women, for a preliminary count of $5 \cdot 4$ handshakes. Suppose Alice and Barb are two of the women. Our count of $5 \cdot 4$ counts the handshake between Alice and Barb twice—once among Alice's 4 handshakes with other women, and once among Barb's 4 handshakes with other women. So, here we have to divide by 2, since $5 \cdot 4$ counts each handshake twice, once for each woman. This gives us $5 \cdot 4/2 = 10$ handshakes between two women.

Turning to handshakes between a man and a woman, each of the women shakes hands with 4 men, for a preliminary count of $5 \cdot 4 = 20$ handshakes. Suppose Alice is one of the women and Carl is one of the men. The handshake between Alice and Carl is only counted once, just among Alice's 4 handshakes with men. So, we don't divide the preliminary count by 2, because each handshake between a woman and a man is only counted once. There are 20 handshakes between a woman and a man.

Combining the handshakes between two women with those between a woman and a man, we have $10 + 20 = 30$ handshakes.

□

Problem 14.20:

(a) How many diagonals does a triangle have?

(b) How many diagonals does a quadrilateral have?

(c) How many diagonals does a pentagon have?

(d) How many diagonals does a hexagon have?

(e) Find a formula for the number of diagonals in a polygon with n sides, where n is an integer greater than 2.

Solution for Problem 14.20:

(a) A triangle has 0 diagonals.

(b) A quadrilateral has 2 diagonals.

(c) As shown at the left below, a pentagon has 5 diagonals.

A Pentagon and Its Diagonals   A Hexagon and Its Diagonals

(d) A hexagon and its diagonals are shown at the right above. Rather than counting the diagonals directly, we count the diagonals by thinking about each vertex. Each vertex can connect to the other 5 vertices, but 2 of these connections are edges, not diagonals. So each vertex has $5 - 2 = 3$ diagonals. (This is a lot like the handshaking problem! Thinking of a diagonal as a handshake between two vertices, each vertex "shakes hands" with 3 other vertices.)

There are 6 vertices of a hexagon and each connects to 3 vertices by a diagonal, so it appears that there are $6 \cdot 3 = 18$ diagonals. However, this counts each diagonal twice, once for each vertex at its endpoints. To correct for this, we must divide by 2, giving $18/2 = 9$ diagonals.

(e) We can use our process from part (d) for any polygon. A polygon with n sides has n vertices. As in part (c), each vertex can connect to the other $n - 1$ vertices, but 2 of these connections are edges, not diagonals. So each vertex has $(n - 1) - 2 = n - 3$ diagonals.

Since each of the n vertices has $n-3$ diagonals, it appears that there are $n(n-3)$ diagonals. But again, this counts each diagonal twice, once for each vertex at its endpoints. So, we correct our count by dividing by 2, giving $n(n - 3)/2$ diagonals for a polygon with n sides. Checking, we see that this formula does give us the values we found in the first four parts.

□

14.4.1 There are five girls in a tennis class. How many different doubles teams of two girls each can be formed from the students in the class? *(Source: MOEMS)*

14.4.2 A club has 12 members and needs to choose 2 members to be co-presidents. How many different pairs of co-presidents are possible?

14.4.3 Two students are needed to work in the school store during the lunch hour every day, and four students volunteer for this work. What is the greatest number of days that can be arranged in which no pair of the four students work together more than once? *(Source: MOEMS)*

14.4.4 Six people participated in a checkers tournament. Each participant played exactly three games with each of the other participants. How many games were played in all? *(Source: MOEMS)*

14.4.5 A sports conference has 12 teams in two divisions of 6. How many games are in a complete season for the conference if each team must play every other team in its own division twice and every team in the other division once?

14.4.6★ Find a formula for the sum of the first n even integers: $2 + 4 + 6 + \cdots + 2n$.

14.4.7★ How many interior diagonals does an icosahedron have? (An **icosahedron** is a 3-dimensional figure with 20 triangular faces and 12 vertices, with 5 faces meeting at each vertex. An **interior diagonal** is a segment connecting two vertices that do not lie on a common face.) **Hints:** 12, 103, 93

14.5 Probability

Now we turn from counting to **probability**. Unfortunately, while even most three-year-olds know what "counting" means, the concept of probability is a bit difficult to describe precisely.

Let's start with an example. Suppose we have a coin, where one side is heads, and the other side is tails. If we flip the coin over and over and over again, we expect that about half the time we'll flip heads and about half the time we'll flip tails. We express this mathematically by saying that the **probability** that a coin flip will turn up heads is $\frac{1}{2}$.

This is what we mean by probability of an outcome: it's the fraction of times that we expect an outcome to occur if we perform the experiment over and over. Notice that we can't say the *exact* fraction of times we have success. This is the difficulty in defining probability. Probability only exists because we are trying to measure an event that is not definite.

In basic examples, we'll compute probability by counting the number of equally likely outcomes, then counting how many of these outcomes are "successes." Our probability of success is the ratio of the number of successful outcomes to the total number of possible outcomes. For instance, in our coin-flipping example above, there are 2 possible outcomes (heads and tails), and 1 successful outcome (heads), so the probability of flipping heads is $\frac{1}{2}$.

But we have a very important consideration:

> **Important:** We must be sure that each possible outcome is equally likely.

Problems

Problem 14.21: The faces of a fair 6-sided die are numbered ⚀, ⚁, ⚂, ⚃, ⚄, ⚅. ("Fair" means that each side is equally likely to be rolled.) What is the probability that when the die is rolled, a ⚁ is facing up?

Problem 14.22: What is the probability that when a fair 6-sided die is rolled, an odd number faces up?

Problem 14.23: What is the greatest possible probability for any event? What is the least possible probability for any event?

Problem 14.24: A standard deck of cards has 52 cards divided into 4 suits, each of which has 13 cards. Two of the suits ($\heartsuit$ and $\diamond$, called "hearts" and "diamonds") are red, and the other two ($\spadesuit$ and $\clubsuit$, called "spades" and "clubs") are black. The cards in the deck are placed in random order (usually by a process called "shuffling"). What is the probability that the top two cards are both red?

Problem 14.25: Suppose we have 2 fair 6-sided dice numbered from ⚀ to ⚅. If we roll them both, then what is the probability that the two numbers shown sum to 7?

Let's start with a basic example.

Problem 14.21: The faces of a fair 6-sided die are numbered ⚀, ⚁, ⚂, ⚃, ⚄, ⚅. ("Fair" means that each side is equally likely to be rolled.) What is the probability that when the die is rolled, a ⚁ is facing up?

Solution for Problem 14.21: When we roll the die, there are 6 equally likely outcomes: ⚀, ⚁, ⚂, ⚃, ⚄, or ⚅. In this problem, there is only one "successful" outcome, namely when a ⚁ comes up. Therefore, the probability that a ⚁ is rolled is the 1 successful outcome divided by the total of 6 equally likely outcomes, or $\frac{1}{6}$. □

As we discussed in the introduction to this section, the way to interpret this probability is that if we were to roll our die many, many times, we would expect that about $\frac{1}{6}$ of our rolls would come up ⚀.

In Problem 14.21 we see the basic way to calculate probabilities.

> **Concept:** If all outcomes are **equally likely**, then the probability of success is
>
> $$\frac{\text{Number of successful outcomes}}{\text{Number of possible outcomes}}.$$

Here's another example with our trusty die:

Problem 14.22: What is the probability that when a fair 6-sided die is rolled, an odd number faces up?

Solution for Problem 14.22: In this problem, as in Problem 14.21, there are 6 equally likely outcomes. Three of those outcomes are successful: a ⚀, ⚂, or ⚄. Therefore, the probability is $\frac{3}{6} = \frac{1}{2}$. □

Now that we've done a couple of basic probability problems, let's ask some important general questions about probability.

Problem 14.23: What is the greatest possible probability for any event? What is the least possible probability for any event?

Solution for Problem 14.23: Since the probability of an event occurring is essentially the proportion of times that we expect the event to occur, the largest the probability could be is 1. This occurs when the event happens every time.

Another way to look at this is to recall that for any event, we have

$$\text{Probability of success} = \frac{\text{Number of successful outcomes}}{\text{Number of possible outcomes}}.$$

Clearly the number of successful outcomes cannot be greater than the number of possible outcomes, so the probability must be no greater than 1. If every outcome is successful, then the number of successful outcomes equals the number of possible outcomes, and the probability is 1. For example, if the event is "a single die roll is less than 10," then the probability is 1, since there are 6 successful outcomes out of 6 possible outcomes.

Similarly, the smallest the probability could ever be is 0. This occurs when the event cannot happen, so the number of successful outcomes is 0. For example, if the event is "a single die roll is 8," then the probability is 0, because there are 0 successful outcomes out of 6 possible outcomes. □

> **Important:** When working on a probability problem, if you ever get a probability that's less than 0 or greater than 1, then you've made a mistake! All probabilities are greater than or equal to 0, and less than or equal to 1.

Let's try a slightly more complicated problem.

> **Problem 14.24:** A standard deck of cards has 52 cards divided into 4 suits, each of which has 13 cards. Two of the suits ($\heartsuit$ and $\diamond$, called "hearts" and "diamonds") are red, and the other two ($\spadesuit$ and $\clubsuit$, called "spades" and "clubs") are black. The cards in the deck are placed in random order (usually by a process called "shuffling"). What is the probability that the top two cards are both red?

Solution for Problem 14.24: Since all choices of the first two cards are equally likely, we need to count the total number of possibilities for the first two cards, and also the number of ways that the first two cards are both red.

First we count the total number of ways to draw two cards. There are 52 ways to pick the first card, then 51 ways to pick the second card, for a total of $52 \cdot 51$ possibilities.

Next we count the number of successful possibilities, meaning the number of ways to draw two red cards. There are 26 ways to pick a red card first (since there are 26 total red cards), then there are 25 ways to also pick a second red card (since there are 25 red cards remaining after we've chosen the first card). Thus, there are a total of $26 \cdot 25$ successful possibilities.

Therefore, the probability is

$$\frac{\text{Number of successful outcomes}}{\text{Number of possible outcomes}} = \frac{26 \cdot 25}{52 \cdot 51} = \frac{25}{102}.$$

□

> **Problem 14.25:** Suppose we have 2 fair 6-sided dice numbered from ⚀ to ⚅. If we roll them both, then what is the probability the two numbers shown sum to 7?

Solution for Problem 14.25: We might incorrectly think like this:

> **Bogus Solution:** Any number from 2 to 12 could occur, so there are 11 possibilities. 7 is one of those, so the probability is 1/11.

The error here is that the 11 possibilities are **not equally likely**. For example, rolling a sum of 7 is more likely than rolling a sum of 2. In order to correctly compute probability, we need to count equally likely outcomes, and then determine how many of those possibilities result in a sum of 7. But how can we count equally likely outcomes for the sum of two dice?

There are 6 equally likely outcomes for each die, so there are $6 \cdot 6 = 36$ total equally likely outcomes for both dice together. It may be easier to see this if you think of one of the dice as being black and the other as being white. There are 6 outcomes for the black die and 6 outcomes for the white die, for a total of $6 \cdot 6 = 36$ outcomes for the pair of dice. The outcomes that sum to 7 are ■ ⬚, ■ ⬚, ■ ⬚, ■ ⬚, ■ ⬚, and ⬚ ⬚, for a total of 6 equally likely successful outcomes. Therefore, the probability of rolling a sum of 7 is $\frac{6}{36} = \frac{1}{6}$. □

We can see all of the possible equally likely outcomes for the two dice in the following table:

	Die #1					
	▪	▪▪	▪▪▪	▪▪▪▪	▪▪▪▪▪	▪▪▪▪▪▪
▪	2	3	4	5	6	7
▪▪	3	4	5	6	7	8
▪▪▪	4	5	6	7	8	9
▪▪▪▪	5	6	7	8	9	10
▪▪▪▪▪	6	7	8	9	10	11
▪▪▪▪▪▪	7	8	9	10	11	12

Die #2 is the label for the rows.

Notice that 6 of the entries in the above table are 7, and there are 36 total entries in the table, so the probability of rolling a 7 is $\frac{6}{36} = \frac{1}{6}$.

Exercises

14.5.1 Suppose we roll a fair 6-sided die. What is the probability that

(a) a ▪▪▪ is rolled?

(b) an even number is rolled?

(c) a perfect square is rolled?

14.5.2 Suppose that we have an 8-sided die with 2 red sides, 5 yellow sides, and a blue side. What is the probability of rolling a yellow side?

14.5.3 Consider a standard deck of 52 cards (as described in Problem 14.24). The deck is randomly arranged. What is the probability that

(a) the top card is a ♠?

(b) the top card is a 9?

(c) the top card is a face card (a Jack, Queen, or King)?

(d) the top card is black and the second card is red?

(e) the top card is a 3 and the second card is an 8?

(f) the top two cards are both Aces?

14.5.4 Suppose we flip four coins simultaneously: a penny, a nickel, a dime, and a quarter. What is the probability that

(a) they all come up heads?

(b) the penny and nickel both come up heads?

(c)★ at least 15¢ worth of coins come up heads?

14.5.5 Suppose that we roll two fair 6-sided dice. What is the probability that the two numbers rolled sum to 5?

14.5.6 Two dice are thrown. What is the probability that the product of the two numbers is a multiple of 5? *(Source: AMC 8)*

14.5.7★ A pair of 8-sided dice has the sides of each die numbered 1 through 8. Each side has the same probability of landing face up. What is the probability that the product of the two numbers on the sides that land face-up is greater than 36? *(Source: AMC 8)*

14.5.8★ At a party, there are only single women and married men with their wives. The probability that a randomly selected woman is single is $\frac{2}{5}$. What fraction of the people in the room are married men? *(Source: AMC 8)*

14.6 Summary

In this chapter, we learned how to use arithmetic to solve counting problems.

> **Important:** Don't just blindly add, subtract, multiply, and divide—think about what you're doing!

Counting a list of numbers like $1, 2, 3, \ldots, 38$ is easy! Counting many other lists of numbers is easy too: use arithmetic to convert it into a list that looks like $1, 2, 3, \ldots$. The number of items in the list $a, a + 1, \ldots, b - 1, b$, where $a \le b$ are integers, is $b - a + 1$.

> **Concept:** When presented with a complicated problem, try to reduce or simplify it to a simpler problem that you know how to solve.

Counting items which lie in one or more overlapping sets requires a thoughtful use of addition and subtraction. We can use a Venn diagram to help keep track of the thought process. When using a Venn diagram, we should initially try to fill in numbers that correspond exactly to a single region of the diagram. We may have to place variables in our diagram: if so, it's usually wise to choose our variable to represent the answer to the problem.

> **Concept:** When assigning a variable, it's usually best to let your variable represent the answer to the problem.

When counting multiple independent events, we multiply: the number of ways that A **and** B can occur is

(the number of ways A can occur) **times** (the number of ways B can occur).

Sometimes our later choices depend on our earlier choices, so our counting must take that into consideration.

Casework can often help us break a counting problem into more manageable pieces. We split the possibilities into exclusive cases, meaning that every outcome shows up in exactly one case. Then, to count the total, you simply add the counts for each case. Casework requires you to be organized and careful, and to make sure that you don't omit any outcomes in your cases.

> **Concept:** When faced with a series of independent choices, one after the other, we **multiply** the number of options at each step. When faced with exclusive options (meaning we can't choose more than one), we **add** the number of options.

To count pairs of items, we first count the number of ways to select 2 items from our group, and then divide by 2 because we've counted each pair twice (once in each order). In general, if we have n items, then there are $\frac{n(n-1)}{2}$ pairs of items.

> **Important:** For any positive integer n,
> $$1 + 2 + \cdots + (n - 1) + n = \frac{n(n + 1)}{2}.$$

If all outcomes are *equally likely*, then the probability of success is

$$\frac{\text{Number of successful outcomes}}{\text{Number of possible outcomes}}.$$

It is very important that all of the outcomes are equally likely!

When working on a probability problem, if you ever get a probability that's less than 0 or greater than 1, then you've made a mistake! All probabilities are greater than or equal to 0, and less than or equal to 1.

Most probability problems are just two counting problems: counting the number of total outcomes and counting the number of successful outcomes. So we can take advantage of all of the counting techniques that we've learned to solve probability problems as well.

14.26   How many numbers are in the following lists?

(a) $-7, -6, -5, \ldots, 23, 24$

(c) $3.5, 6.5, 9.5, 12.5, \ldots, 87.5, 90.5$

(b) $7, 14, 21, \ldots, 686$

(d) $86, 82, 78, \ldots, 14, 10$

14.27   In a group of 25 girls, 8 joined the track team, 13 joined the math team, and 6 joined both teams. How many of the girls did not join either team? *(Source: MOEMS)*

14.28   There are 40 students in Mrs. Rusczyk's first grade class. If there are three times as many students with blond hair as with blue eyes, 3 students with blond hair and blue eyes, and 15 students with neither blond hair nor blue eyes, how many students have blue eyes?

14.29   You have 4 shirts, 3 pairs of pants, and 6 hats. How many outfits can you make consisting of one shirt, one pair of pants, and one hat?

14.30   A haunted house has six windows. In how many ways can Georgie the Ghost enter the house by one window and leave by a different window? *(Source: AMC 8)*

14.31   How many 3-letter combinations can be formed if the first letter must be a vowel (A, E, I, O, or U), and the second letter must be different from the third letter?

14.32   How many 5-digit numbers have the second digit odd and the fifth digit at least four times the second digit?

14.33   Pat Peano has plenty of 0's, 1's, 3's, 4's, 5's, 6's, 7's, 8's, and 9's, but he has only twenty-two 2's. How far can he number the pages of his scrapbook with these digits? *(Source: AMC 8)*

14.34   How many positive, even three-digit numbers exist such that the sum of the hundreds digit and the tens digit equals the units digit? *(Source: MATHCOUNTS)*

14.35   A baseball league has nine teams. During the season, each of the nine teams plays exactly three games with each of the other teams. What is the total number of games played? *(Source: MOEMS)*

14.36   Tyler has entered a buffet line in which he chooses one kind of meat, two different vegetables, and one dessert from the selections below. If the order of food items is not important, how many different meals might he choose?
Meat: beef, chicken, pork
Vegetables: baked beans, corn, potatoes, tomatoes
Dessert: brownies, chocolate cake, chocolate pudding, ice cream
(Source: AMC 8)

14.37 A singles tournament had six players. Each player played every other player only once, with no ties. If Helen won 4 games, Ines won 3 games, Janet won 2 games, Kendra won 2 games, and Lara won 2 games, how many games did Monica win? *(Source: AMC 8)*

14.38 Two fair 6-sided dice are rolled. What is the probability

(a) that "doubles" are rolled (that is, the two dice show the same number)?

(b) that the sum rolled is greater than 3 but less than 7?

(c) that at least one of the dice shows a ⊡?

14.39 A bag contains some marbles, all of the same size. Eight of them are black. The rest are red. The probability of drawing a red marble from the bag is $\frac{2}{3}$. Find the total number of red marbles in the bag. *(Source: MOEMS)*

14.40 A box contains 5 white balls and 6 black balls.

(a) A ball is drawn out of the box at random. What is the probability that the ball is white?

(b) Two balls are drawn out of the box at random. What is the probability that they both are white?

14.41 If one neglects the ":", certain times displayed on a digital watch are palindromes. Three examples are $\boxed{1:01}$, $\boxed{4:44}$, and $\boxed{12:21}$. How many times during a 12-hour period will be palindromes? *(Source: AMC 8)*

14.42 Diana and Apollo each roll a standard die obtaining a number at random from 1 to 6. What is the probability that Diana's number is larger than Apollo's number? *(Source: AMC 8)*

Challenge Problems ▶

14.43 Which integers n satisfy $\frac{1}{2} > \frac{1}{n} > \frac{3}{100}$, and how many such integers are there?

14.44 My classroom has 11 rows of chairs, with 11 chairs in each row. The chairs in each row are numbered from 1 to 11.

(a) How many chairs have odd numbers?

(b)★ Suppose we replaced all of the occurrences of "11" in this problem with n, where n is an odd number. Can you find a formula in terms of n for the number of chairs with odd numbers? Is the formula different if n is even?

14.45 There are 7 married couples at a party. At the start of the party, every person shakes hands once with every other person except his or her spouse. How many handshakes are there?

14.46 When writing the numbers from 1 to 500, how many times will you write the digit 3?
Hints: 134, 71

14.47 In a sports league, there are 20 total teams, divided into 4 divisions of 5 teams each. Over the course of a season, each team plays each of the other teams in its own division 3 times, and each of the other teams in the other divisions twice. How many games does the league have in a complete season?

14.48 Keiko tosses one penny and Ephraim tosses two pennies. What is the probability that Ephraim gets the same number of heads that Keiko gets? *(Source: AMC 8)*

14.49 If two dice are tossed, what is the probability that the product of the numbers showing on the tops of the dice is greater than 10? *(Source: AMC 8)*

14.50 Paco uses a spinner to select a number from 1 through 5 inclusive, each with equal probability. Manu uses a different spinner to select a number from 1 through 10 inclusive, each with equal probability. What is the probability that the product of their numbers is less than 30? *(Source: MATHCOUNTS)*

14.51 In Park School's 8th grade, 33 students like volleyball, 34 like softball, 39 like basketball, 20 like volleyball and softball, 10 like volleyball and basketball, 8 like softball and basketball, 3 like all three sports, and 12 like none of these sports. How many students are in Park School's 8th grade? *(Source: MOEMS)* **Hints:** 163, 114

14.52★ In my fencing club, there are twice as many boys who are in high school as there are boys who are in middle school. Of the students in the club who are in middle school, there are three times as many girls as there are boys. Half of the girls who are in the club are in high school. If there are 72 people in my fencing club, how many are middle school boys?
Hints: 58

14.53★ There are 120 seats in a row. What is the fewest number of seats that must be occupied so that the next person to be seated must sit next to someone? *(Source: AMC 8)*

14.54★ In how many ways can you spell the word NOON in the grid below? You can start on any letter, then on each step you can move one letter in any direction (up, down, left, right, or diagonal). You cannot visit the same letter twice. **Hints:** 80

NNNN
NOON
NOON
NNNN

14.55★ Two-thirds of the dogs at the dog pound are pit bulls. Half the dogs at the pound are female, and three-quarters of the male dogs at the pound are pit bulls. If there are 14 female pit bulls at the pound, how many dogs are at the pound?

14.56★ We connect dots with toothpicks in a grid as shown at right. If there are 10 horizontal toothpicks in each row and 20 vertical ones in each column, how many total toothpicks are there? *(Source: AMC)* **Hints:** 145

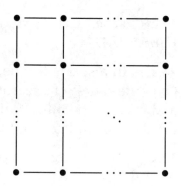

14.57★ I have 120 blocks. Each block is one of 2 different materials, 3 different colors, 4 different sizes, and 5 different shapes. No two blocks have exactly the same of all four properties. I take two blocks at random. What is the probability the two blocks have exactly two of these four properties the same? *(Source: AIME)* **Hints:** 48

  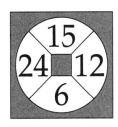 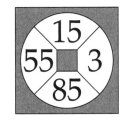

An idea which can be used only once is a trick. If one can use it more than once it becomes a method.

– George Pólya and Gabor Szegö

CHAPTER **15**

Problem-Solving Strategies

We finish the book with a chapter covering common general strategies for tackling problems. These strategies have a common goal:

> **Concept:** Simplify the problem.

15.1 Find a Pattern

Much of learning consists simply of observing patterns. Solving math problems is no different. An excellent problem solver is playful and experiments with problems. Often these experiments reveal patterns that lead to a solution.

Problem 15.1: What is the 2010th letter in the sequence below?

$$ABCDEDCBAABCDEDCBAABCDEDCBAABCDEDC\ldots$$

Problem 15.2: In this problem, we find the units digit (ones digit) of 2^{2011}.

(a) Find the units digit of each of the first 8 powers of 2, starting with 2^1.

(b) Find the units digit of 2^{2011}.

Problem 15.3: Michelle's Number Recycling Machine obeys two rules:

1. If an inserted number has exactly one digit, double the number.

2. If an inserted number has exactly two digits, compute the sum of the digits.

The first number Michelle inserts is 1. Then every answer she gets is inserted back into the machine until fifty numbers are inserted. What is the fiftieth number to be inserted? *(Source: MOEMS)*

Problem 15.4: In the figure below, each row of *'s has two more *'s than the row above it. Altogether, how many *'s are contained in the first 30 rows?

```
        *
      *   *   *
    *   *   *   *   *
  *   *   *   *   *   *   *
  :     :     :     :   ·.
```

Problem 15.1: What is the 2010th letter in the sequence below?

ABCDEDCBAABCDEDCBAABCDEDCBAABCDEDC...

Solution for Problem 15.1: We certainly don't want to write out 2010 letters! Fortunately, the letters follow a clear pattern. The same 9-letter block repeats over and over:

ABCDEDCBA.

We'll have to write this block over and over many times before reaching the 2010th letter. To figure out how many times, we divide 2010 by 9, which has quotient 223 and remainder 3. So, in writing the first 2010 letters, we write this repeating block 223 times, and then write 3 more letters. Therefore, the 2010th letter is *C*. □

In Problem 15.1, the pattern is part of the problem statement. In many problems, the pattern isn't given in the problem, and we must discover it by experimenting.

Problem 15.2: What is the units digit (ones digit) of 2^{2011}?

Solution for Problem 15.2: Computing 2^{2011} by hand will take a while. Many calculators aren't able to output all the digits of such a large number, so even using a calculator may not help solve the problem. Instead, we'll have to play with the problem a bit by computing several powers of 2 and looking for a pattern. Starting from 2^1, the first eight powers of 2 are

$$2, 4, 8, 16, 32, 64, 128, 256.$$

At first, it may not be obvious that there's a pattern. But remember, the problem asks for the units digit of 2^{2011}, so let's look at just the units digits of the numbers in this list:

$$2, 4, 8, 6, 2, 4, 8, 6.$$

The same block of 4 digits repeats twice. Will this pattern continue forever?

Important: Noticing a pattern isn't enough. We have to be sure that the pattern continues in order to use it to solve a problem. This usually means that we have to figure out why the pattern occurs.

The units digit of the product of two integers is the same as the units digit of the product of the units digits of the integers. For example, the units digit of $342 \cdot 486$ is the same as the units digit of $2 \cdot 6$. So, all we have to consider are the units digits of the powers of 2.

We start with 2, and multiplying any number that ends in 2 by 2 gives a number that ends in 4. This means that any 2 in the list of units digits of powers of 2 must be followed by a 4. Similarly, 4 must be followed by 8, and 8 must be followed by 6. Since $6 \cdot 2$ ends in 2, the next units digit is 2 again. We already know that after 2 comes 4, after 4 comes 8, and after 8 comes 6. Then, we're back to 2 yet again. So, we see that the units digits repeat the cycle 2, 4, 8, 6 over and over.

Now our goal is to figure out which digit is 2011th if we repeat the cycle 2, 4, 8, 6 until we have 2011 terms. 2011 divided by 4 has quotient 502 and remainder 3. So, we will write the cycle 502 times, and then write 3 more terms to get to the 2011th term. Therefore, the 2011th term is 8, so the units digit of 2^{2011} is 8.

Notice that we don't even have to find the quotient when 2011 is divided by 4. All we really care about is the remainder. Since the remainder is 3, we know that to get to the 2011th term, we have to write three more terms after writing the last complete cycle 2, 4, 8, 6. $\square$

It's very easy to be off by one term when using patterns to solve a problem as we did in Problem 15.2. For example, suppose we wanted to find the units digit of 2^{2000}. Following our work in the previous problem, we find the remainder when we divide 2000 by 4. The remainder is 0, so do we take the first term in the cycle 2, 4, 8, 6, or do we take the last?

To get to the 2000th term, we write the cycle $2000/4 = 500$ times and then write *no more extra terms*. We write the 2000th term when we write the last term of the cycle for the 500th time. So, the units digit of 2^{2000} is 6.

WARNING!! Be careful not to be off by one term when using patterns to solve a problem.

One way to check that you're not off by one is to test small cases. For example, to test our reasoning above for the units digit of 2^{2000}, we can consider what happens when 2 is raised to smaller exponents that are multiples of 4. Both 2^4 and 2^8 end in 6, which gives us more confidence that our answer for 2^{2000} is correct.

Problem 15.3: Michelle's Number Recycling Machine obeys two rules:

1. If an inserted number has exactly one digit, double the number.

2. If an inserted number has exactly two digits, compute the sum of the digits.

The first number Michelle inserts is 1. Then every answer she gets is inserted back into the machine until fifty numbers are inserted. What is the fiftieth number to be inserted? *(Source: MOEMS)*

Solution for Problem 15.3:   As with the previous problem, we experiment a bit and hope we find a pattern. Following the two given rules, the first several numbers Michelle's machine produces are

$$1, 2, 4, 8, 16, 7, 14, 5, 10, 1, 2, 4, 8.$$

Once the machine produces 1 for a second time, we know that the machine will repeat the first 9 numbers over and over. Since 50 divided by 9 leaves a remainder of 5, the 50th number in the list is the same as the 5th in this repeating block of numbers. This means that the 50th number in the list is 16. □

Problem 15.4: In the figure below, each row of *'s has two more *'s than the row above it. Altogether, how many *'s are contained in the first 30 rows?

```
          *
        *   *   *
      *   *   *   *   *
    *   *   *   *   *   *   *
    :   :   :     :   ⋱
```

Solution for Problem 15.4:   First, we simplify the problem by getting rid of the symbols, and instead write the number of *'s in each row. The numbers of *'s in the rows are

$$1, 3, 5, 7, 9, 11, \dots .$$

So, to count all the *'s in the first 30 rows, we could add the first 30 positive odd numbers. But instead, let's add up shorter lists and look for a pattern.

Concept: Considering a simpler version of a problem can help us solve the original problem.

The first 5 such sums are

$$1 = 1,$$
$$1 + 3 = 4,$$
$$1 + 3 + 5 = 9,$$
$$1 + 3 + 5 + 7 = 16,$$
$$1 + 3 + 5 + 7 + 9 = 25.$$

Each sum is a perfect square! The sum of the first 2 odd numbers is 2^2, the sum of the first 3 odd numbers is 3^2, the sum of the first 4 odd numbers is 4^2, and so on.

We now expect that the sum of the first 30 positive odd numbers is $30^2 = 900$. But we still have to figure out why summing the first n positive odd numbers results in n^2. Now that we know what to look for, there are a number of ways to see why it is true.

One way is to use what we learned back on page 62 about consecutive squares. There, we learned that
$$a^2 + 2a + 1 = (a + 1)^2.$$

The first square is just the first positive odd number: $1^2 = 1$. To get from 1^2 to 2^2, we add the odd number $2 \cdot 1 + 1$:
$$1^2 + 2 \cdot 1 + 1 = 2^2.$$

Then, to get from 2^2 to 3^2, we add the next odd number, $2 \cdot 2 + 1$:

$$2^2 + 2 \cdot 2 + 1 = 3^2.$$

And so on:

$$3^2 + 2 \cdot 3 + 1 = 4^2,$$
$$4^2 + 2 \cdot 4 + 1 = 5^2,$$
$$5^2 + 2 \cdot 5 + 1 = 6^2.$$

We can also use some clever diagrams to explain why summing the first n positive odd numbers equals n^2:

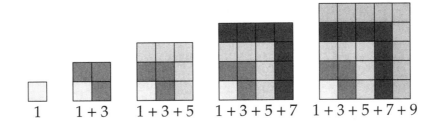

1   1 + 3   1 + 3 + 5   1 + 3 + 5 + 7   1 + 3 + 5 + 7 + 9

Now, we can confidently state that there are 900 *'s total in the first 30 rows. □

Exercises

15.1.1 It takes exactly 74 colored beads on a string to make a necklace. The beads are strung in the following order: one red, one orange, two yellow, one green, and one blue. Then the pattern repeats, starting again with one red bead. If the first bead of the necklace is red, what is the color of the last bead used to make the necklace? *(Source: MATHCOUNTS)*

15.1.2 The **Fibonacci sequence** begins

$$1, 1, 2, 3, 5, 8, 13, 21, 34, 55.$$

Each term of the sequence after the second term is the sum of the two terms before it. The sequence continues forever. For example, the eleventh term is $34 + 55$, or 89. How many of the first 60 terms of this sequence are odd numbers?

15.1.3 In the table of numbers below, what number is directly above 119?

$$
\begin{array}{ccccccc}
& & & 1 & & & \\
& & 2 & 3 & 4 & & \\
& 5 & 6 & 7 & 8 & 9 & \\
10 & 11 & 12 & 13 & 14 & 15 & 16 \\
\end{array}
$$

$$\cdots \qquad \vdots \qquad \cdots$$

15.1.4 All of the even numbers from 2 through 288, except those ending in 0, are multiplied together. What is the units digit (ones digit) of the product? **Hints:** 100

15.2 Make a List

If a strategy is good enough to allow Santa Claus to distribute presents to all the children in the world, it ought to be good enough to help us solve some math problems.

Problems

Problem 15.5: Find a two-digit positive integer with all these properties:

- the tens digit is larger than the ones digit (units digit),
- the difference between the digits is greater than 3,
- the sum of the digits is greater than 10, and
- the integer is a multiple of 12.

(Source: MOEMS)

Problem 15.6: Elizabeth spent exactly $7 for some 15-cent stamps and some 31-cent stamps. How many 15-cent stamps did she buy?

Problem 15.7: A **partition** of a positive integer n is a way of writing n as the sum of positive integers in which the order of the numbers in the sum doesn't matter. For example, the partitions of 3 are 3, $2 + 1$, and $1 + 1 + 1$. We consider $2 + 1$ and $1 + 2$ to be the same, so there are 3 partitions of 3. How many partitions of 6 are there?

Problem 15.5: Find a two-digit positive integer with all these properties:

- the tens digit is larger than the ones digit (units digit),

- the difference between the digits is greater than 3,

- the sum of the digits is greater than 10, and

- the integer is a multiple of 12.

(Source: MOEMS)

Solution for Problem 15.5: It would take way too long to test every single two-digit number. We narrow our search by first focusing on just one of the properties. But which one?

Concept: When faced with several restrictions in a problem, it's often best to consider the most restrictive first.

Each of the first three properties is satisfied by quite a few two-digit numbers, but there aren't many two-digit multiples of 12. So, we start by listing the multiples of 12:

$$12, 24, 36, 48, 60, 72, 84, 96.$$

Now that we have a short list of possible solutions, we can quickly go through the other properties and eliminate possibilities from this list. Since the tens digit must be larger than the ones digit, we can eliminate the first four numbers in the list, leaving

$$\cancel{12}, \cancel{24}, \cancel{36}, \cancel{48}, 60, 72, 84, 96.$$

The next property, that the difference between the digits is greater than 3, eliminates 96:

$$\cancel{12}, \cancel{24}, \cancel{36}, \cancel{48}, 60, 72, 84, \cancel{96}.$$

Finally, since the sum of the digits must be greater than 10, we can eliminate 60 and 72, and we are left with 84 as the answer to the problem. □

Problem 15.6: Elizabeth spent exactly $7 for some 15-cent stamps and some 31-cent stamps. How many 15-cent stamps did she buy?

Solution for Problem 15.6: We often start word problems by assigning variables and writing equations. Let's try that here. First, we note that $7 is 700 cents. If we let a be the number of 15-cent stamps and b be the number of 31-cent stamps, then we must have

$$15a + 31b = 700.$$

That's all we know about a and b, and this equation isn't terribly helpful. We could just guess values of a or b and hope we get lucky, but there are a lot of possibilities.

Instead, we take a more organized approach. After paying for all the 31-cent stamps, the amount remaining must be divisible by 15 cents. So, we imagine that Elizabeth starts with 700 cents and pays for the 31-cent stamps one at a time. We then list the number of cents she has remaining at each step, looking for a multiple of 15:

$$700, 669, 638, 607, 576, 545, 514, 483, 452, 421, 390.$$

Since 390 is divisible by both 3 and 5, it is divisible by 15. Elizabeth spent $700 - 390 = 310$ cents on 31-cent stamps, so she bought 10 31-cent stamps. With the other 390 cents, she bought $390/15 = 26$ 15-cent stamps.

You might have noticed that we could have saved a lot of work with a little bit of thinking. Instead of buying the 31-cent stamps one at a time, we might have noticed that the number of 31-cent stamps she bought must have been a multiple of 5. This is the only way the number of cents left for 15-cent stamps could be a multiple of 5. So, we can shorten our list by buying five 31-cent stamps at a time. Each block of five 31-cent stamps costs $5 \cdot 31 = 155$ cents, so our list is

$$700, 545, 390.$$

We reach the desired multiple of 15 much faster this way! Furthermore, it's easy with this method to see why there are no other combinations she could have bought. If we continue the list, we have

$$700, 545, 390, 235, 80.$$

The only multiple of 15 in this list is 390. So, the only way she can buy 31-cent stamps and 15-cent stamps is if she spends 390 cents on 15-cent stamps and 310 cents on 31-cent stamps. $\square$

In the previous problem, we saw that doing a little bit of thinking before listing can sometimes shorten the amount of listing you have to do. In the next problem, we see that sometimes we need to do some careful thinking just to make sure we have a complete list.

Problem 15.7: A **partition** of a positive integer n is a way of writing n as the sum of positive integers in which the order of the numbers in the sum doesn't matter. For example, the partitions of 3 are 3, $2 + 1$, and $1 + 1 + 1$. We consider $2 + 1$ and $1 + 2$ to be the same, so there are 3 partitions of 3. How many partitions of 6 are there?

Solution for Problem 15.7: If we just start listing partitions of 6 as we think of them, it will be hard to know when we've found them all. So, we should take an organized approach.

> **Concept:** Organized lists are much more useful than disorganized lists.

One way to organize the partitions is to group them based on the largest number in the partition. Obviously, there's only one partition that has 6, namely

$$6.$$

Similarly, there's only one partition in which 5 is the largest number:

$$5 + 1.$$

The partitions with 4 as the greatest number are

$$4 + 2,$$
$$4 + 1 + 1.$$

The partitions with 3 as the greatest number are

$$3 + 3,$$
$$3 + 2 + 1,$$
$$3 + 1 + 1 + 1.$$

The partitions with 2 as the greatest number are

$$2 + 2 + 2,$$
$$2 + 2 + 1 + 1,$$
$$2 + 1 + 1 + 1 + 1.$$

The only partition with 1 as the greatest number is

$$1 + 1 + 1 + 1 + 1 + 1.$$

Altogether, we count 11 partitions of 6. □

Exercises ▶

15.2.1 In Problem 15.6, why did we choose to imagine buying the 31-cent stamps one at a time, rather than starting with buying the 15-cent stamps?

15.2.2 I am less than 6 feet tall but more than 2 feet tall. My height in inches is a multiple of 7 and is also 1 more than a multiple of 6. What is my height?

15.2.3 List all two-digit positive integers that satisfy both of the following:

1. The tens and ones digits are consecutive numbers, and

2. The integer is the product of two consecutive numbers.

(Source: MOEMS)

15.2.4 If a number is divided by 3, the remainder is 0. If the number is divided by 5, the remainder is 4. If the number is divided by 11, the remainder is 7. The number has two digits. What is the number?

15.2.5★ The three-digit number 114 has a **digit sum** of $1 + 1 + 4$, or 6. How many three-digit positive integers have a digit sum of 6? **Hints:** 85, 88

15.3 Draw a Picture

The old adages "Seeing is believing" and "A picture is worth a thousand words" are applicable to many math problems. Naturally, this is often true of geometry problems, but it's also true of some problems that don't appear to be about pictures at all.

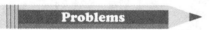

Problem 15.8: Wally the wandering walrus swims 6 miles north, then 3 miles east, then 3 miles north, then 15 miles west. How far is he from where he started? (You can assume Earth is flat for this problem.)

Problem 15.9: A frog is at the bottom of a 12-meter well. Each morning he climbs up 5 meters. Each night he slides down 3 meters. If he starts climbing on a Sunday, on which day will he reach the top of the well and escape?

Problem 15.10: Abel, Bernoulli, Cantor, and Descartes have a race. Bernoulli finished between Abel and Descartes. Cantor is happy that he didn't finish last, and Descartes bragged all day long about beating Abel. If no one finished between Cantor and Abel, then in what order did the participants finish?

Problem 15.11: Below are the pairs of cities connected by direct flights by GetUThere Airlines. For each pair of cities, there are flights in both directions. Is it possible to get from Boston to Philadelphia on a series of GetUThere flights?

Boston—New York	Baltimore—Washington	Buffalo—Newark
Buffalo—Albany	Philadelphia—Erie	New York—Washington
New York—Baltimore	Erie—Newark	Albany—Philadelphia
Newark—Albany	Baltimore—Boston	Newark—Philadelphia

We start with a problem in which drawing a picture is a pretty obvious first step.

Problem 15.8: Wally the wandering walrus swims 6 miles north, then 3 miles east, then 3 miles north, then 15 miles west. How far is he from where he started? (You can assume Earth is flat for this problem.)

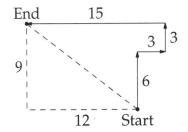

Solution for Problem 15.8: At the right, the solid arrows show Wally's path. As shown in the dashed right triangle, Wally wanders 9 miles north and 12 miles west in total. Applying the Pythagorean Theorem, or recalling the $\{9, 12, 15\}$ Pythagorean triple, we find that Wally ends 15 miles from where he started. □

Problem 15.9: A frog is at the bottom of a 12-meter well. Each morning he climbs up 5 meters. Each night he slides down 3 meters. If he starts climbing on a Sunday, on which day will he reach the top of the well and escape?

Solution for Problem 15.9: What's wrong with this solution:

> **Bogus Solution:** Since he climbs up 5 meters each morning and slides back 3 meters each night, he moves upward 2 meters total each day of the week. Therefore, he will climb 12 meters in 12/2 = 6 days. He starts climbing on a Sunday, so his sixth day of climbing is the following Friday.

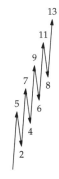

We see the flaw in this reasoning when we draw a picture that shows both his climbs and his slides. Our picture is shown at the right. We draw up arrows for the climbs and down arrows for the slides, and note the total height climbed at each step. We see that his height first goes over 12 meters after the fifth climb, so he escapes the well on the fifth day of climbing. He starts climbing on a Sunday, so his fifth and last day of climbing is a Thursday. □

Concept: A quick sketch can help prevent errors.

Problem 15.10: Abel, Bernoulli, Cantor, and Descartes have a race. Bernoulli finished between Abel and Descartes. Cantor is happy that he didn't finish last, and Descartes bragged all day long about beating Abel. If no one finished between Cantor and Abel, in what order did the participants finish?

Solution for Problem 15.10: We need a good way to organize the information in the problem. Each piece of information eliminates possibilities. For example, because Bernoulli finished between Abel and Descartes, we know that Bernoulli did not finish first or last. We visualize this information by making a table with a row for each racer and a column for each position. We place X's in the 1st and 4th columns of

	1st	2nd	3rd	4th
Abel				
Bernoulli	X			X
Cantor				
Descartes				

Bernoulli's row to indicate that Bernoulli didn't finish in either of these positions.

Next, we place an X in Cantor's 4th column since Cantor wasn't last. Because Descartes beat Abel, we know that Abel wasn't first and Descartes wasn't last. Placing X's for these facts as well, we now have the table at the right.

	1st	2nd	3rd	4th
Abel	X			
Bernoulli	X			X
Cantor				X
Descartes				X

Now, it's clear that Abel must have been 4th, since none of the other runners could have been 4th. We then immediately know that Cantor was 3rd, since no one was between Cantor and Abel. We place O's in Abel's 4th column and Cantor's 3rd column to indicate that we know these placements. We then can place X's in the remainder of Abel's and Cantor's rows, and in the remainder of the 3rd column.

	1st	2nd	3rd	4th
Abel	X	X	X	O
Bernoulli	X		X	X
Cantor	X	X	O	X
Descartes			X	X

	1st	2nd	3rd	4th
Abel	X	X	X	O
Bernoulli	X	O	X	X
Cantor	X	X	O	X
Descartes	O	X	X	X

Now we have the full story. There's only one possibility left for Bernoulli, 2nd place, and only Descartes could have been in 1st place. The completed chart is shown at the left, and the order of the racers was

Descartes, Bernoulli, Cantor, Abel.

We can check our answer by making sure that this order agrees with all the information in the problem. In the finishing order we found above, Bernoulli is between Abel and Descartes. Cantor is not last, Descartes beats Abel, and no one is between Cantor and Abel. □

Problem 15.11: Below are the pairs of cities connected by direct flights by GetUThere Airlines. For each pair of cities, there are flights in both directions. Is it possible to get from Boston to Philadelphia on a series of GetUThere flights?

Boston—New York	Baltimore—Washington	Buffalo—Newark
Buffalo—Albany	Philadelphia—Erie	New York—Washington
New York—Baltimore	Erie—Newark	Albany—Philadelphia
Newark—Albany	Baltimore—Boston	Newark—Philadelphia

Solution for Problem 15.11: We know that Boston and Philadelphia are not connected by a direct flight, but we can't tell whether or not there's a sequence of flights that goes from Boston to

Philadelphia. To help hunt for such a sequence, we draw a picture that includes all the flights. We make each city a point, and connect each pair of points that is connected by a direct flight. The result is shown below:

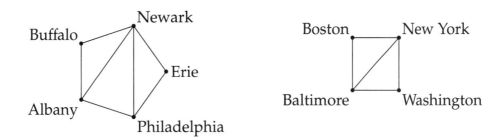

Now it's obvious that there is no way to get from Boston to Philadelphia. □

> **Sidenote: Graph theory** is a powerful field of mathematics that we can use to study connections between pairs of items. In Problem 15.11, we constructed a **graph** to represent connections between cities. The points in the graph for the cities are called **vertices** and the connections are **edges** of the graph.

Exercises

15.3.1 A lumberjack can cut a log into five pieces in 20 minutes. How long would it take to cut a log of the same size and shape into seven pieces?

15.3.2 The lengths of three rods are 6 cm, 10 cm, and 11 cm. How can you use these rods to measure a length of 15 cm?

15.3.3 Albert's house is 5 miles east of Belle's house and 3 miles west of Carnot's house. Dolly's house is 6 miles east of Carnot's house, and 4 miles east of Eli's house. Frank's house is 5 miles north of Eli's house and 8 miles north of Greta's house. To the nearest tenth of a mile, how far apart are Belle's house and Greta's house?

15.3.4 A man wearing red pants has red shoes. A man with blue pants has blue shoes. A man with green pants has green shoes. They exchange shoes so that each man is wearing one shoe from each of the other two men. After they leave, you only remember that the man in green pants had a red shoe on his right foot. What color shoe is each man wearing on each foot?

15.3.5★ One line divides a plane into two regions. Two lines can divide a plane into at most four regions. What is the maximum number of regions possible using eight lines? **Hints:** 66

15.4 Work Backwards

In some math problems, we are given the situation at the end of a process and must figure out what happened to bring about that end. We can often solve these problems by working backwards from the end, reversing each step in the process described in the problem.

Problem 15.12: David buys a Beanie Baby. He later sells it to Jessica and loses $3 on the deal. Jessica makes a profit of $6 by selling it to Bryan for $25. How much did David pay for the Beanie Baby? *(Source: MOEMS)*

Problem 15.13: Danielle chooses a number. She multiplies it by 3, then adds 6, then divides by 3, and finally subtracts 6. Her end result is 4. What number did she choose?

Problem 15.14: The surface of a pond is being covered by oil leaking from a pipeline. The amount of surface area covered by the oil is doubling each day. At this rate, the surface of the pond will be completely covered with oil at the end of the twenty-fifth day. What fraction of the surface area of the pond will be covered by oil at the end of 20 days? *(Source: MATHCOUNTS)*

Problem 15.15: Alice gave Bob as many dollars as Bob had. Bob then gave Alice as many dollars as Alice then had. At this point, each had 24 dollars. How much did Alice have at the beginning?

Problem 15.16: In a sequence of five integers, the third integer is the sum of the previous two, the fourth integer is the sum of the previous three, and the fifth integer is the sum of the previous four. If the sum of the five integers is 248, what is the third integer in the sequence? *(Source: MATHCOUNTS)*

Problem 15.12: David buys a Beanie Baby. He later sells it to Jessica and loses $3 on the deal. Jessica makes a profit of $6 by selling it to Bryan for $25. How much did David pay for the Beanie Baby?

Solution for Problem 15.12: Rather than starting at the beginning by assigning a variable to the price David paid for the Beanie Baby, we start at the end. Jessica made a profit of $6 by selling the Beanie Baby for $25, so she must have bought it for $25 − $6 = $19. David lost $3 when he sold the Beanie Baby for $19, so he must have bought it for $19 + $3 = $22. □

Problem 15.13: Danielle chooses a number. She multiplies it by 3, then adds 6, then divides by 3, and finally subtracts 6. Her end result is 4. What number did she choose?

Solution for Problem 15.13: Just for fun, let's try working this problem "forwards." Let x be Danielle's number. We build an expression step by step for her final number:

Danielle's action	Resulting expression
Multiply by 3	$3x$
Add 6	$3x + 6$
Divide by 3	$(3x + 6)/3$
Subtract 6	$(3x + 6)/3 - 6$

We know that this final number must equal 4, so we have an equation:

$$\frac{3x + 6}{3} - 6 = 4.$$

It would be awfully easy to make a mistake while setting up or solving this equation. Let's try going backwards and see if that's easier.

We'll start with the end result, 4, and we'll go backwards through the steps, undoing each. For example, Danielle's last step was "subtract 6." Going backwards, we add 6 to see that Danielle's number was 10 before she subtracted 6. Here's what we find when we start with 4 and go backwards through the steps, undoing each:

Danielle's action	Undo action	Resulting number
Subtract 6	Add 6	10
Divide by 3	Multiply by 3	30
Add 6	Subtract 6	24
Multiply by 3	Divide by 3	8

Therefore, Danielle started with 8. (Note that $x = 8$ satisfies our earlier equation.) $\square$

Our "work backwards" solution to Problem 15.13 is closely related to solving the equation we wrote for the problem. Here's the equation we wrote for the problem:

$$\frac{3x + 6}{3} - 6 = 4.$$

Now, let's go through the "Undo actions" from our table, in order:

Undo action	Resulting equation
Add 6	$\dfrac{3x + 6}{3} = 10$
Multiply by 3	$3x + 6 = 30$
Subtract 6	$3x = 24$
Divide by 3	$x = 8$

So, our "working backwards" is essentially just solving the equation without writing the equation in the first place!

Problem 15.14: The surface of a pond is being covered by oil leaking from a pipeline. The amount of surface area covered by the oil is doubling each day. At this rate, the surface of the pond will be completely covered with oil at the end of the twenty-fifth day. What fraction of the surface area of the pond will be covered by oil at the end of 20 days? *(Source: MATHCOUNTS)*

Solution for Problem 15.14: What's wrong with this solution:

Bogus Solution: Since 20 days is $\frac{20}{25} = \frac{4}{5}$ of the number of days it takes to cover the whole pond, $\frac{4}{5}$ of the pond must be covered at the end of 20 days.

This solution assumes that the amount the oil spreads each day is the same. But that's not the case! For example, on the fourth day the amount covered by oil doubles, which means that it increases by the same amount as was covered on all three previous days *combined*.

The portion of the pond covered doubles each day when going forwards in time. So, if we go backwards in time, the amount of the pond covered is halved each day. Since the pond is completely covered at the end of the twenty-fifth day, $\frac{1}{2}$ is covered at the end of the twenty-fourth day. Going back another day, the portion covered at the end of the twenty-third day is $\frac{1}{2} \cdot \frac{1}{2} = \frac{1}{4}$. Similarly, we have:

End of Day	Portion Covered
25	1
24	$\frac{1}{2}$
23	$\frac{1}{4}$
22	$\frac{1}{8}$
21	$\frac{1}{16}$
20	$\frac{1}{32}$

The pond is $\frac{1}{32}$ covered with oil at the end of 20 days. $\square$

Problem 15.15: Alice gave Bob as many dollars as Bob had. Bob then gave Alice as many dollars as Alice then had. At this point, each had 24 dollars. How much did Alice have at the beginning?

Solution for Problem 15.15: Solving this with algebra would require two variables and great care in setting up equations. Let's try going backwards. They both finish with $24. In the final step, Alice receives as much money as she has. So, she doubles her money to end up with $24. Therefore, she must have previously had only $12, and Bob gave her $12 more. Since Bob has $24 dollars after giving Alice $12, he must have had $36 before giving Alice any money.

Going back one more step, we know that Alice has $12 and Bob has $36 after Alice gives Bob money. Since Alice gave Bob as much money as Bob already had, Bob doubled his money to get to $36. Therefore, he originally had $18 before Alice gave him $18 more. Alice had $12 after giving the $18 to Bob, so she started with $12 + $18 = $30 dollars.

> **Important:** It's particularly important to check our answer when working
> backwards to solve a complicated problem. We can usually do so
> by using our answer and working forwards through the problem.

We check that Alice starting with $30 and Bob with $18 does indeed end with both of them having $24:

Action	Alice's amount	Bob's amount
Start	$30	$18
Alice gives Bob the amount Bob had	$12	$36
Bob gives Alice the amount Alice had	$24	$24

Our answer checks out, so Alice started with $30. □

All four of these problems have one key feature in common. Each tells a story in which we know the end, and are trying to figure out what the situation was sometime earlier. This is a huge clue to try working backwards from the known end situation.

> **Concept:** When we know a lot about the end state of a problem, and want to
> know where we started, we should try working backwards.

Problem 15.16: In a sequence of five integers, the third integer is the sum of the previous two, the fourth integer is the sum of the previous three, and the fifth integer is the sum of the previous four. If the sum of the five integers is 248, what is the third integer in the sequence? *(Source: MATHCOUNTS)*

Solution for Problem 15.16: We know something about the end situation, so let's work backwards. The sum of all five integers is 248. But the sum of the first four integers equals the fifth integer. So, the sum of the first five integers is double the fifth integer. Therefore, the fifth integer is 248/2 = 124 and the sum of the first four integers is 124.

Similarly, the fourth integer is the sum of the first three integers, so the sum of the first four integers is double the fourth integer. This makes the fourth integer $124/2 = 62$, and the sum of the first three integers is also 62.

We take one more step backwards. The third integer is the sum of the first two integers, so the sum of the first three integers is double the third integer. Therefore, the third integer is $62/2 = 31.$ $\square$

Exercises ▶

15.4.1 Granny Smith has $63. Elberta has $2 more than Anjou and Anjou has one-third as much as Granny Smith. How many dollars does Elberta have? *(Source: AMC 8)*

15.4.2 Suppose you enter an elevator at a certain floor. Then the elevator moves up 6 floors, down 4 floors, and up 2 floors. You are then at floor 7. At which floor did you initially enter the elevator?

15.4.3 Early one morning, Joy took out one-half of the coins from her coin bank, and in the evening she put in 10 coins. The next morning, she took out one-third of the coins in the bank, and that evening she put in 4 coins. The next morning, she took out one-half the coins in the bank, leaving 16 coins. How many coins were in the bank to begin with?

15.4.4 A list of 8 numbers is formed by beginning with two given numbers. Each new number in the list is the product of the two previous numbers. Find the first number if the last three are shown:

$$\underline{\ ?\ }, \ \underline{\ \ \ }, \ \underline{\ \ \ }, \ \underline{\ \ \ }, \ \underline{\ \ \ }, \ \underline{16}, \ \underline{64}, \ \underline{1024}.$$

(Source: AMC 8)

15.4.5 Serena and Visala had a combined total of $180. Serena then gave Visala $20, and then Visala gave Serena a quarter of the money Visala had. After this, they each had the same amount. How much money did Serena start with?

15.5 Summary

In this chapter, we discussed four powerful problem-solving strategies. As you continue your math studies, you will use these strategies on all sorts of problems:

- Find a pattern
- Make a list
- Draw a picture
- Work backwards

All four of these strategies have a common goal:

> **Concept:** Simplify the problem.
>

 REVIEW PROBLEMS ▶

15.17 The last Monday of a particular month is on the 27th day of the month. What day of the week is the first day of the month?

15.18 Glen, Harry, and Kim each like a different sport among tennis, baseball, and soccer. Glen does not like baseball or soccer. Harry does not like baseball. Name the favorite sport of each person. *(Source: MOEMS)*

15.19 In a "Tribonacci" sequence, each number after the third number is the sum of the preceding three numbers. For example, if the first three numbers are 5, 6, and 7, then the fourth number is 18 because $5 + 6 + 7 = 18$, and the fifth number is 31 because $6 + 7 + 18 = 31$. The first five numbers of another Tribonacci sequence are $P, Q, 86, 158$, and 291 in that order. What is the value of P? *(Source: MOEMS)*

15.20 In the table below, all the positive integers are arranged in columns. Under what letter will the number 100 appear?

A	B	C	D	E	F
		1	2	3	4
10	9	8	7	6	5
11	12	13	14	15	16
22	21	20	19	18	17
23	24	25	26	27	28
⋮	⋮	⋮	⋮	⋮	⋮

(Source: MOEMS)

15.21 Find the largest integer that is less than 1000, two more than a multiple of 3, two more than a multiple of 5, and odd.

15.22 Terri produces a sequence of positive integers by following the three rules below. She starts with a positive integer, then applies the appropriate rule to the result, and repeats.

Rule 1: If the integer is less than 10, multiply it by 9.

Rule 2: If the integer is even and greater than 9, divide it by 2.

Rule 3: If the integer is odd and greater than 9, subtract 5 from it.

Here is a sample sequence: 23, 18, 9, 81, 76, ... Find the 98th term of the sequence that begins 98, 49, ... *(Source: AMC 8)*

15.23   Adnan began with a number. He divided his number by 2, subtracted 6 from the quotient, took the square root of the difference, added 1 to the square root, and took the square root of the sum. His final result was 3. What was Adnan's original number? *(Source: MOEMS)*

15.24   In the table below, the integers from 100 down to 0 are arranged in columns P, Q, R, S, and T. Write the letter of the column that contains the number 25.

P	Q	R	S	T
	100	99	98	97
93	94	95	96	
	92	91	90	89
85	86	87	88	
	84	83	82	81
77	78	79	80	

. . . .

(Source: MOEMS)

15.25   Luyi went to a store where she spent one-half of her money and then $16 more. She then went to another store where she spent one-third of her remaining money and then $16 more. She then had $4 left. How much did she have when she entered the first store?

15.26   Find the units digit (ones digit) of 3^{80}.

15.27   Three generous friends, each with some cash, redistribute their money as follows: Ami gives enough money to Jan and Toy to double the amount of money that each has. Jan then gives enough to Ami and Toy to double their amounts. Finally, Toy gives Ami and Jan enough to double their amounts. If Toy has $36 when they begin and $36 when they end, what is the total amount that all three friends have? *(Source: AMC 8)*

15.28   Two-thirds of the people in a room are seated in three-fourths of the chairs. The rest of the people are standing. If there are 6 empty chairs, how many people are in the room?

15.29   A box contains gold coins. If the coins are equally divided among six people, four coins are left over. If the coins are equally divided among five people, three coins are left over. If the box holds the smallest number of coins that meets these two conditions, how many coins are left over when equally divided among seven people? *(Source: AMC 8)*

15.30   Suppose there is a special key on a calculator that replaces the number x currently displayed with the number given by the formula $1/(1 - x)$. For example, if the calculator is displaying 2 and the special key is pressed, then the calculator will display -1 since $1/(1 - 2) = -1$. Now suppose the calculator is displaying 5. After the special key is pressed 100 times in a row, what decimal number will the calculator display? *(Source: AMC 8)*

15.31   You want to bring a wolf, a goat, and a cabbage across a river. You are the rower and don't get out of the boat. The wolf wants to eat the goat, and the goat wants to eat the cabbage, but neither will happen as long as you are near. Besides yourself, there is room for only one item in the boat. How can you bring all three across the river?

15.32 How many partitions of 7 are there? (See Problem 15.7 on page 554 for the definition of a partition.)

15.33 Four people come to a river in the night. There is a narrow bridge that can hold only two people at a time. Because it's night, a torch has to be used when crossing the bridge, but the people only have 1 torch among them. Person *A* can cross the bridge in 1 minute, person *B* in 2 minutes, person *C* in 5 minutes, and person *D* in 8 minutes. When two people cross the bridge together, they must move at the slower person's pace. The torch burns out in 15 minutes. Find a way for all four people to get across the bridge before the torch burns out.

15.34 There are positive integers that have these properties:

1. the sum of the squares of their digits is 50, and

2. each digit is larger than the one to its left.

What is the largest integer with both properties? *(Source: AMC 8)*

15.35 Cindy walks at a constant rate of 2 miles per hour. She leaves home to walk to her friend Jenny's house at 9 am. When she is halfway there, she thinks that she left her phone at home. She turns around and begins to walk back home, but when she is halfway home (from where she turned around), she finds her phone. She turns back around to walk to Jenny's and arrives there at 10 am. How far apart are Cindy's house and Jenny's house? **Hints:** 43

Challenge Problems

15.36 There are 24 four-digit positive integers that use each of the four digits 2, 4, 5, and 7 exactly once. Listed in numerical order from smallest to largest, what integer is in the 17th position in the list? *(Source: AMC 8)*

15.37 One half of the water is poured out of a full container. Then one third of the remainder is poured out. Continue the process: one fourth of the remainder for the third pouring, one fifth of the remainder for the fourth pouring, etc. After how many pourings does exactly one ninth of the original water remain? **Hints:** 109

15.38 Consider all pairs of positive integers in which both numbers are less than 10. The two integers in each pair can be the same or be different. How many different products are possible if the two integers are multiplied? **Hints:** 59

15.39 A 2-by-2 square is divided into four 1-by-1 squares. Each of the small squares is to be painted either white or gray. In how many different ways can the painting be accomplished so that no gray square shares its top or right side with any white square? There may be as few as zero or as many as four small gray squares. *(Source: AMC 8)*

15.40 A certain calculator has only two keys [+1] and [×2]. When you press one of the keys, the calculator automatically displays the result. For instance, if the calculator originally displayed "9" and you pressed [+1], it would display "10". If you then pressed [×2], it would display "20". Starting with the display "1", what is the fewest number of keystrokes you would need to reach "200"? *(Source: AMC 8)* **Hints:** 98, 127

15.41 The product of three positive integers (not necessarily different) is 40. How many sets of 3 integers have this property if the order of the 3 integers in a set does not matter?

15.42 How many paths with length 8 units are there from A to B along the grid at the right? Notice that one segment in the grid is missing! We cannot travel along the missing segment. **Hints:** 51

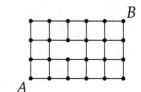

15.43

(a) Marco starts hiking on a path at noon, and stops at 8 p.m. He rests until noon the following day, and then starts hiking back towards his original starting point along the same path. He gets back to the starting point 8 hours after he starts walking. He doesn't necessarily walk at a constant rate either day. Show that there is a point on the path that Marco visits at the exact same time on both days.

(b) Suppose Marco only takes 4 hours on his return trip. Must there still be a point on the path that Marco visits at exactly the same time on both days?

15.44 In the game of Triball, each team has three players. In my Triball league, each player is on exactly two different teams, and no two players are teammates on two different teams. What is the smallest possible number of players in my Triball league? **Hints:** 30, 32

15.45 Find the last two digits (the tens digit and the units digit) of 7^{2011}.

15.46★ Sixtown is a country with six towns. Each pair of towns is directly connected by either a train route or by an airplane route. Explain why there must be three towns such that all three are directly connected to each other by the same mode of transportation. **Hints:** 160, 141

15.47★ A **cryptarithm** is a math puzzle in which the digits in a simple equation are replaced with letters. Each digit is represented by only one letter, and each letter represents a different digit. So, for example, we might represent $51 + 50 = 101$ as $AB + AC = BCB$. In the cryptarithm $SEND + MORE = MONEY$, what digit does the letter Y represent?

15.48★ Five married couples get together at a party. At the start of the party, each person shakes hands with everyone they didn't know before the party. After all the handshakes, Kyle, one of the husbands, asks everyone else how many hands they shook. He received each number from 0 to 8 as an answer once. How many hands did Kyle shake?

Hints to Selected Problems

1. What angles (or sums of angles) can you relate $\angle BPC$ to?

2. Can you find a power of two that's near 100, 1000, or 10000?

3. When trying to find a formula, it's often best to first solve the problem for specific values. Find the area when $s = 8$.

4. For what values of n is $6n$ among the values you found in the previous hint?

5. For what integers t is $\sqrt{t}$ an integer?

6. Is the desired region part of another figure whose area you can find?

7. How do you find the least common multiple of a group of numbers? What must be true about k in order for lcm$[12, 15, 20, k]$ to be 420?

8. After extending diagonal $\overline{SQ}$, you should have some right triangles to work with. Unfortunately, all we know about these triangles are the lengths of their hypotenuses, and we need their legs to find areas....

9. When solving word problems, one of our most useful strategies is finding two expressions for the same quantity, and then setting them equal.

10. Try the problem with a quadrilateral: can all of the angles of a quadrilateral be acute?

11. Look at Hint 147.

12. Consider a simpler problem; how did we solve the problem about polygon diagonals in the text?

13. If a number is not a multiple of 6, then what must be true about its prime factorization?

14. So, each term in the second sum is how many times the corresponding number in the first sum?

15. Let's say that a student "touches" a locker if she either opens or closes the locker. Which students touch locker 6? Which students touch locker 7? Locker 8? Locker 9?

16. Is there a right triangle that has the desired segment as a side?

17. Problems involving rates and work can often be solved by thinking about how much work is done per unit of time.

18. What do you know about the angles of a decagon? What does this tell you about the number of acute angles a decagon could have?

19. We know that the diagonals of a kite are perpendicular. But the diagonals of this kite don't even intersect! Diagonal $\overline{PR}$ is outside the kite, and diagonal $\overline{SQ}$ is inside it. What about the lines (not just the line segments) containing those diagonals?

20. We can find the areas of some complicated figures by rearranging them into figures whose areas we can find.

21. Must we have $x - y > 0$? Why or why not?

22. We'll have to find some more lengths to find the shaded area. Look at the unshaded pieces: what kind of triangles are they?

23. Try Hint 72.

24. Add the greatest two lengths in each triple. In each case, how does the sum relate to the smallest length?

25. What shape does Rebecca's path form? What angles of this shape do you know?

26. The inequality chain $a > b > c$ means that $a > b$ and $b > c$ both hold.

27. Each of these triangles is part of a larger triangle in the diagram.

28. If $a \div b$ is an integer, then how are a and b related?

29. Simplify the problem. What if we replaced 10^{93} with just 10^3? 10^4? 10^5?

30. Draw a picture. Let each player be a point. What will teams be?

31. How must the prime factorization of a divisor of 2520 be related to the prime factorization of 2520?

32. Each team is a triangle connecting three points. How many points do you need to satisfy the conditions in the problem?

33. Don't forget squares whose sides aren't horizontal or vertical lines!

34. What are the digits of the number?

35. How do you get from one perfect square to the next quickly?

36. If you put the numbers that are divisible by 3 in one list, and the numbers that are divisible by 5 in another list, then which list is 15 in? How does the answer to that affect your counting?

37. What's the nearest multiple of 8?

38. Consider a simpler problem. How would you handle the problem if you replaced the mixed numbers with integers?

39. The desired region is part of sector AOB. What is the other part of the sector?

40. By how many meters would Robert beat Sam if the race were 50 meters? 100 meters? 150 meters?

41. What number are we not allowed to divide by?

42. What fraction of students in Central Middle School are boys with blond hair?

43. Draw a diagram!

44. I'll bet Hint 164 is pretty good.

45. The diagonals split the quadrilateral into four pieces. Do you know how to find the areas of those pieces? Can you easily combine a pair of these pieces to make another figure whose area is easy to find?

46. a divided by b is $\frac{a}{b}$, and b divided by c is $\frac{b}{c}$, and a divided by c is $\frac{a}{c}$. What can we do with $\frac{a}{b}$ and $\frac{b}{c}$ to get $\frac{a}{c}$?

47. Make a list of the first 20 positive perfect squares.

48. Not all problems have pretty solutions. Sometimes you have to get your hands dirty with some pretty grungy casework.

49. Can you write 2^{12} as a power of 8?

50. What does quadrilateral $ABCD$ tell you about $x + y$?

51. For the dots that are 1 step away from B, it's obvious how many paths there are to B that only go upward or rightward at each step. What about the dots that are 2 steps away from B? Or the dots that are 3 steps away from B?

52. How far must the largest number be from the average of the original list?

53. We are given the areas of triangles. $\overline{QT}$ and $\overline{QR}$ are bases of triangles.

54. Sometimes thinking of the average of a list of numbers as "balancing" the list helps solve problems.

55. How have we dealt with fractions in equations in the past?

56. What useful extra line might we add to the diagram?

57. Simplify the problem. How would you handle $99 \cdot 44$, $999 \cdot 444$, or $9999 \cdot 4444$?

58. Assign a variable.

59. We have $2 \cdot 3 = 1 \cdot 6$ and $3 \cdot 4 = 2 \cdot 6$. So, we have to be careful, since some products will appear multiple times. How can we be organized in writing all the possible products?

60. *RPSU* is a quadrilateral!

61. Zeros at the end of a number—what number does that make you think about multiplying by?

62. How many train-lengths does the train travel to clear the tunnel?

63. I see five little triangles. I also see five larger triangles!

64. We are given one equation involving AB and CD. How are $\overline{AB}$ and $\overline{CD}$ related to the triangles mentioned in the problem?

65. It's easier to substitute into *simple* expressions than to substitute into complicated expressions.

66. Draw a picture. Keep adding lines. Count the regions you have each time. Do you see a pattern in your results?

67. Draw all three long diagonals.

68. That expression in the square root looks scary. What if the problem were just $\sqrt{z} = \frac{10}{\sqrt{z}}$? Then could you figure out what to do? How about just $a = \frac{10}{a}$?

69. Count the number of new regions made each time you add a line. Do you see a pattern in these results?

70. 4 is the square of 2. Can you write 4^5 as the square of some number?

71. How many times does 3 appear as the tens digit?

72. You'll get more information from Hint 11.

73. How can you get 10's in the product?

74. How do these lengths affect the *ratio* of these areas?

75. In the text, we learned a strategy for infinite decimals. But an infinite decimal can be written as an infinite sum of fractions!

76. It might help to think outside the box on this one.

77. If the squares of two numbers are equal, then what do we know about the two numbers? (Remember, the numbers don't have to be positive!)

78. What do the prime factorizations of lcm$[a, b]$ and gcd(a, b) tell you about the prime factorizations of a and b?

79. $\overline{AB}$ is a base of $\triangle ABD$ and $\overline{CD}$ is a base of $\triangle BDC$. Notice anything interesting about these triangles?

80. Experiment. Start from an N in the corner—how many options do you have? What if you start from an N that's not in a corner?

81. Assign a variable so you can write expressions and set up equations. What's often a useful way to assign a variable in a ratio problem?

82. All of the exponents in the prime factorization of a perfect square must be even. What similar fact is true about the exponents in the prime factorization of a perfect cube?

83. How is the measure of each interior angle related to the measure of its corresponding exterior angle?

84. Can the numbers in the problem be written with the same exponent?

85. What is a good way to organize the three-digit numbers whose digit sum is 6?

86. Each right triangle has a hypotenuse among the sides of the original triangle.

87. We don't know a divisibility rule for 45, but we do know divisibility rules for some of the divisors of 45.

88. How many start with 6? How many start with 5?

89. Suppose Dave has $\$x$ before betting half his money on a hand. How much will he have if he wins? How much will he have if he loses?

90. Are there any simple fractions nearby?

91. Multiplying an integer by 10 means you add a 0 to the end of the integer. How do you get factors of 10?

92. Compare $\sqrt{x}$ to something simpler. Is it greater than 1?

93. Each vertex is connected to how many other vertices by an interior diagonal of the icosahedron?

94. Can you relate $\angle PBC + \angle PCB$ to any other angles (or sums of angles)?

95. Use a variable to write expressions for how many games Kyle's team won and lost.

96. We need an altitude length. When we draw an altitude in an acute triangle, we split the triangle into two right triangles.

97. Compare the first 3 terms of the sum in this part to your answers in the first 3 parts.

98. It's not immediately obvious what our first few presses should be if we want to get from 1 to 200 as fast as possible. If we just double 7 times, we'll get to 128. Then what? If it's not obvious how to proceed going forwards....

99. One step at a time. What variable can you solve for immediately?

100. We aren't multiplying the same units digit over and over again. But we are multiplying the same group of units digits over and over again.

101. The lune is part of a larger figure whose area we can find. So is the triangle.

102. The distributive property works with sums of three numbers just like it does with sums of two numbers: $w(x + y + z) = wx + wy + wz$.

103. Each vertex is connected to how many other vertices by an edge of the icosahedron?

104. How long would it take one worker to build the whole road? What fraction of the road does one worker complete in one day?

105. What do the two triangles have in common?

106. Start by finding one pair x and y.

107. Can you use the same steps you used to tackle the first hint to find the formula?

108. It's often best to think of percent increases and decreases in terms of multiplying the original quantity by some number.

109. What fraction of the water remains after 1 pour? After 2 pours? After 3 pours?

110. What length do you need in order to determine the area of ABC? What length do you need in order to determine the area of $ABCD$?

111. Approach the problem in pieces. What can you figure out right away from the given information?

112. How much other stuff?

113. If c is the cost of the comic book in cents, then what other quantities in the problem can you express in terms of c?

114. So, you should start with three circles!

115. What length-finding strategies do you know?

116. Each base in the second sum is double a base in the first sum.

117. What fraction of the pool is filled each hour?

118. The product of two positive numbers must be positive. By what can we multiply $x - y$ in order to get terms $3x$ and $3y$?

119. Can you write it as a power of 9?

120. Let x be the amount each person gave Ott.

121. There's only one obvious place to draw a median. Where should you then draw heights?

122. The count you did for the first hint included a lot of multiples of 5. How many?

123. If we know what fraction of the book Chandra reads, then we can figure out how many pages she reads.

124. What do you know about a number whose digits sum to 18?

125. How would you solve similar problems that are simpler-looking, like $\frac{3}{7} = \frac{h}{3}$, or $\frac{3}{h} = \frac{h}{27}$? Do the square roots really make the problem much different?

126. What kind of triangle is $\triangle ABC$?

127. What is probably the last button we'll press if we get from 1 to 200 as fast as possible?

128. AD is in both of the given ratio relationships.

129. Don't let the weird words fool you; this problem is just like many others you've solved in the section.

130. It's a word problem. What is our usual strategy for word problems?

131. How might the prime factorization of the number help you?

132. If you are given two numbers, how can you tell if their quotient will be positive?

133. We worked with infinite decimals by multiplying by 10. What number might we multiply by here?

134. Can you split the problem into cases you can handle?

135. Can you write the ratio in an easier-to-use form?

136. Let h be the height from A to $\overline{BC}$. What are the areas of $\triangle ABM$ and $\triangle ACM$?

137. Can you write 7^4 as the square of a number using exponent laws?

138. How do you usually find the least common multiple and the greatest common divisor of two numbers? Can you use that process to start from the given values of lcm[a, b] and gcd(a, b) to learn about a and b?

139. Problems involving averages can often be solved by thinking about sums.

140. Simplify the problem. If x is Douglas's favorite number, then how would you express the number we form by writing a 0 at the end of his favorite number?

141. Is it possible for one town to be connected to exactly two towns by train and exactly two towns by airplane?

142. To what other angles in the diagram can you relate angles of the star?

143. Multiplying $\underbrace{9999\ldots9}_{\text{94 nines}}$ by $\underbrace{4444\ldots44}_{\text{94 fours}}$ looks hard. Is there a really long number that's easy to multiply $\underbrace{4444\ldots44}_{\text{94 fours}}$ by?

144. Simplify the problem first. Count the numbers less than 1000 that are divisible by 2 and 3.

145. How many horizontal rows of toothpicks are there?

146. Simplify the problem. Find x^2.

147. Hint 44. Yeah, Hint 44 is the way to go.

148. How do you find the number halfway between −97 and 133 on the number line?

149. How long would the base have to be if the legs each have length 1? Is such a triangle possible?

150. We are given that $AB : AD = 2 : 5$, and that AB and AD are both integers. Could AD possibly be 4? Why or why not? Just from these given facts, what are the possible values of AD?

151. Simplify the problem first.

152. Let E and F be the endpoints of the fold, where F is the endpoint closest to B. Let $BF = x$. Can you build some equations now?

153. What do you know about the sum of the *interior* angles of a polygon?

154. This problem involves dividing by 9. What key insight did we make in the text to help us learn how to test for divisibility by 9?

155. Get rid of the square root. What must the expression inside the radical equal?

156. There's water, and there's other stuff.

157. If you multiply a fraction by $\frac{2}{2}$, you don't change the value of the fraction.

158. Solve a similar, simpler problem.

159. Assign a variable. Write an equation.

160. Let each town be a point.

161. If you multiply a 5-digit number and a 10-digit number, what are the possibilities for the number of digits in the product?

162. What must you do to $\sqrt{x}$ to get x?

163. This sure looks like a Venn diagram problem, but there are three categories!

164. Hint 23 might be the best one for this problem. Or maybe Hint 147.

Index

www.artofproblemsolving.com

The Art of Problem Solving (AoPS) is:

• Books

For over 25 years, *the Art of Problem Solving* books have been used by students as a resource for the American Mathematics Competitions and other national and local math events.

> *Every school should have this in their math library.*
> – Paul Zeitz, past coach of the U.S. International Mathematical Olympiad team

Visit our site to learn about our textbooks, which form a full math curriculum for high-performing students in grades 6-12.

• Classes

The Art of Problem Solving offers online classes on topics such as number theory, counting, geometry, algebra, and more at beginning, intermediate, and Olympiad levels.

> *All the children were very engaged. It's the best use of technology I have ever seen.*
> – Mary Fay-Zenk, coach of National Champion California MATHCOUNTS teams

• Forum

As of April 2019, the Art of Problem Solving Forum has over 395,000 members who have posted over 8,100,000 messages on our discussion board. Members can also join any of our free "Math Jams".

> *I'd just like to thank the coordinators of this site for taking the time to set it up... I think this is a great site, and I bet just about anyone else here would say the same...*
> – AoPS Community Member

• ...and much, much more!

Membership is **FREE**! Come join the Art of Problem Solving community today!